INTERNATIONAL SERIES OF MONOGRAPHS ON

ORGANIC CHEMISTRY

GENERAL EDITORS: D. H. R. BARTON and W. DOERING

VOLUME 7

Interpretation of the
ULTRAVIOLET SPECTRA
of
NATURAL PRODUCTS

Interpretation of the

ULTRAVIOLET SPECTRA

of

NATURAL PRODUCTS

by

A. I. SCOTT

Professor of Organic Chemistry
University of British Columbia
Vancouver

A Pergamon Press Book

THE MACMILLAN COMPANY

NEW YORK

1964

THE MACMILLAN COMPANY
60 Fifth Avenue
New York 11, N.Y.

This book is distributed by
THE MACMILLAN COMPANY
pursuant to a special arrangement with
PERGAMON PRESS LIMITED
Oxford, England

Library of Congress Catalog Card Number 62–9187

To W. Conover and L. Armstrong

CONTENTS

PREFACE

THE origin of this book is a series of encounters with natural product chemists in search of their chromophores. I have tried to collect within these covers sufficient information to aid the organic, analytical and bio-chemist in his constant search for analogous or (hopefully) exact structural examples to match the ultraviolet spectrum of his current series of compounds, of either natural or synthetic origin. The template of natural product chemistry was chosen for the simple reason that most empirical work of correlative nature has stemmed from the study of materials isolated from biological sources. The emphasis is squarely laid on available correlative data, model systems and, wherever possible, working rules to aid the organic chemist in a qualitative sense. Thus, rigorous theoretical approaches to the calculation of spectra are not treated and many interesting topics which include mechanistic photochemistry, optical rotatory power, ligand field theory, fluorescence and phosphorescence are not discussed. I have simply tried to guide both novice and experienced workers to the source of the recorded spectrum of a variety of naturally occurring structures and to indicate the methods applicable to the solution of structural problems within the limits of the electron absorption spectrum.

The first six chapters contain, largely in tabular form, the classes of chromophore of frequent recurrence in the realm of natural products. Chapter seven, kindly contributed by Dr. C.J.W. Brooks (Glasgow University) is intended to serve as a reference source for biochemical and analytical workers. The concluding chapters provide selective but, I hope, representative examples of the power of the interpretative method as outlined in the earlier part of the book. Many hundreds of excellent examples are available and I should welcome comments and suggestions from readers for future expansion of the second part of the work.

It is indeed fortunate that, unlike some of the more recent spectral methods, there has been an element of timelessness in ultraviolet spectral studies. For this reason, I hope that readers and critics alike will forgive the delay in publication – a result of printing difficulties (the manuscript was completed in Spring 1961).

Many colleagues helped in all directions and I am happy to acknowledge the encouragement of my Editor, Professor D.H.R. Barton F.R.S. whose fluent use of spectroscopic assignments gave me the idea of writing this book. At all times Professor R.A. Raphael F.R.S. offered helpful comment while Drs. J.C.D. Brand, C.J.W. Brooks, K.H. Overton and M.C. Whiting drew my attention to many important references.

My debt to Professor W.D.Ollis is profound, since he not only read the entire manuscript as part of his summer vacation, but provided keen criticism at every step of the way. Miss P.A.Dodson prepared the index and the onerous task of typing was performed uncomplainingly by Miss B.Porter.

Authors, editors and publishers (where noted) co-operated fully in giving permission to reproduce diagrams. Finally, a word of gratitude to my wife for her patient help.

A.I.SCOTT

INTRODUCTION

THE investigation of the structure and chemistry of naturally occurring compounds has intrigued the organic chemist since the initiation of his subject. The exponential increase in the rate of successful structural elucidations in the last decade owes a great deal to the empirical correlations developed for assignment of characteristic absorption in the infrared, ultraviolet and, more recently, n.m.r. spectra of organic molecules. The transparency of many groupings (and often large segments), of complex molecules to that part of the electromagnetic spectrum between 190 and 400 mμ, defined herein as the ultraviolet region, imposes *per se* a limitation of usefulness on the results of interpretation of absorption bands in this region. However, when taken in conjunction with the wealth of detail provided by infrared and n.m.r. bands, such a combination of data from three instrumentally accessible regions, when correctly interpreted, in many cases may lead to structural proposals of value to the natural product chemist. Such formulations may then be tested by appropriate chemical transformation with spectroscopic control. In this way, the process of degradation and structural assignment is aided by spectroscopic assignments, which admittedly are of an empirical nature at this time, but none the less are useful to the organic chemist.

This short introduction to the interpretation of the ultraviolet spectra of some natural products is written from such an empirical standpoint in the hope that these correlations, which constitute an ever-increasing part of the language of the organic chemist, may form not only a useful working guide to the application of ultraviolet data in structural work, but may also stimulate the evolution of further assignments as they arise in this continually expanding subject of structure–spectra correlation.

DEFINITIONS AND CONCEPTS

Wavelength

Electromagnetic radiation is characterized by either its wavelength (λ) or by its frequency (ν). These quantities are related by equation (1):

$$\lambda\nu = c \tag{1}$$

where c is the velocity of light, whereas the energy of the radiation is given by the Planck equation (2):

$$E = h\nu \tag{2}$$

The latter equation indicates that frequency is a more fundamental quantity than wavelength, and many of the theoretical papers on spectroscopy use wavenumbers ($\sigma = \lambda^{-1}$ with λ in cm) rather than wavelength. However, in correlative studies on natural products it is customary to express the absorption in terms of λ in millimicrons (mμ; 1 mμ = 10^{-7} cm), or less frequently in ångströms (Å; 1 Å = 10^{-8} cm). We have used mμ throughout the present work for such assignments. A selection of wavelengths, with corresponding wavenumber and energy values (from equations (1) and (2)) appear in Table 1. Since radiation of wave-

TABLE 1. WAVELENGTH-ENERGY RELATIONSHIPS

λ(mμ)	180	200	300	400
σ(cm^{-1})	55,555	50,000	33,333	25,000
ΔE (kcal/mole)	160	143	95	72

length 200 mμ thus corresponds to an energy of *ca.* 143 kcal/mole, it is not surprising that the irradiation of organic structures should lead to such phenomena as *trans* → *cis* isomerization, cleavage of C—C bonds, and generation of free radicals.

Having defined the unit of wavelength as the millimicron (1 mμ), we can specify the limits of the electronic spectrum (30–300 kcal/(mole)) as extending from 800 to 100 mμ. Above 800 mμ we enter the near-infrared, while below 100 mμ lies the soft X-ray region. For physiological reasons, the visible region is defined as 400–800 mμ. The ultraviolet region is subdivided into the far ultraviolet (100–190 mμ) and near ultraviolet (190–400 mμ). Owing to the absorption of the shorter wavelengths by constituents of the atmosphere, it is necessary that measurements appreciably below 190 mμ should be carried out *in vacuo*. Experimentation in the far or vacuum ultraviolet region is difficult and much work in this field remains to be done. Our interest is mainly confined to the region 190–400 mμ, although, since there is no doubt that the essential process of energy absorption followed by excitation of electrons occurs in the 400–700 mμ region, we shall have occasion to discuss electronic absorption spectra in the visible region.

In the cases of a few molecules where symmetry factors are favourable, it has been possible to arrive at theoretical prediction of wavelength of absorption from energy considerations and the use of equations (1) and (2). We shall, however, confine our discussion to the empirical approach throughout.

Absorption Intensity

The second fundamental characteristic required to define absorption of monochromatic light of wavelength λ, is the *intensity* of absorption. This is given by equation (3)

$$\ln\left(\frac{I_0}{I}\right) = kn \tag{3}$$

where I_0 and I are the respective intensities of the incident and transmitted light and n is the number of molecules of absorbant in the light path. For substances in solution n is proportional to the molar concentration of solute (c) and to the length (l) of the cell that contains the solution. Transferring to decadic logarithms we have

$$\text{optical density} = \log_{10}\left(\frac{I_0}{I}\right) = \varepsilon \cdot c \cdot l \tag{4}$$

Equation (4), which should be thought of as an experimental relationship, is described as the *Beer–Lambert Law*. The left side of (4) is variously described as the absorbance or *optical density* of the solution, symbolized by d. The commercial spectrophotometer provides a direct measurement of d either as a recorded trace or scale reading.

The term ε is the *molecular extinction coefficient* which is the normal unit of absorption intensity. Note that ε is a pure number whose units are $l\,\text{mole}^{-1}\text{cm}^{-1}$ and from (4) we have

$$\varepsilon = \frac{d \times \text{M.W.}}{c \times l} \tag{5}$$

where c is in grams per litre. Where the molecular weight of the compound is unknown, the expression $E_{1\,cm}^{1\%}$ (sometimes called E value) is used where

$$\varepsilon = E_{1\,cm}^{1\%} \times 0 \cdot 1 \text{ M.W.}$$

We have seen that the *wavelength* of absorption of a molecule is determined by the *energy* of the appropriate electronic transition. The *extinction coefficient* is controlled by the *size* of the absorbing species and the *probability* of the transition. It can be shown[1] that

$$\varepsilon = 0 \cdot 87 \times 10^{20}\,Pa \tag{6}$$

where P is the transition probability and a is the cross-sectional target-area, which from X-ray and electron diffraction is $\sim 10\,\text{Å}$. This gives $\varepsilon \sim 10^5$ for a transition of unit probability. The highest recorded values are in the order of *ca.* $\varepsilon = 10^5$ although the Oxford School has recently obtained ε values of 10^6 in the poly-yne series[2]. Conventionally, ε values of 10^4 or more are termed high, 10^3–10^4 medium, and $\varepsilon < 10^3$ low intensity absorptions. An absorption of 100–1000 corresponds to a transition of low probability ($P = 0 \cdot 01$ or less) and such low intensity is sometimes termed a forbidden transition.

Another fundamental value derivable from the tenets of electromagnetic theory is the *oscillator strength* (f) given by

$$\varepsilon = 0 \cdot 464 \times 10^9\,f/\varDelta v \tag{7}$$

where $\Delta\nu$ is the range of wavenumbers (reciprocal wavelengths) over which the electronic transition extends[3]. We may regard (f) as the measure of the number of electrons per molecule taking part in the transitions responsible for the absorption of light. We shall have occasion to refer to calculations using f values in Chapter 2.

An empirical method of intensity calculation has been developed by Platt[4a] for benzenoid compounds and was recently extended by Mason[4b] to the heteroaromatic series. Benzene has an absorption band near 260 mμ (ε 100), there being no change of dipole moment during the electronic transitions associated with this band. Replacement of a —CH= group by —N= or a hydrogen atom by a substituent, leads to perturbation and thence to dipole moment changes which are observed in the regular increase of the intensity of the 260 mμ band. For a given substituent, Platt has shown that equation (8) is valid:

$$I_a - I_0 = M_a^2 \tag{8}$$

where I_a is the intensity of the 260 mμ band for the substituted compound, I_0 is that of the parent, benzene, and M_a is the *spectroscopic moment* of substituent (a), which is positive for electron-releasing ($+M$) and negative for electron-attracting ($-M$) substituents.

Then for polysubstitution:

$$I_{ab} - I_0 = M_a^2 + M_b^2 + 2M_aM_b \qquad (para) \tag{9}$$

and
$$I_{ab} - I_0 = M_a^2 + M_b^2 - M_aM_b \qquad (ortho \text{ or } meta). \tag{10}$$

A set of M_a values has been evolved† and accounts qualitatively for the observed intensities of substituted benzenes and naphthalenes, the latter series making use of the 320 mμ band of naphthalene. Extension to pyridines and more complex N-heteroaromatic compounds has been described.[4b]

It is now agreed that the Beer–Lambert Law is fundamentally true, although its application is not so general as was once believed. The law is, however, rigorously obeyed when a *single species* gives rise to the observed absorption. Deviations from the law may be observed:

(i) when different forms of the absorbing system are in equilibrium; in this case it is often meaningful to measure the absorption at different values of pH. This results in a change of intensity for a given wavelength band, the change in ionic species being inversely proportional to the relative extinction coefficients. This means that there will be one point common to all the extinction curves which is constant for all values of pH. Such a point is called an isosbestic point and the presence of an isosbestic point for any given system is indicative that a number of equilibrium forms are present.

† see p. 181

(ii) When complexes occur between pairs of solute molecules (association) or between solute and solvent (e.g. H-bonding).

(iii) When there is thermal equilibrium between the ground state and a low-lying electronically excited state, as in some forms of thermochromism.

(iv) Beer's Law is not obeyed by fluorescent compounds or compounds changed chemically by ultraviolet irradiation.

Presentation of Absorption Spectra

For practical purposes it is convenient and customary to present the spectra of organic compounds in graphical form as a plot of $\log \varepsilon$ or ε/wavelength (in $m\mu$) with increasing wavelengths from left to right. However, as a result of

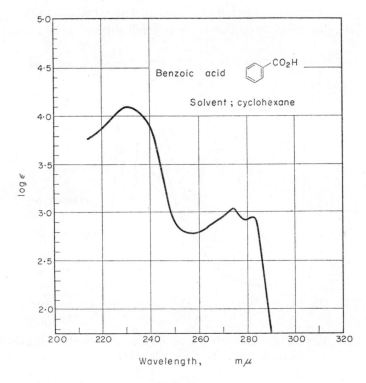

FIG. 1. Absorption Curve of benzoic acid in cyclohexane (after Friedel and Orchin No. 71).

publication policy and usage, it is probably true to say that less than 5% of ultraviolet spectra reported in the literature since 1930 have been presented in graphical form. A typical curve is illustrated in Fig. 1, and most investigators record their spectra in this way, although the results are published in the form: λ_{max} (in $m\mu$); $\log \varepsilon$ or ε. Sometimes the minimum λ_{min} is also reported. Projects in hand for the presentation of many reference spectra in graphical form[5] should aid identification by inspection as many subtleties hitherto unsuspected might be revealed by graphical presentation of data — at the same time visual comparison would be facilitated. It is also frequently necessary to subtract and add absorption curves during the course of a structural investigation, so that although we shall concern ourselves in this volume mainly with the correlation of λ_{max} and intensity values with structural features, the construction of an absorption curve is still a most important operation. The tedium of such a process is now largely removed by the advent of the commercial recording spectrophotometer.

Solvents

In Fig. 2 we illustrate the effect of changing from hydrocarbon to hydroxylic solvent for the case of phenol. The loss of fine structure in the latter case is quite typical, the broad band due to H-bonded solvent–solute complexes re-

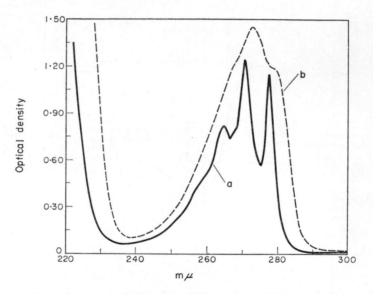

FIG. 2. Absorption curve of phenol in: (a) iso-octane, (b) ethanol. (Coggleshall and Lavy, *J. Amer. Chem. Soc.*, **70**, 3283, 1948.)

placing the fine structure present in hexane solution. The fine structure revealed in the latter solvent illustrates the principle that non-solvating or non-chelating solvents produce a spectrum near to that obtaining in the gaseous state. Common solvents and their "window" regions are shown in Table 2.

Experimental Methods and Instrumentation

Detailed descriptions of the apparatus and technique of absorption spectrophotometry are so numerous that there is no need to mention them in this book

TABLE 2. MINIMUM WAVELENGTHS FOR COMMON SOLVENTS USED IN SPECTROSCOPY

Solvent	Abbreviation†	Wavelength (mμ) of cut-out	
		1 mm cells	10 mm cells
Cyclohexane	C	190	195
Hexane	H	187	201
Carbon tetrachloride	CCl$_4$	245	257
Chloroform	Ch	223	237
Methylene dichloride	CH$_2$Cl$_2$	215	220
Ethanol	A	198	204
Methanol	MeOH	198	203
Water	W	187	191
Dioxan	D	–	–

† Adopted throughout this work.

except to say that the modern instrument is expected to be accurate to within 2 mμ in λ and 5% in ε. Frequent calibration of the instrument is essential for accuracy of spectral correlations.

Chromophores

Although ultraviolet absorption marks the excitation of electrons from their ground state, the nuclei which the electrons hold together determine the strength of the binding. Thus, the characteristic energy of a transition, and hence the wavelength of absorption, is a property of a group of atoms rather than of electrons themselves. When such absorption occurs the group producing it is called a *chromophore*. We suggest that this general definition should be adopted in preference to other usages. Structural changes affecting such a group of atoms can be expected to modify its absorption. The way in which spectra may be used to derive structural information is the main theme of this book. It must be stated at the outset (spectroscopists need read no further) that at present the relationships we have chosen to discuss between electronic light absorption and molecular structure of complex molecules form empirical, but none the less useful working guides for the organic chemist. Some knowledge of the commonly occurring chromophoric systems is therefore an essential requirement of the practising natural product chemist.

The three indispensable contributions to electronic absorption are the single bond (σ-electrons), the multiple bond (π-electrons) and the unshared electron pair (p-electrons)†. We shall not discuss free radical absorption (unpaired electrons) or ionic spectra (charge electrons).

† For a comprehensive and up-to-date review of the nature and nomenclature of electronic transitions see reference 13.

σ-Absorption

Compounds containing only σ-valency electrons are the saturated hydrocarbons which absorb below 170 mμ and give rise to intense bands corresponding to $N \rightarrow V$ and $N \rightarrow R$ transitions[6, 7]. The latter type of transition is also called a Rydberg transition. In Table 3 will be found a representation of such

TABLE 3. TYPES OF TRANSITION[7a]

Transition	λ (mμ)	Electron excited	Symbol†
$N \rightarrow V$	<150	σ	$C\!-\!H \rightarrow \bar{C}\overset{+}{H}$
$N \rightarrow R$ (Rydberg)	<150	σ	$C\!-\!C \rightarrow \overset{+}{C}\!\cdot\!C$
$N \rightarrow R$	<150	σ	$C\!-\!R \rightarrow \overset{+}{C}\!\cdot\!R$
$n \rightarrow \sigma^*$	~195	p	$\ce{>C-\ddot{N}-} \rightarrow \ce{C^*\dot{N}-}$
$n \rightarrow \sigma^*$	185	p	$\ce{>C-\ddot{O}-C<} \rightarrow \ce{>C^*\dot{O}-C<}$
$n \rightarrow \sigma^*$	195	p	$\ce{>C-\ddot{S}-H} \rightarrow \ce{>C^*\dot{S}-H}$
$n \rightarrow \sigma^*$	190	p	$\ce{>C=\ddot{O}} \rightarrow \ce{>C\overset{\sigma^*}{=}\dot{O}}$
$n \rightarrow \pi^*$	280	p	$\ce{>C=\ddot{O}} \rightarrow \ce{>C\overset{\pi^*}{=}\dot{O}}$
$\pi \rightarrow \pi^*$	~190	π	$\ce{>C=C<} \rightarrow \ce{>C\cdots C<}$
$\pi \rightarrow \pi^*$	~214	π	$\ce{>C=C-C=C<} \rightarrow \overset{*}{\ce{C-C-C-C}}$
Electron transfer (E.T.)	215–250	π	$\ce{>C=C-C=X} \rightarrow \overset{\oplus}{\ce{>C}}\ce{-C=C-}\overset{\ominus}{\ce{X}}$
	215–250	π	(phenyl)$\ce{-C=X}$

† The geometrical representation of the excited state in terms of molecular orbital treatment has been formulated for some simple molecules (ref. 13). The symbols in Table 3 are intended as convenient shorthand, pending a completely generalized notation.

TABLE 3 — (contd.)

Transition	λ (mμ)	Electron excited	Symbol
Electron transfer (E.T.)	215–250	$p - \pi$	
	215–250	$p - \pi$	
Local Excitation ($\pi \to \pi^*$)	180–255	π	
Hyperconjugation	—	σ	

absorptions together with the wavelengths at which they occur. These lie outside the range of the commercial instruments, the transparency of saturated hydrocarbons to 190 mμ making them ideal solvents for spectroscopy (Table 2).

Absorption due to Electron Lone Pairs (p-electrons) .

The non-bonding *p*-electrons are held more loosely than the σ-electrons and undergo Rydberg ($N \to R$) transition at correspondingly higher wavelength. From equation (2) the ionization potentials shown in Table 4 have been deter-

TABLE 4. $N \to R$ TRANSITIONS AND IONIZATION POTENTIALS OF SATURATED COVALENT MOLECULES, R—X[7]

Compound	$N \to R$ band (mμ)	Ionization potential (eV)
MeNH$_2$	115	10·8
MeOH	115	10·8
MeSH	125	9·9
EtCl	114	10·9
EtBr	114	10·9
EtI	121	10·3

mined spectroscopically. In addition to these bands in the far ultraviolet, atoms in the first row of the periodic table bound to carbon show a *p*-orbital electron transition to an antibonding σ-orbital (symbolized σ^*), the transition being described as $n \to \sigma^*$ where *n* denotes the orbital of the non-bonding *p*-electron in the ground state. Some $n \to \sigma^*$ frequencies appear in Table 1.1 (p. 16).

π-electrons

Unsaturated or multiple bond electrons present in olefinic, carbonyl or nitroso compounds for example, show Rydberg transitions in the 120–180 mμ region (10·5 eV). More importantly for diagnostic purposes, several of these chromophores have absorption in the more accessible regions of the spectrum. Thus olefins have intense bands between 180 and 205 mμ ($\varepsilon \sim 10^4$) which are assigned to the transition of a π-electron from its orbital to an antibonding (π^*) orbital, symbolized $\pi \to \pi^*$. For doubly bound nuclei of different atoms, other transitions are possible. The simple ketones for example display weak absorption ($\varepsilon \sim 15$) near 280 mμ, corresponding to promotion of the non-bonding electron of oxygen to an antibonding π orbital ($n \to \pi^*$ band), a second band of high intensity being found near 190 mμ, ascribed to the $n \to \sigma^*$ transition.

CONJUGATION OF CHROMOPHORES

The presence of *non-interacting* chromophores in an organic molecule gives rise to absorption corresponding to the simple summation of the contributing absorptions. Conjugation of like or unlike chromophores gives rise to new and intense absorption bands in the 210–260 mμ region of the spectrum.

$\pi \to \pi^*$ Absorption

Conjugation of like chromophores, as exemplified by butadiene,

$$CH_2{=}CH{-}CH{=}CH_2,$$

produces absorption at 217 mμ ($\varepsilon \sim 10^4$) corresponding to the promotion of a π-electron to the antibonding π^* orbital ($\pi \to \pi^*$ transition). Such absorption is affected by the further conjugation of p-electron systems with such a chromophore. Thus the presence of an atom X, with non-bonding electrons, can give rise to excited states represented for example by:

$$\ddot{X}{-}C{=}C{-}C{=}C \to \overset{\oplus}{X}{=}C{-}C{=}C{-}\overset{\ominus}{C}{-}$$

The result of such an extension of the chromophore is a shift to longer wavelength. Braude[3] has classified this type of transition as π–p absorption, although the overall effect is that of the transfer of an electron from a p-orbital to an antibonding π-orbital. Similarly, the absorption spectrum of benzene (I) is sometimes regarded as π–π* absorption. Substitution by a grouping with p-electrons once again causes a red shift by a process symbolized as in II. Shifts to longer wavelengths are also occasioned by alkyl groups, both in aromatic and alicyclic conjugated systems. Such effects are symbolized by Braude as π–σ absorption, which may be explained in terms of hyperconjugation (III, arrows).

I   II   III

Whether we regard the effect as inductive or hyperconjugative in nature, there remains no doubt that an application of empirical rules of shift as described in Chapters 2 and 3 has proved rewarding in structural investigation.

Electron–Transfer Absorption

The conjugation of *unlike* chromophores (as IV) gives rise to transitions involving the transfer of one electron from an ethylenic π-orbital to the C=O π-orbital (IV → V)

IV   V

Similarly, the new intense bands which appear in the spectrum of benzenoid compounds on introduction of a substituent with available *p*-electrons ($+M$ substituent) or one with electron-withdrawing properties ($-M$ substituent) may be assigned to the transfer of an electron to or from the benzene π-orbital system, symbolized in VI and VII. Longuet-Higgins and Murrell[8], whose con-

VI   VII

vention we have adopted because of its general applicability, describe such a transition as an electron transfer, symbolized as an E.T. absorption band. The π–π* band of olefins and aromatic compounds, and the $n \rightarrow \pi$* bands of carbonyl compounds are described as local excitation (L.E.) bands. It is felt that this nomenclature avoids some of the confusing terms which have been used previously. A selection of synonymous descriptions of various absorption types is included in Table 5. Note that in some other systems of nomenclature distinction is not made between π–π* and E.T. bands.

TABLE 5. TRANSITION AND SHIFT NOMENCLATURE [7, 7a, 8, 9, 13].

Transition (mμ)	Preferred notation †	Alternative notation
C=C (190)	$\pi \to \pi^*$	—
C=C—C=C (214)	$\pi \to \pi^*$	K-Band
C=C—C=O (215–230)	E.T.	K-Band
(> 300)	L.E. of C=O $(n \to \pi^*)$	R-Band
⬡ (180, 203, 255)	L.E.	E_1, E_2, B-Bands††
⬡—C$\stackrel{X}{\diagdown}$	E.T.	K-Band
⬡—$\ddot{\mathrm{X}}$	E.T. or $p - \pi$	$\pi -- p$
Shift		
$\xrightarrow{\lambda}$	Red (to longer wavelength)	Bathochromic
$\xleftarrow{\lambda}$	Blue (to shorter wavelength)	Hypsochromic

† Used throughout this work.
†† Alternative spectroscopic nomenclature for these transitions will also be found in references 7 (a) and 13.

As an example of the use of this nomenclature consider the case of dimethylaniline (VIII). The 296 mμ band corresponds to the displaced 255 mμ (L.E.) band of benzene. The 250 mμ absorption is intense, and marks the electron

NMe$_2$ CHO

VIII   IX

λ_{max} 200, 250, 296 mμ[10] λ_{max} 241, 279, 320 mμ[11]

transfer, while the 200 mμ band corresponds to the 203·5 mμ (L.E.) band of benzene. Benzaldehyde (IX) has a three banded spectrum. The weak intensity band at 320 mμ is assigned to the local excitation $(n \to \pi^*)$ of the carbonyl group displaced from 280–300 mμ. The 279 mμ band of benzaldehyde corresponds to the L.E. band of benzene (255 mμ) and the 241 mμ peak marks the E.T. transition. We shall have occasion to note the profound effect of steric hindrance on the E.T. bands of several classes of organic molecule.

Charge–Resonance Spectra[3]

The effect of introducing a permanent charge into a chromophoric system is shown in the difference between the absorption spectra of triphenylmethane (X) and its ion (XI). The resonance of the charge in cyanine dyes (as XII) is also an example of this effect. An important example[12] from the chemistry of vision is the charge-resonance spectrum of indicator yellow (part formula XIII) in acid solution, λ_{max} 440 mμ. Indicator yellow is produced from the major pig-

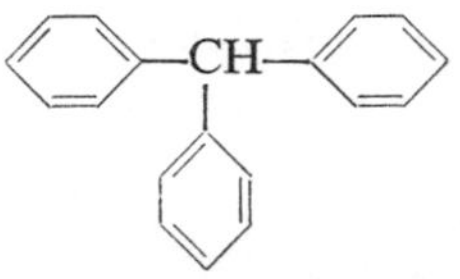

X λ_{max} 264 mμ 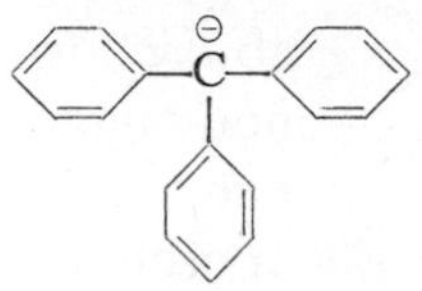   XI λ_{max} 282, 480 mμ

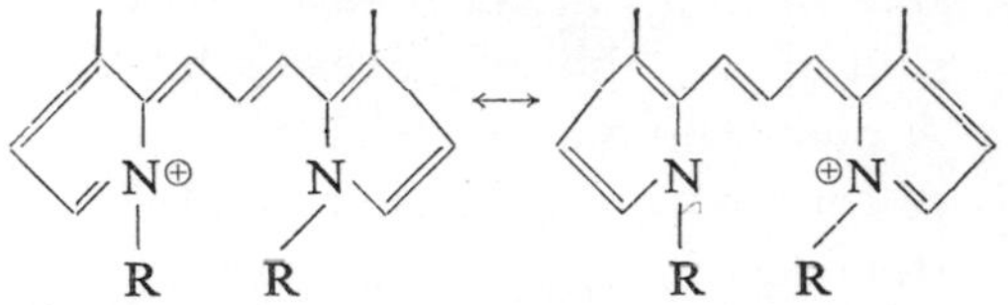

XII

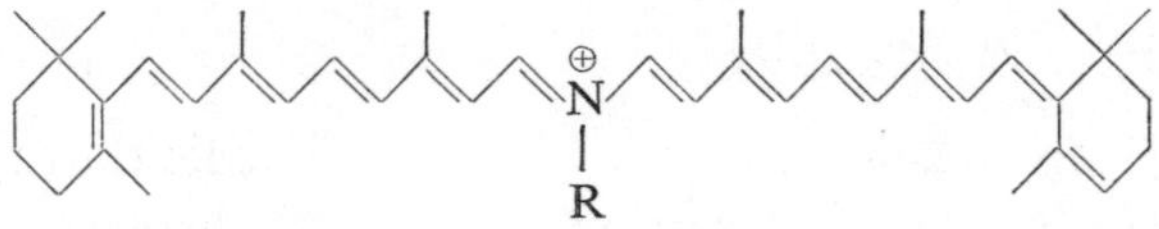

XIII

ment of the retina, rhodopsin, on illumination and is a vitamin A aldehyde-protein complex. Charge–resonance spectra are probably of great significance in many biological systems, but are not discussed further in this work as the requisite details of structure–spectral relationships have, not as yet, been sufficiently developed.

Bibliography of Ultraviolet Spectroscopy

The reading list given on p. 432 is recommended for amplification of many of the topics considered herein and for valuable information regarding theory, experimentation and instrumentation.

SYMBOLS AND DEFINITIONS

λ	wavelength
λ_{max}	wavelength at an absorption maximum
λ_{min}	wavelength at an absorption minimum
$m\mu$	millimicron $= 10^{-7}$ cm
Å	ångström unit $= 10^{-8}$ cm
ν	frequency
ε	molecular extinction coefficient
$E_{1\,cm}^{1\%}$	absorption of a 1% solution in cell length 1 cm
$n \to \sigma^*$	non-bonding $\to$ antibonding sigma orbital transition
$n \to \pi^*$	non-bonding $\to$ antibonding pi orbital transition
$\pi \to \pi^*$	pi orbital $\to$ antibonding pi orbital transition
E.T.	electron transfer
L.E.	local excitation
Red shift	shift of λ_{max} to longer wavelengths (bathochromic)
Blue shift	shift of λ_{max} shorter wavelengths (hypsochromic)
Isosbestic point	A point common to the absorption spectral curves of a pH dependent equilibrium of molecular species
Sh.	shoulder
i.	inflexion
Hyperchromic shift	intensity increase
Hypochromic shift	intensity decrease.

REFERENCES

1. E. A. BRAUDE, *Nature, Lond.*, **155**, 753 (1945); *J. Chem. Soc.*, 379, (1950).
2. M. C. WHITING, Private communication.
3. E. A. BRAUDE, *Determination of Organic Structures by Physical Methods* (edited by BRAUDE and NACHOD), pp. 131–95, Academic Press, New York (1955).
4(a). J. R. PLATT, *J. Chem. Phys.*, **19**, 263 (1951).
4(b). S. F. MASON, *Recent Work on Naturally Occurring Nitrogen Heterocyclic Compounds*, Chem. Soc. Special Publication, No. 3, p. 139 (1955).
5. A. P. I. Spectrograms, Project 44.
6. W. C. PRICE, *Chem. Rev.*, **47**, 257 (1947).
7. F. A. MATSEN, *Technique of Organic Chemistry*, vol. IX, p. 629, Interscience, London (1956).
7(a). J. W. SIDMAN, *Chem. Rev.*, **58**, 689 (1958).
8. H. C. LONGUET-HIGGINS and J. N. MURRELL, *Proc. Phys. Soc.*, **68**A, 60 (1955); J. N. MURRELL, *J. Chem. Soc.*, 3779 (1956).
9. A. E. GILLAM and E. S. STERN, *An Introduction to Electronic Absorption Spectroscopy*, Arnold, London (1957).
10. H. B. KLEVENS and J. R. PLATT, *J. Amer. Chem. Soc.*, **71**, 1714 (1949).
11. S. IMANISHI, *J. Chem. Phys.*, **19**, 389 (1951).
12. R. A. MORTON, *Nature, Lond.*, **153**, 69 (1944); F. D. COLLINS, *ibid.*, **171**, 469 (1953).
13. S. F. MASON, *Quart. Rev. Chem. Soc.*, **15**, 287 (1961).

CHAPTER 1

SINGLE CHROMOPHORES

1.1. ABSORPTION DUE TO ELECTRON LONE PAIRS IN SATURATED SYSTEMS

IN the main, the first absorption maximum of covalently saturated compounds containing hetero-atoms and corresponding to an excitation of a p-orbital electron to an antibonding orbital ($n \rightarrow \sigma^*$) occurs at a wavelength too short for ready measurement by conventional instruments. A further disadvantage in applying diagnosis to systems containing this type of chromophore is that the relatively weak bands tend to be obscured by other, more active, absorbing groups present in the natural product. This is particularly evident in the case of $\geq$C—O—, $\geq$C—Hal and $\geq$C—N— functions. Several representative members of this category are listed in Table 1.1.

Alcohols and Ethers

The transparency of the $\geq$C—O—R chromophore down to 185 mμ, although placing the grouping outside the category of an absorbing species for all practical purposes, explains the wide use of alcohol, ether, and water as spectroscopic solvents.

Sulphides

The $\geq$C—S—R moiety, although showing absorption of moderate intensity at 195 and 215 mμ, has not hitherto been quoted extensively in diagnostic studies. Di- and polysulphides, however, give rise to low intensity absorption ($\varepsilon \sim 300$) in the easily accessible range of the ultraviolet spectrum. In particular, the biologically active 6,8-thioctic acid (No. 14) has a band at 334 mμ (ε 160). The effect of ring size on the —S—S— absorption is also noted (Nos. 13, 15, 16).

TABLE 1.1. $n \rightarrow \sigma^*$ ABSORPTION OF COVALENTLY SATURATED SYSTEMS

	λ_{max} (mμ)	ε	Solvent	Reference
Alcohol				
1. CH_3OH	177	200	H	(1)
Sulphide				
2. $CH_3CH_2 \cdot S \cdot CH_2CH_3$	194	4600	H	(2)
	215	1600		
Amines				
3. $(CH_3)_3N$	199	3950	H	(3)
4. $(C_2H_5)_2NH$	193	2500	H	(4)
5. $(C_2H_5)_2NH \cdot HCl$	185	–	W	(4)
Alkyl halides				
6. CH_3Cl	173	200	H	(5)
7. C_3H_7Br	208	300	H	(6)
8. CH_3I	259	400	H	(6)
9. CH_2Cl_2	216†	–	–	(7)
10. $CHCl_3$	229†	–	–	(7)
11. CCl_4	236†	–	–	(7)
Disulphides				
12. $C_2H_5 \cdot S \cdot S \cdot C_2H_5$	194	5500	H	(8)
	250	380		
13.	334	160	A	(9)
14.	334	100	A	(9, 10)
15.	295	300	A	(9)
16.	252	475	A	(9)
Peroxide				
17. $CH_3 \cdot O \cdot O \cdot CH_3$	<220	–	H	(11)
Ozonide				
18.	<220	–	H	(12)

† Transmission ceases in this area: these values are not true maxima.

Amines (Table 1.2)

The saturated $-\overset{|}{\underset{|}{C}}-\overset{|}{N}-$ linkage gives rise to fairly intense absorption in the 200 mμ region. Thus trimethylamine (No. 3) has λ_{max} 199 mμ ($\varepsilon \sim$ 3950). Some correlation between the structure and electronic absorption of saturated amines

TABLE 1.2. ABSORPTION OF SATURATED AMINES

Amine	λ_{max} (mμ)	ε	Solvent	Reference
1. Et$_2$NH	193	2500	H	(4)
2. Et$_2$NH·HCl	<185	–	W	(4)
3. Me$_3$N	199	3950	H	(3)
4.	200	4000	V	(15)
5.	213	1600	E	(16)
6.	214	2300	E	(16)
7.	218	1700	E	(16)
8.	215	3100	E	(16)
9.	214	5000	E	(16)

is illustrated in Table 1.2. As might be expected, addition of mineral acid causes a blue shift in the spectrum of saturated amines, a reflection of the reduced delocalization of the lone pair now involved in salt formation (Nos. 1, 2).

Alkyl Halides[5, 6, 7]

The effect of increasing electronegativity in the series alk I, alk Br, alk Cl is evident from their decreasing λ_{max} values (Table 1.1). Inspection of the λ_{max} values of the series $CH_3Cl \rightarrow CCl_4$ reveals that while methylene chloride is a satisfactory solvent down to 225 mμ and frequently used in ozonization studies, the high end absorption of chloroform renders it unsatisfactory for use below 230 mμ (1 mm cells).

Ozonides and Peroxides[11, 12]

The —O—O— chromophore absorbs at *ca.* 200 mμ. Ozonides $\left[\underset{}{>}C\underset{\underset{O}{\diagdown\diagup}}{\overset{O—O}{\diagup\diagdown}}C< \right]$ although having λ_{max} at <200 mμ can be estimated by using ε values at 220 mμ.

It may be inferred from the rather meagre data presented above that absorption due to the lone pair has not found extensive use in natural product studies. This is so not only because of the weak and inaccessible nature of such absorption, but also because in many cases it is a more informative operation to examine the infrared absorption where characteristic vibration and stretching frequencies of saturated linkages are not necessarily masked by the presence of groupings of considerable chromophoric activity. However, for very accurate spectral correlations it may be useful to determine the end absorption of a saturated framework and to use this as a "background" factor while examining the effect of placement of active chromophores within the framework. This has in fact been carried out in the case of the isolated double bond[21].

1.2. OLEFINS

The electronic transition ($\pi \rightarrow \pi^*$) observed in the spectrum of olefinic compounds may be ascribed to the local excitation of a π-electron to an anti-

TABLE 1.3. $\pi \rightarrow \pi^*$ ABSORPTION OF ACYCLIC OLEFINS (IN n-HEPTANE)

Olefin		λ_{max} (mμ)	ε	Reference
1.	$CH_2=CH_2$	162·5	15,000	(17)
		174·3	5500	
2.	$CH_3(CH_2)_5CH=CH_2$	177	13,000	(17)
3.	$C_5H_{11}CH\overset{t}{=}CH \cdot CH_3$	179	15,000	(17)
4.	$C_5H_{11}CH\overset{c}{=}CH \cdot CH_3$	183	13,000	(17)
5.	$(CH_3)_2C=C(CH_3)_2$	196·5	11,500	(18)

bonding π-orbital. It is a necessary consequence that the C—C bond is free to rotate, thus accounting for the phenomenon of photo-induced *cis–trans* iso-merism. The position of maximal absorption of the *acyclic* double bond occurs in the 180 mμ region (Table 1.3). Small differences are discernible in the spectra of *cis*- and *trans*-disubstituted olefins (Nos. 3, 4) but, here again, infrared assign-ments form a superior method of diagnosis. However, the tetra-substituted double bond (No. 5), difficult to detect by other physical means, does absorb at a wavelength (~ 200 mμ) within the compass of modern instruments.

Alicyclic Olefins

The spectrum of cyclohexene resembles that of a *cis*-2-alkene. The effect of progressive alkyl (or ring residue) substitution on the cyclohexene spectrum may be seen by reference to Table 1.4. Before considering the data reproduced in this table, it is convenient to recall the classification of the double bond types one is likely to encounter in natural products. In a recent study, Ellington and Meakins[19] have classified olefins in the following way:

		Type
[Compounds containing no double bond]		*a*
Cis-disubstituted	$\overset{H}{\underset{C}{>}}C=C\overset{H}{\underset{C}{<}}$	*b*
Trans-disubstituted	$\overset{H}{\underset{C}{>}}C=C\overset{C}{\underset{H}{<}}$	*c*
Exo-methylene	$\overset{C}{\underset{C}{>}}C=CH_2$	*d*
Tri-substituted and exo- to a ring	$\overset{H}{\underset{C}{>}}C=C\overset{C}{\underset{C}{<}}$	*e*
Tetra-substituted	$\overset{C}{\underset{C}{>}}C=C\overset{C}{\underset{C}{<}}$	
	Not exocyclic	*f*
	exo- to 1 ring	*g*
	exo- to 2 rings	*h*

Returning now to Table 1.4, it should be noted that the λ_{max} values are corrected for stray light effects which often make accurate location of true maxima in the 190–200 mμ region rather difficult. From the fairly representative range of steroidal olefins studied, the following generalizations may be made:

TABLE 1.4. ABSORPTION DATA FOR ALICYCLIC OLEFINS [18]

No.	Compound	Type	Solvent	λ_{max} (mμ)	ε
1.		b	C	190	7250
			A	194	4580
2.		f	C	196·5	11,500
			A	198	13,200
3.		f	C	194·5	8900
			A	196	8150
4.		$b+f$	C	193	8500
			A	195	7600
5.		$2b+f$	C	191·5	7800
			A	195	6500
6.		b	C	189	6500
			A	194	3500
7.		b	C	196·5	8900
			A	197	7600
8.		f	C	193	10,300
9.		b	C	190	6400
10.		b	C	190	6400
11.		b	C	190	7100
12.		e	C	194	10,700
13.		e	C	197	13,200
			A	199	14,000

† Implies cholestane residue.

TABLE 1.4—(contd.)

No.	Compound	Type	Solvent	λ_{max} (mμ)	ε
14.		e	A	199	9200
15.		e	C	193	8300
16.		e	C A	193 197	9000 7800
17.		b	C	190·5	7800
18.		e	C	189·5	6900
19.		e	C A	190·5 195·5	8500 6400
20.		f	C	199	8300
21.		e	C A	193·5 196·5	7600 7100

TABLE 1.4—(contd.)

No.	Compound	Type	Solvent	λ_{max} (mμ)	ε
22.		b	C A	193 197	10,700 9200
23.		h	C A	206 205	11,200 11,800
24.		h	C A	203 201·5	12,500 12,100
25.		e	C A	192·5 197	8400 6800
26.		h	C A	199 200	14,800 14,500
27.		g	C A	205 204	8300 8700

TABLE 1.5. CLASSIFICATION OF OLEFIN ABSORPTION [19, 20]

	Type	λ_{max} (mμ) †	λ_{max}	ε_{210}
—CH=CH—	b, c	196	6200–7500	200–1900
>=CH₂	d	195–196	8700–9300	2200–2500
—CH=C⟨C C	e	195–196	8100–9700	1400–3200
—CH=C⟨C C at △ 7:8*		196–197	5700–7500	4300–4700
C C >C=C< C C	f	196–198	7300–9000	3400–4700
C C Ring >C=C< Ring C C	h	204	11,300–12,200	10,000–10,700

† For EtOH.
* Steroid numbering.

(a) The tetra-substituted double bond exocyclic to two rings (type *h*) (as A) can be recognized with certainty both from its band position ($\lambda_{max} \sim 204$ mμ) and its intensity (log $\varepsilon > 4.0$) of absorption.

A

(b) The overlap between λ_{max} values for other types (*b–g*) (Table 1.5) of double bond does not allow of unequivocal assignment of substitution pattern.

(c) It is evident that the *position* of a double bond within the steroid or triterpene framework is an important factor in the location of maximal absorption.

Thus, at present, the measurement of true maxima of olefins using commercially available instruments cannot be used (except in the cases noted) to permit assignment of double bond type. This conclusion is reached by Meakins[19], who showed (Table 1.5), in a study related to that summarized in Table 1.4, that only type *h* bonds were clearly distinguishable. The results of these related studies (Tables 1.4 and 1.5) are sufficient to indicate the scope of the application of ultraviolet analysis to the problem using routine equipment. In a previous study. Bladon *et al.*[20] had shown that consideration of intensity values of an olefin at selected wavelengths above the position of maximal absorption allows of a fairly reliable diagnosis. These intensity values are summarized in Table 1.5, column 5, for wavelength 210 mμ. Thus, use of the

TABLE 1.6. ABSORPTION OF ALICYCLIC OLEFINS (AFTER TURNER[21])

No.	Compound type	Bond type	λ_{max} (mμ)†	ε	Av. λ_{max}
1.		b	183	7500	
2.		b	183	6750	182–188
3.		b	185	9700	
4.		"e"	188	7100	
5.		e	189	7500	188–193
6.		"e"	210	5400	
7.		f	200	8900	
8.		f	200	7000	196–200
9.		h	208	11,200	

† Hexane solution.

combined data in Table 1.5 would permit unequivocal identification of both type h and Δ^7-trisubstituted olefins, the latter displaying abnormally low ε_{max} values.

These difficulties have been resolved to a certain extent by Turner[21]. Using a modified vacuum ultraviolet spectrophotometer which allows of facile measurement to 180 mμ this author was able to determine the real maxima of a number of steroid and terpene olefins in hexane and acetonitrile solutions. The values for λ_{max} (measured from the published graphs) are shown in Table 1.6 and demonstrate that even with this further instrumental refinement†, the band head in many cases is sufficiently broad[64] to cause overlap of average frequencies of specific bond types listed in Tables 1.5 and 1.6. Some typical spectra of isolated double bonds are shown in Fig. 1.1 (a), (b).

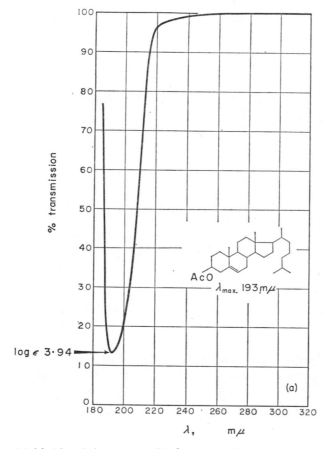

FIG. 1.1 (a) Absorbtion curve of 3 β-Acetoxycholest-5-ene in cyclohexane. (After Stich, Rotzer and Reichstein, *Helv. Chim. Acta*, **42**, 1484, 1959.)

The presence of a second double bond separated by at least two single bonds from an ethylenic centre will, in general, give rise to the spectrum obtained by summation of the contributing absorption bands. This principle of summation (and subtraction) of spectra of non-conjugated chromophores has

† For a recent critical review of double bond absorption measurement see reference 63.

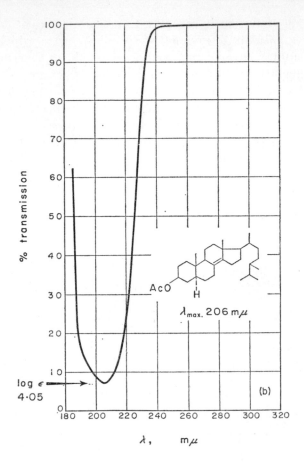

FIG. 1.1 (b) Absorption curve of 3β-acetoxyergost-8,14-ene in cyclohexane. (After Stich, Rotzer and Reichstein, *Helv. Chim. Acta*, **42**, 1484, 1959.)

been used with excellent results in many natural product studies. The operation of this concept may, however, become fraught with difficulty when the geometry of the molecular species imposes chromophoric interaction leading to new and often unpredictable spectral properties.

Polar Substituents

The attachment of a hetero-atom bearing a lone electron pair (e.g. O, N, S, Hal.) to an ethylenic double bond allows a more probable electronic transition of the following type to operate:

The maximum shifts in the predicted sense ($N \approx S >$ Hal. $> O$) is illustrated by the examples in Table 1.7. Thus, while the presence of a methoxyl group (No. 2) produces a moderate shift ($+28$ mμ), the —SMe and —NMe$_2$ groups (Nos. 4, 5) display a large displacement to the red ($+60$ mμ).

TABLE 1.7. EFFECT OF POLAR GROUPS ON OLEFIN ABSORPTION

		λ_{max} (mμ)	ε	Solvent	Reference
1.	CH$_2$=CH$_2$	162·5	15,000	H	(17)
2.	CH$_2$=CH—OMe	190	10,000	–	(22)
3.	CH$_2$=CH—Cl	185	10,000	–	(22)
4.	CH$_2$=CH—SMe	228	8,000	–	(22)
5.	EtCH=CH—N⟨⟩	228	10,000	–	(23)
6.	⟨⟩	ca. 180	10,000		(24)
7.	NH·COMe ... H	240	6660	A	(25)
8.	...N... Et	238	7200	E	(16)

Ring Size

Reference to Table 1.4 (Nos. 1, 7, 8) reveals that the size of alicyclic ring containing an isolated double bond does not impose a predictable effect upon the position of maximal absorption.

1.3. ALKYNES

Acetylene shows maximal absorption at 173 mμ in the vapour state, although Table 1.8 includes several systems containing the triple bond in isolation, it is obvious that the main absorption is outside the useful range of the ordinary spectrophotometer. The alkylated acetylenes do, however, show weaker absorption (ε 100) at *ca.* 220 mμ.

TABLE 1.8. ABSORPTION OF SIMPLE ALKYNES[17, 26]

	λ_{max} (mμ)	ε	Solvent
HC≡CH	173	6000	V
CH$_3$(CH$_2$)$_5$—C≡CH	185	2200	H
	222·5	120	
CH$_3$(CH$_2$)$_4$—C≡C—CH$_3$	177·5	10,000	H
	196	2000	
	222·5	160	

1.4 CARBONYL COMPOUNDS

Acyclic Ketones

The absorption bands of non-conjugated ketones and aldehydes at 280 and 190 mμ correspond to two possible excitations of one of the oxygen lone pair electrons (L.E. bands). In the long wavelength transition the electron is raised to the antibonding π-orbital ($n \rightarrow \pi^*$ transition) while the shorter wavelength band is ascribed to the $n \rightarrow \sigma^*$ transition of the $>$C=O group.† This rather weak absorption is exemplified by acetone which has λ_{max} 279 (ε 13) and 188 (ε 1860) mμ in hexane. Spectral analysis of simple ketones is thus difficult, the long wavelength band being not only very weak but often broad, and the low wavelength band is found at the limit of instrumental reach. Most studies have been concerned with measurement of the former band, and several examples are given in Table 1.9. Although it would appear that progressive alkyl or ring residue substitution of the α-hydrogen atom produces a fairly regular bathochromic shift (Nos. 1, 2, 3, 4, 6) this effect has not found application in structural studies.

Cyclopropyl Ketones

The hyperconjugative effect of the attachment of a cyclopropane residue to the carbon atom α to a carbonyl group is reflected in a shift of the $n \rightarrow \sigma^*$ band. to the accessible (210 mμ) region of the spectrum (Nos. 47–52).†† The $n \rightarrow \pi^*$ band undergoes an intensity increase without much change in maximal wavelength.

Alicyclic Ketones

Cyclohexanone (λ_{max} 285 mμ) absorbs at the same wavelength as a di-alkylated acetone. As in the acyclic series, further alkyl substitution displaces the $n \rightarrow \pi^*$ band to over 300 mμ in the case of the 2,2,6,6-tetrasubstituted deriv-

† see p. 8
†† This absorption may be a modified E. T. band

TABLE 1.9. SELECTIVE ABSORPTION OF SATURATED KETONES

No.	Compound	$n \to \pi^*$ band		$n \to \sigma^*$ band		Solvent	Reference
		λ_{max}	ε	λ_{max}	ε		
A. Acyclic							
1.		270·6 279	16 13	— 188	— 1860	A C	(27)
2.		277	19·4	—	—	A	(27)
3.		281	21·2	—	—	A	(27)
4.		285	21·2	—	—	A	(27)
5.		281	17·5	—	—	A	(27)
6.		295	20	—	—	A	(27)
7.		281	33	—	—	A	(28)
8.		279	23	—	—	A	(28)
9.		281	28	—	—	A	(28)
B. Alicyclic							
10.		280	18	—	—	H	(29)
11.		299	20	—	—	H	(29)
12.		285	14	—	—	H	(29)
13.		281	12	—	—	H	(29)

TABLE 1.9—(contd.)

No.	Compound	$n \to \pi^*$ band		$n \to \sigma^*$ band		Solvent	Reference
		λ_{max}	ε	λ_{max}	ε		
B. Alicyclic—(contd.)							
14.		283	14	—	—	H	(30)
15.		290	23	—	—	H	(30)
16.		293	40	—	—	H	(30)
17.		305	21	—	—	H	(30)
18.		296 292	26 35	189 195·5	2400 1500	C A	(18)
19.		279	30	194	1660	A	(18)
20.		293	32	195	6000†	A	(18)
21.		280	40	—	—	A	(31)
22.		287	40	—	—	A	(31)

† C=C and C=O intensities superimposed.

TABLE 1.9—(contd.)

No.	Compound	$n \to \pi^*$ band		$n \to \sigma^*$ band		Solvent	Reference
		λ_{max}	ε	λ_{max}	ε		
B. Alicyclic—(contd.)							
23.†		291	32	—	—	A	(31)

No.	Compound	λ_{max}	ε	$\Delta\lambda$	Solvent	Reference
C. Halogenated Ketones						
24. (= 22)		287	40	0	A	(31)
25.		313	158	+26	A	(31)
26.		282	40	−4	A	(31)
27.		286	23	0	A	(31)
28.		282	39	−4	A	(31)
29.		279	40	−7	A	(31)

† β-Amyrane residue.

TABLE 1.9—(contd.)

No.	Compound	λ_{max}	ε	$\Delta\lambda$	Solvent	Reference
	C. Halogenated Ketones—(contd.)					
30.		256–258	72	−30	MeOH	(32)
31.		280	18	−6	A	(32)
	D. Ketols and their Acetates†					
32.		280	40	0	A	(31)
33.		299·5	59	+19·5	A	(31)
34.		290	85	+10	A	(31)
35.		298	29·5	0	A	(31)
36.		313	49	+15	A	(31)

† See also references (65) and (66)

TABLE 1.9—(contd.)

No.	Compound	λ_{max}	ε	$\Delta\lambda$	Solvent	Reference
37.		285·5	47	—12·5	A	(31)
E. Cyclopentanones						
38.		289	32	0	A	(31)
39.		297·5	29	+8·5	A	(31)
40.		306	100	+17	A	(31)
41.		312	89	+23	Ch	(31)
42.	†	293	—	0	A	(33)
43.		316	—	+23	A	(33)
44.		316	—	+23	A	(33)

† Androstane residue

TABLE 1.9—(contd.)

No.	Compound	λ_{max}	ε	$\Delta\lambda$	Solvent	Reference
45.		299	—	0	A	(33)
46.		316	—	+17	A	(33)

No.	Compound	$n \rightarrow \pi^*$		$n \rightarrow \sigma^*$		Solvent	Reference
		λ_{max}	ε	λ_{max}	ε		
F. Cyclopropyl Ketones							
47.		270	21·3	206	1310	A	(34)
48.		280	35	210	2470	A	(35)
49.		275	62	214	2990	A	(35)
50.		—	—	215	2650	A	(36)
51.		293	60	213	2650	A	(37)
52.		288	56	215 214	4400 4500	A A	(38) (61)

ative (No. 17). This same shift is evident in the case of steroidal ketones (*cf*. No. 19 with, say, Nos. 18 and 20) where not only substitution pattern but also the *position* of the $>C=O$ group within the tetracyclic framework appears to influence the λ_{max} value (*cf*. Nos. 20 and 21). The high-intensity ($n \to \sigma^*$) band is not affected in a regular way by such substitution.

Polar Substituents

Cookson[31] has analysed the effect of polar substituents on the $n \to \pi^*$ band of saturated cyclic ketones. In the case of conformationally rigid steroid and triterpenoid ketones, a distinction between equatorial (*e*) and axial (*a*) halogen, hydroxyl and acetoxyl groups attached to the α-carbon atom is possible. Examples (Nos. 21–45) will be found in Table 1.9. The average shifts are summarized below and serve to complement the corresponding infrared values[13]:

α-Substituent	$\Delta\lambda(m\mu)$	
	e	*a*
Cl	$-\ 7$	$+22$
Br	$-\ 5$	$+28$
OH	-12	$+17$
OAc	$-\ 5$	$+10$

I
λ_{max} 309 mμ

II
λ_{max} 279 mμ

Example. Let us consider the epimeric 3β-acetoxy-6-bromocholestan-7-ones. The 6β-isomer (I) has an axial bromo substituent capable of electronic interaction with the $>C=O$ group at position 7 and absorbs at 309 mμ, a bathochromic shift of 26 mμ compared with the unsubstituted ketone. The 6α-isomer (II) on the other hand absorbs at a wavelength 4 mμ less than the parent ketone, the latter having λ_{max} 283 mμ.

Ring Size

In general, the ring size of a cycloalkanone is determined conclusively by examination of the carbonyl stretching frequency in the 1700–1800 cm^{-1} region of the infrared spectrum. Additional confirmation can be provided,

III

especially in the five or six-membered examples, by determination of the λ_{max} value (Nos. 11, 12, Table 1.9). This could be of real diagnostic value in the case of a chromophore such as III, where resolution† of the $>C=O$ stretching frequency may be insufficient. Here, the ultraviolet spectrum (λ_{max} 300 mμ; ε, 20) should provide the required confirmation of a cyclopentanone chromophore.

α-Diketones

The acyclic α-diketones (e.g. diacetyl) exist in the preferred *S-trans* configuration (IV). The spectrum contains *two* weak bands (ε, 10–20) at *ca.* 280 and 450 mμ respectively (Table 1.10). On the other hand, *cyclic* α-diketones as V (a)

TABLE 1.10. α-DICARBONYL COMPOUNDS

	λ_{max} (mμ)	ε	Solvent	Reference
CH₃CO·CHO	{444 {280	14 20	E	(39)
CO·CHO H	440	20	A	(40)
CH₃·CO·CO·CH₃	{420 {282	10 19	A	(39)
$n = 1$	466	31	A	(41)
$n = 2$	380 298	11 29	A	(41)
$n = 3$	337 299	34 34	A	(41)
$n = 4$	343 295	21 34	A	(41)
$n = 14$	384 296	22 43	A	(41)

often exist in the diosphenol form V (b), a chromophore treated separately in Chapter 2. However, when enolization is prevented either by substitution of the

IV   V (a)   V (b)

† The integrated intensity value will of course indicate the presence of two carbonyl functions.

methylene groups α to the dicarbonyl function or by operation of unfavourable steric effects[14], the cyclic α-diketones show the two weak $n \rightarrow \pi^*$ bands, the displacement of the longer wavelength band reflecting the degree of inter-action between the $\rangle C=O$ groups. The maxima for the ascending series of non-enolizable α-diketones are given in Table 1.10. Examination of the data reveals that while cyclopentanedione (azimuthal angle $<10°$) shows CO–CO interaction comparable with acyclic diketones, a minimum interaction is reached at ring size seven ($\theta = 90°$). The low wavelength ($n \rightarrow \sigma^*$) band occurs in the 195–200 mμ region.

β-Diketones

The ultraviolet spectra of β-di- and tri-ketones are dependent on the degree of enolization of the species under examination. The enolization (VI $\rightarrow$ VII) may be suppressed by steric or solvent effect. Thus when measured in a polar

$$R—CO \cdot CH_2 \cdot COR' \rightleftharpoons R—\underset{\underset{OH}{|}}{C}=CH \cdot CO \cdot R'$$

VI   VII

solvent, the spectrum of acetyl acetone shows that the molecule exists mainly in the diketo form (VIII). However, in a hydrocarbon solvent where the enol form is stabilized by intramolecular hydrogen bonding, we observe the spectrum of a β-hydroxy-α,β-unsaturated ketone (IX). Addition of sodium hydroxide solution shifts the maximum even further to the red (X).[64]

$CH_3—CO \cdot CH_2 \cdot CO \cdot CH_3$ $\rightleftharpoons$

λ_{max} 274 (ε 1500) mμ in water λ_{max} 271 (ε 12,000) mμ in hexane

VIII   IX

H$^{\oplus}$ ↑↓ OH$^{\ominus}$

λ_{max} 294 mμ in N NaOH (ε 20,000)

X

In very dilute ethanolic solution, the spectrum of cyclic β-diketones shifts from 260 to ca. 280 mμ due to intervention of charged ionic species (as X). This effect is considered further in Chapter 2.

Aldehydes

The $n \rightarrow \pi^*$ band of saturated aldehydes occurs at *ca.* 290 mμ ($\varepsilon \sim 15$), while the low wavelength band is at 193 mμ in acetaldehyde. α-Alkyl substitution does not appear to affect the 290 mμ band to a measurable extent (Table 1.11), except in the case of angular aldehydes (No. 3).

Carboxylic Acids, Esters and Lactones

The —CO$_2$R grouping absorbs weakly ($\varepsilon \sim 40$) at 200–205 mμ, a combination of intensity and maximal position which renders diagnosis by electronic absorption almost impossible. There is little difference (± 2 mμ) in the λ_{max} value of an acid, its alkyl ester and the corresponding sodium salt (Table 1.11). Progressive alkyl substitution raises the λ_{max} value to *ca.* 213 mμ (No 7).

α-Keto Acids[22]

The presence of a $>$C$=$O group in the α-position to the carboxyl chromophore (as in pyruvic acid XI) does not produce a typical α-diketone absorption. The spectrum of oxalic acid (XII) would also be regarded as typical of the —CO—CO— chromophore.

TABLE 1.11. MAIN ABSORPTION MAXIMA OF ALDEHYDES, ACIDS AND AMIDES

	λ_{max} (mμ)	ε	Solvent	Reference
1. CH$_3 \cdot$CHO	{193 {292	– 15	H	(18)
2. Me$_3$C$\cdot$CH$=$O	193	45	A	(18)
3. CHO (structure)	309	40	A	(62)
4. CH$_3 \cdot$CO$_2$H	197	60	H	(4)
5. CH$_3 \cdot$CO$_2$Et	201	50	W	(4)
6. CH$_3 \cdot$CO$_2$Na	210 (infl.)	150	W	(4)
7. CH$_3$(CH$_2$)$_{14}$CO$_2$H	210	49·5	W	(42)
8. CH$_3$(CH$_2$)$_{14}$CH(CH$_3$)$\cdot$CH(CH$_3$)$\cdot$CO$_2$H	213	144	A	(42)
9. CH$_3 \cdot$CH$_2$CONH$_2$	175	7000	H †	(43)
10. CH$_2$—CO NH CH$_2$—CO	191	15,200	CH$_3$CN	(43)

† Containing 2% propionitrile.

The same considerations in respect of enolization mentioned in the case of β-diketones apply to the α-keto acids. A fuller discussion of this topic will be reserved until the next chapter.

$$CH_3 \cdot CO \cdot CO_2H \qquad\qquad HO_2C \cdot CO_2H$$

λ_{max} 210 (ε 400) mμ λ_{max} 185 (ε 4000) mμ

330 (ε 7) mμ 250 (ε 50) mμ

XI   XII

Amides and Imides

The use of a vacuum ultraviolet spectrophotometer has enabled Turner[43] to measure the $n \rightarrow \sigma^*$ band of amides with accuracy. In acetonitrile and hexane solution the —CO·NH— chromophore absorbs at 175 mμ. Imides have λ_{max} *ca.* 190 mμ with approximately twice the intensities of the simple amides. The relevant data are presented in Table 1.11.

1.5. ABSORPTION BY THE —N=X GROUPING (TABLE 1.12)

Azomethines

Absorption by the $>C=N-$ group is summarized for some representative examples (Nos. 1–5) in Table 1.12. The low wavelength band at 200 mμ suffers a red shift (+80 mμ) on salt formation (Nos. 1, 2, 3). This effect is to be contrasted with the change to shorter wavelength occasioned by the addition of mineral acid to ethanolic solutions of saturated amines (p. 17). Attachment of a hydroxyl group to the nitrogen atom, although increasing the intensity, does not bring the λ_{max} value into the accessible region. Thus, the oximes of saturated carbonyl compounds do not serve as useful derivatives for spectral–structural correlation.

Nitriles

The unconjugated —C≡N grouping is transparent to 190 mμ and the aliphatic nitriles have found application as solvents for measurement of $>C=C<$ and $>C=O$ absorption in the region 190–210 mμ[21].

Azo Compounds

Aliphatic azo compounds show weak absorption (ε, 10) at about 350 mμ ($n \rightarrow \pi^*$ transition). The corresponding N-oxides (R—N=N—R) are char-
$$\downarrow$$
$$O.$$

TABLE 1.12. ABSORPTION OF THE —N=X CHROMOPHORE

	λ_{max} (mμ)	ε	Solvent	Reference
A. Imines				

1.   H$_2$N—C—NH$_2$·HCl
        ‖
       NH
	265	15	W	(44)

2.   HO$_2$C·CH$_2$·N—C—NH$_2$
          │ ‖
        Me NH
	<220	30–50	W	(44)

3.	255–8	1000	A	(45)
4. >=NOH	193	2000	A	(46)
5. >=NONa	265	200	A	(46)
B. Azo and Azoxy Compounds				
6. >—N=N—< CN CN	345	12	A	(47)

7.   Me—N=N—Me
        ↓
        O
	217
	274
		7250
		43
			A	(48)

8.   >—N=N—<
       ↓
       O
	220·5
	275
		7000
		52
			A	(48)

C. Diazo Compounds				
9. CH$_2$=$\overset{+}{N}$=$\overset{-}{N}$	347·5	4·5	A	(49)
10. EtO$_2$C—CH=$\overset{+}{N}$=$\overset{-}{N}$	⎰249 ⎱377·5	10,050 16	A	(50)
11. HO$_2$CCH(NH$_2$)CH$_2$OCOCH=$\overset{+}{N}$=$\overset{-}{N}$	250·5	19,700	pH 7	(51)
D. Nitroso Compounds				
12. >—N=O	300 665	100 20	E	(52)
13. Br—>—N=O	645	–	iso P	(53)

TABLE 1.12—(contd.)

	λ_{max} (mμ)	ε	Solvent	Reference
E. Nitro Compounds				
14. CH$_3$·NO$_2$	278	20	P	(54)
15. 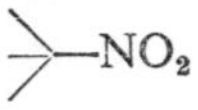 >—NO$_2$	276	27	A	(54)
F. Nitrate				
16. Et·O·NO$_2$	255–60	17	P	(54)
G. N-nitroso				
17. Et—N—N=O	233 350	7400 90	A	(55)
H. Nitrite				
18. nBu—O—N=O	218 313–84 (bands at 10 mμ intervals)	1050 20–40	A	(55)
I. Azide				
19. Et—N=N=N	222 287	150 20		(56)
J. Isocyanate				
20. NaNCO	265	13	W	(46)
21. EtNCS	250	1200	H	(57)

acterized by absorption bands at 220 mμ (ε, 7000) and at 275 mμ (ε, 50). For example, the naturally occurring macrozamin (XIII)[48] has a spectrum almost identical with that of azoxymethane (No. 7, Table 1.12).

$$Me—N=N—CH_2—O—C_6H_{10}O_4—O—C_5H_9O_4$$
$$\downarrow$$
$$O$$

XIII

Diazo Compounds

The $\overset{O}{\overset{\|}{—C}}—CH=\overset{+}{N}=\overset{-}{N}$ chromophore which is found in the amino acid azaserine (XIV) has λ_{max} 250 mμ (ε, 20,000). The striking similarity of this absorption to that of diazoacetic ester (No. 10) was used as confirmatory evidence during

$$N_2CHCO·O·CH_2·CH(NH_2)·CO_2H$$

XIV

the structural elucidation of this mould metabolite.[51] Diazo alkanes absorb weakly at *ca.* 350 mμ.

Nitroso, Nitro Compounds, Azides and Thioisocyanate

Absorption maxima (for a few representative examples) are included in Table 1.12, not because of the frequency of their occurrence in nature, but rather because the isolation of compounds containing groups such as —NO$_2^*$ (β-nitropropionic acid; chloromycetin) and —N=C (xanthocillin-X) from natural sources would indicate that references to such data might be desirable.

1.6. THIOCARBONYL COMPOUNDS

Simple thioketones (R$_2$C=S) are rather unstable. The examples in Table 1.13 are consequently restricted to compounds in which the $>$C=S grouping is

XV

stabilized by the attachment of electron-donating functions such as —NR$_2$.

In this environment the $-\overset{\overset{\text{S}}{\|}}{\text{C}}-$X chromophore shows intense absorption (ε 20,000) in the 250 mμ region. In connection with rotatory dispersion studies

TABLE 1.13. ABSORPTION OF THIONES AND SULPHOXIDES

	λ_{max}	ε	Solvent	Reference
H$_2$N·C·NH$_2$ $\overset{\|}{\text{S}}$	252	15,000	W	(44)
H$_2$N·C·NH·NH$_2$ $\overset{\|}{\text{S}}$	243	13,800	A	(58)
⬡—S—Me ↓ O	210	2500	A	(59)
CH$_3$SO·CH$_2$·CH=CH$_2$	210 / 239	2500 / 2500	A / H	(60)

* See *Proc. Chem. Soc.*, 182 (1963).

some steroidal thioketones have been prepared[68]. Thus XV has λ_{max} 492mμ (ε 12·9) and 239mμ (ε 8770) in dioxan.

Sulphones and Sulphoxides

Sulphones are transparent to 180 mμ but the sulphoxide ($-S \rightarrow O$) grouping gives rise to a solvent dependent maximum (210–230 mμ) as will be seen by reference to Table 1.13.

REFERENCES

1. G. HERZBERG and G. SCHEIBE, *Z. phys. Chem.*, B 7, 390 (1930).
2. E. A. FEHNEL and M. CARMACK, *J. Amer. Chem. Soc.*, **71**, 84 (1949).
3. E. TANNENBAUM, E. M. COFFIN and A. J. HARRISON, *J. Chem. Phys.*, **21**, 311 (1956).
4. H. LEY and B. ARENDS, *Z. phys. Chem.*, B 17, 177 (1932).
5. C. R. ZOBEL and A. B. F. DUNCAN, *J. Amer. Chem. Soc.*, **77**, 2611 (1955).
6. W. AUMULLER, H. FROMHERZ and C. O. STROTHER, *Z. phys. Chem.* B 37, 30 (1937).
7. J. R. LACHER, L. E. HUMMEL, E. F. BOHMFALK and J. D. PARK, *J. Amer. Chem. Soc.*, **72**, 5486 (1950).
8. H. MOHLER and J. SORGE, *Helv. Chim. Acta*, **23**, 1200 (1940).
9. J. A. BARLTROP, P. M. HAYES and M. CALVIN, *J. Amer. Chem. Soc.*, **76**, 4348 (1954).
10. R. C. THOMAS and L. J. REED, *ibid.*, **78**, 6151 (1956).
11. A. RIECHE and K. KOCH, *Ber. dtsch. chem. Ges.*, **75**, 1016 (1942).
12. A. RIECHE, R. MEISTER and H. SANTHOFF, *Liebigs Ann.*, **553**, 187 (1942).
13. *Inter alia* R. N. JONES and co-workers, *J. Amer. Chem. Soc.*, **74**, 2828 (1952).
14. E. WENKERT and B. G. JACKSON, *ibid.*, **80**, 211 (1958).
15. L. W. PICKETT, M. E. CORNING, G. M. WIEDER, D. A. SEMENOW and J. M. BUCKLEY, *ibid.*, **75**, 1618 (1953).
16. N. J. LEONARD and D. M. LOCKE, *ibid.*, **77**, 437 (1955).
17. J. R. PLATT, H. B. KLEVENS and W. C. PRICE, *J. Chem. Phys.*, **17**, 466 (1949).
18. K. STICH, G. ROTZLER and T. REICHSTEIN, *Helv. Chim. Acta*, **42**, 1480 (1959).
19. P. S. ELLINGTON and G. D. MEAKINS, *J. Chem. Soc.*, 697 (1960).
20. P. BLADON, H. B. HENBEST and G. W. WOOD, *ibid.*, 2727 (1952).
21. D. W. TURNER, *ibid.*, 30 (1959).
22. E. A. BRAUDE, *Ann. Rep. Chem. Soc.*, **42**, 105 (1945).
23. K. BOWDEN, E. A. BRAUDE, E. R. H. JONES and B. C. L. WEEDON, *J. Chem. Soc.*, 45 (1946).
24. L. W. PICKETT, M. MUNTZ and E. M. McPHERSON, *J. Amer. Chem. Soc.*, **73**, 4862 (1951).
25. G. ROSENCRANZ, O. MANCERA, F. SONDHEIMER and C. DJERASSI, *J. Org. Chem.*, **21**, 520 (1956).
26. W. C. PRICE and A. D. WALSH, *Trans. Faraday Soc.*, **41**, 381 (1945).
27. F. O. RICE, *J. Amer. Chem. Soc.*, **42**, 727 (1920).
28. R. P. MARIELLA and R. R. RAUBE, *ibid.*, **74**, 518 (1952).
29. S. W. BENSON and G. B. KISTIAKOWSKY, *ibid.*, **64**, 80 (1942).
30. Mme. RAMART-LUCAS and M. CORNUBERT, *Bull. Soc. Chim.*, 4, **53**, 744 (1933).
31. R. C. COOKSON, *J. Chem. Soc.*, 282 (1954); R. C. COOKSON and S. H. DANDEGAONKER, *ibid.*, 352 (1955).
32. C. DJERASSI, I. FORNAGUERA and O. MANCERA, *J. Amer. Chem. Soc.*, **81**, 2383 (1959).
33. J. FISHMAN and C. DJERASSI, *Experientia*, **16**, 138 (1960).
34. G. W. CANNON, A. A. SANTILLI and P. SHENIAN, *J. Amer. Chem. Soc.*, **81**, 1660 (1959).
35. R. H. EASTMAN, *ibid.*, **76**, 4115 (1954).

36. G. Büchi and D. M. White, *J. Amer. Chem. Soc.*, **79**, 750 (1957).
37. M. Palmade and G. Ourisson, *Bull. Soc. Chim.*, **5**, 886 (1958).
38. D. Arigoni, H. Bosshard, G. Büchi, O. Jeger and L. J. Krebaum, *Helv. Chim. Acta*, **40**, 1732 (1957).
39. S.-T. Woo and S.-T. Chang, *Trans. Faraday Soc.*, **41**, 157 (1945).
40. G. A. Fleisher and E. C. Kendall, *J. Org. Chem.*, **16**, 573 (1951).
41. N. J. Leonard and P. M. Mader, *J. Amer. Chem. Soc.*, **70**, 2707 (1948).
42. J. Cason and G. Sumrell, *J. Org. Chem.*, **16**, 1177 (1951).
43. D. W. Turner, *J. Chem. Soc.*, 4555 (1957).
44. A. Castille and E. Ruppol, *Bull. Soc. chim. Biol.*, **10**, 623 (1928).
45. O. E. Edwards, E. H. Clarke and B. Douglas, *Canad. J. Chem.*, **32**, 235 (1954).
46. H. Ley and H. Wingchen, *Ber. dtsch. chem. Ges.*, **67**, 501 (1934).
47. C. G. Overberger, M. T. O'Shaunessy and H. Shalit, *J. Amer. Chem. Soc.*, **71**, 2661 (1949).
48. B. W. Langley, B. Lythgoe and L. S. Rayner, *J. Chem. Soc.*, 4191 (1952).
49. A. Hantzsch and J. Lifschitz, *Ber. dtsch. chem. Ges.*, **45**, 3011 (1912).
50. K. L. Wolf, *Z. phys. Chem.*, **B17**, 46 (1932).
51. S. A. Fussari, T. H. Haskell, R. P. Frohardt and Q. R. Bartz, *J. Amer. Chem. Soc.*, **76**, 2881 (1954).
52. E. C. C. Baly and C. H. Desch, *J. Chem. Soc.*, **93**, 1747 (1908).
53. G. N. Lewis and M. Kasha, *J. Amer. Chem. Soc.*, **67**, 994 (1945).
54. R. N. Haszeldine, *J. Chem. Soc.*, 252 (1953).
55. R. N. Haszeldine and B. J. H. Mattinson, *ibid.*, 4172 (1955).
56. Yu N. Sheinker, *Dokl. Akad. Nauk. SSSR*, **77**, 1043 (1951).
57. M. Pestemer and B. Litschauer, *Monatsh. Chem.*, **65**, 239 (1935).
58. K. L. Evans and A. E. Gillam, *J. Chem. Soc.*, 565 (1943).
59. H. P. Koch, *ibid.*, 2892 (1950).
60. P. Karrer, N. J. Antia and R. Schwyzer, *Helv. Chim. Acta*, **34**, 1392 (1951).
61. D. H. R. Barton, P. de Mayo and M. Shafiq, *J. Chem. Soc.*, 140 (1958).
62. L. F. Fieser and M. Fieser, *Steroids*, p. 778 and refs. cited, Reinhold, New York (1959).
63. T. H. Applewhite and R. A. Micheli, *Tetrahedron Letters*, **16**, 560 (1961).
64. J. H. Chapman and A. C. Parker, *J. Chem. Soc.*, 2675 (1961).
65. C. Djerassi, J. Fishman and T. Nambara, *Experientia*, **17**, 565 (1961).
66. J. Fishman and T. Nambara, *Chem. and Ind.*, 79 (1961).
67. G. S. Hammond, W. G. Borduin and G. A. Guter, *J. Amer. Chem. Soc.*, **81**, 4682 (1959).
68. C. Djerassi, *Optical Rotatory Dispersion*, McGraw-Hill, New York (1960).

CHAPTER 2

CONJUGATED CHROMOPHORES

INTENSE selective absorption in the region 200–300 mμ may be taken as evidence that at least two chromophores are present in a conjugated state within the molecule. As discussed earlier (p. 10) such an array of *like* chromophores allows the probable transition of a mobile π-electron to an antibonding orbital. Diene, polyene and poly-yne spectra fall into this category. The conjugation of *unlike* chromophores, as I, results in the possibility of an electron transfer; such a transition is responsible for the main intense absorption band (E.T. band) corresponding to the dipole state (II). In some cases it

$$>\!C\!=\!C\!-\!C\!=\!X \xrightarrow{\;h\nu\;} >\!\overset{\oplus}{C}\!-\!C\!=\!C\!-\!\overset{\ominus}{X}$$

$$\text{I} \qquad\qquad\qquad \text{II}$$

is also possible to locate the weak, displaced $n \rightarrow \pi^*$ (L.E.) band of the $>\!C\!=\!X$ moiety. We shall also see how steric and electronic effects operate on the absorption spectra of conjugated systems. Although our treatment is empirical in nature, the value of the correlations developed on this basis is evident from the number of successful cases which have yielded to interpretation using the concepts described in the sequel. In fact, we may safely state that a minimum requirement of the aspiring natural product chemist is a conversance with the rules available for the calculation of maxima of diene and enone systems. We must also make the important proviso that the investigator must be cognisant of the consequences of apparent exceptions to and contradictions of the existing rules, which must always be regarded as valuable working hypotheses rather than as completely rigid laws of light absorption.

2.1. CONJUGATED DIENES

The absorption of butadiene at 217 mμ (ε 21,000) corresponds to a transition of a π-electron to an antibonding orbital (III $\rightarrow$ IIIa) $\pi - \pi^*$.

$$\text{III} \qquad\qquad \text{IIIa} \qquad\qquad \text{IV}$$

The conjugated dienes are particularly suitable for interpretative analysis since changes in their substitution patterns and geometry have been correlated with spectral shifts to a higher degree than in any other chromophoric system. The parent butadiene and its alkylated derivatives exist in the preferred S-*trans* conformation (III). The S-*cis* conformer (IV), which for practical purposes may be considered only to occur when embodied in a ring system, reflects the necessary increase in electron repulsion by a red shift (40 mμ) in the case of cyclohexadiene (λ_{max} 256 mμ). In accord with the original inference of Mulliken[1a] the intensity of absorption of the S-*cis* dienes is generally considerably lower (ε, 10,000–15,000) than that of the fully transoid dienes (ε, 20,000–30,000). The effect of ring size on diene absorption is illustrated in Table 2.1 (Nos. 17 to 20).

The cyclic dienes, then, fall into two categories, the *heteroannular* dienes (as V) congeneric with butadiene and the *homoannular* dienes (as VI) derived

V   VI

from cyclohexadiene. Now, it is a fortunate consequence of the electronic transitions responsible for the absorption bands of dienes that there is a regular and significant variation of λ_{max} with substitution pattern, a circumstance adumbrated during 1935–1940 by the work of Fieser[1b], Dannenberg[27] and Gillam[2] and later (1941) codified with powerful effect by Woodward[1c] in the form of two rules for the prediction of diene absorption maxima, based on a standard wavelength (217 mμ) for butadiene. The original Woodward rules are summarized as follows:

(1) each alkyl substituent or ring residue attached to the diene chromophore displaces λ_{max} by 5 mμ towards longer wavelengths; and

(2) each exocyclic double bond causes a further displacement of +5 mμ, the effect being twofold if the bond is exocyclic to two rings.

VII   VIII

Example 1. 2,3-Dimethylbutadiene (VII).[1b]

λ_{max} (calc) = 217 + 2 × 5 (alkyl subst.) = 227 mμ

λ_{max} (obs) = 226 mμ.

Example 2. Cholesta-4,6-diene (VIII).[5]

λ_{max} (calc.) = 217 + 3 × 5 (ring residues (*a*)) + 5 (*exo* $>$C$=$C$<$)
          = 237 mμ

λ_{max} (obs.) = 234 mμ.

TABLE 2.1. ABSORPTION OF DIENES AND TRIENES

No.	Compound	λ_{calc}	λ_{obs}	ε	Reference
A. Acyclic and Heteroannular					
1.		214	217	21,000	(2)
2.		229	228	8500	(3)
3.		234	241	23,000	(4)
4.		239	239	17,300	(5)
5.		234	235	19,000	(5)
6.	AcO	234	235	19,000	(5)
7.	EtO	240	241	22,600	(5)
8.	MeS	264	268	22,600	(5)
9.	Br	239	238	23,000	(5)
10.	R	244	242	10,000	(5)
11.	CO_2Me	244	237	10,200	(6)

TABLE 2.1—(contd.)

No.	Compound	λ_{calc}	λ_{obs}	ε	Reference
A. Acyclic and Heteroannular—(contd.)					
12.		244	250	25,000	(7)
13.		239	237·5	16,000	(8)
14.		244	243	—	(9)
15.		289	283	33,000	(5)
B. Homoannular dienes					
16.		—	238·5	3400	(2)
17.		263	256	8000	(2)
18.		—	248	7500	(10)
19.	$(CH_2)_6$	—	223	5000	(11)
20.	$(CH_2)_9$	—	232	—	(12)
21.		273	262	6400	(13)

TABLE 2.1—(contd.)

No.	Compound	λ_{calc}	λ_{obs}	ε	Reference
22.		278	272·5	7000	(14)

B. Homoannular dienes—(contd.)

23.		273	275	10,000	(5)
24.		353	355	19,700	(15)
25.		?	285	9100	(15)

C. Diexo dienes

26.		—	248	15,800	(16)
27.		—	249 / 240	11,480 / 9800	(16)
28.		—	220	5500	(17)
29.		—	220	ca. 6000	(18)
30.		—	220	ca. 6000	(18)

Vinyl cyclopropane

31.		—	210	8700	p. 347

Fieser's modification[15] of the Woodward diene rules is based on a large number of examples of steroid spectra and simply lowers the "basic diene" value by 3 mμ. A value of 253 mμ is assigned to the unsubstituted homoannular

TABLE 2.2. RULES OF DIENE ABSORPTION

Parent heteroannular diene	214
Parent homoannular diene	253
Increments for	
Double bond extending conjugation	30
Alkyl substituent or ring residue	5
Exocyclic double bond	5
Polar groupings : OAc	0
OAlk	6
SAlk	30
Cl, Br	5
— NAlk$_2$	60
Solvent correction	0
	λ_{calc} = Total

system. The Fieser modification together with some more recent additions is given in Table 2.2.

IX

Example 3. Ergosta-5,7,22-triene (IX).

$$\lambda_{max} \text{ (calc.)} = 253 \text{ (parent)} + 4 \times 5 \text{ (ring residues:}$$
$$\text{(a) bonds)} + 2 \times 5 \text{ (exo C=C)}$$
$$= 283 \text{ m}\mu$$

$$\lambda_{max} \text{ (obs)} = 282 \text{ m}\mu \text{ (}\varepsilon, 11,900\text{).}[5]$$

Table 2.1 provides a selection of diene maxima, together with the values calculated from Table 2.2. Many examples will also be found in two important works[5,15] from which our selection has been, in part, prepared.

Solvent

While diene maxima are relatively insensitive to solvent change, it is desirable to use ethanol as reference.

Stereochemistry

The effect of geometrical requirements on the *intensity* of diene absorption is evident in the 7,14-steroidal dienes (No. 10) which, although calculated accurately as heteroannular dienes (λ, 244 mμ), have ε values of 10,000 comparable with homoannular or S-*cis* diene intensity.

The energy requirement of the $\pi \rightarrow \pi^*$ transition responsible for the selective absorption of conjugated dienes becomes increased by loss of planarity due to overcrowding, ring strain or a combination of these factors. Thus, the di-exocyclic dienes (as X) absorb at wavelengths unpredictable from Table 2.2

X

since they combine homoannular type geometry with a vulnerability to loss of planarity. Some relevant examples (26–30) are included in Table 2.1.

Accumulation of data within specialized branches of natural product chemistry is continually providing us with new and hitherto unsuspected spectral correlations, often of a most subtle nature. For instance, the experienced worker in the triterpene field is well aware of the changes in position of *subsidiary maxima* accompanying the main absorption band of the 7,9 (11)-dienes on going from the euphol to the lanostane framework. This particular phenomenon is illustrated by the data below.[54] The triple maxima are not implied in any way

R	λ_1	λ_2	λ_3	(in mμ)
A. Lanostane type	236	243	251	
B. Euphol type	233	240	247·5	

by the diene rules but are, in fact, used empirically to "fingerprint" the framework containing the chromophore.

Polar Substituents

Small but regular displacements are effected by the introduction of sub-stituents bearing lone pairs into the diene system. These are noted in Table 2.2 and differ in some respects from shifts reported elsewhere[15]. It is felt that our values represent the best fit over a large number of examples.

Ring Size

It is important to recall that the diene rules discussed above are applicable to all acyclic and heteroannular dienes, but only to homoannular dienes contained in a *six-membered ring*. Thus, considerable deviation from 256 mμ (cyclohexadiene) maximum is found in the alicyclic dienes of increasing size (Table 2.1) a minimum value of λ_{max} being reached at the nine-membered diene. Conversion factors to other ring sizes from Table 2.2 have not yet been invoked for purposes of rigorous calculation. It is reasonable to expect, however, that the correct choice of a suitable "parent" value should lead to satisfactory extension of the existing rules.

2.2. POLYENES

When the number of C=C units (n) in a conjugated polyene chain reaches 5 or 6, the absorption enters the visible (400 mμ) region, e.g. (XI) ($n = 9$) has λ_{max} 469 mμ (ε, 162,000) in hexane.[23]

XI. – all-*trans*-5,6-Dihydro-α-carotene

Inspection of the longest wavelength bands of the ascending series of methyl polyenes (Table 2.3) reveals that as far as $n = 6$, the average increment for each C=C extending conjugation is constant at about 30 mμ. Thereafter, the increment approaches a limiting value. Several equations have been deduced relating chain length and absorption maxima (via energy level differences). For polyenes where $n < 6$ we have the Lewis–Calvin[102] equation

$$\lambda^2 = k\,n. \tag{1}$$

Where $n > 6$ the polyene series show a convergence which necessitates the finding of parameters for the following equations:

$$\lambda = a\{1 - b\cos[\pi/n - 1]\}^{0\cdot5} \tag{2[103]}$$

$$\lambda = 1\cdot23 \times 10^{-4}/[18\cdot8\,(2n + 1)^{-1} + V_0(1 - \tfrac{1}{2}n)^{-1}] \tag{3[104]}$$

$$\lambda = D(1 - a^{2n-2}). \tag{4[105]}$$

TABLE 2.3. LONGEST WAVELENGTH ABSORPTION MAXIMA OF THE ALL-trans POLYENES,

$$R \left[CH \overset{t}{=} CH \right]_n R$$

R	n	λ_{max}	$\varepsilon \times 10^{-3}$	Solvent	Reference
H	3	267·5	56	H	(19)
Me	3	274·5	30	H	(20)
H	4	304	–	H	(19)
Me	4	310	76·5	H	(20)
H	5	334	118	H	(21)
Me	5	342	122	H	(20)
Me	6	380	146·5	Ch	(20)
Me	7	401	–	Ch	(20)
Me	8	411	–	Ch	(20)
[structure]	8	426	132	Et₂O	(22)

The parametric values will not detain us further, as Nayler and Whiting have pointed out[20] that none of these equations provides accurate fit for the observed maxima of the dimethylpolyenes.† Although qualitative agreement is

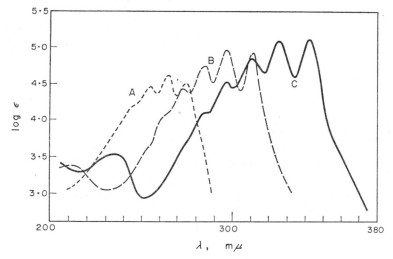

FIG. 2.1. Absorption spectra of dimethylpolyenes $CH_3(CH=CH)_nCH_3$ (in hexane). A, $n = 3$; B, $n = 4$; C, $n = 5$. (Nayler and Whiting, *J. Chem. Soc.*, 3042, 1955.)

generally found, a differential plot $[(\lambda_{n+1} - \lambda_n)/n]$ reveals that equations (2), (3) and (4) do not predict a point of inflection found at $n = 7$, even with allow-

† The Lewis–Calvin equation (1) as well as providing the simplest guide to the prediction of λ_{max} accords fairly well with recent data[116]

ance for experimental error in band head location. Hirayama[106] has offered a wide choice of parameter to meet a selection of polyene types in equation (5)

$$\lambda^2 = A - BC^N \tag{5}$$

where N is a value of n modified to meet structural and substitutional requirements. However, these attempts to find an *exact* structure–spectral relationship in the polyenes are in fact baulked by neglect of such factors as interacting non-conjugated π-electron systems[106], the presence of non-coplanar trimethyl cyclohexenyl groups[107] and the appearance of "half" and "quarter"-length chromophores due to the appearance of geometrical isomerism in some of the more extended systems. Also, the polyenes exhibit many subsidiary maxima which, as we shall see in Chapter 9, may be informative as to subtleties of stereochemistry. Some typical spectra of the dimethyl polyenes are illustrated in Fig. 2.1.

The absorption intensity of the first (longest wavelength) band approaches a limiting value and obeys the simple chromophore–area theory[106–108] (Braude) which requires that the oscillator strength f should show a linear increase with n where

$$f = 4 \cdot 3 \times 10^{-9} \int \varepsilon \, d\bar{\nu}. \tag{6}$$

As an approximation, it is suggested that for simple polyenes

$$\varepsilon_{\max} = 20,000 \, n. \tag{7}$$

2.3. ENYNES

Conjugation of $\rangle C{=}C\langle$ and $-C{\equiv}C-$ is marked by an absorption spectrum with $\lambda_{\max}$ 223 mμ and a characteristic inflection at 230 mμ, the latter serving as a distinguishing feature between diene and enyne absorption. Table 2.4 includes some representative enyne ($\pi - \pi^*$) assignments. The effect of terminal alkyl substitution on the position of the main band and the inflection is exemplified by the entry B 4.

2.4. DIYNES AND POLY-YNES (TABLE 2.4)

The spectra of conjugated acetylenes are characterized by a series of medium intensity ($\pi \to \pi^*$) bands (ε, 200–300) regularly spaced at intervals of 2300 cm^{-1} and, where n exceeds 2, a set of high intensity ($\varepsilon \sim 10^5$) peaks (ascribed to a Rydberg transition) separated by 2600 cm^{-1} intervals provides immediate recognition of the poly-yne chromophore (Fig. 2.2). The "spiky" appearance of the solution spectrum has been of great diagnostic value during the isolation and

TABLE 2.4. PRINCIPAL MAXIMA OF CONJUGATED ACETYLENES (ETHANOL SOLUTION)

	λ_L	ε_L	λ_A	ε_A
A. *Dimethylpoly-ynes*[21]				
$Me(C{\equiv}C)_n Me$				
n				
2	—	—	250	160
3	207	135,000	306	120
4	234	281,000	354	105
5	260·5	352,000	394	120
6	284	445,000	—	—
B. *Enynes*[25]	λ	ε	$\lambda_{infl.}$	ε
$CH{\equiv}C{-}CH{=}CH{\cdot}CH_2OH$	223	14,000	—	—
2. $CH{\equiv}C{-}CMe{=}CH{\cdot}CH_2OH$	223·5	13,000	228	11,500
3. $CH{\equiv}C{-}CH{=}CMe{\cdot}CH_2OH$	223	13,000	231	11,000
4. $nBu{-}C{\equiv}C{-}CH{=}CH{\cdot}CH_2OH$	228	15,000	238	11,500

C. *Enediynes*[26]

1. $nPr{-}(C{\equiv}C)_2{-}CH\overset{cis}{=}CH{\cdot}CHO$

λ_{max}	220·5	229·5	248·5	278	283	295	314
$10^{-3}\,\varepsilon$	15	20	19	10	8·9	21	23

2. $MeCH{=}CH{-}(C{\equiv}C)_2{-}CH{=}CH{\cdot}CH_2OH$

λ_{max}	218	237	246·5	262·5	277·5	294·5	314
$10^{-3}\,\varepsilon$	26·5	30	24	7·4	14	21·5	18

purification of these substance from natural sources (Fig. 8.6). The ε values of the first maximum of the high intensity band series (Table 2.4) approach a value of 80,000 n.

2.5. ENONE ABSORPTION

As discussed above, the conjugation of a double bond with a carbonyl group leads to intense absorption (log ε 3·9–4·3) corresponding to transfer of a π-electron from the ethylene orbit to the $>C{=}O$ orbit. We designate this absorption as an electron transfer (E.T. band) as defined on p. 11 and reserve the symbolism $\pi \to \pi^*$ (frequently used in the literature) for the conjugation of *like* chromophores (e.g. dienes). The E.T. band is found between 220 and 250 mμ in simple enones. A second characteristic absorption band (ε, 50–100) appears at 310–30 mμ and corresponds to the displaced $n \to \pi^*$ band of the $>C{=}O$ group. Whereas the E.T. band is affected in a regular way by both alkyl and electron-donating substituents, the $n \to \pi^*$ band shows no such

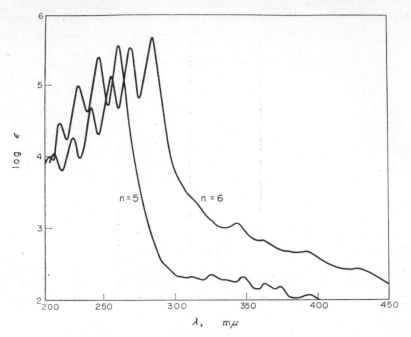

FIG. 2.2. Absorption spectra of dimethylpoly-ynes $CH_3(C{\equiv}C)_nCH_3$ (in alcohol).
(Cook, Jones and Whiting, *J. Chem. Soc.*, 2886, 1952.)

dependence but rather exhibits a complementary set of shifts engendered by conformational changes at the γ-position. Let us now consider the E.T. and L.E. bands in turn.

E.T. Absorption (Table 2.7)

The prediction of the maxima of the intensely-absorbing E.T. bands of α,β-unsaturated ketones can be made in a reliable way by use of Woodward's rules which may be summarized as follows:

(1) The average value for mono alkylated enones is 224 mμ.

(2) The substitution for hydrogen of an alkyl group on the α or β-position of an α,β-unsaturated ketone causes a red shift of *ca.* 11 mμ.

(3) Where the double bond occupies an exocyclic location, a further shift of $+5$ mμ is observed.

Take the case of mesityl oxide (XII); the β,β-substitution

$$CH_3{>}C{=}CH{-}\overset{\displaystyle O}{\overset{\displaystyle \|}{C}}{-}CH_3$$

XII

λ, 237 mμ (ε, 12,600)

XIII

λ, 241 mμ (ε, 16,000)

pattern predicts λ 235 mμ. Testosterone (XIII) carries the same substituents (β,β-ring residues) but has in addition its $\rangle$C=C$\langle$ in an *exo*cyclic location leading to λ_{calc} 240 mμ. It is not surprising to find that the E.T. band is solvent dependent. Correction factors are available (Table 2.5) from the measurement of λ_{max} for testosterone and Δ^4-cholestenone in a variety of solvents. As many more examples become available, modifications and extensions of the original Woodward rules continue to be made. From a study of the ultraviolet absorption of a large number of steroids Fieser has formulated an extensive range of parameters to deal with many combinations of enone and dienone systems. Table 2.6 shows a selection of such values together with some modified data in current usage. Representative examples of several classes of enone system will be found in Table 2.7 together with the calculated λ value. The intensity of the E.T. band is usually 10,000–15,000 unless steric hindrance to coplanarity is present, as, for example, in the acetyl cyclohexene systems (Nos. 5–10) where the overlap of methyl groups reaches a maximum at No. 8 (ε_{max}, 1400) which probably exists in the strongly hindered S-*trans* or S-*cis* form. There is evidence from dipole moment studies that mesityl oxide (No. 3) in fact adopts the S-*cis* conformation by virtue of the large overlap of bulky methyl groups in the S-*trans* form. Again, within a rigid framework the S-*cis* form may be imposed

TABLE 2.5. SOLVENT CORRECTIONS† FOR ENONE ABSORPTION[27]

Solvent	Abbreviation	Correction (mμ)
Ethanol	A	0
Methanol	MeOH	0
Dioxan	D	+5
Chloroform	Ch	+1
Ether	E	+7
Water*	W	−8
Hexane	H	+11
Cyclohexane**	C	+11

† Calculated from the λ values of Δ^4-cholesten-3-one in the appropriate solvent. These values may be applied to λ_{calc} from Table 2.6.

* U. Westphal and B. A. Ashley, *J. Biol. Chem.*, **233**, 57 (1958).

** Author's unpublished observation.

by the geometrical requirements present (e.g., Nos. 17, 47, 48, 49). These observations find theoretical interpretation of a qualitative nature by the well established relation between the integrated intensity and the square of the effective chromophore length. Thus for (XIV) and (XV) the ratio of the integrated absorption intensities is 0·65, as compared with 0·68 for the ratio of the squares of chromophore lengths (m^2/n^2)[101]. However, it is not always

TABLE 2.6. RULES OF ENONE ABSORPTION

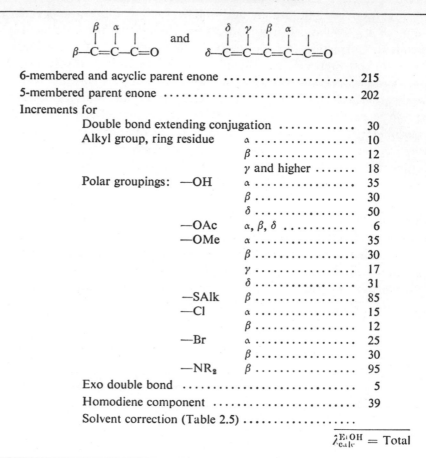

$$\overset{\beta}{\underset{\beta}{|}} \overset{\alpha}{\underset{C}{|}} \overset{}{\underset{C}{=}} \overset{}{\underset{C}{=}} O \quad \text{and} \quad \overset{\delta}{\underset{\delta}{|}} \overset{\gamma}{\underset{C}{|}} \overset{\beta}{\underset{C}{|}} \overset{\alpha}{\underset{C}{|}} \text{—C=C—C=C—C=O}$$

6-membered and acyclic parent enone		215
5-membered parent enone		202
Increments for		
Double bond extending conjugation		30
Alkyl group, ring residue	α	10
	β	12
	γ and higher	18
Polar groupings: —OH	α	35
	β	30
	δ	50
—OAc	α, β, δ	6
—OMe	α	35
	β	30
	γ	17
	δ	31
—SAlk	β	85
—Cl	α	15
	β	12
—Br	α	25
	β	30
—NR₂	β	95
Exo double bond		5
Homodiene component		39
Solvent correction (Table 2.5)		

$$\lambda_{calc}^{EtOH} = \text{Total}$$

a simple matter to separate intensity effects due to adoption of S-*cis* geometry and to loss of planarity by steric hindrance, since these are frequently merged

XIV   XV

λ 249 (ε 6890)   λ 249 (ε 12,400)

To return now to the calculation of maxima, the homoannular dienones may be treated as the heteroannular systems (i.e. an increment of 30 mμ for a double bond extending conjugation) with an additional factor of + 39 mμ for the homodiene component (*cf.* 214 and 253 for the basic dienes). Let us now consider two examples in detail.

(XVI)   (XVII)

Example 1. Cholesta-4,6-dien-3-one (XVI).

$$\lambda_{(calc)}^{EtOH} = 215 \text{ (parent)} + 12 \text{ (β-subst.)} + 18 \text{ (δ-subst.)}$$
$$+ 30 \text{ (C=C ext. conj.)} + 5 \text{ (exo C=C)}$$
$$= 280 \text{ m}\mu.$$
$$\lambda_{(obs)}^{EtOH} = 284 \text{ m}\mu.^{5}$$

Example 2. 3β-Acetoxy-7-oxolanosta-5,8,11-triene (XVII).

$$\lambda_{(calc)}^{EtOH} = 215 \text{ (parent)} + 10 \text{ (α-subst)} + 12 \text{ (β-subst)}$$
$$+ 18 \text{ (δ-subst.)} + 30 \text{ (C=C ext. conj.)} + 39 \text{ (homodiene}$$
$$\text{component)}$$
$$= 324 \text{ m}\mu.$$
$$\lambda_{(obs)}^{EtOH} = 256 \text{ and } 327 \text{ m}\mu.^{15}$$

In the second example the cross conjugated enone (Δ^5-component) is not included in the calculation since it is considered to be the less active chromophore. The band at 256 mμ may however be due to its (displaced) transition (λ_{calc} 244 mμ) or to the appearance of the $\Delta^{8,9}$-7 ketone system (λ_{calc} 249 mμ). Cross conjugated dienones may, in general, be analysed on the premise that the more probable transition determines the position of λ_{max}. This receives at least a partial explanation in terms of the exaltation mechanism involving electron transfer from an essentially ethylenic orbit to a carbonyl group orbit. The same effect is observed in No. 27. Interesting examples of cross conjugation are provided by Nos. 35 and 36 which are noted without interpretative comment until many more examples are at hand. The increment for a cyclopropane ring extending conjugation is indicated in No. 37.

Polar Substituents (Table 2.7)

Application of the increments listed in Table 2.6 have been made for some alkoxyl, hydroxyl and halogen compounds in Table 2.7. It should be noted that our values (Tables 2.6) differ in some respects from the increments listed elsewhere[15, 110].

Diosphenol Absorption (Table 2.7)

A particular case of polar substitution concerns the diosphenol chromophore which arises via the enolization of a cyclohexan-1,2-dione (a) → (b). Here, the hydroxyl group on the α-carbon atom is responsible for the characteristic band at 270 mμ in, say, cholestan-2,3-dione (No. 18) (λ_{calc}, 262 mμ). Addition of dilute alkali shifts the maximum to 300 mμ (b) → (c), whilst acetylation low-

(a)   (b)   (c)

ers the absorption to *ca.* 235 mμ in the diosphenyl acetate (No. 20). As expected, the corresponding enol ether (No. 19) absorbs at the parental value of 264 mμ. The enol content of cycloalkan-1,2-diones may be calculated from the intensity of absorption at the parental wavelength compared with ε_{max} for the corresponding enol ether.

Ring Size (Table 2.7)

The rules of enone absorption apply to acyclic† and six-membered ketones When we consider the λ_{max} values of cyclopentenones it is clear that the maxima predicted by the enone rules are consistently 10–15 mμ higher than the observed value. Consideration of the available data leads us to a new parent value for the *endo*cyclic 5-ring unsaturated ketones of 202 mμ. Using the increments available in Table 2.6, we find that Nos. 38–46 show an average deviation of ± 3 mμ from the calculated value. An exception is No. 39 ($+ 7$ mμ) which is close to the disubstituted value. As more examples come to light it will be interesting to test the increments of Table 2.6 on new systems. Two recent examples are worked in detail below.

Example 3. Isotetrahydrolactucin dienone (XVIII).

XVIII

λ, 281 (ε 14,000) mμ[41].

$$\lambda_{calc}^{EtOH} = 202 \text{ (parent)} + 12 \ (\beta) + 36 \ (\gamma + \delta) + 5 \text{ (exo C=C)}$$
$$+ 30 \text{ (C=C ext. conj.)}$$
$$= 285 \text{ m}\mu.$$

† This category includes acylcycloalkenes.

Example 4. 2-Hydroxycyclopent-2-en-1-one (XIX).

$$\text{XIX}$$

$$\lambda,\ 247\ (\varepsilon,\ 8000)\ m\mu^{40},$$

$$\lambda_{calc}^{EtOH} = 202 + 12\ (\beta\text{-C}) + 35\ (\alpha-\text{OH})$$

$$= 249\ m\mu.$$

The exocyclic cyclopentenones conform to the parent value of 215 mμ (Table 2.6) for calculation of maxima (Nos. 47–49).

Trienones and Polyenones

The above rules may be applied to trienones in which the most active chromophore is always considered for purposes of calculation. Where $n > 6$, the effect of a $>$C=O group at the end of the polyene chain does not contribute a measurable bathochromic displacement with respect to the parent polyene absorption

Enediones (Table 2.7)

The cross conjugated —CO—C=C—CO— moiety is frequently encountered in steroid and triterpene studies and may be present in one of four geometrical forms which we have named homo-*cisoid* (XX), hetero-*cisoid* (XXI), e mi*cisoid* (XXII) and fully *transoid* (XXIII). Detailed calculations for predic-

XX	XXI	XXII	XXIII
λ, 224 †	λ, 255–263 †	λ, 252 †	λ, 275 †
227*	259*	244*	249*

tion of these types are not available. We have indicated the approximate location of λ_{max} under each type† and other examples will be found in Table 2.7 (Nos. 50–63). These include —CO—C=C—CO$_2$H which may be calculated reliably by using the alkyl substituent value for the —CO$_2$H group. Further diagnosis is possible in the case of No. 56 where a shift of $+16$ mμ is found in

† λ_{obs} (average).
* λ_{calc} is indicated by asterisk.

TABLE 2.7. ELECTRON TRANSFER (E.T.) BANDS OF ENONE SYSTEMS†

No.	Compound	λ_{calc}*	λ_{obs}	ε	Reference
A. Acyclic					
1.		215	219	3600	(28)
2.		225	221	6450	(28)
3.		239	237	12,600	(28)
4.		249	249	—	(28)
B. Acetyl cyclohexenes					
5.		237	232	12,500	(29)
6.		237	232	12,000	(29)
7.		249	245	6500	(29)
8.		249	243	1400	(29)
9.		281	281	20,800	(29)
10.		281	278 / 228	4500 / 11,600	(29)

† In ethanol, or corrected to ethanolic values (Table 2.5).
* $\lambda = \lambda_{max}$ in mμ.

TABLE 2.7—(contd.)

No.	Compound	λ_{calc}	λ_{obs}	ε	Reference
B. Acetyl cyclohexenes—(contd.)					
11.	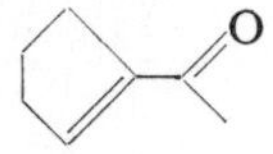	237	239	13,000	(30)
12.	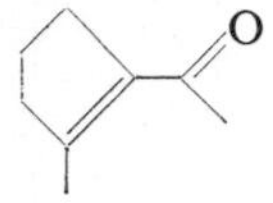	249	253	10,000	(30)
C. Cyclohexenones					
13.	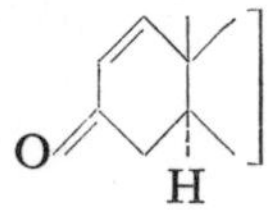	227	230	10,000	(5)
14.	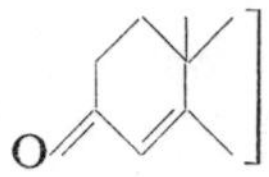	244	241	16,600	(5)
15.	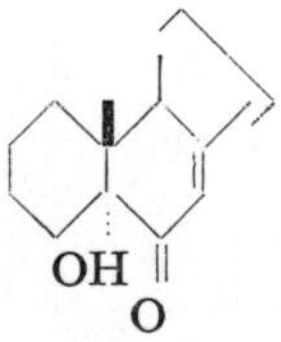	244	252	13,400	(5)
16.	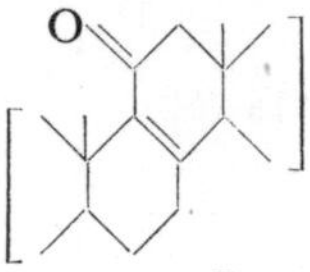	249	254	9100	(5)
17.	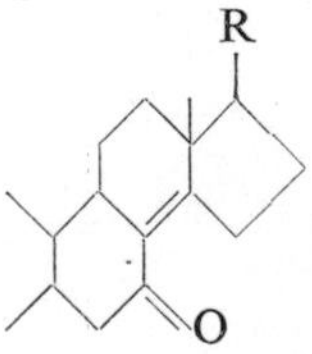	259	262	9500	(5)
18.	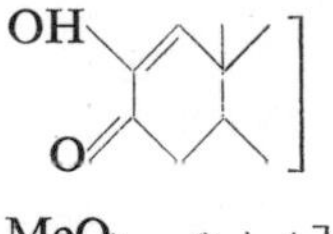	262	270 300†	8500 12,000	(5)
19.	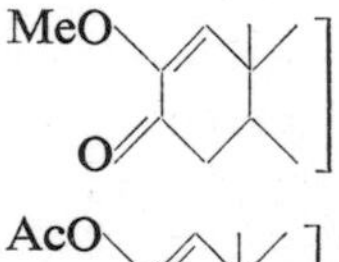	262	264	5000	(31)
20.	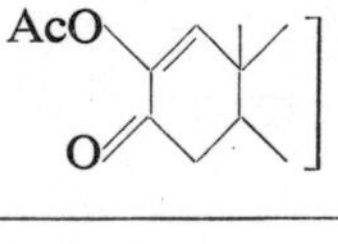	233	237	8900	(5)

† in 0·1 N NaOH.

IUS 3a

TABLE 2.7—(contd.)

No.	Compound	λ_{calc}	λ_{obs}	ε	Reference
C. Cyclohexenones —(contd.)					
21.		279	281	7000	(5)
22.		250	244	9500	(5)
23.		252	256	7600	(32)
24.		269	287	13,000	(5)
25.		245	248	18,750	(32a)
26.		239	239	12,270	(32a)
27.		244	244	15,000	(5)
28.		227	240	12,000	(33)
29.		286	290	12,600	(5)

TABLE 2.7—(contd.)

No.	Compound	λ_{calc}	λ_{obs}	ε	Reference

C. Cyclohexenones — (contd.)

No.	Compound	λ_{calc}	λ_{obs}	ε	Reference
30.		303	239 292	4000 13,000	(5)
31.		302	300 365	5000 600	(33)
32.		324	327	4500	(33)
33.		349	230 278 348	18,000 3720 11,000	(5)
34.		356	348	26,500	(5)
35.		?	224 298	15,600 5060	(34)
36.		—	284	6310	(35)
37.		—	266	13,700	(36)

TABLE 2.7—(contd.)

No.	Compound	λ_{calc}	λ_{obs}	ε	Reference
D. Cyclopentenones					
38.		214	218	9500	(30)
38a.		214	212		(37)
39.		214	221	—	(37)
40.	nC_6H_{13}	224	229	—	(37)
41.		229	226	7400	(28)
42.		236	235	—	(37)
43.		241	240	16,000	(38)
44.	Br	256	251	10,800	(39)
45.	OMe	249	246	9200	(40)
46.	CO_2H	278	281	14,000	(41)

TABLE 2.7—(contd.)

No.	Compound	λ_{calc}	λ_{obs}	ε	Reference
E. Exo cyclopentenones					
47.		259	259	13,000	(42)
48.		230	228	8000	(43)
49.		230	230	10,000	(44)
F. Enediones					
50.			252	11,000	(27)
51.		—	255	11,000	(5)
52.		—	263 375	9200 460	(45)
53.		—	275	15,000	(46)
54.		227	222	12,000	(47)

TABLE 2.7—(contd.)

No.	Compound	λ_{calc}	λ_{obs}	ε	Reference
F. Enediones—(contd.)					
55.		239	237	11,000	(48)
56.		249	247	8500	(49)
57.		249	248	14,800	(49)a
58.		249	246	9800	(50)
59.		239	242	8000	(51)
60.		236	243		(52)
61.		309	311	20,500	(52)
62.		—	284	7900	(54)

TABLE 2.7—(contd.)

No.	Compound	λ_{calc}	λ_{obs}	ε	Reference
G. Enediones—(contd.)					
63.		—	330 384†	17,700 11,000	(55)

† in 0·1 N NaOH.

alkaline solutions. A generalized statement[110] that "no increment should be added for $>C{=}O$ extending the conjugation of an enone" is only applicable in the cases of types XX and XXI. The effective length of the transoid system (XXIII) must, in part, be responsible for its exalted value. No. 61, a diene–dione, may be calculated by regarding it as a vinylogous homo-*cisoid* (type XX) ene-dione, i.e. by allowing no increment for the second $>C{=}O$ group.

β-Diketones and β-Triketones (Table 2.7)

Extensive studies of the degree of enolization of β-diketones and β-keto-esters have demonstrated that in acyclic systems the equilibrium is not only solvent-dependent but is quite simply related to the solvent polarity (Z-value)[111]. Thus the keto-form as XXIV is stabilized by solvents which can form intermolecular hydrogen bonds with the solute. In water, acetyl acetone (XXIV;

$$R{-}CO{-}CH_2{-}CO{-}R \ \rightleftharpoons$$

$\lambda_{calc} = 280$ (ε, 30) $\lambda_{calc} = 279$ ($\varepsilon \sim 13,000$)

XXIV   XXV

R=Me) has λ_{max}, 274 mμ (ε 1500) corresponding to 15% enolization, whilst in hexane we find a value of $\varepsilon_{max}^{271} = 12,000$, representing almost complete pre-dominance of the intra-molecularly bonded *cisoid* form XXV. In the cyclic β-diketones (Table 2.8) such a steric situation is impossible, so that the *trans*-fixed cycloalkane 1-3-diones show only simple dicarbonyl absorption in iso-octane solution[112] at 290 mμ. In acidic methanol or ether the enol XXVII

TABLE 2.8. β-DIKETONES AND TRIKETONES (IN EtOH)

No.	Compound	λ_{max}	ε	Reference
1.		255	12,600	(60)
2.		258	12,000	(61)
		282†	18,000	
3.		255	13,200	(62)
4.		290	5,100	(63)
5.		231 277	10,000 10,000	(64)
6.		233 276	13,500 13,500	(62)
7.		255	13,200	(61)

† In 5×10^{-5} M solution.

appears (at 252 and 242 mμ, respectively). The generation of the enolate anion which is observed in basic solution at 282 mμ (ε 26,000) forms a useful diagnostic process for the cyclic β-diketones. Table 2.8 contains some examples

which are relevant to natural product studies. For ease of presentation the ketones are represented by the non-enolized form. It is interesting to note that dilution of ethanolic solutions to *ca.* 5×10^{-5} M displaces the maximum to that of the ionic species (No. 2b). The β-triketones which are found in nature, e.g. angustione (No. 6) show characteristic twin maxima at 230 and 280 mμ. The cyclopentan-1,3-dione (No. 7) is present as the enol in ethanolic solution and absorbs at 255 mμ (calculated, 259 mμ).

"Second Order Effects" (Table 2.9)

We have already noted two types of steric effect on enone absorption. Firstly the loss of planarity and the possibility of S-*cis* geometry due to steric overcrowding in the acetyl cyclohexenes and leading to low ε values, and secondly a geometrical effect in the ene-diones resulting in changes of effective chromophore area and hence ε values. The E.T. band may be affected in yet another, less predictable manner, by what we have chosen† to call "second-order" or "homoconjugative" interactions between spatially favoured combinations of the excited state $\left(\overset{+}{C}-C=C-\overset{-}{O}\right)$ and various sources of either lone pair electrons, π-electrons or positive charge. For example, the introduction of a non-conjugated double bond into keto ester 4 (Table 2.9) shifts λ_{max} from 220 to 245 mμ. In all probability a low wavelength band (*ca.* 210 mμ) is also present in the diene, and the whole spectrum ascribed to a transition involving the "homo" conjugation of the second double bond (as XXIX). In this particular

XXIX

example, however, an alternative explanation might simply be that the conformational change cyclohexene → cyclohexadiene favours a change in the main contributing chromophore from unsaturated ester + non-planar acetyl (220 mμ) to conjugated acetyl + non-planar acid (245 mμ). Nos. 7–10 provide more obvious manifestations of the effect of a heteroatom on the E.T. band.

† But seen p. 77 for recent nomenclature.

TABLE 2.9. "SECOND-ORDER" ELECTRON TRANSFER EFFECTS

No.	Compound	λ_{calc}	λ_{obs}†	ε	Reference
1.		237	239	13,000	(56)
2.		237	240 276	5300 1750	(56)
3.		237	232	12,500	(56)
4.		249	220 (!)	6000	(56)
5.		249	215 245	3000 2000	(56)
6.		244	238	15,400	(57)
7.		244	232·5	14,100	(57)
8.		244	229	15,600	(57)
9.		244	230	—	(58)
10.		244	229	—	(58)
11.		229	232	16,500	(59)

† In EtOH.

TABLE 2.9—(contd.)

No.	Compound	λ_{calc}	λ_{obs}	ε	Reference
12.		229	222 241	10,000 12,000	(59)

The positive charge is prevented from developing on the C=C—C=O grouping most effectively by $\overset{+}{>}NMe_2$ (No. 8) which absorbs at 15 mμ lower than the calculated value. This category of observation is invaluable in the study of complex alkaloidal systems. Nos. 11 and 12 provide an interesting example of the effect of an apparently remote lactone moiety on the principal absorption band of $\Delta^{14,15}$-16 steroidal ketones.

We have seen that judicious application of the empirical rules summarized in Table 2.6 provides a reliable working guide to the substitution pattern of the enone and dienone chromophores. We have also taken cognizance of the value of apparent exceptions to the rules. Correctly interpreted, the latter can provide meaningful data which may corroborate or refute suspected nuances of stereochemical environment. We shall now consider the low intensity enone band, which in favourable cases, can provide useful conformational information.

$n \rightarrow \pi^*$ Enone Absorption

The displaced local excitation of the $>C=O$ group absorbs at 300–350 mμ (log ε 1–2) and in ethanol appears as a somewhat ill-defined maximum. In hexane solution several bands are discernible in the 300–350 mμ region. These bands are not affected in any regular way by alkyl substitution (Table 2.10). However, substitution of the γ-position of an α,β-unsaturated ketone with a grouping with available lone pairs of electrons results in a regular shift of the $n \rightarrow \pi^*$ band, depending on whether the substituent is present in the axial or equatorial conformation, the former arrangement providing better hyperconjugative contributions from the σ-electrons of the $>C-X$ bond, or alternatively, a deeper involvement of the p-electrons of X, with the π-orbital of

6β (a)

6α (e)

XXX $\lambda_{n \rightarrow \pi^*}^{hexane}$ 314, 323·5, 336, 349 and 367 mμ

TABLE 2.10. $n \to \pi^*$ TRANSITIONS IN ENONE SYSTEMS (IN HEXANE)

No.	Compound	λ_{max}	ε	Reference
1.		340	60	(65)
2.		338	100	(66)
3.		322·5 333 344 357 374	23 26 27·5 21 9·5	(67)
4.		304 332	33 36	(67)
5.		329	63	(67)

$\Delta\lambda$ (mμ) for substitution at C_6 in XXX

Substituent	e	a
Cl	+3	+14
Br	+5	+20
OH	+2	+ 7
OAc	+2	+10

the enone. Let us take Δ^4-cholestenone (XXX) as our parent enone. By a careful study of the maxima of $n \to \pi^*$ absorption, Cookson[113] has found that the following increments permit differentiation of axial and equatorial substitution at C_6. The entire $n \to \pi^*$ band appears as a series of maxima in hexane and the increments listed above are average values determined from the shift of each peak. The E.T. band remains unaffected for all practical purposes.

β,γ-Unsaturated Ketones

It is convenient at this point to consider the non-conjugated β,γ-unsaturated ketones (which are in equilibrium with their α,β-unsaturated isomers) since their three-banded spectrum has recently[68] been subjected to analysis with the following results:

Cyclohex-3-enone (XXXI) has λ_{max} 187, 217 and 277 mμ (Table 2.11). The low wavelength band (180 mμ) is assigned to a displaced ethylenic $\pi \to \pi^*$ transition (1), the 217 mμ band to a non-classical E.T. band (2) which some-

XXXI   XXXII

times appears as a shoulder rather than a maximum. The third band (277 mμ) almost certainly marks the $n \to \pi^*$ transition (3) and shows an exalted intensity value without wavelength shift. In the bornenone (XXXII), however, the third band is at 305 mμ (ε 290) which would indicate more efficient overlap of the C=C and C=O chromophores. A previous study by Cookson[14] had already drawn attention to the relationship between orbital overlap and $n \to \pi^*$ intensity and λ values Some pertinent examples are collected in Table 2.12. A

TABLE 2.11. ABSORPTION MAXIMA† OF β,γ-UNSATURATED KETONES[68]

	$\lambda_{\pi \to \pi^*}$ (ε)	$\lambda_{\text{E.T.}}$ (ε)	$\lambda_{n \to \pi^*}$ (ε)
	192 (7000)	210sh. (5600)	290 (51)
	187 (7000)	217 (2500)	277 (107)
	185 (2800)	200 (3200)	292 (107)
	185 (2000)	210 (3000)	305 (290).

† In hexane.

TABLE 2.12. $n \rightarrow \pi^*$ BANDS OF β,γ-UNSATURATED KETONES (IN ETHANOL)

No.	Compound	λ	ε	Reference
1.		290	80†	(69)
2.		280	19	(70)
3.		293	190	(71)
4.		285	50	(5)
5.		289·5	145	(72)
6.		290	400	(73)
7.		295	315	(74)
8.		300	1170	(75)

TABLE 2.12—(contd.)

No.	Compound	λ	ε	Reference
9.	Ph·CH$_2$·COMe	288	145	(76)
10.	Ph·CH$_2$·CH$_2$·COMe	285	150	(77)
11.	[structure =O]	293–316	10	(78)
12.	[structure O]	327	18	(78)

particularly striking effect† is provided by parasantonide (No. 8) λ_{max}, 300 mμ (ε 1170). Transitions which lead to a bond in the excited state between atoms not bonded in the ground state are termed *photodesmotic*[114].

2.3. α,β-UNSATURATED ALDEHYDES

The E.T. band of α,β-unsaturated aldehydes is affected by alkyl substitution in the expected sense. Taking 207 mμ as the basic chromophore (= acrylaldehyde), application of the usual alkyl increments ($\alpha - 10$; $\beta - 12$) gives fairly reliable agreement (Table 2.13). Forbes[19] has recently pointed out that the increment for introduction of a second β-alkyl substituent in unsaturated aldehyde and ketone systems is often greater than 12 mμ. However, the value of the increments in current usage is in fact a good *average* applicable to a very wide range of examples and agreement to within 5 mμ is generally found. The $n \rightarrow \pi^*$ band of the unsaturated aldehydes appears at *ca.* 320 mμ in ethanol solution.

Carbonyl Derivatives

The familiar derivatives used for the characterisation of ketones and aldehydes include the *oximes, semicarbazones, thiosemicarbazones* and *2,4-dinitrophenylhydrazones*. Many important complex natural ketones do not form such derivatives for steric reasons. Also, since the ultraviolet and infrared spectra of the parent are, in fact, much more informative, we consider it sufficient to list approximate wavelength values of the principal absorption bands

† Now surpassed[115] in intensity by (i), $\varepsilon_{n \rightarrow \pi^*} \sim 6000$

Ph—[structure]=O (i)

TABLE 2.13. E.T. MAXIMA OF α,β-UNSATURATED ALDEHYDES (IN EtOH)

No.	Compound	λ_{calc}	λ_{obs}	ε	Reference
1.	$CH_2=CH-CH=O$	207	207	11,200	(79)
2.	$CH_3 \cdot CH=CH-CH=O$	219	217	17,900	(79)
3.	$CH_2=CMe-CH=O$	217	216	11,000	(79)
4.	$CH_3 \cdot CH=C \cdot CH=O$ $\overset{|}{Me}$	229	226	16,100	(79)
5.	$Me_2C=CMe \cdot CH=O$	241	245	13,000	(79)
6.	⬡=CH·CH=O	236	238	16,000	(79)
7.	—CHO	241	240	8000	(80)
8.	CHO	229	235	14,000	(80)

of such derivatives (Table 2.14). We note that no distinction between through-conjugated and cross-conjugated dienones is possible on the basis of their semicarbazone and 2,4-dinitrophenylhydrazone maxima and again that these maxima are relatively insensitive to changes in the substitution pattern of the enone.

TABLE 2.14. APPROXIMATE LOCATION OF MOST INTENSE BAND
OF CARBONYL COMPOUNDS AND THEIR DERIVATIVES (EtOH)

	Saturated $>C=O$	$-C=C-C=O$	$(C=C)_2 C=O$	⬡=O
Carbonyl compound	187	230	260	240
Semicarbazone	229	265	300	300
Thiosemicarbazone	270	300	—	—
Oxime	—	235	—	—
2,4-Dinitrophenylhydrazone	360	380	400	400

2.4. α,β-UNSATURATED ACIDS AND ESTERS

It is possible to predict with fair accuracy ($\pm 5 \, m\mu$) the position of λ_{max} for simple unsaturated acids and their alkylated derivatives. Crotonic acid displays E.T. absorption at 205 $m\mu$ (ε, 14,000). Taking the monosubstituted value as 208 $m\mu$, Nielsen[81] has summarized the absorption of the acids as follows:

	$\lambda \, (\pm 5 \, m\mu)$
Monosubstituted (β)	208
Disubsituted (α,β or β,β)	217
Trisubstituted (α,β,β)	225
Increment for C=C extending conjugation	30
Increment for C=C exocyclic	5

Table 2.15 contains selected examples of acids with up to three double bonds in conjugation. The shift on going from —CO_2H to —CO_2Alk is not usually greater than 2 $m\mu$.

2.5. UNSATURATED LACTONES (TABLE 2.16)

A wide diversity of lactone types has been uncovered during structural investigations on natural products. For the simpler unsaturated lactones (Nos. 1 to 3) end absorption has been recorded in the literature. The first two entries give ε values at selected wavelengths. However, it would now be instructive to examine the position of maximal absorption of these simpler compounds (as has been done for No. 3) since structure–spectrum relationships should be meaningful. The documentation of butenolide spectra is now so extensive that its various modes of occurrence in nature are readily recognizable from spectral considerations (Nos. 4, 5, 6). The related α-pyrones (No. 7) absorb at 300 $m\mu$. Penicillic acid (16, 17), ascorbic acid (10), patulin (15) and reductic acid types are also illustrated. The effect of alkali on the spectrum of α-hydroxybutenolides (No. 11) is characteristic and quite comparable to the diosphenol shift ($+40 \, m\mu$). The analogy is maintained in the spectrum of the acetate (No. 12). A similar type of shift occurs in α-keto esters and acids on going from neutral to basic solution ($\Delta\lambda + 33 \, m\mu$).

2.6. UNSATURATED AMIDES AND LACTAMS (TABLE 2.17)

Unsaturated amides absorb at 200 $m\mu$ (ε, 8,000). A second band (ε, 1000) appears in the spectrum of α,β-unsaturated *lactams* at 240–50 $m\mu$.

TABLE 2.15. α, β-UNSATURATED ACIDS AND ESTERS† (IN EtOH)

No.	Compound	λ	ε	Reference
A. Acyclic				
1.	$CH_2{=}CH{-}CO_2H$	200	10.000	(81)
2.	$CH_2{=}CMe \cdot CO_2H$	210	—	(81)
3.	HOCH$_2$—⟩—CO$_2$H	206	8000	(81)
4.	$MeCH{\overset{t}{=}}CH \cdot CO_2H$	205	14,000	(81)
5.	$MeCH{\overset{c}{=}}CH \cdot CO_2H$	205·5	13,500	(81)
6.	$CH_3CH{\overset{t}{=}}CMe \cdot CO_2H$	213	12,500	(81)
7.	$CH_3CH{\overset{c}{=}}CMe \cdot CO_2H$	216	9000	(81)
8.	$Me_2C{=}CH \cdot CO_2H$	216	12,000	(81)
9.	$Me_2C{=}CMe \cdot CO_2H$	221	9700	(81)
10.	Me⟩C=C—CO$_2$Et / Et	CH$_2 \cdot$CO$_2$H	219	9200	(81)
B. Alicyclic				
11.	—CO$_2$H	222	10,500	(81)
12.	—CO$_2$H	217	10,000	(81)
13.	—CO$_2$H	222	9900	(81)
14.	—CO$_2$H	231	10,500	(81)
15.	CO$_2$Me / —CO$_2$H	228	10,000	(81)
16.	CH·CO$_2$H	220	14,000	(81)

† Acid → ester shift ≯ ± 2 mμ.

TABLE 2.15—(contd.)

No.	Compound	λ	ε	Reference
B. *Alicyclic—(contd.)*				
17.	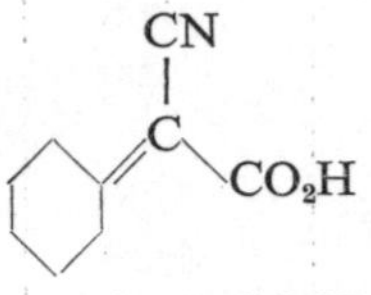 (structure: cyclohexylidene with C(CN)CO₂H)	235	12,500	(81)
18.	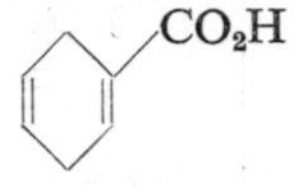 (structure: cyclohexadiene with CO₂H)	236	2100(!)	(81)
19.	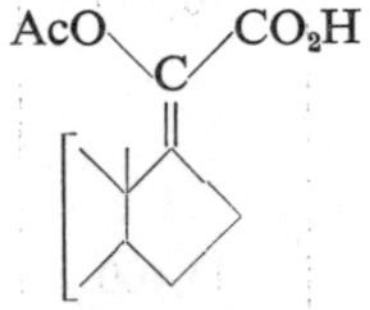 (structure: bicyclic with AcO, C, CO₂H)	228	11,600	(82)
20.	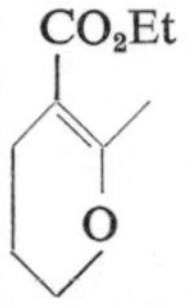 (structure: ring with CO₂Et, O)	248	12,500	(83)
C. *Diene and Triene Acids*				
21.	MeO₂C—CH$\overset{c}{=}$CH—CH$\overset{c}{=}$CH—CO₂H	258	20,900	(84)
22.	MeO₂C—CH$\overset{t}{=}$CH—CH$\overset{t}{=}$CH—CO₂H	257	29,400	(84)
23.	MeCH$\overset{t}{=}$CH—CH$\overset{c}{=}$CH—CO₂H	260	16,200	(84)
24.	MeCH$\overset{t}{=}$CH—CH$\overset{t}{=}$CH—CO₂H	263	25,800	(84)
25.	MeO₂C—CMe=CH—CH=CH—CH=CMe·CO₂H (all *trans*)	315	44,000	(84)

2.7. CONJUGATED AZOMETHINES (TABLE 2.18)

The $\text{>C=}\overset{|}{\text{C}}\text{—}\overset{|}{\text{C}}\text{=N—}$ chromophore displays E.T. absorption at 220 mμ. A pronounced shift to the red (+ 60 mμ) takes place on acidification. We have included oxime and di-azomethine (No. 7) absorption in this category.

TABLE 2.16. E.T. BANDS OF α,β-UNSATURATED LACTONES (IN EtOH)

No.	Compound	λ_{max}	ε	Reference
1.		220† 225 235	7500 5000 900	(85)
2.		220† 225 230	5700 4450 3100	(85)
3.		205	10,700	(84)
4.		217	15,400	(5)
5.		271	18,000	(5)
6.		335	29,000	(5)
7.		300	5450	(5)
8.		230	16,000	(86)
9.		230	11,200	(87)

† λ_{max} 220; values for approaching λ's given (for aqueous solution).

TABLE 2.16—(contd.)

No.	Compound	λ_{max}	ε	Reference
10.		245 300†	10,000 5400	(88)
11.		233 272†	8400 5200	(89)
12.		218	10,500	(89)
13.		236	16,000	(90)
14.		220	16,000	(90)
15.		275,5	13,300	(91)
16.		270	23,000	(92)
17.		282	18,500	(92)

† In 0·01 N alkali.

TABLE 2.17. UNSATURATED AMIDES AND LACTAMS

No.	Compound	λ_{max}	ε	Solvent	Reference
1.		213	7000	W	(93)
2.		200	4660	W	(93)
3.	—CONH₂	220	—	A	(94)
4.	—CONH₂	213	—	A	(94)
5.	—CONH₂	218	—	A	(94)
6.		204 240	8400 1200	MeOH	(93)
7.		241	1470	A	(95)
8.		251	1120	A	(95)

2.8. CONJUGATED NITRILES (TABLE 2.18)

α-cyano crotonic acid absorbs at 215 mμ (ε, 9700), whilst the unsaturated nitriles (8) and (9) (Table 2.18) have their principal absorption at 213 mμ. Second-order effects are discernible in (9). Example (10) gives a value of $+ 65$ mμ for β-nitrogen substitution on the $\overset{|}{>}\!C\!=\!C\!-\!C\!\equiv\!N$ moiety, partially restored to the parent value on acidification.

TABLE 2.18. CONJUGATED AZOMETHINES (IN EtOH)

	λ	ε	Reference
A. $\quad$ —C=N—			
1. $CH_3CH=CH—CH=N—C_4H_9$	220	23,000	(96)
2. $\quad$ >C=C—C=N<	274–278	20,000	(97)
3.	286	24,300	(98)
4.	328	48,700	(98)
5. MeCH=CH—CH=NOH	230·5	17,800	(99)
6. MeCH=CMe·CMe=NOH	229·5	16,900	(99)
7. R—N=CMe—CMe=N—R	206 209	17,000 18,500	(100)
B. —C≡N (in hexane)			
8.	213	10,000	(101)
9.	213 240 349	9100 5400 5600	(101)
10.	278 216 272	18,300 2400 } in acid 1800 }	(101)

2.9. CUMULATED SYSTEMS—ALLENES, KETENS AND CARBODIIMIDES[99]

$CH_2=C=CH_2$	$Et_2C=C=O$	$Et-N=C=N-Et$
XXXIII	XXXIV	XXXV
λ, 170 (ε 4000)	λ, 227 (ε 360)	λ, 230 (ε 4000)
227 (ε 630)	375 (ε 20)	270 (ε 25)

These all show medium absorption at 230 mμ. A weaker transition is also evident in the spectra of XXXIV and XXXV ($n \rightarrow \pi$*?).

REFERENCES

1(a). R. S. MULLIKEN, *J. Chem. Phys.*, **7**, 121 (1939).

1(b). L. F. FIESER, *Natural Products Related to Phenanthrene*, 2nd ed., p. 398, Reinhold, New York (1937).

1(c). R. B. WOODWARD, *J. Amer. Chem. Soc.*, **64**, 72 (1942).

2. H. BOOKER, L. K. EVANS and A. E. GILLAM, *J. Chem. Soc.*, 1453 (1940).

3. J. C. LUNT and F. SONDHEIMER, *ibid.*, 2957 (1950).

4. E. A. BRAUDE and C. J. TIMMONS, *ibid.*, 2000 (1950).

5. L. DORFMAN, *Chem. Rev.*, **53**, 47 (1953).

6. D. H. R. BARTON and C. J. W. BROOKS, *J. Chem. Soc.*, 257 (1951).

7. L. RUZICKA, A. GROB and F. VAN DER SLUYS-VEER, *Helv. Chim. Acta*, **22**, 788 (1939).

8. W. SANDERMANN, *Ber. dtsch. chem. Ges.*, **74**, 160 (1941).

9. M. C. DAWSON, T. G. HALSALL and R. E. H. SWAYNE, *J. Chem. Soc.*, 590 (1953).

10. E. PESCH and S. L. FRIESS, *J. Amer. Chem. Soc.*, **72**, 5756 (1950).

11. R. W. FAWCETT and J. O. HARRIS, *J. Chem. Soc.*, 2673 (1954).

12. M. F. BARTLETT, S. K. FIGDOR and K. WIESNER, *Canad. J. Chem.*, **30**, 291 (1952).

13. E. D. PARKER and L. A. GOLDBLATT, *J. Amer. Chem. Soc.*, **72**, 2151 (1950).

14. L. F. FIESER and W. P. CAMPBELL, *ibid.*, **60**, 159 (1938).

15. L. F. FIESER and M. FIESER, *Steroids*, pp. 15–24, Reinhold, New York (1959).

16. A. T. BLOMQUIST, J. WOLINSKY, Y. C. MEINWALD and D. T. LONGONE, *J. Amer. Chem. Soc.*, **78**, 6057 (1956).

17. A. T. BLOMQUIST and D. T. LONGONE, *ibid.*, **79**, 3916 (1957).

18. W. J. BAILEY, R. L. HUDSON and C.-W. LIAO, *ibid.*, **80**, 4358 (1958).

19. G. F. WOODS and L. H. SCHWARTZMAN, *ibid.*, **70**, 3394 (1948).

20. P. NAYLER and M. C. WHITING, *J. Chem. Soc.*, 3037 (1955).

21. A. D. MEBANE, *J. Amer. Chem. Soc.*, **74**, 5227 (1952).

22. F. BOHLMANN, *Ber. dtsch. chem. Ges.*, **84**, 545 (1951).

23. L. ZECHMEISTER, A. L. LE ROSEN, W. A. SCHROEDER, A. POLGAR and L. PAULING, *J. Amer. Chem. Soc.*, **65**, 1940 (1943).

24. C. L. COOK, E. R. H. JONES and M. C. WHITING, *J. Chem. Soc.*, 2883 (1952).

25. E. A. BRAUDE and E. R. H. JONES, *ibid.*, 122 (1946) and previous papers.

26. I. BELL, E. R. H. JONES and M. C. WHITING, *ibid.*, 1313 (1958).

27. H. DANNENBERG, *Abhandl. preuß. Akad. Wiss.*, **21**, 3 (1939).

28. L. K. EVANS and A. E. GILLAM, *J. Chem. Soc.*, 815 (1941).

29. E. A. BRAUDE and E. S. WAIGHT, *Progress in Stereochemistry* (edited by W. KLYNE) Vol. I, Ch. 4, Butterworth, London (1954).

30. W. M. Schubert and W. A. Sweeney, *J. Amer. Chem. Soc.*, **77**, 2297 (1955).
31. D. Lavie and D. Willner, *ibid.*, **82**, 1668 (1960).
32. C. Djerassi, G. Rosencranz, J. Romo, S. C. Kaufmann and J. Pataki, *ibid.*, **72**, 4534 (1950).
32(a). A. W. Allan, Ph. D. Thesis, Glasgow (1959).
33. F. Wessely, J. Kotlan and W. Metlesies, *Monatsh. Chem.*, **85**, 69 (1954).
34. L. F. Fieser, K. Nakanishi and W. Y. Huang, *J. Amer. Chem. Soc.*, **75**, 4719 (1953).
35. J. Meinwald and P. C. Lee, *ibid.*, **82**, 699 (1960).
36. R. B. Bates, G. Büchi, T. Matsuura and R. R. Schaffer, *ibid.*, **82**, 2327 (1960).
37. R. L. Frank, R. Armstrong, J. Kwiatek and H. A. Price, *ibid.*, **70**, 1379 (1948).
38. D. H. R. Barton and P. de Mayo, *J. Chem. Soc.*, 142 (1956).
39. T. L. Jacobs and N. Takahashi, *J. Amer. Chem. Soc.*, **80**, 4865 (1958).
40. K. Bernauer, *Liebigs Ann.* **588**, 230 (1954).
41. D. H. R. Barton and C. R. Narayanan, *J. Chem. Soc.*, 963 (1958).
42. H. E. Stavely and G. N. Bollenback, *J. Amer. Chem. Soc.*, **65**, 1285 (1943).
43. P. L. Julian, E. W. Meyer and H. C. Printy, *ibid.*, **70**, 3872 (1948).
44. Hooper *et al.*, *Antibiot. Chemother.* **5**, 585 (1955).
45. D. H. R. Barton, P. de Mayo and J. C. Orr, *J. Chem. Soc.*, 2239 (1958).
46. E. R. H. Jones and T. G. Halsall, *Fortschritte der Chemie organischer Naturstoffe*, XII, 44.
47. R. B. Woodward, *Angew. Chem.* **69**, 50 (1957).
48. B. D. Davies, *J. Amer. Chem. Soc.*, **75**, 5567 (1953).
49. H. H. Appel, C. J. W. Brooks and K. H. Overton, *J. Chem. Soc.*, 3322 (1959).
49(a). H. H. Appel, J. D. Connolly, K. H. Overton and R. P. M. Bond, *ibid.*, 4685 (1960).
50. G. Büchi and E. W. Warnhoff, *J. Amer. Chem. Soc.*, **81**, 4434 (1959).
51. K. Wiesner, Z. Valenta, W. A. Ayer, L. R. Fowler and J. E. Francis, *Tetrahedron*, **4**, 87 (1958).
52. M. Sutter and E. Schlittler, *Helv. Chim. Acta*, **32**, 1855 (1949).
53. D. H. R. Barton, R. Bernasconi and J. Klein, *J. Chem. Soc.*, 511 (1960).
54. D. H. R. Barton, J. F. McGhie, M. K. Pradhan and S. A. Knight, *ibid.*, 876 (1955).
55. S. M. Kupchan, C. I. Ayres, M. Neeman, R. Hensler, T. Masamune and S. Rajago-palan, *J. Amer. Chem. Soc.*, **82**, 2242 (1960).
56. E. R. H. Jones, G. H. Mansfield and M. C. Whiting, *J. Chem. Soc.*, 4073 (1956).
57. E. M. Kosower and D. C. Remy, *Tetrahedron*, **5**, 281 (1959).
58. V. Georgian, *Chem. and Ind.*, 930 (1954); 1480 (1957).
59. P. Wieland, K. Heusler, H. Ueberwasser and A. Wettstein, *Helv. Chim. Acta*, **41**, 74 (1958).
60. E. G. Meek, J. H. Turnbull and W. Wilson, *J. Chem. Soc.*, 811 (1953).
61. R. B. Woodward and E. R. Blout, *J. Amer. Chem. Soc.*, **65**, 562 (1943).
62. W. Chan and C. H. Hassall, *J. Chem. Soc.*, 2860 (1955).
63. H. Smith, *ibid.*, 803 (1953).
64. A. J. Birch, *ibid.*, 3026 (1951).
65. H. S. French and L. Wiley, *J. Amer. Chem. Soc.*, **71**, 3702 (1949).
66. W. C. J. Ross, *J. Chem. Soc.*, 25 (1945).
67. R. C. Cookson and S. H. Dandegaonker, *ibid.*, 1651 (1955).
68. H. Labhart and G. Waginère, *Helv. Chim. Acta*, **42**, 2219 (1959).
69. H. F. Gray, R. S. Rasmussen and D. D. Tunnicliff, *J. Amer. Chem. Soc.*, **69**, 1630 (1947).
70. A. J. Birch, *J. Chem. Soc.*, 593 (1946).
71. K. Heusler and T. Reichstein, *Helv. Chim. Acta*, **36**, 398 (1958).
72. K. Stich, G. Rotzler and T. Reichstein, *ibid.*, **42**, 1480 (1959).
73. K. Wiesner, Z. Valenta, J. F. King, R. K. Mangdal, L. G. Humber and Shô Itô, *Chem. and Ind.*, 173 (1957).
74. R. C. Cookson and N. S. Wariyar, *J. Chem. Soc.*, 2302 (1956).

75. R.B.WOODWARD and E.G.KOVACH, *J. Amer. Chem. Soc.*, **72**, 1009 (1950).

76. W.D.KUMLER, L.A.STRAIT and E.L.ALPEN, *ibid.*, **72**, 1463 (1950).

77. S.F.MARSOCCI and SCOTT MACKENZIE, *ibid.*, **81**, 4513 (1959).

78. D.BIQUARD, *Bull. Soc. Chim. Fr.*, **8**, 55 (1941).

79. W.F.FORBES and R.SHILTON, *J. Amer. Chem. Soc.*, **81**, 786 (1959).

80. J.W.BATTY, I.M.HEILBRON and W.E.JONES, *J. Chem. Soc.*, 1556 (1939).

81. A.T.NIELSEN, *J. Org. Chem.*, **22**, 1539 (1957).

82. K.HEUSLER, P.WIELAND and A.WETTSTEIN, *Helv. Chim. Acta*, **41**, 997 (1958).

83. F.E.VADER, *ibid.*, **35**, 215 (1953).

84. U.EISNER, J.A.ELVIDGE and R.P.LINSTEAD, *J. Chem. Soc.*, 1372 (1953).

85. E.R.H.JONES, T.Y.SHEN and M.C.WHITING, *ibid.*, 230 (1950).

86. A.ROSSI and H.SCHINZ, *Helv. Chim. Acta*, **31**, 473 (1948).

87. H.SCHINZ and M.HINDER, *ibid.*, **30**, 1349 (1947).

88. H.DAHN and H.HAUTH, *ibid.*, **40**, 2249 (1957).

89. C.DJERASSI and W.RITTEL, *J. Amer. Chem. Soc.*, **79**, 3528 (1957).

90. P.A.PLATTNER and L.M.JAMPOLSKY, *Helv. Chim. Acta*, **26**, 687 (1943).

91. R.B.WOODWARD and G.SINGH, *J. Amer. Chem. Soc.*, **72**, 1428, 5351 (1950).

92. R.A.RAPHAEL, *J. Chem. Soc.*, 1508 (1948).

93. R.H.MAZUR, *J. Amer. Chem. Soc.*, **81**, 1454 (1959).

94. O.H.WHEELER, *ibid.*, **78**, 3216 (1956).

95. O.E.EDWARDS and T.SINGH, *Canad. J. Chem.*, **32**, 683 (1954).

96. H.C.BARANY, E.A.BRAUDE and M.PIANKA, *J. Chem. Soc.*, 1898 (1949).

97. J.L.JOHNSON, M.E.HERR, J.C.BABCOCK, H.E.FONKEN, J.E.STAFFORD and F.W.HEYL, *J. Amer. Chem. Soc.*, **78**, 430 (1956).

98. N.J.LEONARD and J.A.ADAMCIK, *ibid.*, **81**, 595 (1959).

99. A.E.GILLAM and E.S.STERN, *Electronic Absorption Spectroscopy*, 2nd ed., p.119, Arnold, London (1957).

100. E.A.BRAUDE, *Ann. Rep.*, **42**, 105 (1945).

101. K.SCHENKER and J.DRUEY, *Helv. Chim. Acta*, **42**, 1960 (1959).

102. G.N.LEWIS and M.CALVIN, *Chem. Rev.*, **25**, 273 (1939).

103. W.KUHN, *Helv. Chim. Acta*, **31**, 1780 (1948).

104. H.KUHN, *J. Chem. Phys.*, **17**, 1198 (1949).

105. M.J.S.DEWAR, *J. Chem. Soc.*, 3544 (1952).

106. E.A.BRAUDE, *ibid.*, 1902 (1949).

107. E.A.BRAUDE, *ibid.*, 1890 (1949).

108. E.A.BRAUDE, *ibid.*, 370 (1950).

109. R.B.WOODWARD, *J. Amer. Chem. Soc.*, **63**, 1123 (1941); *ibid.* **64**, 72, 76 (1942).

110. Ref. (99), p. 232.

111. E.M.KOSOWER, *J. Amer. Chem. Soc.*, **80**, 3253 (1958), and following papers.

112. B.EISTERT and F.GEISS, *Tetrahedron*, **7**, 1 (1959).

113. C.W.BIRD, R.C.COOKSON and S.H.DANDEGAONKER, *J. Chem. Soc.*, 3675 (1956).

114. E.M.KOSOWER, W.D.CLOSSON, H.L.GOERING and J.C.GROSS, *J. Amer. Chem. Soc.* **83**, 2013 (1961).

115. R.C.COOKSON and S.MACKENZIE, *Proc. Chem. Soc.* 423 (1961).

116. M.C.WHITING, Private Communication.

117. G.S.HANUNOND, W.G.BORDUIN and G.A.GUTER, *J. Amer. Chem. Soc.*, **81**, 4682 (1959).

CHAPTER 3

C-AROMATIC COMPOUNDS

THE widespread occurrence of aromatic rings among natural products as a result of the biosynthetic pathways involving shikimate and acetate metabolism has led to a fairly intensive search for correlation between physical property and structural feature in these compounds. The infrared spectrum forms the most generally applicable method of recognition of the presence of a C-aromatic ring but, as we shall see, valuable information may be gleaned from a careful study of the ultraviolet absorption of certain classes of aromatic compound.

It is an unfortunate consequence of the nature of aromatic absorption that, as a whole, the interpretation of the ultraviolet spectra of benzenoid derivatives is not so facile as that of the alicyclic compounds. No well defined set of rules is, as yet, available for the calculation of maxima, even on the most empirical basis, because the most characteristic band of the substituted benzene ring which corresponds to a transfer of an electron from the ring to a $-M$-substituent, or to the ring from a $+M$-substituent with available p-electrons, is in many cases only slightly affected by changes in the nature of substitution. Furthermore, in spite of attempts† to classify shifts of maxima engendered by introduction of polar substituents, the steric and electronic interplay in situations more complex than the disubstituted derivatives renders the employment of data derivable from simple model systems so hazardous that the natural product chemist is well advised to search for a very close analogy for a suspected chromophoric system – in many cases such a quest will involve the synthesis of a meaningful model compound.

In spite of these difficulties, certain spectral features of a limited number of chromophoric arrays have been used with telling effect in structural studies. These include the measurement of the spectra of acidic and basic aromatic compounds at varying pH values, and the correlation of shifts of certain absorption bands with change of solvent. Such techniques will be illustrated in this and succeeding chapters which, however, will be concerned mainly with a survey of some of the chromophores of common occurrence in nature. These have been collected in tabular form for ease of reference.

† See for example Refs. (2) and (3).

3.1. BENZENOID HYDROCARBONS (TABLE 3.1)

The spectrum of the aromatic parent, benzene (I) displays considerable fine structure, both in the vapour state and in hexane solution, a property which is not shared to the same degree by its congeners. The use of hydroxylic solvent tends to smooth out fine structure through solvent–solute interaction, whereas in hydrocarbon solvent it is possible to observe the effects of intramolecular interactions more clearly (Fig. 3.1). Where relevant, measurement of maxima

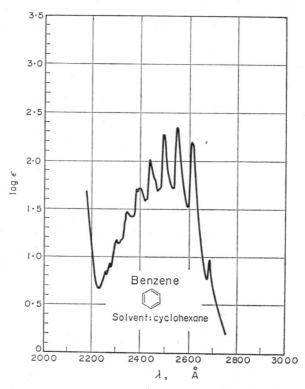

Fig. 3.1. Absorption spectrum of benzene in cyclohexane (Friedel and Orchin, No. 7).

in both types of solvent can form a complementary armament (see, for example, o-hydroxyacetophenone, p. 114). The three-banded spectrum of benzene will be considered as one chromophore as defined on p. 7; this treatment not only simplifies the consideration of the spectra of substituted benzenes, but further minimizes the use of a nomenclature system which is not required within the scope of this volume. Benzene absorbs at 184 (ε60,000), 203.5 (ε7400) and 254 (ε204) mμ in hexane solution. These maxima may be considered as the L.E. bands of the benzene chromophore. Increasing alkyl substitution causes displacement of the 254 mμ band (λ_3) to the red, an effect which reaches its limit at tetrasubstitution. The bathochromic shift occasioned by alkyl substitution may be considered as an inductive effect, although views have been expressed recently that these phenomena may be ascribed to hyperconjugation[89]. Comparison of the spectra of 1,2,3-trimethylbenzene

I, 254 mμ (ε 204)   II, 266 mμ (ε 360)   III, 263 mμ (ε 250)

(II) with that of methyl indane (III) reveals a close but possibly fortuitous correspondence in wavelength and intensity of maximal absorption, for indane itself has λ_{max}, 273 mμ (ε 1600) which would not be expected on the basis of comparison with o-xylene (λ_{max}, 262 mμ (ε 300)). Further examples of the effect of steric strain engendered by attachment of a hydroaromatic ring to the benzene nucleus are discernible in the comparison of tetralin (No. 12) with the octahydroanthracene (No. 14). The spectrum of the latter is typical of that of a benzene ring embedded in an alicyclic framework.

3.2. PHENOLS AND THEIR ETHERS (TABLE 3.2a)

Phenol (No. 1) exhibits a long wavelength band at 270 mμ (ε, 1450) which is considered to be the displaced and intensified L.E. band of benzene (254 mμ). The intense absorption of phenol at 210 mμ (ε, 6000) marks an E.T. transition in which a p-electron of oxygen is transferred to the π-orbital of the ring. The latter process requires less energy in the anion (V) and in anisole (No. 3). In the acetylated phenols, e.g. o-cresyl acetate, the lone pair on oxygen is not available for such transfer (VI; arrows) and a return to the spectrum of toluene is observed.

IV   V   VI

VII

TABLE 3.1. BENZENOID HYDROCARBONS

No.	Compound	λ_1	ε_1	λ_2	ε_2	λ_3	ε_3	Solvent	Reference
1.		184	(60,000)	203·5	(7400)	254	(204)	H	(1)
2.		—		206·5	(7000)	254	(160)	MeOH	(2)
3.		—		210	(8300)	262·5	(300)	MeOH	(3)
4.		—		212	(7200)	264·5	(300)	MeOH	(3)
5.		193	(54,000)	212	(8000)	274	(460)	H	(1)
6.		—		—		266	(305)	H	(1)
7.		—		—		266	(360)	H	(1)
8.		—		—		275	(835)	H	(1)
9.		—		—		279	(820)	H	(1)
10.		—		—		270	(365)	H	(1)
11.		—		—		272	(300)	H	(1)
12.		—		—		267 / 274	(560) / (560)	iso O	(4)
13.		—		—		263	(250)	iso O	(4)
14.		—		—		275 / 285	(1700) / (1800)	A	(5)
15.		—		—		260 / 267 / 273	(1000) / (1400) / (1600)	H	(6)

TABLE 3.2a. PHENOLS, PHENYL ETHERS AND ACETATES

No.	Compound	λ_1	(ε_1)	λ_2	(ε_2)	Solvent	Reference
1.	OH (phenol)	210·5	(6200)	210	(1450)	W	(2)
2.	O⊖ (phenolate)	235	(9400)	287	(2600)	N NaOH	(2)
3.	OMe	217	(6400)	269	(1480)	W	(2)
4.	OAc	—		261	(300)	H	(7)
5.	OH / OH (catechol)	214	(6300)	275·5	(2300)	pH 3	(3)
6.	O⊖ / OH	236·5	(6800)	292	(3500)	pH 11	(3)
7.	OH / OH (resorcinol)	216	(6800)	273·5	(1900)	pH 3	(3)
8.	OH / O⊖	236	(8000)	287	(2900)	pH 11	(3)
9.	OH / HO (hydroquinone)	—		295	(3100)	A	(8)
10.	O⊖ / HO	—		283		A/NaOH	(8)
11.	OH / HO OH	—		267·5 / 271	(450) / (388)	A	(9)
12.	O⊖ / ⊖O O⊖	252	(20,000)	350	(8730)	OH⁻	(9)

TABLE 3.2a—(contd.)

No.	Compound	λ_1	(ε_1)	λ_2	(ε_2)	Solvent	Reference
13.		—		261·5	(361)	A	(9)
14.		—		292	(3160)	A	(10)
15.		—		266·5	(708)	A	(10)
16.		—		267·5	(682)	A	(9)
17.		244·5	(5440)	275	(4530)	OH⁻	(9)
				357	(4680)		
18.		—		259	(240)	A	(10)
19.		—		279	(1950)	C	(5)
				286	(1780)		
20.		—		280	(2300)	A	(11)
				285	(2000)		
21.		—		280	(2270)†		(12)
22.		—		268	(775)†		(12)

† Average value.

TABLE 3.2a—(contd.)

No.	Compound	λ_1	(ε_1)	λ_2	(ε_2)	Solvent	Reference
23.	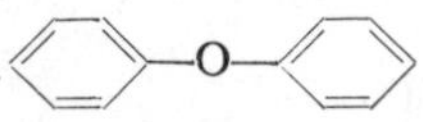	255	(11,000)	272 278	(2000) (1800)	C	(21)
24.	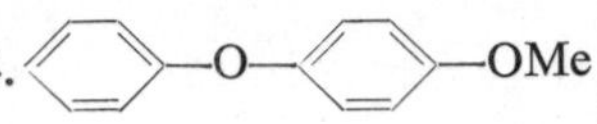 —OMe	230	(13,200)	280 288	(2700) (2500)	C	(14)
25.	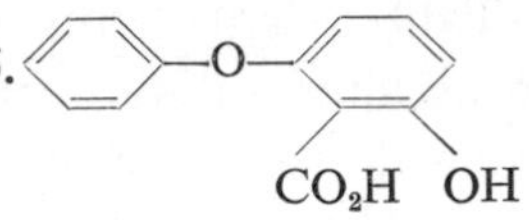 CO_2H OH	—		316	(6000)	A	(15)
26.	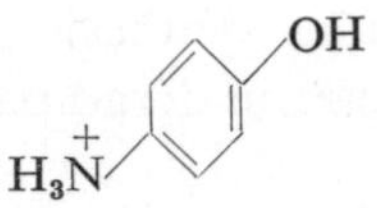 OH $H_3\overset{+}{N}$	218·5	(6240)	262·5	(1450)	W	(2)
27.	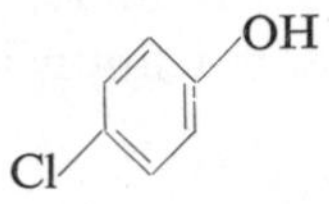 OH Cl	225	(8900)	279·5	(1600)	0·1 N HCl	(2)
28.	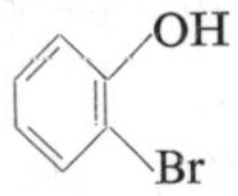 OH Br	—		279	(2800)	A	(16)
29.	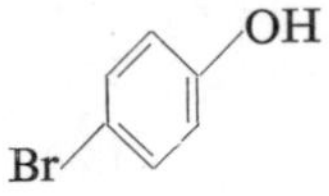 OH Br	—		284·5	(1650)	A	(16)
30.	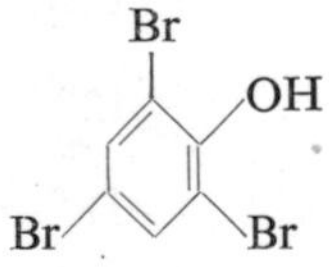 Br OH Br Br	—		295	(3200)	A	(16)

Thus estrone acetate (VII) has λ_{max}^{EtOH} 260 mμ (ε 1640)[13]. (cf. o-xylene, λ_{max} 262·5 (ε 300)).

A shift of the long wavelength band (λ_2) of ca. +20 mμ on passing from neutral to alkaline solution forms a useful method of recognition of the presence of the monohydric phenol chromophore (Nos. 2, 19). For catechols and resorcinols a similar shift is observed (Tables 3.2a, 3.2b), However, the long wavelength band of the hydroquinones undergoes a blue shift on passing from neutral to alkaline solution. This observation has been applied to the solution of a structural problem in the following way. The assignation of the appropriate

IUS 4 a

structures to the isomeric bromolactones VIII and IX was tentatively made on the basis

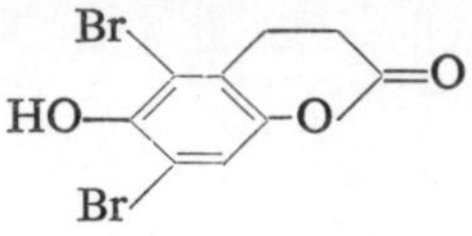

VIII

$\Delta \lambda - 40\,m\mu$

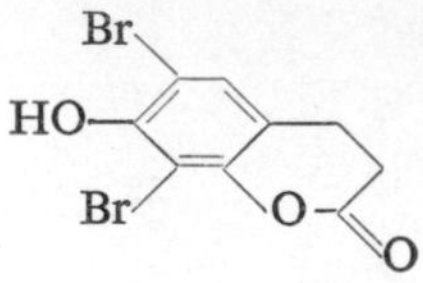

IX

$\Delta \lambda + 17\,m\mu$

of the respective shifts of the long wavelength band (λ_2) (Table 3.2(b)). Thus the lactone of structure (VIII) opens to a hydroquinone in alkaline solution and displays a blue shift, whereas (IX) hydrolyses in alkali to a dibromoresorcinol and this is accompanied by a bathochromic displacement. The assignment of structure made on this basis was confirmed by unambiguous synthesis of the parent lactones VIII(a) and IX(a) (Table 3.2b) whose spectra undergo parallel shifts in alkaline solution.

The interpretation of the spectra of polyhydric phenols is more difficult (Table 3.2a) and their sensitivity to alkali is an added complication in diag-

TABLE 3.2 b. EFFECT OF ALKALI ON THE SPECTRA OF DIHYDRIC PHENOLS

	Neutral soln. λ_2 (mμ)	Alkaline soln. λ_2 (mμ)	$\Delta\lambda_2$
Phenol	270	287	+17
Catechol	275·5	292	+16·5
Resorcinol	276	290	+13·5
Hydroquinone	295	283	−12
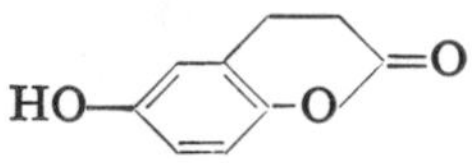 VIII (a)	286	265	−21
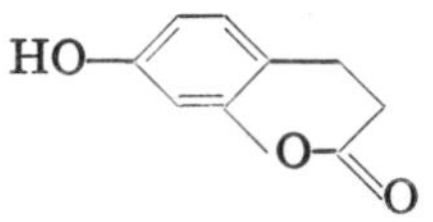 IX (a)	280	295	+15

nosis by the alkaline shift principle. In these cases, complete acetylation produces the spectrum of the parent hydrocarbon system (Nos. 13, 15, 18). The information derived from the spectroscopic modification of Gibb's test (Chapter 7) may also prove meaningful.

Diphenyl ethers absorb at slightly longer wavelengths than the corresponding anisoles, indicating some conjugative interaction between the benzene rings. The bulk of the phenoxyl group may also cause loss of coplanarity of an adjacent chromophore with the benzene ring (Section 3.5). The effect of halogen substitution on phenol absorption illustrated by No. 27–30. We note that the *p*-aminophenol cation (No. 26) has its maximum close to that of phenol itself, indicating that the electron transfer of the aniline component (Section 3.8) is inhibited by salt formation.

3.3. STYRENES AND STILBENES (TABLE 3.3)

The spectrum of styrene contains a main band at 248 mμ, whose intensity and position are susceptible to loss of coplanarity (No. 1–8). In addition, characteristic subsidiary maxima at 282 and 291 mμ (displaced benzenoid absorption) provide useful diagnostic features. The introduction of hydroxyl groups on the ring does not affect the main band in a regular way although the 290 mμ absorption is intensified and a shift of the main band of *ca.* 10 mμ to longer wavelengths occurs on *para*-substitution (No. 11–18).

The sensitivity of the 248 mμ bands to conformational environment may be judged by comparison of indene (No. 9) with 1,2-dihydronaphthalene (No. 8), the latter spectrum showing a displacement of + 10 mμ compared with that of methylstyrene (No. 2). Further stereochemical subtleties are revealed by the positions of the maxima of the isomeric dehydro-estrone systems (X), (XI) and (XII)[12]:

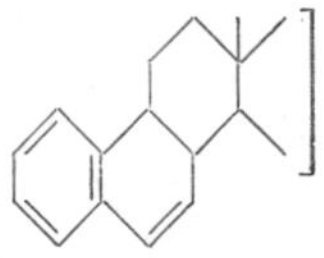

X	XI	XII
λ, 262 (9000)	λ, 275 (17,000)	λ, 264 (19,000)

Stilbenes

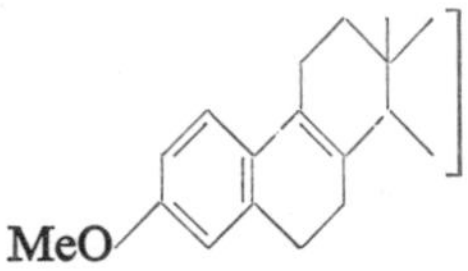

In addition to the principal band near 280 mμ, stilbenes absorb near 220 mμ The *cis*-stilbenes absorb at shorter wavelengths than the *trans*-isomers as a con

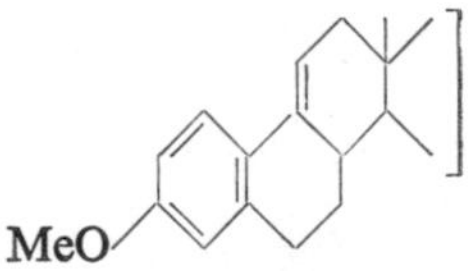

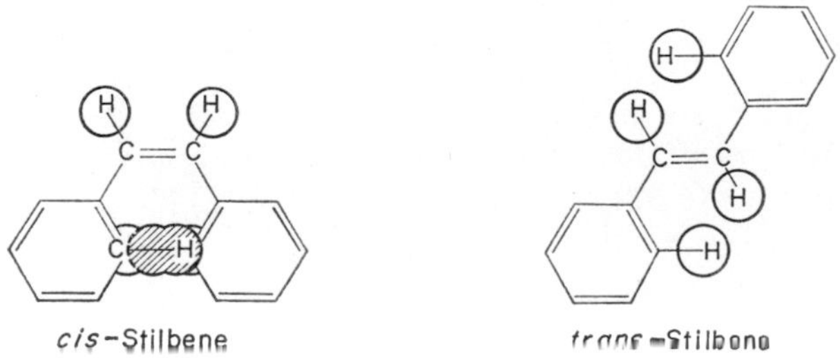

cis-Stilbene   *trans*-Stilbene

FIG. 3.2

TABLE 3.3. STYRENE AND STILBENE ABSORPTION

No.	Compound	λ_1 (ε_1)	λ_2 (ε_2)		Solvent	Reference
A. Styrenes						
1.		248 (14,000)	282 291	(750) (500)	A	(17, 18)
2.		251 (17,000)	284 293	(950) (600)	A	(17, 18)
3.		243 (11,500)	285i	(300)	A	(17, 18)
4.		245 (11,600)	286 297	(1100) (800)	A	(5)
5.		245 (7000)	—		O	(20)
6.		235 (inflection)	—		A	(4)
7.		240 (8000)	—		A	(22)
8.		262 (10,500)	296	(700)	H	(23)
9.		249 (11,000)	280 290	(450) (250)	A	(23)
10.		259·5 (13,500) 269 (11,750)	290 301·5	(4000) (4000)	A	(24)
11.	MeO HO	260 (15,850)	305	(7000)	A	(25)
12.	O O	264 (15,500)	303	(6600)	A	(26)

TABLE 3.3—(contd.)

No.	Compound	λ_1 (ε_1)		λ_2 (ε_2)		Solvent	Reference
A. Styrenes—(contd.)							
13.	OMe	250	(11,500)	—		A	(29)
14.	MeO	250	(8500)	293	(2150)	A	(30)
15.	OH	267	(8000)	298	(2850)	A	(20)
				308	(2550)		
16.	OMe	265	(8500)	296	(2400)	A	(30)
				307	(2000)		
17.	OAc	265	(7000)	300	(1800)	A	(30)
18.	OMe	265	(7800)	298	(2130)	A	(30)
B. Stilbenes							
19.	*trans* $C_6H_5CH{=}CHC_6H_5$	228	(16,400)	295·5	(29,000)	A	(31)
20.	*cis* $C_6H_5CH{=}CHC_6H_5$	224	(24,400)	280	(10,500)	A	(31)
21.	OH HO OH HO	—		330	(2,600)	A	(32)
22.		218	(22,000)	280	(5000)	A	(33)
		240	(12,000)				

sequence of their shorter effective chromophoric length (Fig. 3.2). The decreased intensity at 280 mμ of the *cis*-stilbene chromophore reflects the steric hindrance to coplanarity by overlap at the *ortho*-positions. Hydroxylic substitution raises λ_{max}, especially for the *para*-derivatives. The tetrahydroxystilbene (No. 21: *trans*-form) has been isolated from hardwood extractives[32].

In the α,β-dialkylstilbenes (e.g. No. 22), steric interference between both pairs of alkyl and phenyl groups affects the spectrum profoundly, the main band now appearing at 240 mμ with only moderate absorption near 280 mμ (ε 5000).

3.4. AROMATIC CARBONYL COMPOUNDS

The effects of various $+ M$ and $- M$ substituents on the absorption bands of benzene have been discussed by Doub and Vandenbelt[2,3]. In a most detailed survey these authors have attempted to relate the nature and pattern of substitution to the effect on the 203·5 mμ band of benzene. Now, although this treatment has some merit in the case of alkyl substitution, the availability of p-electrons in the groupings —OR, —NR$_2$, etc., and the polarizability of moieties such as $>$C=O, —CN, —NO$_2$ allow the operation of an electron transfer (E.T.) transition[80,81], which is a characteristic of the composite molecule R—S, where R and S represent different chromophores separated by a single bond. In effect, this means that the 210 mμ band of phenol does not correspond to the 203·5 mμ of benzene, since the former absorption represents the transfer of an electron from the p-orbital of oxygen to a π-orbital of the ring system.

Although the empirical approach of Doub and Vandenbelt may be regarded as without basis in terms of current theory, this does not detract from the usefulness of their compilation. By consideration of a number of disubstituted benzenes these authors arrived at $\Delta\lambda$ values for some sixteen substituents (in hydroxylic solvent) where

$$\Delta\lambda = (\lambda_{max} - 203\cdot5)\ m\mu \tag{1}$$

and λ_{max} is the wavelength of the principal (or primary) absorption band. Straight-line relationships were found for the plot of $\Delta\lambda$ (for certain series of p-disubstituted benzenes) against the product of the contributing substitutional increments $(\Delta\lambda' \times \Delta\lambda'')$. A refinement was then made using the value λ_0 ($= 180$ mμ). The observed increment for a disubstituted benzene then becomes

$$\Delta\lambda_0 = \lambda_{max} - 180 \tag{2}$$

and the contributing substitutional parameters are found from equation (3)

$$\delta\lambda_0' \times \delta\lambda_0'' = 24\cdot05 \times \Delta\lambda_0. \tag{3}$$

The plot of $\Delta\lambda_0$ against the products of the contributing $\delta\lambda_0$ values shows a widely applicable straight-line relationship for p-disubstitution, while the o- and

m-derivatives are plotted against the *sum* of the $\delta\lambda_0$ values. Table 3.4(a) includes a selection of $\delta\lambda_0$ values. It is important to recall that this treatment is only applicable to substituents of opposite electronic effect, involving an o–p-directing group in presence of a m-directing group. The combination of two similarly orienting groups results in a spectrum approximating to that of the stronger chromophore. The qualitative nature of this method may be illustrated

XIII	XIV	XV
λ, 251 mμ	λ, 251 mμ	λ, 276 mμ

for the isomeric hydroxy acetophenones (XIII, XIV, XV). From the additivity relationships for $\delta\lambda_0$ values (Table 3.4a) we have (for all *three* isomers)

$$\lambda_{calc} = 180 + 36 \cdot 1 \, (OH) + 63 \cdot 3 \, (COMe)$$

$$= 279 \cdot 4 \text{ m}\mu.$$

Using equations (2) and (3) $\lambda_{calc} = 276$ mμ.

These results are satisfactory for the p-isomer but do not provide an accurate means of predicting the maxima of the o- and m-derivatives.

TABLE 3.4a. $\delta\lambda_0$ VALUES FOR BENZENE SUBSTITUTION

Substituent	$\delta\lambda_0$ (mμ)	Substituent	$\delta\lambda_0$ (mμ)
—H	24·05	—CN	43·9
—NH$_3^+$	25·6	—CO$_2^-$	44·7
—CH$_3$	29·6	—CO$_2$H	50
—Cl	29·3	—NH$_2$	50
—Br	31·5	—O$^-$	55
—OH	36·1	—COCH$_3$	63·3
—OMe	36·8	—CHO	68·9
—SO$_2$NH$_2$	37·5	—NO$_2$	91·6

However, the electron transfer absorptions of substituted benzaldehydes and acetophenones are sharply divided into transitions characteristic of *ortho-*/*meta-*substitution on the one hand and to the *para-*disubstituted series on the other.[2, 3, 10, 24] The *ortho-* and *meta-*isomers give rise to *two* E.T. bands in the 230–300 mμ region, whereas the corresponding *para-*compound shows only *one* intense E.T. band, at wavelengths consistently longer than those of the principal E.T. bands of the *o-/m*-series (Figs. 3.3, 3.4). Further, the *ortho*-substituent may have steric requirements which involve overlap with, say, the methyl group of acetophenone. This may lead to a decrease in the intensity of absorption and/or a wavelength shift[45] (blue or red). A unifying molecular orbital treatment of this phenomenon

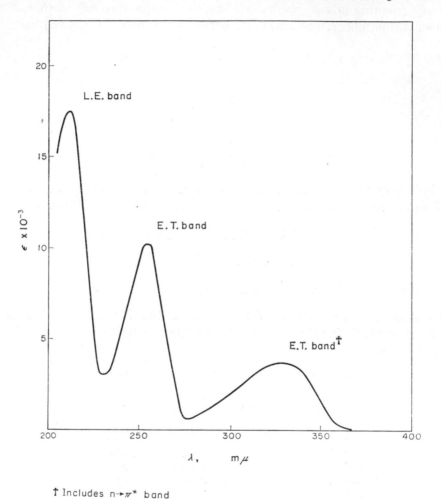

† Includes n→π* band

Fig. 3.3. Absorption curve of *o*-hydroxyacetophenone (in 0·1N HCb).

has appeared[82], but for our present purpose it is only necessary to recognize the possibility of an anomalous spectrum if the model of the chromophore under study displays serious steric overlap of this nature. It has been pointed out by Murrell[81] that the E.T. band of a given molecule may be recognized by its susceptibility to the loss of coplanarity by steric hindrance. Further, the fundamental difference between the *o-/m*- and *p*-transitions can be explained and the appropriate energies of transition calculated by quantum-mechanical treatment[83] of the simple disubstituted benzene case.

In view of the fundamental nature of these transitional differences, it seems to us that the E.T. bands due to conjugation of the unlike chromophores, Ph—CX=Y, should be affected in a regular way by the introduction of *ortho-*, *meta-* and *para*-substituents. Our treatment differs from previous correlative

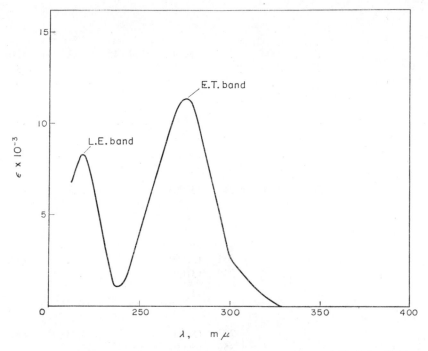

FIG. 3.4. Absorption curve of *p*-hydroxyacetophenone (in 0·1 N HCl).

studies in that it is necessary to find a parent E.T. chromophore value to which a common set of increments may be added. Thus the method of calculation which will be developed in the sequel forms a useful, if empirical, treatment of aromatic spectra based on principles similar to those available for calculation of the E.T. maxima of alicyclic and aliphatic chromophores (Chapter 2).

Ketones and Aldehydes (Table 3.4b)

In hydroxylic solvent acetophenone exhibits a four-banded spectrum with maxima at 199, 246, 278 and 320 mμ (ε 20,000; 13,200; 1000 and 50, respectively). The bands at 199 and 278 mμ may be assigned to the displaced 188 and 255 mμ bands of benzene. The weak absorption at 320 mμ marks the L.E. ($n \rightarrow \pi^*$) band of the $>$C=O group and is usually masked by more intense bands in this region engendered by further substitution of the molecule. The electron transfer band at 246 mμ will be considered as the parent chromophore for all combinations of a benzene ring with a ketonic function (XVIa). For substituted benzaldehydes,

TABLE 3.4b. AROMATIC KETONES AND ALDEHYDES

No.	Compound	Benzenoid bands	E.T. bands		$n \to \pi^*$ band	Solvent	Reference
A. Ketones							
1.		199 (20,000) 278 (1000)	243	(12,600)	320 (45)	A	(10) (34)
2.		281 (1200)	242 245	(8700) (8300)	331 (50)	A	(35)
3.		280 (400)	242	(3600)	—	A	(36)
4.		—	251 329	(9300) (3100)	—	A	(34)
5.		—	257 359	(5600) (5000)	—	OH⁻	(34)
6.		—	246 305	(11,000) (3820)	—	A	(34) (37)
7.		220·5 (10,700)	276	(13,500)	330 (60)	A	(34)
8.		—	277 314	(13,800) (7000)	—	A/H⁺	(34)
9.		—	333	(26,000)	—	OH⁻	(34)

TABLE 3.4b.—(contd.)

No.	Compound	Benzenoid bands	E.T. bands	$n \to \pi^*$ band	Solvent	Reference
A. Ketones—(contd.)						
10.		223 (12,600)	291 (17,800) 333 (2510)	—	A	(34)
11.		281 (1000)	238 (5860)	—	A	(34)
12.		227 (13,100)	285 (15,500)	—	A	(9)
13.		—	318·5 (22,400)	—	OH⁻	(9)
14.		—	295 (14,000)	—	A	(39)
15.		—	248 (11,600) 292 (1700)	—	MeOH	(40)
16.		—	243 (12,300)	—	A	(40)
17.		270 (1700)	254 (18,000)	330 (160)	A	(41)
18.		—	251 (11,000) 342 (1600)	—	A	(42)

TABLE 3.4b.—(contd.)

No.	Compound	Benzenoid bands		E.T. band		$n \rightarrow \pi^*$ band	Solvent	Reference
A. Ketones—(contd.)								
19.	Cl, MeO, OH, OH, MeO, OH, OMe, Me, O	—		296	(18,000)	—		(43)
20.	HO, OH, MeO, Cl, Me, Cl, CO₂H, OH, O	—		285	(16,000)	—		(44)
B. Aldehydes								
21.	CHO	20 280 289	(1400) (1200)	242 248	(14,000) (12,500)	330– 350 (50)	H	(35)
22.	CHO (Me)	291	(1700)†	243 251	(12,500) (13,000)	322 (45)	H	(35)
23.	CHO (Me)	279	(1200)	251 257	(15,000) (12,500)	326 (30)	H	(35)
24.	CHO (Me, Me, Me)	—		264 300	(14,500) (100)†	—	H	(35)
25.	CHO, OH	—		255 325	(19,000) (3020)	—	A	(34)
26.	CHO, OMe	—		253 319·5	(11,000) (4000)	—	A	(34)
27.	CHO	—		247 302	(10,000) (2900)	—	H	(45)

† Benzenoid and E.T. superimposed.

TABLE 3.4b.—(contd.)

No.	Compound	Benzenoid bands	E.T. bands	$n \rightarrow \pi^*$ band	Solvent	Reference
B. Aldehydes—(contd.)						
28.	CHO / HO—	221† (13,800)	282 (17,500)	332(180)	A	(34)
29.	CHO / HO₂C—	—	253 (16,000) 288 (1950)	—	A	(45)

No.	Compound	Benzenoid bands	E.T. bands	Solvent	Reference
C. Extended Systems					
30.		220 (12,500)	286 (22,500)	A	(5)
31.		230 (14,000) 238 (13,500)	300 (16,000) 320 (15,000)	A	(5)
32.	MeO—	233 (10,000)	318 (26,000)	A	(5)
33.	AcO—	223 (11,000)	289 (22,000)	A	(5)
34.	$(CH=CH)_2COMe$	233 (6000)	320 (33,000)	A	(5)
35.	$(CH=CH)_nCHO$				(46)
	$n = 1$		322 (30,500)	Ch.	(46)
	$n = 2$	249 (10,800)	352 (42,000)	Ch.	(46)
	$n = 3$	272 (8000)	382 (52,000)	Ch.	(46)
	$n = 7$	275 (12,300)	304 (11,600) 351 (9900) 457 (90,200)	Ch.	(46)

† Combined with p–π (E.T.) band of HO—⟨⟩—

TABLE 3.4 b.—(cotd.)

No.	Compound	Benzenoid bands	E.T. bands	Solvent	Reference
C. Extended Systems—(contd.)					
36.			294 (17,000)	A	(47)
37.		233 (14,000)	324 (23,700)	A	(48)
38.		261 (15,700)	371 (34,000)	A	(48)

a parent value of 250 mμ is taken to represent the E.T. absorption. A selection of spectra of carbonyl systems will be found in Table 3.4b.

XVIa   R = Alkyl or ring residue λ^* † = 246 mμ
XVIb   R = H λ^* = 250 mμ

Let us now consider the substitution of acetophenone by a variety of groupings in the *o-*, *m-* and *p-*positions as reflected in the *position* of the 246 mμ band. Intensity changes become important in this treatment where operation of the "*ortho*" effect depresses ε to such an extent that only a shoulder remains at the expected wavelength of absorption. This usually requires heavy 2,6-disubstitution (e.g. 2,4,6-trimethylacetophenone, Table 3.4b, No. 3). For purposes of calculation of the approximate location of the E.T. bands of aromatic ketones, the increments shown in Table 3.4c have been found to provide predicted values to within 5 mμ for many examples. A selection of these will be found in Table 3.4d together with the deviation ($\Delta \lambda^*$) values. Intensities have been omitted in order to simplify the presentation. Of the thirty-four examples in Table 3.4d, twenty-six are within 5 mμ, five within 7 mμ and the remaining three are, respectively, 9, 14 and 20 mμ in error. Thus 2,4,6-trimethylaceto-

† $\lambda^* = \lambda_{max}$ in EtOH, MeOH or aqueous solutions.

phenone $(-20\ m\mu)$ has λ_{max} 246 mμ (ε 3600), revealing the extent of loss of coplanarity of the conjugate functions contributing to the electron transfer. The intensity of absorption obeys approximately a $\cos^2\theta$ law. The anomalous position of the 2,6-dihydroxyacetophenones (ca. $+10\ m\mu$) may be ascribed to similar loss of coplanarity, although 3-hydroxy-4-aminoacetophenone $(-14\ m\mu)$ cannot be

TABLE 3.4c. CALCULATION OF THE PRINCIPAL E.T. BAND OF SUBSTITUTED BENZENE DERIVATIVES, Ar—COR (IN EtOH)

		$\lambda*$† (mμ)
Parent chromophore: PhCOR		
R = Alkyl or ring residue		246
R = H		250
R = OH, OAlk		230
Increment for each substituent:		
—Alkyl or ring	o-, m-	3
residue	p-	10
—OH, —OMe, —OAlk	o-, m-	7
	p-	25
—O⁻	o-	11
	m-	20
	p-	78††
—Cl	o-, m-	0
	p-	10
—Br	o-, m-	2
	p-	15
—NH₂	o-, m-	13
	p-	58
—NHAc	o-, m-	20
	p-	45
—NHMe	p-	73
—NMe₂	o-, m-	20
	p-	85

† $\lambda* = \lambda_{max}$ in EtOH.

†† This value may be decreased markedly by steric hindrance to coplanarity.

explained on this basis. The spectral data for the last compound was, however, recorded at pH 6 and some difference might be found for alcoholic solution.

We are now in a position to extend our calculations to examples of some complexity and of relevance to our theme of natural product chemistry. Hydroxylic solvent (usually ethanol) is taken as reference because the E.T. band under review is least susceptible to intramolecular effects in this solvent. Solvation effects in alkylated acetophenones have been discussed in detail by Schubert[90], Braude[33] and Morton[34] and we shall consider these at a later stage (p. 114). Let us now examine the detailed calculation of λ_{max} for a number of polycyclic ketones.

TABLE 3.4d.—E.T. BANDS OF SUBSTITUTED ACETOPHENONES (IN EtOH)

	λ^*_{calc}	λ^*_{obs}	$\Delta\lambda^*$	Reference
Acetophenone	[246]	243	—	
2-Me	249	245	—4	(35)
4-Me	256	256	0	(2)
2,4,6-tri-Me	262	242	—20†	(36)
2-OH	253	252	—1	(34)
3-OH	253	250·5	—2·5	(3)
4-OH	271	275	+4	(2)
2,4-di-OH	278	275	—3	(49)
2,4-di-OH (anion)	331	328	—3	(49)
3,4-di-OH	278	274	—4	(49)
3,4-di-OH (anion)	344	342	—2	(49)
2,5-di-OH	260	256	—4	(49)
2,6-di-OH	260	270	+10†	(37)
2,6-di-OMe	260	260	0	(50)
2,4,6-tri-OH	285	285·5	+0·5†	(9)
2,4,6-tri-OH-ω-Me	285	285	0	(38)
2,4-di-OH-5,6-di-Me	284	285	+1	(37)
2,4-di-OH-3,5-di-Me	284	285	+1	(37)
2,4-di-OH-3,6-di-Me	284	291	+7†	(37)
2,6-di-OH-3-Et	263	272	+9†	(50)
2,4-diOMe-5-Me-ω-diMe	281	288	+4	(50)
2,4,6-tri-OH-3-Me·	288	291	+3	(10)
2-NH$_2$	259	259	0	(51)
3-NH$_2$	259	262	+3	(51)
4-NH$_2$	304	311	+7	(2)
2-NHAc	266	266	0	(51)
3-NHAc	266	257–60(Sh)	—6	(51)
4-NHAc	291	289	—2	(51)
2-NMe$_2$	266	266	0	(51)
4-NMe$_2$	331	331	0	(51)
2,4-di-Cl	256	252	—4	(49)
3,4-di-Cl	256	254	—2	(49)
2,5-di-Cl	246	240	—6	(49)
2-OH-4-NH$_2$	311	325	+14††	(49)

† "*ortho*" effect predicted.
†† At pH 6 in aqueous solution.

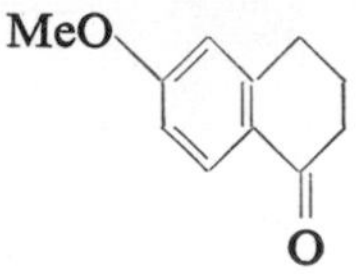

XVII 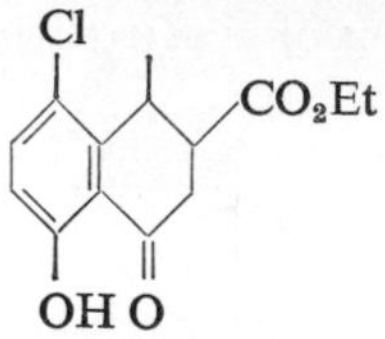   XVIII 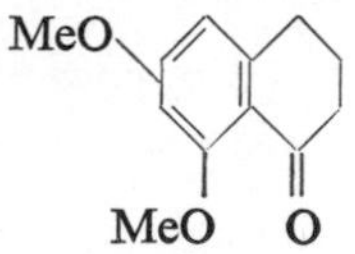   XIX

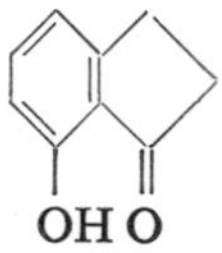

XX 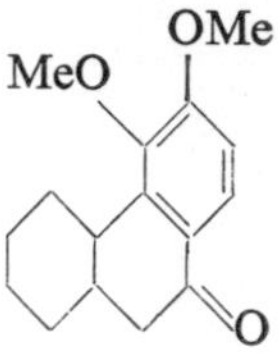   XXI 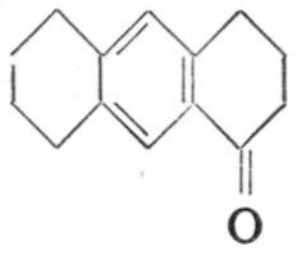   XXII

Example 1. 6-Methoxytetralone (XVII).

$\lambda^{*\dagger}_{calc}$ = 246 (parent chromophore) + 3 (*o*-ring residue) + 25 (*p*-OMe)

     = 274 mμ

λ_{obs} = 276 mμ (ε 16,500).[84]

Example 2. 3-Carbethoxy-4-methyl-5-chloro-8-hydroxytetralone (XVIII).

λ^{*}_{calc} = 246 + 3 (*o*-ring residue) + 7 (*o*-OH)

     = 256 mμ

λ_{obs} = 257 mμ (ε 8000).[85]

Example 3. 6,8-Dimethoxytetralone (XIX).

λ^{*}_{calc} = 246 + 3 (*o*-ring residue) + 7 (*o*-OMe) + 25 (*p*-OMe)

     = 281 mμ

λ^{*}_{obs} = 275 mμ (ε 8500).[86]

Example 4. 7-Hydroxyindanone (XX).

λ^{*}_{calc} = 246 + 3 (*o*-ring residue) + 7 (*o*-OH)

     = 256 mμ

λ_{obs} = 255 mμ (ε 8200).[53]

Example 5. 3,4-Dimethoxy-10-oxo-octahydrophenanthrene (XXI).

λ^{*}_{calc} = 281 mμ

λ_{obs} = 278 mμ (ε 10,000).[87]

* $\lambda^{*} = \lambda^{EtOH}_{max}$.

† λ_{max} values for aromatic carbonyl compounds are constant (within 2mμ) for EtOH, MeOH, H$_2$O and mixtures of these solvents.

TABLE 3.4e. E.T. BANDS OF SUBSTITUTED AROMATIC KETONES

No.	Compound	λ^*_{calc}	λ^*_{obs}	Reference
1.		249	248	(40)
2.		249	249	(40)
3.		251	253	(68)
4.		249	243	(40)
5.		254	254	(5)
6.		291	290	(52)
7.		274	273	(53)
8.		255	252·5	(54)
9.		262	256·6	(54)

Example 6. 9-Octahydro-1-oxoanthracene (XXII).

λ_{calc} = 246 + 3 (*o*-ring residue) + 3 (*m*-ring residue) + 10 (*p*-ring residue)

= 262 mμ

λ_{obs} = 262 mμ (ε 12,000).[5]

Further examples will be found in Table 3.4e.

Substituted *benzaldehydes* may be treated in exactly the same way, with the parent chromophore value of 250 mμ (XVIb). Table 3.4f summarizes calculated and observed values for some substituted benzaldehydes. The *ortho*-effect is not so pronounced in the aldehyde series, as the overlap now involves the aldehydic-H atom and the *ortho*-substituent.

We have emphasized that the foregoing treatment is strictly applicable only to spectra determined in hydroxylic solvent.† In non-polar solvents, e.g. hexane, the operation of intramolecular chelation effects becomes evident in the shift of the second (long wavelength) E.T. band of *ortho*-substituted aldehydes and

TABLE 3.4f. E.T. BANDS OF SUBSTITUTED BENZALDEHYDES (EtOH)

Compound	λ^*_{calc}	λ^*_{obs}	$\Delta\lambda^*$	Reference
Benzaldehyde	[250]	250	—	
2-Me	253	253	0	(51)
3-Me	253	251	−2	(51)
4-Me	260	259	−1	(51)
2,4,6-tri-Me	266	264	−2	(35)
2-OH	257	256	−1	(34)
2-OH (anion)	261	264	+3	(3)
3-OH (anion)	270	267	−3	(3)
4-OH	275	282	+7	(51)
4-OH (anion)	328	330	+2	(2)
2,4-di-OH	282	278	−4	(49)
2,4-di-OH (anion)	339	331	−8	(49)
2,6-di-OH-4-OEt-3-Me	292	295	+3	(10)
2-OH,3-OMe	264	265	+1	(50)
2-NMe₂	270	271	+1	(51)
4-NMe₂	335	337	+2	(51)
2-NMe₂-5-Me	273	270(sh)	−3	(3)
2-OH-5-Cl	257	255	−2	(49)
2-OH-5-Cl (anion)	261	260	−1	(49)
4-OH-3,5-di-Me	281	290	+9	(16)
4-OH-2,6-di-Me	281	286	+5	(16)
4-OMe-3,5-di-Me	281	265	−16†	(16)
2-OMe	257	254	−3	(51)
3-OMe	257	255	−2	(51)
4-OMe	275	280	+5	(51)

† See p. 109.

ketones. Indeed, these effects have been correlated with structural changes in studies by Morton and his collaborators[10, 34] whose work has recently been extended by Conover[19] to the chromophores of the tetracycline series.

Morton's results demonstrate that while o-hydroxy carbonyl compounds undergo a blue shift of the second E.T. band (330 mμ) on etherification, the m-isomers show no difference of this band for the change OH → O-Alk (Table 3.4g). Further, while the hydroxy compounds absorb at essentially the same wavelength

TABLE 3.4g. LONG WAVELENGTH ABSORPTION OF o-HYDROXY AND o-ALKOXY-ALDEHYDES AND -KETONES (AFTER CONOVER[19])

	Hydrocarbon† solvent		Hydroxylic† solvent	
	o-OH	o-OAlk	o-OH	o-OAlk
Benzaldehyde	329	310	325	320
Acetophenone	329	300	327	305
Tetralone	331	307*	335	317*
Indanone	314	306	316	312

	Excess alkali (o—O$^\ominus$)	Shift on etherification (λ_{OH}—λ_{OMe})	Shift on ionisation† ($\lambda_{O^\ominus}$—λ_{OH})
Benzaldehyde	383	19	58
Acetophenone	365	29	38
Tetralone	372	24	37
Indanone	364	8	47

† For solvent details, see Ref. (19).
* —OMe in all cases except these which are for—OCH$_2$Ph.

in hydrocarbon and hydroxylic solvent, their ethers show a red shift of the 330 mμ band on changing from ethanol to hexane solution. Again, although the first E.T. bands (246 mμ) show regular displacement in alkali, predictable by the foregoing treatment, the second (long wavelength) bands of o-hydroxybenzaldehyde and o-hydroxyacetophenone show a remarkable variation in the bathochromic shift occasioned by the ionization of the hydroxyl function, in spite of the near identity of their spectra above 300 mμ in neutral solvent. These facts have been cited by Conover in support of solvation–chelation phenomena first adumbrated by Morton. Conover's refinement implies that the H-bond being stronger in the chelated case (5; *intra*) than in the solvated case (4; *inter*) we should expect: (a) larger effects from chelation than from solvation, (b) identical spectra for the o-hydroxy compounds (329 mμ in hexane), (c) a shift in the spectra of the o-methoxy compounds on passing from hydrocarbon to hydroxylic solvent.

$$\qquad \qquad \text{Solvation} \qquad (4)$$

$$\qquad \qquad \text{Chelation} \qquad (5)$$

The role of steric repulsion is important in its effect on the 330 mμ band of this series. Thus we find a greater blue shift for the change o-OH $\rightarrow$ —OMe in acetophenone compared with benzaldehyde. Similarly the spectra of the derived phenoxide ions indicate that, in the excited state of the benzaldehyde series, there is less repulsion than in the acetophenones. The effect of imposition of a rigid geometry is evident in the abnormally small chelation effect shown by 7-hydroxyindanone (Table 3.4g). The corresponding tetralones show the expected solvation–chelation shifts. Extension of this treatment to other systems would seem worthy of investigation.

The cinnamoyl chromophore $\left(\text{Ph—}\overset{|}{\text{C}}\text{=}\overset{|}{\text{C}}\text{—CO—}\right)$ in which an additional double bond extends the conjugation of the aromatic carbonyl system has its E.T. band *ca.* 40 mμ higher than the parent (Table 3.4b). Thus benzylidene acetone and the monobenzylidene ketones (Nos. 30, 36) absorb at 286–295 mμ (ε 20,000). The possibility of *cis–trans*-isomerism of this chromophore should be borne in mind, the *cis*-isomers generally possessing lower values of λ_{max} and ε. It is of interest to compare Nos. 30 and 32 (Table 3.4b) where the effect of introduction of the p-OMe appears to have greater incremental effect ($+32$ mμ) than in the lower series. The effect of placing this extended chromophore in a rigid framework is exemplified by No. 31. The introduction of additional ethylenic absorption increases λ_{max} by *ca.* 30 mμ per unit of unsaturation (Nos. 34, 35).

Benzophenone has λ_{max} 254 (E.T.) 270 (benzenoid) and 333 mμ (C=O, $n \rightarrow \pi^*$). The long wavelength L.E. band of the carbonyl chromophore is masked in the polysubstituted benzophenones by the more intense E.T. bands which arise from the introduction of hydroxyl functions (Nos. 18–20, Table 3.4b).

3.5. BENZOIC ACIDS, ESTERS AND LACTONES (TABLE 3.5a)

Benzoic acid absorbs at 202 (benzenoid) 230 (E.T.) and 279 mμ (benzenoid) in ethanol. The spectrum of the anion shows displacement to slightly *shorter* wavelengths, but the alkyl esters have spectra almost identical with the corresponding acids. Taking 230 mμ as the parent chromophore of the substituted

TABLE 3.5a. BENZOIC ACIDS, ESTERS AND LACTONES

No.	Compound	Benzenoid bands	E.T. bands	Solvent	Reference
A. Acids					
1.	CO_2H (structure)	202 (8000) 279 (550)	228 (10,000)	A	(55)
2.	CO_2H (structure)	205 (12,000) 279 (750)	228 (5100)	A	(55)
3.	CO_2H (structure)	204 (13,200)	236 (13,800)	A	(55)
4.	CO_2H, OH (structure)	204 (23,000)	236 (7250) 307 (370)	A	(55)
5.	$CO_2^{\ominus}$, OH (structure)	—	230·5 (7200) 296 (3500)	pH 9	(3)
6.	$CO_2^{\ominus}$, $O^{\ominus}$ (structure)	—	242 (6900) 306 (3400)	pH 13	(3)
7.	CO_2H, OH (structure)	203 (23,000)	236 (6000) 301 (2450)	A	(55)
8.	CO_2H, HO (structure)	201 (15,000)	251 (12,300)	A	(55)
9.	$CO_2^{\ominus}$, $^{\ominus}O$ (structure)	—	280 (16,300)	OH^-	(2)
10.	CO_2H, MeO, OH (structure)	206 (33,000)	254 (12,400) 294 (5500)	A	(49)
11.	OH, CO_2H, OH (structure)	—	245 (5000) 302 (2500)	A	(56)
12.	OMe, CO_2H, OMe (structure)	276 (1600)	—	A	(56)

TABLE 3.5a—(contd.)

No.	Compound	Benzenoid bands	E.T. bands	Solvent	Reference
A. Acids—(contd.)					
13.		210 (42,000)	270 (7800)	A	(57)
14.		218 (28,000)	275 (9800)	A	(57)
15.		—	245 (6100) 314 (3000)	A	(58)
16.		272 (1660) 277 (1660)	309 (3160)	C	(21)
17.		—	316 (5750)	C	(21)
18.		217 (45,000)	317 (8000)	A	(59)
19.		216·5 (18,500)	248 (3900) 327 (1940)	pH 3·73	(3)
20.		209 (28,000)	240 (7100) 310 (2800)	pH 11	(3)
21.		270 (970)	226·5 (12,300)	2 N HCl	(2)

TABLE 3.5a—(contd.)

No.	Compound	Benzenoid bands	E.T. bands	Solvent	Reference
	A. Acids—(contd.)				
22.		219·5 (9900)	284 (14,000)	pH 3·75	(2)
23.		—	265 (14,900)	0·1 N NaOH	(2)
24.		276 (1450)	229 (9100)	0·1 N HCl	(3)
25.		272·5 (850)	232 (6500)	0·1 N NaOH	(3)
26.		209 (3900) 282 (950)	230 (11,900)	W	(3)
27.		—	230 (10,000) 280 (1000)	A†	(60)
	B. Esters and lactones				
28.		—	232 (16,300)	A	(61)
29.		—	261 (22,200)	A	(61)
30.		—	250 (13,000) 291 (7600)	A	(62)

† 260 (5000) and 295 (2000) in dioxan. Spectra of phthalic anhydrites in alcohol change with time.[60]

TABLE 3.5a—(contd.)

No.	Compound	Benzenoid bands	E.T. bands	Solvent	Reference
30A.	(structure: dimethoxy isochromandione, OMe OMe ring with O, O)	—	260 (10,000) 300 (6000) 328 (6000)	A	(60)
31.	(structure: isochromanone ring with O)	273 (1720) 280 (1660)	227 (9900)	A	(63)
32.	(structure: methyl isochromanone, OMe O)	—	247 (6800) 290 (4500)	A	(64)
33.	(structure: CHO OH substituted isochromanone, OMe O)	214 (18,500)	271 (6900) 304 (3200)	A	(65)
C. Extended Chromophores					
34.	CH=CH—CO$_2$H (phenyl)	trans — cis —	273 (21,000) 264 (9500)	A	(66)
35.	trans CH=CH—CO$_2$Me (MeO-phenyl)	210 (10,800) 226 (12,400)	308 (40,000)	Ch	(67)
36.	(CH=CH)$_3$CO$_2$Me (MeO-phenyl)	254 (7800)	358 (67,000)	Ch	(67)
37.	(CH=CH)$_7$CO$_2$H (HO-phenyl)	318 (10,900) 345 (14,100)	443 (88,000)	Py	(67)
38.	(CH=CH)$_7$CO$_2^{\ominus}$ ($\ominus$O-phenyl)	319 (13,000) 357 (17,000)	460 (91,000)	OH$^-$	(67)

benzoic acids, esters and lactones, application of the increments in Table 3.4b forms a reliable method of predicting the principal E.T. bands of this series. Some typical naturally occurring acid and lactone chromophores will be found in Table 3.5a. The calculated and observed E.T. values for a selection of the simpler derivatives is included in Table 3.5b. The agreement of λ_{calc} with λ_{obs}, is satisfactory ($\pm$ 5mμ) except for certain of the 2,6-disubstituted acids (cf. Nos. 11, 12, Table 3.5a) as expected. In fact, 2,6-dimethyl and 2,6-dichloro-benzoic acids (Table 3.5b) show no E.T. band. The case of the 4,5-dimethoxy-benzoic acids which show consistently low values of λ_{max}, might be explained on the assumption that coplanarity of the 4-OMe group with the ring is hindered by the bulky methoxyl group at position 5. It is interesting to note in this connection that the 3,4,5-trihydroxy- and 3,5-dihydroxy-4-methoxy acids do not exhibit this effect, which, however, is marked in 4-hydroxy-3,5-dimethylbenzaldehyde (Table 3.4f). The other anomalies in the use of the increments of Table 3.4b occur in the amino acid series, e.g. 3,4-diaminobenzoic acid. It is of course essential to measure the spectra of amino acid compounds at the isoelectric point. This introduces the ambiguity of the effect of solvent on the spectrum. Data for the corresponding esters should provide a more meaningful interpretation. We note that the spectra of the amino acids return to that of benzoic acid in acidic medium (Table 3.5a, No. 20) because the ammonium ion is unable to transfer its p-electrons to the ring, as these are now involved in sp^3-bond hybridization. The application of our empirical "rules" to the case of aromatic lactones as exemplified by the naturally occurring ochracin (XXIII) and iso-ochracin (XXIV)[91] discloses that a fair agreement ($\pm$ 6 mμ) between the calculated and observed values for the position of the main E.T. band is reached.

XXIII Ochracin	XXIV iso-ochracin	XXV
λ^*_{calc}, 240 mμ	λ^*_{calc}, 240 mμ	λ^*_{calc}, 255 mμ
λ^*_{obs}, 246 mμ	λ^*_{obs}, 234 mμ	λ^*_{obs}, 255 mμ

The tendency of the phthalide system (as XXIV) to low values of the principal E.T. band is presumably a reflection of the ring strain imposed on the 5-membered lactone. We recall that this effect is not observed in the superficially similar case of tetralone and indanone.

Phthalic and Isophthalic Acids (Tables 3.5a, 3.5b)

The presence of two ($-M$) substituents in the benzene ring leads to a crossconjugation of chromophores. Calculation of E.T. maxima on the basis of the operation of the stronger chromophore in a given system,

TABLE 3.5 b. E.T. BANDS OF SUBSTITUTED BENZOIC ACIDS (EtOH)

Compound	λ^*_{calc}	λ^*_{obs}	$\Delta\lambda^*$	Reference
Benzoic acid	[230]	230	—	
2-Me	233	228	−5	(55)
4-Me	240	241·5	+1·5	(2)
2,6-di-Me	236	—		(55)
2-OH	237	237	0	(3)
2-O$^\ominus$	241	242	+1	(3)
3-OH	237	236·5	−0·5	(3)
4-OH	255	255	0	(3)
2,4-di-OH	262	256	−6	(49)
2,5-di-OMe	262	257	−5	(49)
2,5-di-OH	244	238	−6.	(49)
2,6-di-OH	244	245	+1	(56)
2,4,6-tri-OH	269	262·5	−6·5	(9)
3,4,5-tri-OH	269	270	+1	(57)
3,5-di-OH-4-OMe	269	275	+6	(57)
3,4-di-OH	262	260	−2	(49)
3-OMe, 4-OH	262	260	−2	(49)
2-OAc-3-Me	233	230	−3	(50)
2-OH-4-Me	247	242	−5	(49)
2-OH-4-OMe	262	254	−8	(49)
2-Me-6-OH (ester)	240	244	+4	(50)
2,4-di-OH-6-Me	265	263	−2	(87)
2-NH$_2$	243	248	+5	(3)
4-NH$_2$	288	284	−4	(2)
2-OH-4-NH$_2$	295	301	+6	(49)
2-Me-4-NH$_2$	291	288	−3	(49)
2-Cl-4-NHMe	303	302	−1	(49)
2-Cl, 4-NMe$_2$	315	313	−2	(49)
2,4-di-Cl	240	232	−8	(49)
2,6-di-Cl	230	—	—	(55)
3,4-di-Cl	240	242	+2	(49)
2-NH$_2$, 5-Cl	253	249	−4	(49)
3-NH$_2$	243	250	+7	(3)
2,4-di-NH$_2$	301	317i (pH 4·4)*	+16	(49)
2-Cl-4-NH$_2$	288	282	−6	(49)
2-OH, 5-Cl	237	233	−4	(49)
2-OH, 4,5-di-OMe	269	257	−12	(28)
2-OH, 5-Br	239	233	−6	(49)
2-OMe, 5-Br	239	234	−5	(49)
2-NH$_2$, 5-Cl	243	249	+6	(49)
2-NHAc	250	250	0	(51)
2-NHAc-Me ester	250	250	0	(51)
3-NHAc	250	250 (sh)	0	(51)
3-NHAc-Me ester	250	250	0	(51)
4-NHAc	275	270	−5	(51)
4-NHAc-Me ester	275	274	−1	(51)

* (i) signifies an inflection

TABLE 3.5b—(contd.)

Compound	λ^*_{calc}	λ^*_{obs}	$\Delta\lambda^*$	Reference
Phthalic Acids				
Phthalic acid	(230)	230	—	(3)
4-(Hydroxyiso-propyl)	240	241	+1	(69)
3-OH, 4,5-di-OMe	269	255·5	−13·5	(28)
Isophthalic Acids	(230)	230	—	(3)
4-OH-isophthalic acid	255	255	*O*	(70)
4-OH, 5-Cl-isophthalic acid	255	258·5	+3·5	(70)
4-OMe-isophthalic acid	255	253	−2	(70)
4-OH, 5-NH₂-isophthalic acid	268	*ca.* 275 (sh)	*ca.* +7	(70)
5-(Hydroxyisopropyl)	233	236	+3	(69)

e.g. the *p*-hydroxy benzoic acid unit in 4-hydroxyisophthalic acid(XXV), with no increment for the (weaker) *ortho*-transition leads to the observed value. This analogy is extended to other derivatives in Table 3.5b.

Phenyl benzoate shows intense absorption at 232 mμ, and the increment for a *p*-methoxyl group is again approximately 25 mμ in this molecule. Further ring substitution, as in the *depsides* (No. 30) cannot safely be treated by the simple additive method.

Diphenylether Carboxylic Acids (Nos. 16–18; Table 3.5a)

The electron transfer band of the carboxyl group of these compounds is profoundly affected by the presence of 2- and 2,6-substitution and is often missing from the spectrum. Thus erdin hydrate (No. 18), the product of the treatment of the mould metabolite, erdin, with mineral acid, has λ_{max} at 217 and 317 mμ, which is not significantly different from the spectrum of diphenyl ether itself (λ_{max} 225, 280 mμ). The expected —CO₂H band at 250–260 mμ is suppressed by the effect of the *ortho*-phenoxyl group.

Cinnamic Acids (Table 3.5a)

trans-Cinnamic acid absorbs at 273 mμ (ε, 21,000) in ethanol, representing an increment of 43 mμ for introduction of the unsaturated linkage between the benzene ring and the carboxyl group. The *cis*-isomer (of shorter chromophoric length) has λ_{max} 264 mμ (ε, 9500). Additional unsaturation increases the principal maximum by *ca.* 25 mμ for each double bond introduced (Nos. 35–38).

TABLE 3.6. ABSORPTION MAXIMA OF QUINONES

No.	Compound	λ_{max} (ε)	λ_{max} (ε)	λ_{max} (ε)	Solvent	Reference
	A. Quinones					
1.		242 (24,000)	281 (400)	434 (20)	H	(66) (71)
2.	OMe	254 (15,800)		360 (1560)	Ch	(78)
3.	MeO OMe	256 (14,500)		380 (560)	CH$_2$Cl$_2$	(79)
4.	OMe MeO	282 (13,500)		360–70 (3400)	CH$_2$Cl$_2$	(79)
5.		241 (20,000) 246 (23,500) 251 (19,000) 256 (13,000)		330 (2750)	H	(42)
6.		243 (18,200) 249 (18,200) 260 (19,000) 269 (19,000)		330 (2400)	H	(42)
7.	OH	244 (15,800) 276 (15,800)		331 (2800) 460 (100)	H	(42)

TABLE 3.6—(contd.)

No.	Compound	λ_{max} (ε)	λ_{max} (ε)	λ_{max} (ε)	Solvent	Reference
A. Quinones—(contd.)						
8.		249 (13,200) 262 (10,000)		339 (1500) 425 (4000) 495 (600)	H	(42)
9.		270 (8900)	338 (890)	573 (7000) 625 (830)	H	(42)
10.		243·5 (33,000) 252·5 (51,000) 263 (20,000) 272 (20,000)	325 (5600)	405 (90)	A	(42)
11.		243·5 (25,000) 250 (29,000) 266 (15,000) 276 (13,500)	322 (3000)	406 (6800) 423 (5000)	A	(42)
12.		248 (31,500) 278 (10,700)	315 (5600)	484 (6600)	OH⁻	(42)
13.		225 (37,000) 253 (17,000) 275 (9500) 287 (9500)	330 (5600)	418 (9500) 437 (9500)	A	(42)
14.		274 (34,000) 301 (19,000)	249 (7900)	385 (2000)	A	(42)

TABLE 3.6—(contd.)

No.	Compound	λ_{max} (ε)	λ_{max} (ε)	λ_{max} (ε)	Solvent	Reference
	A. Quinones—(contd.)					
15.	OH O OH (structure) O	254 (23,000) 274 (14,000) 284 (17,000)	—	430 (16,000)	H	(42)
	B. Extended Quinones					
16.	O=⟨⟩=⟨⟩=O	253 (2500) 263 (2350)	—	398 (69,000)	Ch	(72)
17.	(structure) O ... O	285 (13,000)	347 (5000) 362 (5000)	489 (37,000) 584 (7000)	H$_2$SO$_4$	(72)
18.	OH O (structure) OH O	265 (21,000)	340 (5400)	419 (21,000) 444 (31,600) 493 (5900) 526 (10,000) 567 (15,000)	T	(73)

3.6. QUINONES (TABLE 3.6)

The diversity of quinone species of natural origin[88] necessitates a limited choice for inclusion in this section. The data for a selection of these chromophores will be found in Table 3.6. The benzoquinones have spectra characterized by intense absorption at 240–90 mμ (E.T. absorption) together with a weaker band in the 400 mμ region. Naphthoquinones and higher quinones possess multibanded spectra which may be roughly divided into intense E.T. absorption (250–300 mμ), overlapping benzenoid and E.T. bands (330–400 mμ) and weak (n–π*) bands at 400–500 mμ. Substitution by hydroxyl again masks the last of these bands by the generation of intense absorption in 400–500 mμ region [cf.

naphthoquinone (No. 5) and juglone (No. 8)]. As we shall see in Chapter 8, the chromophore of vitamin K is readily recognized as that of a naphthoquinone.

The absorption of extended quinones, e.g. diphenoquinone (No. 16) λ_{max} 398 mμ (ε, 69,000) occurs in the visible region and imparts intense colour to this molecular species. We are now entering a class of compound which, like the anthraquinone series (Table 3.6), is sufficiently complicated to require construction of valid model systems for purposes of identification. Such processes are described in Chapters 8 and 9.

3.7. HIGHER AROMATIC SYSTEMS (TABLE 3.7)

Just as benzene, styrene and benzaldehyde have been considered as basic chromophoric systems with a set of characteristic absorption bands, each susceptible in a particular manner to the influence of electron donating and attracting substituents, so we shall consider naphthalene, anthracene and the higher hydrocarbon systems as basic chromophores in the present discussion of the spectra of natural product systems.

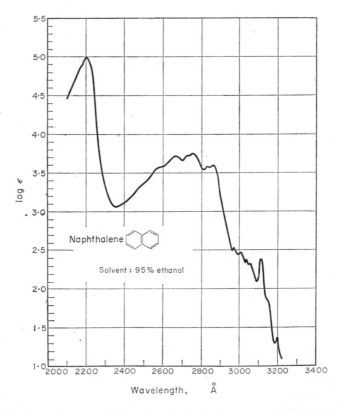

FIG. 3.5. Absorption spectrum of naphthalene (in ethanol) (Friedel and Orchin, No. 195).

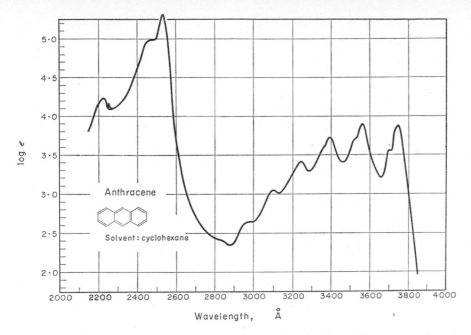

FIG. 3.6. Absorption spectrum of anthracene (in cyclohexane) (Friedel and Orchin, No. 388).

Naphthalene has absorption maxima at 220, 280, 312 and 320 mμ and this four-banded spectrum persists throughout its derivatives with certain modifications due to the appearance of new E.T. transitions. The methyl naphthalenes (Nos. 2–8) are of particular relevance to the terpene chemist, as they represent

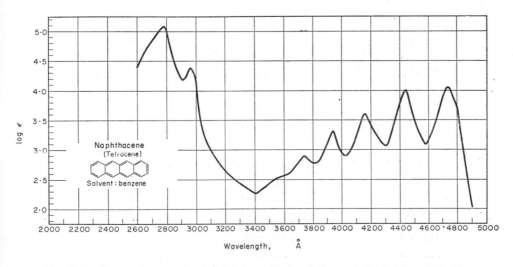

FIG. 3.7. Absorption spectrum of tetracene (naphthacene) (Friedel and Orchin, No. 532).

IUS 5a

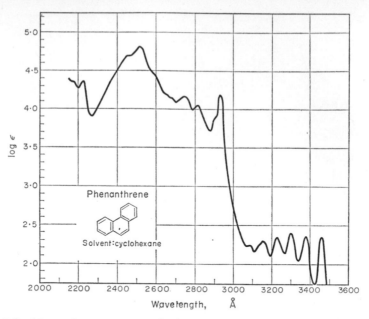

FIG. 3.8. Absorption spectrum of phenanthrene (in cyclohexane) (Friedel and Orchin, No. 341).

TABLE 3.7. ABSORPTION BANDS OF NAPHTHALENES AND HIGHER AROMATIC SYSTEMS[5]
$[\lambda_{max}$ (log ε) IN EtOH]

1. Naphthalene (Fig. 3.5)	2. 1-Methylnaphthalene	3. 2-Methylnaphthalene
220 (5·0)	223 (4·85)	224 (4·9)
275 (3·75)	272 (3·70)	276 (3·65)
286 (3·6)	282 (3·75)	285 (3·5)
312 (2·4)	293 (3·65)	305 (2·7)
320 (1·35)	312 (2·62)	320 (2·7)

4.† 1,5-Dimethylnaphthalene	5.† 2,6-Dimethylnaphthalene	6.† 1,2,5-Trimethylnaphthalene
238 (5·15)	227 (5·05)	230 (4·90)
275 (3·8)	273 (3·7)	288 (3·87)
286 (3·9)	283 (3·55)	324 (2·96)
298 (3·75)	305 (2·1)	
315 (2·7)	310 (2·9)	
321 (2·5)	317 (2·7)	
	323 (3·0)	

† Hydrocarbon solvent.

TABLE 3.7—(contd.)

7.†

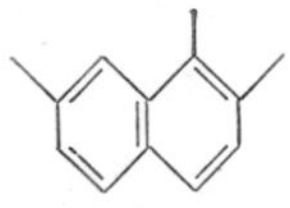

1,2,7-Trimethylnaphthalene

230 (4·96)
281 (3·76)
325 (2·53)

8.†

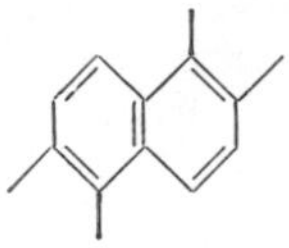

1,2,5,6-
Tetramethylnaphthalene

227 (4·92)
233 (5·01)
286 (3·92)
217 (3·85)
314 (3·33)
322 (3·17)
329 (3·46)

9.

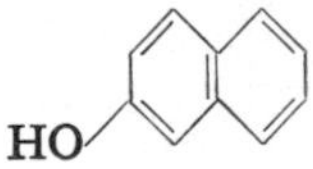

HO

β-Naphthol

230 (4·8)
265 (3·6)
275 (3·65)
285 (3·5)
320 (3·25)

10.

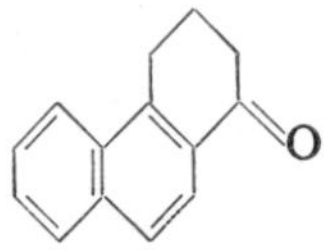

1-Oxo-1,2,3,4-tetrahydrophenanthrene

252 (4.6)
283 (4.0)
295 (3.9)
342 (3.4)

11.

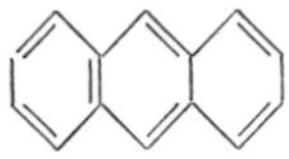

Anthracene

Fig. 3.6†

12.

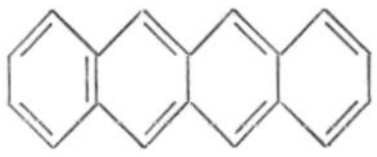

Naphthacene

Fig. 3.7†

13.

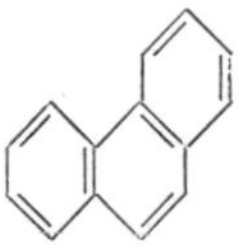

Phenanthrene

Fig. 3.8†

14.

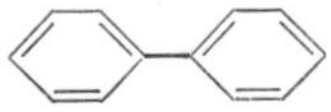

Diphenyl

249 (4·2)

15.

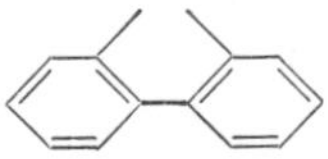

2,2′-Dimethyldiphenyl

270 (3·0)

16.

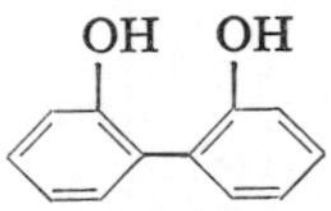

OH   OH

2,2′-Dihydroxydiphenyl

242 (4·0)
285 (3·80)

17.

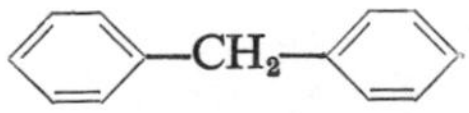

—CH$_2$—

Diphenylmethane

262 (2·69)

† Hydrocarbon solvent

TABLE 3.8. AROMATIC AMINES

No.	Compound	Benzenoid band		E.T. band		Solvent	Reference
1.	NH_2 (aniline)	280	(1430)	230	(8600)	W	(2)
2.	$\overset{\oplus}{N}H_3$ (anilinium)	203 254	(7500) (160)	—		H$^+$	(2)
3.	NHCOMe	—		242	(12,000)	A	(14)
4.	NHCOMe, MeO	—		250	(11,000)	A	(15)
5.	N (dimethyl-o-toluidine)	—		270	(500)	A	(75)
6.	NMe_2	298	(1900)	251	(12,900)	A	(14)
7.	NH_2, OH	—		235 285	(7000) (4000)	A	(5)
8.	NH_2, OH	—		305	(2500)	A	(5)
9.	$\overset{\oplus}{N}H_3$, HO	262·5	(1450)	218	(6240)	H$^+$	(2)
10.	NH_2, NH_2	206 289	(40,000) (2900)	233	(6900)	pH 9	(3)
11.	H_2N, NH_2	210 289	(37,000) (2100)	240	(7300)	pH 9	(3)

common dehydrogenation products of the higher terpene frameworks. Both β-Naphthols (No. 9) has been isolated from natural sources. Anthracenes, phenanthrenes, tetracenes and pyrenes (Figs. 3.5–3.8) are also noteworthy in that they may be isolated as products of dehydrogenation.

The *diphenyls* are included in Table 3.7 as they represent "self" conjugation of the benzene chromophore and display their own characteristic absorption at *ca.* 250 mμ. Steric hindrance to coplanarity of the diphenyl system is reflected in the low intensity value and the return to the simple benzene spectrum in No. 15.

Diphenylmethane with λ_{max} 262 mμ (ε, 490) provides an illustration of the insulating effect of the methylene group producing a benzene-like spectrum.

3.8. AROMATIC AMINES (TABLE 3.8)

Aniline absorbs at 207, 230 and 280 mμ, the central band having an intensity which is characteristic of an electron transfer.[80,81] This assignment is supported by the disappearance of the band from the spectrum on acidification (No. 2). The

TABLE 3.9. BENZONITRILES

No.	Compound	λ^*_{calc}	λ^*_{obs}	$\varDelta\lambda^*$	Reference
1.	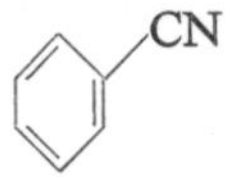 CN	[224]	224	—	(2)
2.	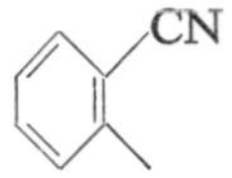 CN	227	228·5	+1·5	(3)
3.	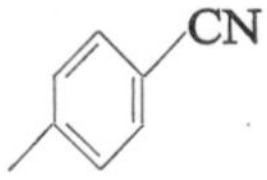 CN	234	234	0	(2)
4.	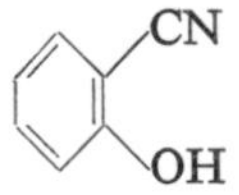 CN OH	231	231	0	(3)
5.	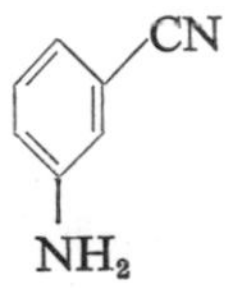 CN NH₂	237	236·5	−0·5	(3)
6.	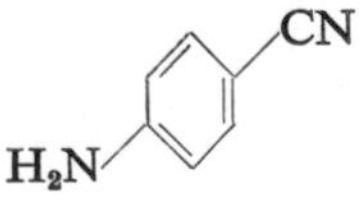 CN H₂N	282	277·5	−4·5	(77)

$$\varDelta\lambda^* = \lambda^*_{obs} - \lambda^*_{calc}$$

p-aminophenol cation again illustrates this phenomenon (No. 8). The remaining examples in Table 3.8 may have use as providing model chromophores for heterocyclic systems.

3.9. BENZONITRILES

These compounds show electron transfer bands of intensities comparable with the corresponding benzoic acids. Taking a value of 224 mμ for the parent chromophore, the increments of Table 3.4b may be successfully applied to calculate the position of the principal E.T. band. This is illustrated for some examples in Table 3.9 (ε values are *ca.* 10^4).

3.10. NITRO COMPOUNDS

Nitrobenzene has λ_{max}, 268·5 mμ (ε, 7800). The strong E.T. band is susceptible to bathochromic shift on introduction of substituents with available *p*-electrons into the ring, but the increments used in the carbonyl and nitrile cases are no longer applicable. Some representative maxima will be found in Table 3.10.

TABLE 3.10. NITRO COMPOUNDS

No.	Compound	Benzenoid bands		E.T. bands		Solvent	Reference
1.	NO$_2$	—		268·5	(7800)	W	(2)
2.	NO$_2$	217	(6700)	285	(9250)	OH$^-$	(2)
3.	NO$_2$ HO	225·5	(6900)	317·5	(10,000)	W	(2)
4.	NO$_2$ H$_2$N	226	(6700)	381	(13,500)	OH$^-$	(2)
5.	NO$_2$ OH	230	(3900)	278·5 351	(6000) (3200)	W	(3)
6.	NO$_2$ NH$_2$	245	(7000)	282·5 412	(5400) (4500)	W	(3)

REFERENCES

1. H. CONRAD–BILLROTH, *Z. phys. Chem.*, **B 29**, 170 (1935).
2. L. DOUB and J. M. VANDENBELT, *J. Amer. Chem. Soc.*, **69**, 2714 (1947).
3. L. DOUB and J. M. VANDENBELT, *ibid.*, **71**, 2414 (1949).
4. *Catalogue of Ultraviolet Spectral Data*, National Bureau of Standards, A.P.I. Project 44.
5. R. A. FRIEDEL and M. ORCHIN, *Ultraviolet Spectra of Aromatic Compounds*, Wiley, New York (1951).
6. R. A. MORTON and A. J. A. DE GOUVEIA, *J. Chem. Soc.*, 911 (1934).
7. P. RAMART–LUCAS and M. J. HOCH, *Bull. Soc. Chim.*, [5], **2**, 327 (1935).
8. G. L. SCHMIR, L. A. COHEN and B. WITKOP, *J. Amer. Chem. Soc.*, **81**, 2228 (1959).
9. T. W. CAMPBELL and G. M. COPPINGER, *ibid.*, **73**, 2708 (1951).
10. R. A. MORTON and Z. SAWIRES, *J. Chem. Soc.*, 1052 (1940).
11. G. ANNER and K. MIESCHER, *Helv. Chim. Acta*, **33**, 1379 (1950).
12. L. DORFMAN, *Chem. Rev.*, **53**, 47 (1953).
13. H. DANNENBERG, *Abhandl. preuss. Akad. Wiss.*, *Math. Naturw. Kl.*, **21**, 3 (1939).
14. H. E. UNGNADE, *J, Amer. Chem. Soc.*, **75**, 432 (1953).
15. H. E. UNGNADE, *ibid.*, **76**, 5133 (1954).
16. A. BURAWOY and J. T. CHAMBERLAIN, *J. Chem. Soc.*, 2312 (1952).
17. C. G. OVERBERGER and D. TANNER, *J. Amer. Chem. Soc.*, **77**, 369 (1955).
18. H. P. KOCH, *J. Chem. Soc.*, 1123 (1948).
19. L. H. CONOVER, *Chem. Soc. Special Publications*, **5**, 48 (1956).
20. K. C. BRYANT, G. T. KENNEDY and E. M. TANNER, *J. Chem. Soc.*, 2389 (1949).
21. H. E. UNGNADE, E. E. PICKETT, L. RUBIN and E. YOUSE, *J. Org. Chem.*, **16**, 1318 (1951).
22. R. B. CARLIN and H. P. LAUDERL, *J. Amer. Chem. Soc.*, **75**, 3969 (1953).
23. R. A. MORTON and A. J. A. DE GOUVEIA, *J. Chem. Soc.*, 916 (1934).
24. B. E. CROSS, J. F. GROVE, J. MACMILLAN and T. P. C. MULHOLLAND, *ibid.*, 2520 (1958).
25. W. COCKER, B. E. CROSS and C. LIPMAN, *ibid.*, 959 (1949).
26. J. PRESS and R. BRUN, *Helv. Chim. Acta*, **37**, 190 (1954).
27. W. M. SCHUBERT and J. D. GARDNER, *J. Amer. Chem. Soc.*, **75**, 1401 (1953).
28. A. ROBERTSON and W. B. WHALLEY, *J. Chem. Soc.*, 848 (1949).
29. H. A. LAITINEN, F. A. MILLER and T. D. PARKS, *J. Amer. Chem. Soc.*, **69**, 2707 (1947).
30. J. F. EASTHAM and D. R. LARKIN, *ibid.*, **80**, 2887 (1958).
31. R. N. BEALE and E. M. F. ROWE, *J. Chem. Soc.*, 2755 (1953).
32. F. E. KING, T. J. KING, D. H. GODSON and L. C. MANNING, *ibid.*, 4477 (1956).
33. E. A. BRAUDE, *ibid.*, 1902 (1949).
34. R. A. MORTON and A. L. STUBBS, *ibid.*, 1347 (1940).
35. E. A. BRAUDE and F. SONDHEIMER, *ibid.*, 3754 (1955).
36. M. T. O'SHAUGHNESSY and W. H. RODEBUSH, *J. Amer. Chem. Soc.*, **62**, 2906 (1940).
37. D. J. CRAM and F. W. CRANZ, *ibid.*, **72**, 595 (1950).
38. R. A. MORTON and Z. SAWIRES, *J. Chem. Soc.*, 1052 (1940).
39. A. SCHMID and T. M. MEIJER, *Helv. Chim. Acta*, **31**, 748 (1948).
40. A. HASSNER and N. H. CROMWELL, *J. Amer. Chem. Soc.*, **80**, 893 (1958).
41. R. N. JONES, *ibid.*, **67**, 2127 (1945).
42. R. A. MORTON and W. T. EARLAM, *J. Chem. Soc.*, 159 (1941).
43. W. J. MC MASTER, A. I. SCOTT and S. TRIPPETT, *ibid.*, 4628 (1960).
44. D. H. R. BARTON and A. I. SCOTT, *ibid.*, 1767 (1958).
45. J. C. DEARDEN and W. F. FORBES, *Canad. J. Chem.*, **36**, 1362 (1958).
46. D. MARSHALL and M. C. WHITING, *J. Chem. Soc.*, 4082 (1956).
47. D. H. R. BARTON, F. MCCAPRA, P. J. MAY and F. THUDIUM, *J. Chem. Soc.*, 1297 (1960).
48. R. H. BURNELL, *ibid.*, 1307 (1958).

49. L. Doub and J. M. Vandenbelt, *J. Amer. Chem. Soc.*, **77**, 4535 (1955).
50. C. J. W. Brooks, Private communication.
51. P. Grammaticakis, *Bull. Soc. Chim.*, [5], **20**, 93, 821, 865 (1953).
52. A. Aebi, A. L. Kapoor and J. Büchi, *Helv. Chim. Acta*, **40**, 569 (1957).
53. R. Pasternack, L. H. Conover, A. Bavley, E. A. Hochstein, G. B. Hess and K. J. Brunings, *J. Amer. Chem. Soc.*, **74**, 1928 (1952).
54. G. D. Hedden and W. G. Brown, *ibid.*, **75**, 3745 (1953).
55. C. M. Moser and A. I. Kohlenberg, *J. Chem. Soc.*, 804 (1951).
56. N. J. Cartwright, J. I. Jones and D. Marmion, *ibid*, 3499 (1952).
57. J. E. Hay and L. J. Haynes, *ibid.*, 2231 (1958).
58. T. Ito and J. B. Neilands, *J. Amer. Chem. Soc.*, **80**, 4645 (1958).
59. D. H. R. Barton and A. I. Scott, *J. Chem. Soc.*, 1767 (1958).
60. Y. Hirshberg, D. Lavie and E. D. Bergmann, *ibid.*, 1030 (1951).
61. G. Cilento, *J. Amer. Chem. Soc.*, **75**, 3748 (1953).
62. T. Davidson and A. I. Scott, Unpublished work.
63. W. A. Schroeder, P. E. Wilcox, K. N. Trueblood and A. O. Dekker, *Analyt. Chem.*, **23**, 1740 (1951).
64. F. A. Hochstein and R. Pasternak, *J. Amer. Chem. Soc.*, **74**, 3905 (1952).
65. J. J. Brown and G. T. Newbold, *J. Chem. Soc.*, 1076 (1954).
66. E. A. Braude, *Ann. Reports Chem. Soc.*, **42**, 105 (1945).
67. D. Marshall and M. C. Whiting, *J. Chem. Soc.*, 537 (1957).
68. J. Klein and E. D. Bergmann, *J. Org. Chem.*, **22**, 1020 (1957).
69. C. F. Heubner and W. A. Jacobs, *J. Biol. Chem.*, **169**, 211 (1947).
70. S. E. Hunt, J. I. Jones and A. S. Lindsey, *J. Chem. Soc.*, 3099 (1956).
71. E. A. Braude, *ibid.*, 490 (1945).
72. B. R. Brown and A. R. Todd, *J. Chem. Soc.*, 1280 (1954).
73. A. Calderbank, A. W. Johnson and A. R. Todd, *ibid.*, 1285 (1954).
74. B. Williamson and W. H. Rodebush, *J. Amer. Chem. Soc.*, **63**, 3018 (1941).
75. P. Grammaticakis, *Bull. Soc. Chim.*, [5], **16**, 134 (1949).
76. P. Ramart–Lucas, *ibid.*, **10**, 13 (1943).
77. A. Burawoy and J. P. Critchley, *Tetrahedron*, **5**, 340 (1959).
78. D. J. Cosgrove, D. G. H. Daniels, J. K. Whitehead and J. D. S. Goulden, *J. Chem. Soc.*, 4821 (1952).
79. J. D. Bu'Lock, *ibid.*, 575 (1955).
80. H. C. Longuet–Higgins and J. N. Murrell, *Proc. Phys. Soc.*, **68A**, 601 (1955) and refs cited therein.
81. J. N. Murrell, *J. Chem. Soc.*, 3779 (1956).
82. E. Heilbronner and R. Gerdil, *Helv. Chim. Acta*, **39**, 1996 (1956).
83. J. Tanaka and S. Nagakura, *J. Chem. Phys.*, **24**, 1274 (1956).
84. R. B. Woodward and R. H. Eastman, *J. Amer. Chem. Soc.*, **66**, 674 (1944).
85. H. Muxfeldt, *Chem. Ber.*, **92**, 3122 (1959).
86. A. Bhati, Private communication.
87. D. Ginsburg and R. Pappo, *J. Chem. Soc.*, 938 (1951).
88. R. H. Thomson, *Naturally Occurring Quinones*, Butterworths, London (1957).
89. W. R. Moore, E. Marcus, S. E. Fenton and R. T. Arnold, *Tetrahedron*, **5**, 179 (1959).
90. W. M. Schubert, J. Robins and J. L. Haun, *J. Amer. Chem. Soc.*, **79**, 910 (1957).
91. J. Blair and G. T. Newbold, *J. Chem. Soc.*, 2871 (1955).

CHAPTER 4

O- AND S-HETEROAROMATIC COMPOUNDS

THE ABSORPTION spectra of furan(I) and thiophen(II) contain bands near 200 and 230 mμ, respectively, which may be compared with the homoannular diene system of cyclopentadiene (III) [λ_{max}, 200 mμ (ε 10,000) and 238·5 mμ (ε 3400)]. Fine structure in the vacuum ultraviolet region (150–190 mμ) is also observed

I   II   III

λ 205 mμ λ 231 mμ λ 200 and 238 mμ

I a   II a

λ 205 mμ λ 221 mμ

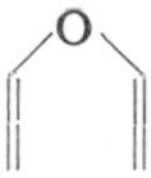

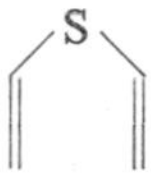

in the spectrum of furan and has been assigned to a Rydberg series. The similarity of the spectra of divinyl ether (Ia) and furan in the one hand, and the differences between those of divinyl sulphide (IIa) and thiophen on the other, suggest that ring conjugation involving the d-orbitals of sulphur may be important and may also explain the aromaticity of the thiophen ring system.

4.1. THIOPHENS

Few naturally occurring compounds containing the thiophen ring have so far been isolated. One interesting example is terthienyl (IV), a blue-fluorescing

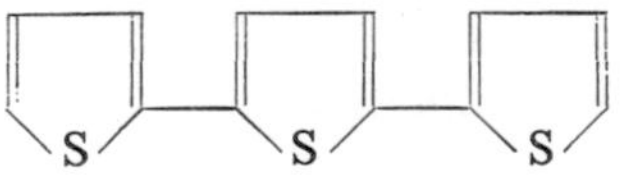

IV   V

λ 255 (ε 10,000) λ 280 (ε 30,000)
350 (ε 23,000)

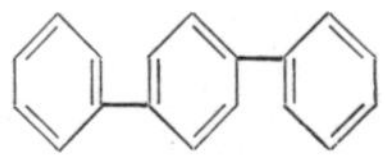

135

constituent of the marigold[11]. The intensity of the absorption of terthienyl may be compared with that of ter-*p*-phenyl (V). Junipal, an acetylenic thiophen of natural origin constitutes a second example (Chapter 8).

4.2. FURANS (TABLE 4.1)

The 205 mμ band of furan is shifted to longer wavelengths by alkylation in the β-position.† The naturally occurring furans with this substitution pattern absorb at 207–212 mμ, e.g. dihydrocolumbin (VI). Di- and tri-alkylated furans

VI   VII

λ 210 (ε 5100)[3] λ 222 (ε 6020)[5]

have λ_{max} near 220 mμ, e.g. menthofuran (VII).

Conjugation of furan with carbonyl groupings gives rise to electron transfer absorption characterized by intense bands ($\varepsilon > 10,000$) in the 240–80 mμ region. Furfural (VIII) and β-furoic acid (IX) represent two of the simpler naturally occurring furans in this category. Evodone (X) has absorption at 265 mμ typ-

VIII   IX

λ 278 mμ λ 238 mμ

X   XI

λ 265 mμ λ 265 mμ

ical of a furyl ketone, e.g. (XI).

---

† The applications of n.m.r. and infrared spectroscopy are particularly rewarding in detection and analysis of furan derivatives.

TABLE 4.1. FURANS AND THIOPHENS

No.	Compound	λ_{max}	ε	Solvent	Reference
1.		199.6 204·6 211 205		H Vap.	(1)
2.					
	i. Marubiin	208 212 216	5620 6520 5000	H	(2)
	ii. Dihydrocolumbin	210	5700	A	(3)
	iii. Limonin	207	7000	A	(4)
3.		222	6020	A	(5)
4.		222	7600	A	(5)
5.		222	6300	A	(5)
6.		290	—	A	(6)
7.	CHO	278	15,800	A	(7)
8.	CO_2Me	245	17,000	A	(8)
9.	CO_2H	238	20,000	A	(9)

TABLE 4.1.—(contd.)

No.	Compound	λ_{max}	ε	Solvent	Reference
10.	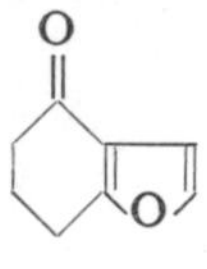	265	4000	A	(10)
11.		231	5600	H	(11)
12.		301	12,300	H	(11)
13.	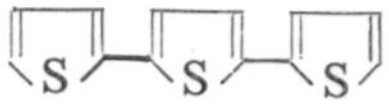	255 350	10,000 23,100	H	(11)

4.3. BENZOFURANS AND DIBENZOFURANS (TABLE 4.2)

The formal analogy between benzofuran (XII) and *o*-hydroxystyrene (XIII) extends to their ultraviolet spectra which are characterized by intense $\pi \to \pi^*$ absorption around 250 mμ, with subsidiary (displaced benzenoid) maxima near 280 mμ. The most common substituent found in the members of this chromo-

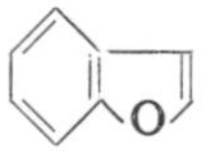

XII

XIII

λ 245, 275, 282 mμ λ 250, 280, 290 mμ

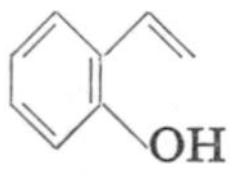

phoric system is the hydroxyl group, which may be introduced via acetate, shikimate or biological hydroxylation sequences *in vivo*. The wavelength shifts engendered by progressive hydroxylation of the benzene ring of benzofuran parallel the corresponding changes in the styrene series. The general effect (cf. Nos. 1, 2, 3) of such substitution is to move the 245 mμ towards longer wavelength with concomitant coalescence of the twin peaks near 280 mμ.

Dibenzofuran has bands at 250 and 280 mμ of almost equal intensity. Again we find that bathochromic displacement of these bands occurs in the hydroxy

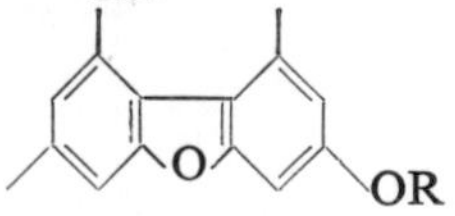

XIV

derivatives although interpretation is complicated by the appearance of several new bands in the spectrum. Pannarol (XIV; R=H) a degradation product of the lichen substance, pannaric acid, exhibits a five-banded spectrum (Table 4.2,

TABLE 4.2. BENZOFURAN AND DIBENZOFURAN ABSORPTION

No.	Compound	λ_1 (ε_1)	λ_2 (ε_2)	λ_3 (ε_3)	Solvent	Reference
1.		245 (12,000)	275 (2800)	282 (3020)	C	(12)
2.		265 (15,000)	—	295 (2950)	MeOH	(13)
3.		226 (24,000) 251 (11,000)	—	280 (3000)	A	(14)
4.		249 (17,400)	—	280 (14,200)	A	(15)
5.		252 (15,700)	—	282 (12,400)	A	(15)
6.		233 (55,000) 267 (29,000)	287 (25,000) 300 (16,000)	312 (25,000)	A	(16)
7.		226 (20,000) 258 (14,200)	—	285 (19,000)	A	(16)

No. 6) which is restored to the spectrum of an alkyl dibenzofuran on acetylation (cf. phenol → phenyl acetate). Thus (XIV; R=Ac) has λ_{max} at 258 and 285 mμ, compared with 2-methyldibenzofuran (λ_{max} 252 and 282 mμ).

4.4. α- AND γ-PYRONES (TABLE 4.3)

Certain features of the spectra of the α-pyrones (i.e. $\alpha, \beta, \gamma, \delta$ dienoic pentanol-ides) have already been noted in our discussion of the unsaturated lactones of the cardiac glycoside series (Chapter 2). 3-Methyl-α-pyrone (XV) has its E.T. band at 300 mμ. The isomeric γ-pyrones (XVI) absorb at considerably shorter

XV   XVI   XVII
λ 300 mμ   λ 245 mμ

wavelengths as might be expected by analogy with the corresponding dienone systems. The γ-pyrones may usually be distinguished from their isomers by chemical means, e.g. salt formation (XVI → XVII).

The tautomeric 4-hydroxy-2-pyrones (keto form XVIII) can give rise to two series of ethers, with α- and γ-pyrone structures (XIX, XX, respectively). While

XVIII   XIX   XX
            λ 280 mμ   λ 240 mμ

the spectrum of XVIII is similar to that of XIX at pH 1–4, above pH 6 maxima at 233 and 276 mμ corresponding to both α- and γ-pyrone-enols are evident. Inspection of the data for some of the entries in Table 4.3 reveals that the introduction of methoxyl groups on the hetero-ring of the α-pyrones does not give rise to the pronounced red shift of the spectrum which is normally associated with this substitution on a system capable of electron-transfer absorption. Indeed, comparison of Nos. 1 and 3 indicates a blue shift for addition of a methoxyl group to the system.

In general, it is found that assignment of α- or γ-pyrone structures to extended chromophores such as that of yangonin (XXI), is possible only when

XXI   XXII   XXIII
λ 360 mμ   λ 314 mμ   λ 276 mμ

TABLE 4.3. PYRONES

No.	Compound	$\lambda_1\ (\varepsilon_1)$	$\lambda_2\ (\varepsilon_2)$	Solvent	Reference
A. α-Pyrones					
1.		—	300 (5000)	A	(17)
2.		233 (—)	276 (—) 284 (—)	pH 7·4 pH 1·1	(18)
3.		—	280 (6460)	A	(18)
4.		233·5 (9850)	332 (14,100)	A	(19)
5.		—	314 (13,500)	A	(20)
6.		—	336 (9550)	A	(21)
7.		—	360 (21,000)	A	(22)
8.		228·5 (20,900) 255 sh. (5000)	315 (12,300)	A	(21)

TABLE 4.3—(contd.)

No.	Compound	$\lambda_1\ (\varepsilon_1)$	$\lambda_2\ (\varepsilon_2)$	$\lambda_3\ (\varepsilon_3)$	Solvent	Reference
B. Coumarins						
9.		— 226 (13,400)	278 (10,500) —	310 (6000) 330 (4900)	A OH⁻	(23) (23)
10.	HO	240 (8000)	—	325 (12,000)	A	(24, 38)
11.	MeO MeO	229 (17,000)	294 (5750)	342 (12,600)	A	(25)
12.		—	266 (22,000)	348 (14,000)	A	(25)
13.		224 (22,000)	253 (5750)	332 (15,000)	A	(25)
14.		240 (25,000)	290 (10,000)	342 (8000)	A	(26)
15.	OMe OMe	222 (25,000)	240 (13,500) 248 (15,900)	268 (20,100) 311 (13,800)	A	(27)
16.	OMe MeO	250 (25,000)		300 (14,000)	A	(28)
17.	OH	—		290 (12,600) 301 i (12,000)	A	(29)
18.	MeO	255 (25,000)	292 (10,000)	342 (8000)	MeOH	(30)

TABLE 4.3—(contd.)

No.	Compound	$\lambda_1\ (\varepsilon_1)$	$\lambda_2\ (\varepsilon_2)$	$\lambda_3\ (\varepsilon_3)$	Solvent	Reference
	B. Coumarins—(contd.)					
19.		255 (17,900)		368 (10,900)	D–W	(31)
	C. Isocoumarin (dihydro)					
20.		212 (20,000)	246 (6500)	314 (4100)	A	(32)
	D. Tocopherol					
21.		—	299 (1000)		A	(33)
	E. γ-Pyrones					
22.			245 (10,000)		A	(34)
23.			315 (5000)		A	(36)
24.			255 (1000)		A	(36)
25.			320 (—)		OH$^-$–A	(35)

TABLE 4.3—(contd.)

No.	Compound	$\lambda_1 (\varepsilon_1)$	$\lambda_2 (\varepsilon_2)$	$\lambda_3 (\varepsilon_3)$	Solvent	Reference
	E. γ-Pyrones—(contd.)					
26.			240 (14,800)		A	(18)
27.			276 (19,500)		A	(20)
28.		250 (17,000)	293 (8570)	354 (15,600)	A	(37)
	F. Chromones					
29.		222 (29,000)	252 (16,500)	330 (7000)	A	(38)
30.		222 (29,000)	243 (23,000)	330 (7000)	A	(38)
31.		249 (27,000)	302 (8,200)	340 (8000)	A	(38)
32.		295 (25,000)	325 (8000)	370 (5000)	A	(39)

TABLE 4.3—(contd.)

No.	Compound	λ_1 (ε_1)	λ_2 (ε_2)	λ_3 (ε_3)	Solvent	Reference
F. Chromones—(contd.)						
33.		237 (14,400)	296 (16,000)	—	A	(40)
G. Flavones (see also Table 4.4)						
34.		250 (17,000)	304 (25,000)	—	A	(41)
35.		269 (18,800)	300 i (13,500)	340 (20,900)	A	(42)
H. Flavonols						
36.		266 (16,700)	367·5 (22,000)		A	(43–45)
37.		259 (20,500)	370 (21,000)			(46)
I. Flavanones (see Table 4.5)						
38.		—	288 (18,000)			(47,61)

TABLE 4.3—(contd.)

No.	Compound	λ_1 (ε_1)	λ_2 (ε_2)	λ_3 (ε_3)	Solvent	Reference
I. Flavanones (see Table 4.5)—(contd.)						
39.		214 (28,000)	290 (17,800)		A	(48)
J. Isoflavones						
40.		—	263 (31,600)	325 i (5130)	A	(45, 49)
41.		—	250 (27,400)	300 (11,240)	A	(49)
K. Coumaranones						
42.		—	284 (22,400)	315 (6030)	A	(50)
43.		234 (11,000)	288 (20,500)	323 (5000)	A	(51)
L. Aurones (see Table 4.7)						
M. Xanthones						
44.		239 (39,000)	261 (12,600)	287 (4200) 337 (6350)	A	(54)

TABLE 4.3—(contd.)

No.	Compound	$\lambda_1 (\varepsilon_1)$	$\lambda_2 (\varepsilon_2)$	$\lambda_3 (\varepsilon_3)$	Solvent	Reference
	M. Xanthones—(contd.)					
45.		237 (36,000) 251 (25,000)	313 (22,400)	337 (12,300)	A	(55)
46.		229 (56,250)	252 (7940)	334 (1990) 380 (800)	A	(55)
47.		231 (10,000)	263 (17,800)	343 (6300) 400 (1600)	A	(55)
48.		242 (37,000) 269 (9000)	309 (23,000)	340 (7000)	A	(56)
	N. Flavan					
49.		207 (43,600)	276 (2200)	–	A	(43)
	O. Flavene					
50.		205 (45,000)	247 (23,800)	272 (7600)	A	(43)

both isomers are available for study. In this favourable situation it is possible to distinguish between the α- and γ-pyrones on the basis of the absorption of the former system at wavelengths consistently longer than the γ-isomer (cf. XXII, XXIII).

4.5. COUMARINS (TABLE 4.3)

Coumarin itself (No. 9), which occurs in many plants, has two main bands in its spectrum at 278 and 310 mμ, which may be assigned to electron-transfer transitions. The spectra of the hydroxylated coumarins have their principal maxima above 300 mμ, although in the polyhydroxy compounds, the E.T. band corresponding to the $p \to \pi$ transfer from oxygen to the ring appears in the 240 mμ region. In *alkaline* solution the spectrum of coumarin undergoes a dramatic change corresponding to opening of the lactone ring and resulting in new bands at 226 and 330 mμ.

Furocoumarins, which occur frequently in nature, give rise to multibanded spectra (e.g. Nos. 14—16) which we shall not attempt to analyse. Other chromophores representative of natural products will be found in Table 4.3.

The tetraphenolic dilactone, ellagic acid (XXIV) of widespread occurrence in the plant kingdom, provides an ideal framework for the illustration of the

XXIV

XXVI

XXV

methods used to interpret the wavelength shifts occasioned by solvent variation on the spectrum of a complex chromophoric system. Studies with flavonoids* (p. 341) reveal that the addition of sodium acetate to an ethanolic solution of a polyphenolic compound selectively ionizes the more acidic phenolic groupings — in the case of ellagic acid those which are *para*- to an aromatic carbonyl group. Such ionization is reflected in the positional changes of the absorption bands of ellagic acid derivatives as summarized in Table 4.3a which may be interpreted as follows. Addition of acetate to a neutral ethanolic solution of ellagic acid produces a new band at 280 mμ which also appears when the dimethyl ether (XXV) containing free p-OH groups is treated similarly, whereas the spectrum of the isomeric ether (XXVI) is unaffected by this reagent (*m*-OH carbonyl system).

* For a recent review see Geissman, *The Chemistry of Flavonoid Compounds*, Macmillian, New York (1962) p. 107.

In alcoholic sodium ethoxide solution, which is known to ionize *all* free phenolic groups, the spectra of XXIV and XXV are identical with the absorption in acetate solution, whereas addition of sodium ethoxide to XXVI produces a yellow solution

TABLE 4.3 a. ABSORPTION MAXIMA (IN mμ) OF ELLAGIC ACID DERIVATIVES[60]

Compound	EtOH	EtOH–NaOAc	EtOH–NaOEt	Acetylated derivative
Ellagic acid	255	256	—	—
		278		
	366	366	—	—
4,4′-Dimethyl ellagic acid (XXV)	253	256	256	239
		278	278	
	361	361	361	368
3,3′-Dimethyl ellagic acid (XXVI)	248	248	270	245
			320	
	372	372	428	347

with an intense band at 438 mμ, tentatively assigned to transitions resulting in a symmetrical extended quinomethine chromophore (XXVI → XXVII).

XXVI   XXVII   +ROH

Acetylation of ellagic acid and its derivatives causes a considerable spectral shift. The changes on acetylation of ellagic acid derivatives are included in Table 4.3a and the empirical relationships derived from this study have been used to assign structures to new alkylation products of the acid[44].

4.6. CHROMONES (TABLE 4.3)

The nucleus of chromone (benzo-γ-pyrone) (XXVIII) constitutes the parent chromophore of the flavonoid, xanthone and anthocyanin systems. The chromones themselves, which occur naturally in hydroxylated form (as XXIX) have, in general, three bands near 250, 300 and 350 mμ, representing the principal

E.T. bands modified by hydroxylic substitution. The increments for progressive

XXVIII   XXIX

λ 250, 310, 350 mμ

hydroxylic substitution follow the trends discussed previously for hydroxy acetophenones, although prediction of maxima on this basis does not appear to be
a rewarding process, probably as a consequence of the cross-conjugation present.

4.7. FLAVONES (TABLE 4.3)

The juxtaposition of cinnamoyl and benzoyl chromophores in the flavones
[e.g. flavone (XXX) and apigenin (XXXI)], precludes any systematic attempt

XXX, Flavone   XXXI, Apigenin

to calculate λ_{max} values *a priori*, but powerful methods for the location of *free
hydroxyl groups* attached to the flavone nucleus have been developed by investigators in this field. These depend on the varying ionizability of diversely
placed hydroxyl function with change of ionizing solvent. As an example, let
us consider apigenin (XXXI) and its isomeric monomethyl ethers, acacetin

XXXII   XXXIII
Acacetin   Genkwanin

$OR^{\ominus}$

XXXII a   XXXIII a

TABLE 4.4. ABSORPTION SPECTRA OF FLAVONES IN NEUTRAL AND BASIC SOLUTIONS[42] [λ_{max} (ε)]

Compound	Neutral EtOH			N/500 (NaOEt EtOH)			$\Delta\lambda_{II}^{OEt\ominus}$
	Band I		Band II	Band I		Band II	
Apigenin (XXXI)	269 (18,800)	300† (13,500)	340 (20,900)	277 (21,900)	330 (13,000)	400 (31,700)	+60
Acacetin (XXXII)	269 (20,300)	298† (16,400)	330 (20,800)	278 (32,600)	295† (21,000)	376 (14,200)	+46
Genkwanin (XXXIII)	269 (17,000)	300† (14,000)	337 (17,000)	269 (13,600)	292† (10,500)	397 (23,800)	+60

† Inflection.

(XXXII) and genkwanin (XXXIII). The spectra of these 5,7,4'-trioxygenated flavones are almost identical in neutral ethanolic solution (Table 4.4) in having bands near 270 and 330 mμ which we call Bands I and II, respectively. The effect of sodium ethoxide solution, which ionizes all free hydroxyl groups, on the position and intensity of these bands is summarized (from Table 4.4) as follows:

(a) When a 7-OH is present

> Band I   270 → 280 mμ (greatly increased ε)
> Band II 330 → 370 mμ (reduced ε).

(b) When a 4'-OH is present

> Band I   270 → 280 mμ (reduced ε)
> Band II 330 → 400 mμ (increased ε).

The red shifts engendered by ionization of the free phenolic groups may be represented as being due to transitions involving the mesomeric anions XXXIIa and XXXIIIa. The obvious value and extension of these correlations will not be developed in further detail at this juncture, but a complete structural problem in flavanol chemistry is discussed in Chapter 9.

4.8. FLAVANONES (TABLE 4.5)

The absence of the flavone 2,3-double bond in the flavanones (as XXXIV) allows the calculation of the principal E.T. band treatment of the molecule as a substituted acetophenone, since the contribution from the isolated ring C

XXXIV λ calc 285 mμ XXXV
        λ obs 292 mμ

chromophore is not important in the region under survey. Calculated and observed maxima for some flavanones will be found in Table 4.5. The deviation (+ 7 mμ) found in the case of (XXXIV) may not be unconnected with the presence of the secondary hydroxyl group at a position α − to the carbonyl group.

By analogy with the flavanone spectra, the *dihydro-isocoumarin* (XXXV) present in *Aspergillus melleus*[32] may be calculated as a substituted benzoic ester (λ_{calc} 240 mμ; λ_{obs} 246 mμ) although the discrepancy may indicate the extent of the effect of ring formation on the main electronic transfer (cf. phthalides, Chapter 3, p. 120).

TABLE 4.5. FLAVANONES[61]

Compound	λ_{calc}	λ_{obs}†	$\varDelta\lambda$
	285	291	+6
	285	285	0
	285	281	−4
	285	294	+9
	285	282	−3
	278	278	0
	285	288	+3

† Inflections occur near 230 mμ in these spectra.

TABLE 4.5—(contd.)

Compound	λ_{calc}	λ_{obs}	$\Delta\lambda$
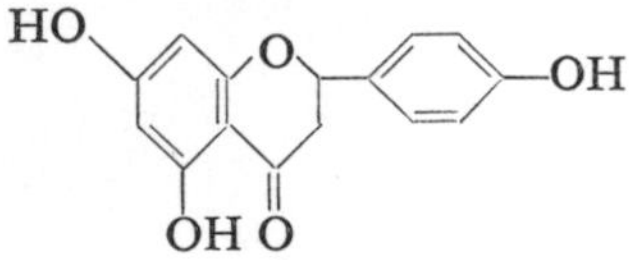	285	290	+5

† Inflections occur near 230 mμ in these spectra.

4.9. ISOFLAVONES

Isoflavones (e.g. genistein, XXXVI) contain cross-conjugated chromone and styrene moieties and the intense absorption near 260 mμ in the spectra of several

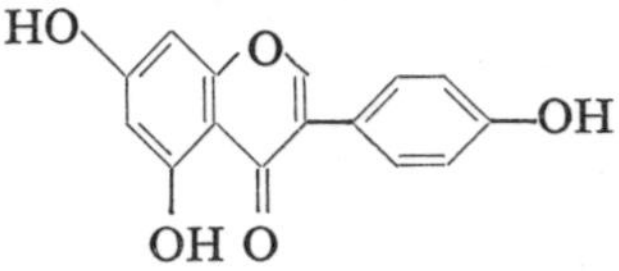

XXXVI

hydroxylated isoflavones (Table 4.6) appears to correspond to the superposition of the principal maxima of each absorbing species. Since the majority of natural isoflavones show this intense peak at 260–70 mμ, it is not usually easy to distinguish substitution pattern from consideration of the spectrum alone. The

TABLE 4.6. ISOFLAVONES [λ_{max} (mμ)][45]

Isoflavone	EtOH	NaOEt–EtOH
5,4,4 -trihydroxy— (genistein)	263	277
5,7-diOH-4'-OMe— (biochanin A)	262·5	275
5,4'-diOH-7-OMe— (prunetin)	262·5	271

use of sodium ethoxide in distinguishing between genistein (XXXVI) and its 4'- and 7-monomethyl ethers on the basis of the shifts to longer wavelength (Table 4.6) would seem to be valid for recognition of the 7-methyl compound (+8·5 mμ) but a distinction between the 4'-methyl ether and the parent is not possible on this basis.

4.10. COUMARANONES (TABLE 4.3)

4,6-Dimethyl-coumaran-3-one (XXXVII) absorbs at 260 mμ, which is the position expected for a dimethyl *ortho*-alkoxy acetophenone. In spite of the con-

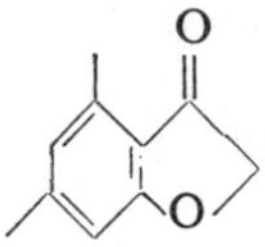

XXXVII

straint of the carbonyl group in the five-membered ring it is possibly surprising that the same increments for aromatic ring substitution may be applied successfully to the calculation of coumaranone maxima.

For both XXXVIII and XXXIX we have λ_{calc} 285 mμ which is in good agreement with the values observed. However, a deviation is found for the

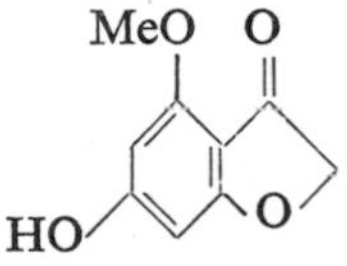

XXXVIII

λ 284 mμ

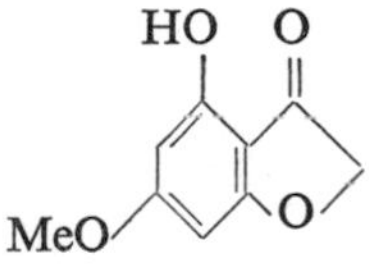

XXXIX

λ 280 mμ

XL λ 318 mμ

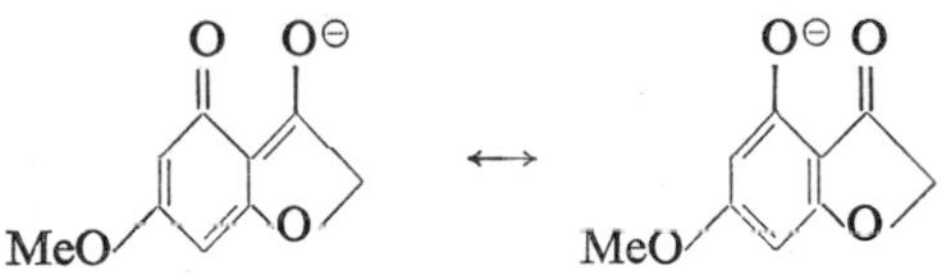

XLI λ 285 mμ

anion (XL) which is expected to show a bathochromic shift of 53 mμ from the parent value of 285 mμ. In fact, the observed maximum is 20 mμ lower than λ_{calc} (= 338 mμ). The discrepancy is conceivably due to steric hindrance to coplanarity in the quinomethine form of the anion (XL). The isomeric anion (XLI) behaves normally (λ_{calc}, 289 mμ).

4.11. AURONES

The spectra of a number of naturally occurring benzalcoumaranones (aurones) have been recorded and interpreted by Geissman and Harborne[53]. The

TABLE 4.7. AURONES [λ_{max} in mμ (ε)][53]

Compound	Band I	Band II	Band III	Band IV
	—	251 (12,600)	316 (18,600)	379 (11,500)
	225 (13,200)	261 (7200)	308 (17,800)	389 (21,400)
	229 (12,600)	257 (8300)	344 (27,000)	—
	—	242 (8500)	321 (14,000)	379 (15,500)
	230 (8500)	273 (9300)	347 (31,000)	—
	—	260 (21,000)	346 (11,700)	405 (30,000)
	254 (8900)	269 (7900)	336 (14,500)	399 (27,500)

majority of aurones (as XLII) show four maxima, two of which are below, and two above 300 mμ. While the former maxima may be attributed to Ph—C=O and Ph—C=C— contributions, of greater interest are the long wavelength

XLII

maxima which are sensitive to hydroxylic substitution of the two chromophoric

species present, namely, Ph—$\overset{|}{C}$=O and PhCH=CH—CO—. Assignment of specific absorption bands has not been made, but rather an empirical working guide has been evolved for the monohydroxyaurones. It is, however, by no means certain that we are comparing equivalent transitions in the parent aurone

TABLE 4.8. LONG WAVELENGTH BANDS OF AURONES[53]

	λ_{ma} (mμ)	$\Delta\lambda$†	$\Delta\lambda$ alk††
Parent	379	—	—
3'-OH	381	+2	—
6 -OH	344	−35	+58
2'-OH	402	+23	—
4'-OH	405	+26	+82
4 -OH	389	+10	—

† $\Delta\lambda = \lambda_{max}$ (OH deriv.) − λ_{max} (parent)
†† $\Delta\lambda$ alk = $\lambda_{max}^{NaOEt-EtOH} - \lambda_{max}^{EtOH}$

(379 mμ) and, for example, 6-hydroxyaurone (344 mμ). The shifts in ethanolic sodium ethoxide of the long wavelength band of the 6- and 4'-derivatives (Table 4.8) parallel those observed for 4-hydroxyacetophenone and for 4-hydroxybenzalacetophenone, respectively.

The polyhydroxyaurones (Table 4.7) have their long wavelength band shifted to the red by 4'-substitution although the 6-OH, 5,6- and 6,7-di-OH compounds have maxima near that of the parent. The corresponding natural aurone glycosides have their maxima shifted between 4 and 6 mμ to the visible compared with their aglycones. The alkaline spectra of the polyhydroxyaurones are complicated by decomposition in this medium.

4.12. CHROMANONES

Chromanones (as XLIII) may again be considered as substituted o-alkoxy-acetophenones like the flavanones and coumaranones. The chromanone

XLIII λ_{max} 283·5 mμ

(XLIII) would be expected to absorb in the same region as a 2,4,6-trialkoxyaceto-phenone (λ_{calc}, 285 mμ) and we observe a close correspondence between cal-culated and recorded values. We also note that the *intensity* of absorption is greater in 2,6-disubstituted ketones of the cyclic series (as XLIII) compared with the corresponding acetophenones, where the carbonyl group may assume a position such that the interplanar angle ($\theta°$) between the C=O and aryl groups is determined by the bulk of the neighbouring substituents. The intensity changes have been found to follow a $\cos^2 \theta$ law†. Such deformation is, of course, for-bidden by the geometrical requirements of the cyclic ketones.

4.13. XANTHONES (TABLE 4.3)

The naturally occurring xanthones contain hydroxyl groups in positions to be expected from consideration of their biogenesis via acetate pathways. Xanth-one itself (XLIV) absorbs at 239, 261, 287 and 337 mμ. The spectra of the hy-droxyxanthones reveal that although the 239 mμ band remains within 10 mμ of this position throughout the series, the 261 mμ band is quite sensitive to changes in hydroxylation pattern. Thus, hydroxyls in the 1-, 4-, 5- and 8-positions, i.e.

XLIV   XLV   XLVI

ortho- and *meta*- to the xanthone carbonyl group cause only slight bathochromic shift of the 261 mμ band. 1,8-Dihydroxyxanthone in fact absorbs at 252 mμ, i.e. 9 mμ below xanthone itself and contains a new band of weak intensity near 400 mμ ($n \rightarrow \pi^*$ transition?). On the other hand, those xanthones which have

† See ref. 33, p. 133.

3- and/or 6-hydroxyl groups, i.e., in the *para*-position to the C=O group, contain an intense maximum near 310 mμ. This surely corresponds to electron transfer of partial chromophore A. The secondary E.T. band of the 3,6-substituted xanthones appears near 340 mμ. We can classify the naturally occurring xanth-

A

ones on this basis. As an example, ravenelin (XLV) has λ_{max} 263, 343 and 400 mμ, indicative of a 1,8-dihydroxyxanthone. The placement of the third hydroxyl was confirmed in this instance by chemical means, but the 3- and 6-positions could have been excluded on spectral grounds. A trioxygenated xanthone recently isolated[56] from *Penicillium patulum* had bands at 269, 309 and 340 mμ. Ferric chloride reaction showed that a hydroxyl was present next to the carbonyl group, and the ultraviolet data favoured placement of the remaining oxygen function at positions 3 and 6 in accord with biogenetic expectation (XLVI R_1= Me; R_2=H). Confirmation was provided by partial methylation to the known xanthone of lichen origin (XLVI; R_1=R_2= Me) which had λ_{max} 254, 306 and 340 mμ.

4.14 FLAVANS, FLAVENES (TABLE 4.3)

5,7,4′-Trihydroxyflavan (XLVII) has absorption [λ_{max}, 276 mμ (ε 2200)] reminiscent of phloroglucinol and this may be considered as a summation of the tri- and mono-oxygenated benzene chromophores. Flavenes [as (XLVIII)] have

XLVII   XLVIII

their principal maxima near 250 mμ (ε ~ 25,000) corresponding to the oxygenated styrene chromophore.

4.15. ANTHOCYANINS (TABLE 4.9)

The spectra of most of the anthocyanins are so similar in the region of maximal absorption (500–550 mμ) that the use of ultraviolet spectroscopy in the determination of the composition of these pigments, and the corresponding

TABLE 4.9. ABSORPTION SPECTRA OF THE ANTHOCYANIDINS[57]

Name	Substitution in (A)			λ_{max}†	λ_{max} 3-glycoside	λ_{max} 3,5-di-glycoside	$\varDelta\lambda^{AlCl_3}$*
	R_1	R_2	R_3				
Pelargonidin	—H	—OH	—H	520	506	504	0
Cyanidin	—OH	—OH	—H	535	523	522	+18
Peonidin	—OMe	—OH	—H	532	523	523	0
Delphinidin	—OH	—OH	—OH	546	535	534	+23
Petunidin	—OMe	—OH	—OH	543	535	533	+24
Malvidin	—OMe	—OH	—OMe	542	535	533	0
Apigeninidin**	—H	—OH	—H	476	—	—	0
Luteolinidin**	—OH	—OH	—H	493	—	—	+52

† In MeOH containing 0·01% HCl; add 10 mμ for change to EtOH—H$^\oplus$.

* $\varDelta\lambda^{AlCl_3} = \lambda_{max}^{AlCl_3-EtOH} - \lambda_{max}^{MeOH-H^\oplus}$ for the aglycone series.

** 3-desoxy series, i.e. (A) where 3-OH = 3-H.

aglycones, the anthocyanidins, presents a difficult problem. An added difficulty in this province of natural product study is that in many cases insufficient amounts of these materials are available in pure condition for accurate intensity

XLIX λ 520 mμ
Pelargonidin chloride

L λ 535 mμ
Cyanidin chloride

LI λ 546 mμ
Delphinidin
Petunidin (3′—OH=3′—OMe)

LII λ 476 mμ
Apigeninidin

measurement. The discussion which follows is, therefore, based on the *position* of the maxima which has been used with advantage in correlating the spectra of certain members of this series with their structure.

(a) *Hydroxylic Substitution*

The visible spectra of all anthocyanidins known to occur in nature as glycosides are listed in Table 4.9. The three main groups of anthocyanin pigment based on pelargonidin (XLIX), cyanidin (L) and delphinidin (LI) may be differentiated by the progressive shift of their maxima to longer wavelength *for a given pattern of glycosidic substitution.* For example, the 3-glycosides of the series XLIX, L and LI absorb at 506, 523 and 535 mμ, respectively. The 3-desoxyanthocyanin (LII) which represents a rarer class of pigment absorbs below 500 mμ.

(b) *3',4'-Dihydroxy Compounds*

Within the classification just established it is possible to distinguish those pigments which bear 3',4'-dihydroxy groups (e.g. cyanidin, delphinidin and petunidin 3-glycosides) from the other anthocyanins by the use of aluminium chloride. Addition of this reagent to an ethanolic solution of a 3',4'-dihydroxy-anthocyanidin evokes a bathochromic displacement (16–35 mμ) of the absorption maximum as summarized in Table 4.9. Such complexing with *vic*-dihydroxy aromatic compounds is, of course, a well known phenomenon, and meaningful spectral data of this type for other natural product systems is available for flavonoids[42,53,57] and for the tetracycline† series in which chelation effects are measured.

(c) *Glycosidic Attachment*

The position of the sugar moiety in the anthocyanins may be deduced from consideration of the data of Table 4.9. Glycosidation in the 3- and 3,5-positions (the usual sites in the natural pigment) causes a blue shift of the maximum of between 7 and 14 mμ. The 5-glycosides on the other hand show a small shift ($\not< 7$ mμ) of the maximum in the same sense. The positions of the bands of 3- and 3,5-glycosides are too close (within 2 mμ) to permit unequivocal assignment. However, Harborne[57] has recently observed that the spectra of all anthocyanidins with sugar or benzoyl in the 5-position show characteristic differences below 500 mμ from those pigments in which the 5-hydroxyl group is free. The spectra of the latter group all show a distinct shoulder between 410 and 450 mμ which is absent from the 5-glycosides. It is therefore a facile process requiring the minimum of material to distinguish between the two main classes of anthocyanin, the 3- and 3,5-glycosides.

† see p. 314.

(d) *Acylated Pigments*[57]

Esters of anthocyanidins with *p*-hydroxycinnamic acid and other hydroxy-aromatic acids have been isolated from natural sources. The esterifying acid may be identified and the number of acyl groups estimated by an examination of the spectrum in the region associated with the acyl component. Experiments with synthetic compounds reveal that the ratio of the intensity of the acyl peak (~300 mμ) to that of the pigment peak (~500 mμ) is an accurate measure of the molar ratio of aromatic acid to anthocyanin in the pigment, the observed spectrum representing a simple addition of the spectra of the contributing chromophores.

The isolation and analytical difficulties associated with the anthocyanins require techniques for structural study which offer the maximum information in return for the minimum of manipulation of small amounts of material. The methods discussed in this section would seem to be ideal in this respect and are furthermore capable of extension to cognate fields.

4.16. DEPSIDONES

Although many depsidones have been isolated from lichens, the ultraviolet data for

LIII λ 270 mμ LIV λ 264 mμ

this class of oxygen heterocycle are meagre. Vicanicin[58] (LIII) absorbs at 270 mμ with an inflection at 324 mμ. It is tempting to treat this molecule as a 2,4-dioxygenated benzoic ester (λ_{calc}, 265 mμ). Similarly the fungal depsidone deschloronornidulin[59] (LIV) also has λ_{calc} 265 mμ and absorbs at 264 mμ (ε 9810). Such calculation becomes hazardous when applied to the main class of depsidone chromophores which have carbonyl groups attached to both aromatic nuclei.

REFERENCES

1. W. C. PRICE and A. D. WALSH, *Proc. Roy. Soc.*, A **179**, 201 (1941); L. W. PICKETT, N. J. HOEF-LICH and T.-C. LIU, *J. Amer. Chem. Soc.*, **73**, 4865 (1951).
2. W. COCKER, B. E. CROSS, S. R. DUFF, J. T. EDWARD and T. F. HOLLEY, *J. Chem. Soc.*, 2540 (1953).
3. D. H. R. BARTON and D. ELAD, *ibid.*, 2085 (1956).
4. D. H. R. BARTON, S. K. PRADHAN, S. STERNHELL and J. F. TEMPLETON, *ibid.*, 255 (1961).

5. R.D.Haworth, A.H.Jubb and J.McKenna, *ibid.*, 1983 (1955).
6. A.Wettstein and K.Miescher, *Helv. Chim. Acta.*, **26**, 631 (1943).
7. G.Mackinnen and O.Temmer. *J. Amer. Chem. Soc.*, **70**, 3586 (1948).
8. J.R.Willard and C.S.Hamilton, *ibid.*, **73**, 4805 (1951).
9. M.Beroza, *ibid.*, **74**, 1585 (1952).
10. A.J.Birch and R.W.Rickards, *Aust. J. Chem.*, **9**, 241 (1956).
11. L.Zechmeister and J.W.Sease, *J. Amer. Chem. Soc.*, **69**, 273 (1947); and preceding papers.
12. J.I.Jones and A.S.Lindsey, *J. Chem. Soc.*, 1836 (1950).
13. J.F.Grove, J.Macmillan, T.P.C.Mulholland and M.A.T.Rogers, *ibid.*, 3949 (1952).
14. H.Bickel and H.Schmidt, *Helv. Chim. Acta*, **36**, 644 (1953).
15. S.Trippett, *J. Chem. Soc.*, 419 (1957).
16. C.A.Wachtmeister, *Acta Chem. Scand.*, **13**, 1855 (1959).
17. J.Fried and R.C.Elderfield, *J. Org. Chem.*, **6**, 566 (1941).
18. J.D.Bu'Lock and H.G.Smith, *J. Chem. Soc.*, 502 (1960).
19. A.H.Harle and L.E.Lyons, *ibid.*, 1575 (1950).
20. D.Herbst, W.B.Mors, O.R.Gottlieb and C.Djerassi, *J. Amer. Chem. Soc.*, **81**, 2427 (1959).
21. W.B.Mors, O.R.Gottlieb and C.Djerassi, *ibid.*, **79**, 4507 (1957).
22. I.Chmielewska, J.Cíéslak, K.Gorczynska, B.Konkik and K.Pitakowska, *Tetrahedron*, **4**, 36 (1958).
23. T.L.Jacobs, D.Danker and A.R.Danker, *J. Amer. Chem. Soc.*, **80**, 864 (1958).
24. R.H. Goodwin and B. Pollock, *Arch. Biochem. Biophys.*, **49**, (1954),
25. F.E.King, J.R.Housley and T.J.King, *J. Chem. Soc.*, 1392 (1954).
26. E.C.Horning and D.B.Reisner, *J. Amer. Chem. Soc.*, **72**, 1514 (1950).
27. F.A.Kincl, J.Romo, G.Rosencranz and F.Sondheimer, *J. Chem. Soc.*, 4163 (1956).
28. H.S.Jois and B.L.Manjunath, *Ber. dtsch. chem. Ges.* **70**, 434 (1937).
29. J.F.Garden, N.F.Hayes and R.H.Thomson, *J. Chem. Soc.*, 3315 (1956).
30. H.Schmid and A.Ebnother, *Helv. Chim. Acta*, **34**, 1982 (1951).
31. K.Bernauer, *Liebigs Ann.*, **588**, 230 (1954).
32. J.Blair and G.T.Newbold, *J. Chem. Soc.*, 2871 (1955).
33. T.J.Webb, L.I.Smith, W.A.Bastedo, H.E.Ungnade, W.W.Prichard, H.H.Hoehn, S.Wawzonek, J.W.Opie and F.L.Austin, *J. Org. Chem.*, **4**, 389 (1939).
34. S.Aronoff, J.B.Harborne *ibid.*, **5**, 561 (1940).
35. J.Fried and E.Titus, *J. Amer. Chem. Soc.*, **70**, 3616 (1948).
36. M.Stacey and L.M.Turton, *J. Chem. Soc.*, 661 (1946).
37. A.Robertson and W.B.Whalley, *ibid.*, 848 (1949).
38. K.Sen and P.Bagchi, *J. Org. Chem.*, **24**, 316 (1959).
39. J.R.Clarke and A.Robertson, *J. Chem. Soc.*, 302 (1949).
39a. T.A.Geissman and J.W.Bolger, *J. Amer. Chem. Soc.*, **73**, 5875 (1951).
40. J.A.Moore and S.Eng, *J. Amer. Chem. Soc.*, **78**, 395 (1956); *ibid.*, **63**, 1717 (1941).
41. S.Aronoff, *J. Org. Chem.*, **5**, 561 (1940).
42. W.D.Ollis, *Recent Developments in the Chemistry of Natural Phenolic Compounds* (edited by W.D.Ollis), Pergamon Press, London (1961).
43. F.E.King, J.W.Clark–Lewis and W.F.Forbes, *J. Chem. Soc.*, 2948 (1955).
44. L.Jurd and R.M.Horowitz, *J. Org. Chem.*, **22**, 1618 (1957).
45. J.B.Harborne, *Chem. and Ind.*, 1142 (1954).
46. E.Wada, *J. Amer. Chem. Soc.*, **78**, 4725 (1956).
47. T.A.Geissman and C.D.Heaton, *ibid.*, **66**, 486 (1944).
48. W.Baker, J.Chadderton, J.B.Harborne and W.D.Ollis, *J. Chem. Soc.*, 1852 (1953).
49. R.B.Bradbury and D.E.White, *ibid.*, 841 (1953).
50. L.A.Duncanson, J.F.Grove, J.Macmillan and T.P.C.Mulholland, *ibid.*, 3555 (1957).

51. T. P. C. Mulholland, *J. Chem. Soc.*, 3987 (1952).
52. T. A. Geissman and L. Jurd, *J. Amer. Chem. Soc.*, **76**, 4475 (1954).
53. T. A. Geissman and J. B. Harborne, *ibid.*, **78**, 832 (1956).
54. R. A. Friedel and M. Orchin, *Ultraviolet Spectra of Aromatic Compounds*, Wiley, New York (1951).
55. P. Yates and G. H. Stout, *J. Amer. Chem. Soc.*, **80**, 1691 (1958).
56. W. J. McMaster, A. I. Scott and S. Trippett, *J. Chem. Soc.*, 4628 (1960).
57. J. B. Harborne, *Biochem. J.*, **70**, 22 (1958).
58. S. Neelakantan, T. R. Seshadri and S. S. Subramanian, *Tetrahedron Letters*, **9**, 1 (1959).
59. F. M. Dean, J. C. Roberts and A. Robertson, *J. Chem. Soc.*, 1432 (1954); F. M. Dean, A. D. T. Erni and A. Robertson, *ibid.*, 3545 (1956).
60. L. Jurd, *J. Amer. Chem. Soc.*, **81**, 4610 (1959).
61. J. B. Harborne and T. A. Geissman, *ibid.*, **78**, 829 (1956).

CHAPTER 5

N-HETEROAROMATIC COMPOUNDS
(MONO-AZINES)

5.1. PYRROLES

THE AROMATICITY of pyrrole (I), which is a consequence of the lone pair of electrons on the nitrogen atom participating in the mobile sextet, is reflected not only in its chemical reactions but also in its absorption spectrum. The bands at 210 and 240 mμ may be compared with the 203 and 255 mμ bands of benzene and with the spectra of thiophen and furan rather than with that of cyclopentadiene (Chapter 4, p. 135). C-Alkyl substitution, however, not only modifies the pyrrole spectrum in the opposite sense from the corresponding alkylbenzenes by shifting the 210 mμ band to *shorter* wavelength, but causes the disappearance of the 240 mμ band. Thus, 2,4-dimethyl-3-ethylpyrrole (cryptopyrrole; II) has a single maximum at 200 mμ (in EtOH) whilst 3,4-dimethyl-pyrrole (Table 5.1) has λ_{max} 203 mμ. Although pyrrole rings are often extremely labile towards mineral acid, cryptopyrrole (II) forms a salt (III) which

is sufficiently long-lived to permit measurement of its absorption spectrum [λ_{max} 260 mμ (ε 5000)]. The position and intensity of this maximum may be interpreted as being due to a transition marking the withdrawal of the nitrogen electron lone pair from the ring, and the appearance of a spectrum of a charged amino-diene, rather than of an N heteroaromatic compound [cf. cyclopentadiene λ_{max} 244 mμ (ε 2500)].

Conjugation of the pyrrole ring with electron-withdrawing functions of the general type >C=X, gives rise to new and intense absorption which has its counterpart in the electron transfer bands of benzenoid compounds (Chapter 3). The electron-transfer band of the pyrrole system is moved to increasingly long wavelengths in the sequence CN < CO_2H < CO_2R < —CH=NOH < CHO < COMe < CO·CO_2R < CH=CHCOMe < CH=CH·COPh for monosubstit-

TABLE 5.1. PYRROLES AND DIPYRRYLMETHANES

No.	Compound	Band I	Band II	E.T. Band	Solvent	Reference
1.		210 (5100)	240 (300)	—	H	(1)
2.		203 (5670)	—	—	A	(2)
3.		200 (7450)	—	—	A	(2)
4.		—	261 (4000)	—	A—H⁺	(2)
5.		—	251 (4100)	290 (16,400)	MeOH	(3)
6.		—	—	262 (12,000)	A	(3)
7.		—	253 (6800)	285 (15,800)	A	(3)
8.		—	—	290 (15,700)	A	(3)
9.		—	—	245 (4800)	A	(3)
10.		232 (9000)	—	258 (5300)	A	(3)

TABLE 5.1—(contd.)

No.	Compound	Band I	Band II	E.T. band	Solvent	Reference
11.†	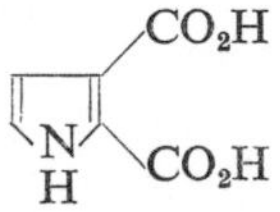 (pyrrole with CO$_2$H, CO$_2$H)	—	—	282 (4200)	A	(3)
12.	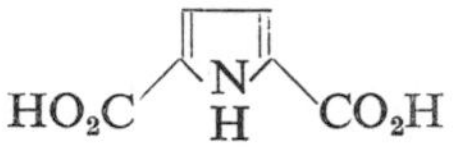 (pyrrole with HO$_2$C, CO$_2$H)	—	—	272 (20,100)	A	(3)
13.	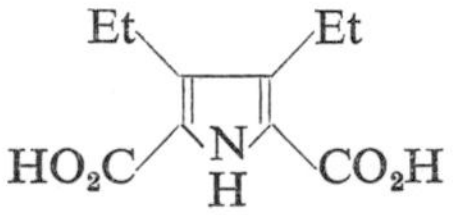 (pyrrole with Et, Et, HO$_2$C, CO$_2$H)	820 (19,600)	—	280 (19,200)	A	(3)
14.	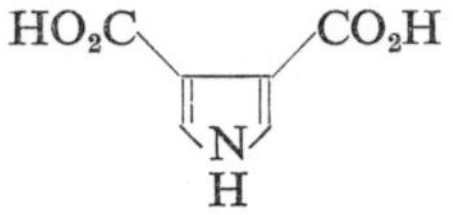 (pyrrole with HO$_2$C, CO$_2$H)	—	—	259 (7300)	A	(3)
15.	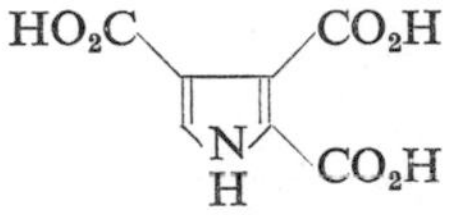 (pyrrole with HO$_2$C, CO$_2$H, CO$_2$H)	—	—	279 (8000)	A	(3)
16.	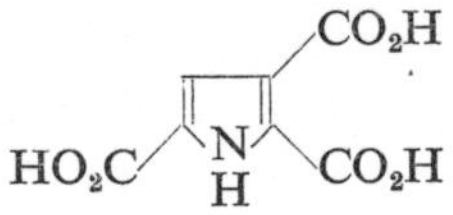 (pyrrole with CO$_2$H, HO$_2$C, CO$_2$H)	—	—	270 (10,300)	A	(3)
17.	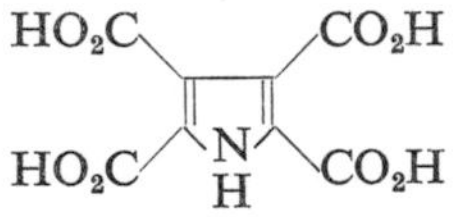 (pyrrole with HO$_2$C, CO$_2$H, HO$_2$C, CO$_2$H)	—	—	277 (7600)	A	(3)

† The ethyl esters of acids 11–17 have their E.T. bands *ca.* 11 mμ higher than those of the acids.

ution at a given position. Another generality which is derivable from the data of Table 5.1 is that the 3-substituted pyrroles absorb at *shorter* wavelengths than the corresponding 2-derivatives. In polysubstituted pyrroles, the most active chromophore usually dominates the spectrum. These generalizations are illustrated by the isomeric aldehydo-esters (IV) and (V) whose spectra are quite

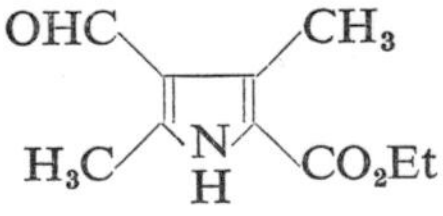

IV

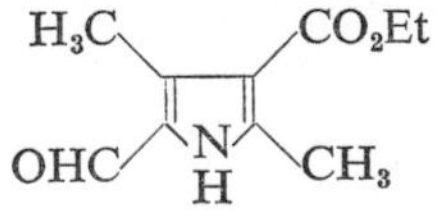

V

similar to those of pyrrole 2- and 3-aldehydes, respectively. The E.T. band of the ester groups is hidden by the aldehyde E.T. band near 290 mμ, the 2-aldehyde absorbing *ca.* 10mμ to the red of the 3-isomer.

The wavelengths of maximal absorption for the E.T. band of the pyrrole mono and dicarboxylic acids and esters lie in the order 3- < 3,4- < 2- < 2,3- and 2,4- < 2,5- which follows the simple additivity relationship (see Table 5.1). From an examination of a series of pyrroles containing electron-transfer bands, Eisner and Gore[3] concluded that intensity values of this class are governed

TABLE 5.1 a. INTENSITIES OF E.T. BANDS OF PYRROLES SUBSTITUTED BY —M GROUPS

Position of substituents	E.T.band intensity $\times 10^{-3}$
2-	13–20
3-	4–5
3,4-	7–10
2,4-	10–17
2,5-	17–22
2,3-	10–12
2,3,5-	9–17

largely by the *position* rather than by the *type* of substituent. The orders of magnitude of intensity values may prove useful in structural determination of new pyrroles, although it is important to assess the effect of steric hindrance to coplanarity for any chromophore with electron transfer absorption since the intensity is usually affected more profoundly than the maximal wavelength position. From Eisner and Gore's data, it would appear that since the 220 to 250 mμ region of absorption in the substituted pyrroles varies in intensity from $\varepsilon = 20,000$ to non-appearance of any defined band, it is meaningful to consider only the electron-transfer band for the purpose of structure correlation. Table 5.1 a summarizes the relevant data.

Dipyrrylmethanes

The linkage of two pyrrole nuclei through saturated carbon as in the di-pyrrylmethane diester (VI) does not cause a substantial change in the spectrum

VI λ 290 (ε 15,700)   VII λ 285 (ε 15,800)

with respect to the corresponding pyrrole. Thus, the spectrum of compound (VI) has an intensity almost equal to that of the model pyrrole (VII) and has almost identical λ_{max}.

5.2. DIPYRROMETHENES (TABLE 5.2)

The complete conjugation of the dipyrromethene (as VIII) in which a polyene is terminated by nitrogen substitution gives intense absorption near 450 mμ. In acid solution the protonated species (as IX) gives a charge transfer absorption spectrum typical of *cyanine dyes*. For example, the perchlorate (IX; R=H; X=ClO$_4^-$) absorbs at 470 mμ. An interesting example of shift to longer wavelength occasioned by steric hindrance to coplanarity appears in the N—Me derivative (IX; R = Me; X=ClO$_4^-$) which has λ_{max} 510 mμ (in CHCl$_3$). Model

TABLE 5.2. DIPYRROMETHENES AND CYANINE DYES

Compound	Band I	Band II	Band III	Solvent	Reference
	225 (10,200)	328 (3400)	447 (35,500)	D	(4)
	—	—	473 (135,000)	Ch	(5)
	—	—	510 (57,000)	Ch	(5)
		—	446 (35,000)	Ch	(6)
	—	—	479 (12,500)	Ch	(6)

compounds revealed that N-alkylation was not expected to produce a large bathochromic shift. The explanation offered by Forster[35] is that the departure from planarity caused by the bulky methyl groups in (IX) decreases the ground-state resonance and lowers the energy difference between ground and excited states — hence the observed red shift. The unification of the theory of steric

VIII λ 447 (ε 35,000)   IX

effects on conjugated systems has been made in a molecular orbital treatment by Heilbronner and Gerdil[39], while M.O. and perturbation theory in relation to cyanine dye spectra have been discussed at length by several authors[38]. These theoretical considerations have been fairly approximate but the main indication is that steric hindrance to coplanarity does not necessarily produce a blue shift from the expected position of absorption although the *intensity* of absorption will always be lowered by such overcrowding. Some relevant data are collected in Table 5.2.

5.3. PORPHINS AND CHLORINS (TABLE 5.3)

We shall deal with the general aspects of porphyrin absorption in this section as a brief introduction to the detailed analysis of naturally occurring pigments of this class which is discussed in some detail in Chapter 8. Porphin (X) con-

X, Porphin   XI, Chlorin

tains the completely unsaturated parent ring system of the porphyrins which also include the chlorins or dihydroporphins. Chlorin (XI) has its longest wavelength absorption maximum above that of porphin (Table 5.3). This is also true of any corresponding chlorin-porphin set, e.g. the octaethyl-chlorin-porphins (XII–XV) The effect of symmetry rather than the absolute level of unsaturation is quite evident for the set porphin-chlorin-tetrahydroporphin as exemplified in Table 5.3.

TABLE 5.3. LONGEST WAVELENGTH ABSORPTION BANDS OF CHLORINS AND PORPHINS
(IN BENZENE)[5]

Symmetry C_{2V}

1. Octaethylchlorin (XII)

λ_{max} 645·5 mμ (ε 168,600)

Symmetry D_{4H}

2. Octaethylporphin (XIII)

λ_{max} 532 mμ (ε 10,800)
λ_{max} 622 mμ (ε 5800)

Symmetry D_{2H}

3. Tetrahydroporphin (XIV)

λ_{max} 721 mμ (ε 150,000)

Symmetry C_{2V}

4. Tetrahydroporphin (XV)

λ_{max} 586 mμ (ε 32,100)
λ_{max} 546 mμ (ε 17,600)

The symmetries of the tetrahydro derivatives (XIV) and (XV) are designated D_{2H} and C_{2V}, respectively. Jackman[5] has employed molecular orbital theory to predict that for a given series, the long wavelength transition occurs in the following order of increasing wavelength: C_{2V} tetrahydroporphin < porphin < chlorin < D_{2H} tetrahydroporphin. The appropriate values for the series delineated in Table 5.3 are 586, 622, 645 and 721 mμ, respectively.

So far we have only been concerned with the *position* of the *longest* wavelength band of porphin spectra, which most easily lends itself to prediction based on calculation using either M.O. or electron-gas models. Valuable empirical correlations between the structures of natural porphyrin types and their spectra in the region 450–700 mμ have been made by a consideration of the relative intensities of the four longest wavelength bands. Inspection of the curve is sufficient to classify the porphyrin as a porphin or chlorin, and the presence of electron-accepting moieties attached to the perimeter of the ring system may be detected by intensity changes corresponding to electron transfer to such acceptors. Some applications of this method are described in Chapter 8, where some typical spectra will also be found. These structural correlations are confined to the spectral region 400–700 mμ. In addition to this "fingerprint" region the porphins and chlorins all absorb strongly ($\varepsilon \geqslant 10^5$) near 400 m$\mu$. This transition is termed the Soret absorption band.

5.4. INDOLES

The indole nucleus occurs intact and in a variety of modifications within the large family of alkaloids which bear its name. The recognition of the presence of the indole chromophore and its diverse ramifications may be made by consideration of the ultraviolet spectrum which forms a most useful method of classification. The spectrum of indole has three bands – at 200, 262 and 280 to 290 mμ which is to be expected by analogy with the naphthalene chromophore. The 262 mμ band is modified in or absent from the spectra of many substituted indoles (Table 5.4; Nos. 2, 4, 6). In Table 5.4 will be found the data for the most commonly occurring chromophoric arrays in the indole alkaloids. The

XVI   XVII   XVIII

XIX   XX λ 248   XXI λ 240

indole chromophore (XVI) is distinguishable from the isomeric α-methylene indoline (XVII) by virtue of the latter's intense absorption near 290 mμ ($\varepsilon > 20,000$). In turn, the indoline chromophore (XVIII) is distinguished by a strong electron transfer band ($\varepsilon > 20,000$) at about 250 mμ which is the position of maximal absorption for NN-dimethyl aniline (XIX) (λ_{max} 250 mμ). The additional bands near 200 and 295 mμ are displaced benzenoid absorption (203·5 and 255 mμ bands). Oxindole (XX) may be compared with acetanilide (XXI) although care must be exercised in such comparisons (see strychnine, below).

Again, the ψ-indoxyl chromophore (XXII) may be compared with that of o-dimethylaminoacetophenone (XXIII) (λ_{max} 266 mμ). The N-acyl indoles show multi-banded spectra with contributions from both indole and

$-\overset{|}{N}-CO-$ conjugated with an aromatic system.

XXII   XXIII

The importance of selection of *valid model compounds* is illustrated by the following example of acylindoline absorption. The molecule of strychnine (XXIV) contains the chromophore of an N-acylindoline (Table 5.4; No. 14). The "obvious" model, N-methylacet-*o*-toluidide (XXV) however has λ_{max} 270 mμ (ε 300). This represents a return to a xylene spectrum occasioned by the steric hindrance to coplanarity with concomitant lowering of the probability of the electron transfer between the nitrogen *p*-electrons and the ring, a situation which in no way duplicates the environment of the N-acyl group in strychnine. The latter base shows a strong E.T. band at 281 mμ with additional bands at 257 and 290 mμ. A close model, in which the N-acyl group is in a conformation propitious for such an electron transfer, is provided by the acylhexahydrocarbazole (XXVI) whose spectrum (λ_{max} 251, 281, 290 mμ) is almost superimposable upon that of strychnine.[15]

XXIV Strychnine   XXV λ 270 (ε 300)

XXVI λ 257 (ε 16,000)

Indolenines (Nos. 16–19) absorb at lower wavelengths and intensities compared with the corresponding indoles. Tautomerism between indole and indolenine forms of substituted indoles has been studied by Witkop, employing both infrared and ultraviolet correlations. The 3-acyl-indoles (e.g. No. 19) may be recognized not only by characteristically intense absorption at about 270 mμ,

TABLE 5.4. INDOLE CHROMOPHORES

No.	Compound	Band I	Band II	Band III	Solvent	Reference
Indoles						
1.		220 (26,000)	262 (6310)	280 (5620) 288 (4170)	C	(6)
2.			—	280 (7080)	A	(7)
3.		220 (30,000)	270 (9000)	295 (5000)	A	(7a)
4.		223 (33,000)	—	280 (5620) 290 (5000)	A	(6)
5.			—	283 (8000) 300 sh (6500)	A	(8)
6.		225 (32,100)	—	291 (5610)	MeOH	(9)
Indoline						
7.		210 (32,000)	254 (25,000)	306 (5500)	A	(10)
Methylene indoline						
8.			293 (45,000)	320 sh (20,000)	A	**(11)**
Oxindole						
9.		—	248 (9350)	279 i (1500)	A	(7)

TABLE 5.4—(contd.)

No.	Compound	Band I	Band II	Band III	Solvent	Reference
	Indoxyl					
10.		230 (25,000)	290 (4000)	—		(12)
	ψ-Indoxyl					
11.		230 (27,500)	256 (6000)	400 (2500)		(13)
	N-Acylindole					
12.		—	242 (20,000)	274 (10,500) 301 (3470)	A	(14)
13.		—	240 (25,000) 268 (22,400)	306 (12,600) 360 (8900)	A	(14)
	N-Acylindoline					
14.		—	257 (16,000)	281 (4200) 290 (3400)	A	(15)
15.		—		292 (4075)		(16)
	Indolenine (ψ-Indole)					
16.		—	262 (4000) 296 (5100)	— —	A H+	(17) (17)

TABLE 5.4—(contd.)

No.	Compound	Band I	Band II	Band III	Solvent	Reference
Indolenine (ψ-Indole) — (contd.)						
17.	(structure)	—	255 (4000)		A	(18)
18.	(structure) NH₂	—	267 (11,200) 260 (9100)	289 (3160) 290 (2500)	A H⁺	(19) (19)
19.	(structure) CHO	251 (17,800) 252 (7500)	270 (13,600) 275 (17,000)	297 (9600) 317 (11,000)	A OH⁻	(20) (20)
20.	(structure) CHOH					
Carbinolamine						
21.	(structure) OH	250 (10,000) 256	295 (2500) 300		H⁺ OH⁻	(21)
β-Carbolinium						
22.	(structure) Me Me			366 (19,000)	A	(20)
23.	(structure) Me Me	233 (32,700)	262–73 (19,600)	313 (20,000) 390 (3910)	A	(20, 22)
24.	(structure)	218 (18,760)	260 (7980)	376 (10,500)	MeOH	(9)
25.	(structure) Me	234 (37,400)	287 (16,300)	347 (4600)	MeOH	(9)
26.	MeO (structure) Me	241 (41,000)	301 (16,100)	336 (4900)	MeOH	(9)

TABLE 5.4 — (contd.)

No.	Compound	Band I	Band II	Band III	Solvent	Reference
β-Carbolinium — (contd.)						
27.	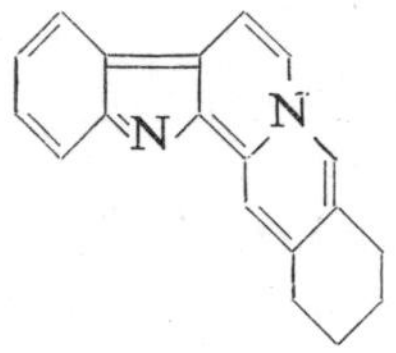	242 (32,400)	295 (13,000)	383 (14,500)	MeOH	(9)
28.	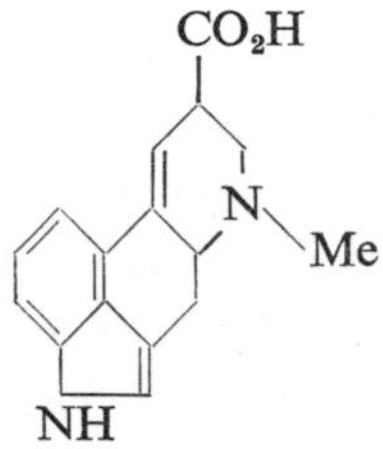	—	310 (10,000)	—		(23)

but also by bathochromic shift of their spectra in alkaline solution, where the enol anion of the indolenine form (XXVIIb) predominates. *β*-Carbolinium and

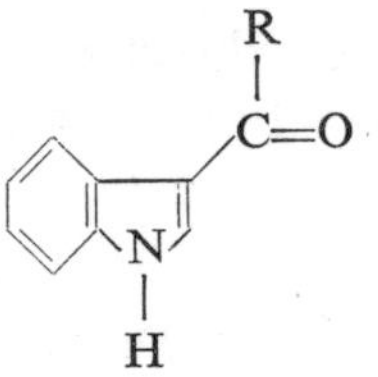

XXVII a

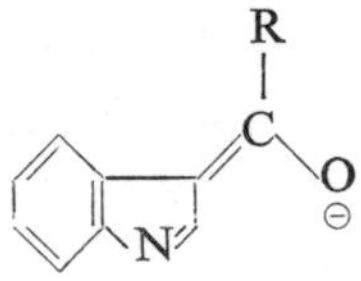

XXVII b

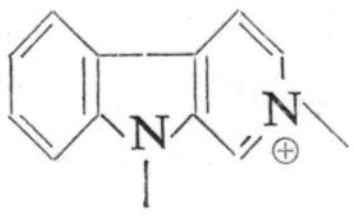

XXVIII

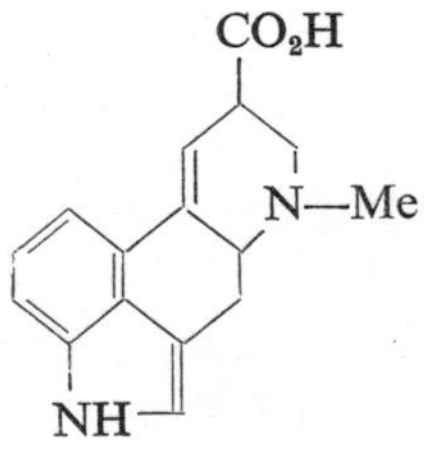

XXIX

related chromophores, e.g. (XXVIII), may be compared with anthracene in absorption characteristics.

The cross-conjugated styrene–indole system of lysergic acid (XXIX) absorbs at 310 mμ (ε 1000).

5.5. PYRIDINE AND ITS DERIVATIVES (TABLE 5.5)

The six-membered monocyclic azines contain certain bands in their ultraviolet spectra which have no counterpart in the spectrum of benzene and its congeners. Pyridine (XXX) absorbs at 195, 251 and 270 mμ in hexane solution, the 270 mμ band showing a dependency on solvent which marks the $n \rightarrow \pi^*$ transition of a non-bonding electron of the N-lone pair to the ring orbital. The $n \rightarrow \pi^*$ bands of the heteroaromatic series may be distinguished by their blue shift for the change hydrocarbon $\rightarrow$ hydroxylic solvent. This shift also provides a measure of the electron-donating capacity of the hetero-atom of the system under study. Acidification of a solution of a compound containing the pyridine nucleus removes this long wavelength band from the spectrum (No. 2; Table 5.5) as the lone pair is now involved in cation formation.

The features of the first $\pi \rightarrow \pi^*$ band (251 mμ) of pyridine and the azines in general may be interpreted on the assumption that this absorption is the counterpart of the 255 mμ band of benzene. Thus the effect of substitution on the 251 mμ band of pyridine is generally bathochromic and follows the trend of benzenoid substitution. In contradistinction, the $n \rightarrow \pi^*$ band is, as a rule, shifted to shorter wavelengths in the presence of o-, p-directing substituents, and to longer wavelengths with m-directing groups. This can be explained by the assumption that the excited state of the $n \rightarrow \pi^*$ transition is stabilized relative to the ground state by electron-accepting and destabilized by electron-donating substituents, the former reducing and the latter increasing the transition energy. A quantitative agreement between calculated and observed intensities of the $\pi - \pi^*$ band of substituted azines can be reached by vector addition of the spectroscopic moments of the appropriate substituents (see Introduction). Some values for spectroscopic moments are given in Table 5.5a.

The effects of solvent and pH changes on the spectrum of pyridine are summarized in Table 5.5. The spectrum of 3-methyl pyridine (No. 3) provides an excellent model for that of nicotine (No. 4).

Hydroxypyridines

The presence of a hydroxyl group α- or γ- to a nitrogen atom in a conjugated system brings into play the proton affinity of the N atom and results in tautomerism to the α- and γ-pyridone structures. The phenomenon is quite general for the N-heteroaromatic compounds and we shall confine our detailed discussion to the case of pyridine with the implicit understanding that the meth-

TABLE 5.5. PYRIDINES

No.	Compound	Band I	Band II	Band III	Solvent	Reference
1.		195 (7500)	251 (2000)	270 (450)	H	(24, 25)
		—	257 (2750)	—	A	(26)
2.		—	256 (5300)	—	H+	(26)
3.	Me	—	263 (3100)	—	OH−	(27)
		—	262·5 (5500)	—	H+	(27)
4.	Me	—	262 (2880)	—	A—OH−	(19)
		—	260 (4790)	—	A—H+	
5.	OMe	<205 (>5300)	269 (3230)	—	pH 7	(28)
		210 (3550)	279 (6200)	—	pH 1	(28)
6.	OH	224 (7230)	293 (5900)	—	pH 6	
		230 (9000)	291 (5070)	—	pH 13	(28)
		209 (3600)	277 (6950)	—	10 N H_2SO_4	
7.	Me, O	226 (6100)	297 (5700)	—	pH 5	(28)
		210 (3500)	279 (6250)	—	10 N H_2SO_4	
8.	OMe	216 (8320)	276 (3960)	—	pH 7	(28)
		224 (4290)	284 (6240)	—	pH 2	
9.	OH	246 (5720)	278 (2320)	315 (3060)	pH 6·8	
		236 (11,000)	298 (4960)	—	pH 13	(28)
		222 (3730)	283 (5840)	—	pH 2	
10.	OH, Cl⊖, Me	249 (8120)	—	320 (5810)	pH 7	(28)
		224 (3790)	288 (5900)	—	pH 2	

TABLE 5.5—(contd.)

No.	Compound	Band I	Band II	Band III	Solvent	Reference
11.	OMe structure	222 (9300) 235 (9500)	235 (2000) —	— —	pH 9 pH 2	(28)
12.	OH structure	— 239 (14,100) 234 (9800)	253 (14,800) 260 (2200) —	— — —	pH 7 pH 13 pH 0	(28)
13.	O structure, N-Me	— 239 (11,800)	260 (18,900) —	— —	pH 7 pH 1	(28)
14.	NH$_2$ structure	229 (9400) 229 (8900)	287 (3800) 300 (5700)	— —	pH 9 pH 1	(29)
15.	NH structure, N-Me	251 (11,700) 255 —	317 (4100) 362 —	— —	pH 14 C	(29)
16.	NH$_2$ structure	231 (8200) 250 (7600)	288 (3000) 315 (3600)	— —	pH 9 pH 1	(29)
17.	NH$_2$ structure	241 (14,000) —	265 (2400) 263 (16,500)	— —	pH 12 pH 1	(29)
18.	NH structure, N-Me	—	268 (16,500)	—	pH 13	(29)

TABLE 5.5—(contd.)

No.	Compound	Band I	Band II	Band III	Solvent	Reference
N-oxides						
19.	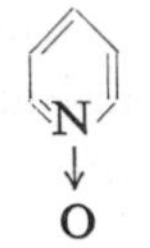	254 (12,000)	—	—	H$_2$O	(30)
20.	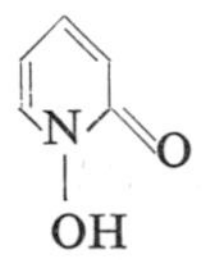	228 (7200) 225 (23,200)	— 244 i(5700)	305 (4600) 323 (6800)	A A—OH$^-$	(31) (31)

TABLE 5.5a. SPECTROSCOPIC MOMENTS[37]

Substituent	Spectroscopic moment (cm m/l)$^{-\frac{1}{2}}$
OH	34
OMe	31
CH$_3$	7
Br	4
H	0
CO$_2$H	−28
—N(Aza)	−38

ods and concepts developed in the ensuing argument are applicable to the solution of many problems of structure among the hydroxy- and amino-azines.

α-*Hydroxypyridines*

The spectrum of 2-hydroxypyridine (XXXI) is reminiscent of that of its N-methyl derivative, N-methyl-2-pyridone (XXXII) but quite different from

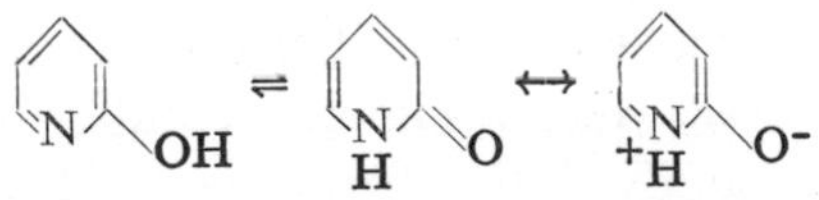

(1)

Enol   Amide   Zwitterion

XXX 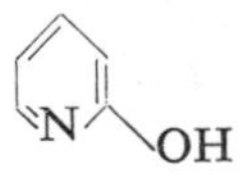   XXXI 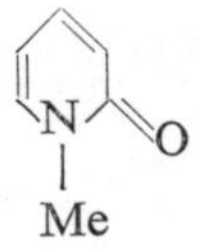   XXXII 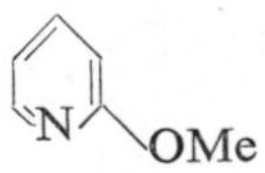   XXXIII

that of the O-Me compound, 2-methoxypyridine (XXXIII), both in organic and aqueous solvents. Even a superficial examination of the data presented in Table 5 5 (Nos. 5–7) reveals that the tautomeric equilibrium (1) of 2-hydroxy-pyridine lies well to the right and favours the amide or zwitterion form. A quantitative treatment is possible if it is assumed that the spectrum of the N-methyl derivative (XXXII) forms a good model for the zwitterionic tautomer of the corresponding hydroxy compound. On this basis the relative amounts of enolic and zwitterionic forms of a given heteroaromatic hydroxy compound *at the iso-electric* pH may be calculated from the relative band intensities of the compound and its N-methyl derivative. The long wavelength bands of the differently charged species of a hydroxyazine occur in the order zwitterion (amide) > anion > cation > enol, provided that bands of corresponding inten-sities are compared. For 2-hydroxypyridine the appropriate values (Table 5.5) are 293, 291, 277 and 269 mμ.

   4-Hydroxypyridine (XXXIV) exists in solution at pH 7 as the amide form (XXXV), λ_{max} 253 mμ, some 40 mμ less than the principal band of 2-pyridone

XXXIV   XXXV   XXXVI   XXXVII

(cf. the isomeric cyclohexadienones, Chap. 2). This conclusion is reached by comparison with the spectra of N-methyl-4-pyridone (XXXVI) and the cor-responding O-methyl compound, 4-methoxypyridine (XXXVII). On the very reasonable assumption that the NMe—(C=C)$_n$CO group provides at least a *qualitative* model for the NH—(C=C)$_n$CO chromophore (where $n = 0, 1, 2$ etc.) it is possible to assign structures to those tautomeric hydroxyazines whose N-methyl and O-methyl derivatives are available.

   The effect of changing from hydroxylic to hydrocarbon solvent causes shifts of up to $+ 30$ mμ in the spectrum of the hydroxy- (but not the methoxy-) azines. Mason has interpreted this observation in terms of greater stabilization of the polar ground state by solvation relative to the excited state. In non-polar solvent the solvation energy of the polar state now being much smaller causes appearance of the maximum at higher wavelength.

   3-Hydroxypyridine exists in tautomeric equilibrium between the enol (XXXVIII) and zwitterion (XXXIX) forms in neutral aqueous solution, a

XXXVIII   XXXIX   XL   XLI

conclusion reached when the summation of the spectra of the methochloride (XL) and 3-methoxypyridine (XLI) was found to duplicate the spectrum of 3-hydroxypyridine. Vitamin B_6 (pyridoxine; XLII) has the spectrum of a 3-hydroxypyridine.

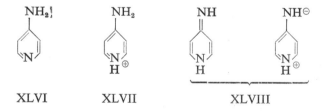

XLII

Aminopyridines

The tautomeric equilibrium of 2-aminopyridine lies on the amine (XLIII) rather than the imine (XLIV) side. This follows from spectral comparison with the N-methylimino compound (XLV) which has absorption unlike that of 2-aminopyridine. Infrared studies of the amino-azines show the presence of the

XLIII   XLIV   XLV

primary amino group. The electronic spectrum of 4-aminopyridine has been considered in some detail by Mason[29]. Measurements on the three accessible ionic species of the monocyclic N-heteroaromatic amines, viz. the neutral amine (XLVI), the cation (XLVII) and the imine or zwitterion ion form

XLVI   XLVII   XLVIII

(XLVIII) show again the wavelength order (for a given band) zwitterion > cation > neutral form. It is also found that for a particular class of pyridine derivative, the long wave bands lie in the order 3 > 2 > 4-substituted pyridine. This is not the order predicted by the charge-transfer model but has been explained in terms of a benzyl anion model.†

It is instructive to compare the shifts of the maxima of the aminoazines on change from hydroxylic to hydrocarbon solvent with the corresponding hydroxy-azine shift. 2-Aminopyridine has λ_{max} 229, 287 mμ in water and 231, 288 mμ

† The M.O. treatment of the azines is described by Mason[28, 29, 41].

in cyclohexane. The change from ethanol to hexane gives a blue shift of 7 mμ in the spectrum of 4-aminopyridine. In sharp contrast, the corresponding hydroxypyridines show red shifts of nearly 30 mμ for the change EtOH → hexane. We discussed above the explanation for the latter phenomenon in terms of solvation stabilization which implies that we accept the view that the *p*-electrons of oxygen are active in the first two electronic transitions of the hydroxy-azines and we are measuring the extent of hydrogen-bonding by the solvent shift. In the case of the amino-azines, the small blue shifts observed may be due to differential stabilization of the excited state in hydroxylic solvent which outweighs the hydrogen-bonding stabilization of the ground state.

Pyridine N-oxides

Just as the spectrum of pyridine ($\varepsilon_{\max}$ 2700) is intensified without wavelength shift by protonation to give the pyridinium ion ($\varepsilon_{\max}$, 5000), so the

XLIX　　　L　　　LI

LII　　　　　LIII　　　　　LIV　　　　　LV

principal band of pyridine N-oxide (XLIX) appears at 245 mμ (ε 12,000) corresponding to the pyridinium oxide mesomer (L) with contributions from the form (LI). A naturally occurring N-oxide is represented by aspergillic acid (LII) (Chapter 6). Studies with model 2-hydroxypyridine N-oxides (as LIII) show that the 1-hydroxypyridone form predominates. Katritzky[31] has recently concluded from basicity and spectral measurements that the pyridone form is generally preferred for 2-hydroxy N-oxides, whereas the amino N-oxides (as LIV) exist in the amino, not in the imino form (LV).

5.6. QUINOLINES AND ISOQUINOLINES (TABLE 5.6)

Introduction of a nitrogen atom into the ring systems of naphthalene and anthracene has a remarkably slight effect on the spectrum between 220 and 400 mμ. Exceptions to this statement occur when we are dealing with tautomeric forms of hydroxy- and aminoquinolines and isoquinolines. Like naphthalene,

TABLE 5.6. QUINOLINES, ISOQUINOLINES AND ACRIDINES

No.	Compound	Band I	Band II	Band III	Band IV	Solvent	Reference
	Quinolines						
1.	(quinoline)	226 (35,500)	—	268–275 (3500)	300 (2000) 313 (2500)	C	(6)
2.	(2-hydroxyquinoline)	224 (26,700)	245 (8520)	270 (6550)	324 (6300)	pH 5·5	(32)
3.	(N-methyl-2-quinolone)	228 (34,100)	245 (10,200)	272 (6900)	375 (6500)	pH 7	(29)
4.	(2-methoxyquinoline)	—		267 (2000)	307 (2070) 318 (2200)	pH 6·8	(32)
5.	(MeO-, OH, Et, Me substituted quinoline)	215 (20,500)	246 (31,300) 255 (29,600)	276 (2200) 287 (3000) 298 (3200)	332 (9000) 346 (9000)	A	(20)
6.	(MeO-, OH substituted quinoline)	217 (18,600)	244 (35,600) 248 (35,500)	284 (3160) 296 (3030)	333 (9000) 347 (9200)	A	(20)
7.	(OMe furoquinoline)	236 (60,000)	309 (9000)	328 (7600)	—	A	(33)
	Isoquinolines						
8.	(isoquinoline)	218 (79,000)	266 (3900)	305 (2000)	318 (3000)	C	(6)
9.	(HO- isoquinoline)	229 (43,600) 225 (25,600)	263 (17,200) 280 (2160)	353 (8040) 319 (700)	—	pH 7·5 C	(32)
10.	(O=, NMe isoquinolone)	230 (34,400)	267 (22,900)	358 (12,200)		pH 10	(32)

TABLE 5.6—(contd.)

No.	Compound	Band I	Band II	Band III	Band IV	Solvent	Reference
Acridines							
11.		250	340	355	380	A	(6)
12.		—	358 (4500)	400 (2800)	—	A	(32)
13.		—	360 (3550)	392 (3550)	—	A	(32)
14.		—	380 (3600)	—	550 (1200)	pH 9	(32)
15.		244 (31,000)	277 (19,000)	322 (8000)	370 (5600) 475 (4000)	A	(34)

quinoline has three bands at 230, 270 and 313 mμ. The *intensity* of the long wavelength band is, however, greater in the azine than in the corresponding hydrocarbon. For naphthalene we have λ_{max} 310 mμ (ε 140), for quinoline λ_{max} 313 mμ (ε 2000) and for isoquinoline λ_{max} 318 mμ (ε 2000). This intensity increase of the $\pi \rightarrow \pi^*$ absorption is predictable by perturbation theory. Mason has compared the observed and calculated intensities of azines. The intensity may be readily derived from equation (1)

$$I_a - I_0 = M_a^2 \tag{1}$$

where I_a is the intensity of the long wavelength band in the substituted nucleus, I_0 that of the unsubstituted nucleus, and M_a the spectroscopic moment[37] of the substituent a. From the table of spectroscopic moments (p. 181) we have the value -38 for the aza-substituent.

For polysubstitution:

$$I_{ab} - I_0 = M_a^2 + M_b^2 + 2M_aM_b \qquad (2) \qquad \cdots p-$$

and

$$I_{ab} - I_0 = M_a^2 + M_b^2 - M_aM_b \qquad (3) \quad \cdots o-/m-$$

where (2) and (3) refer to *para-*, and *ortho-* and *meta-*substituted derivatives, respectively. Qualitative agreement is found between the calculated and observed intensities of the mono-and poly-azines and their derivatives using equations (1)–(3).

The $n \to \pi^*$ bands displayed by many azines (which are identified by their shift to lower wavelength on changing from hydrocarbon to hydroxylic solvent) are not observed in quinoline and isoquinoline, as they (presumably) lie below a $\pi \to \pi^*$ band.

Hydroxyquinolines (Table 5.6)

2-Hydroxyquinoline (LVI) has been shown to exist mainly as the amide (LVII) on the basis of comparison of its spectrum with that of N-methyl-2-

LVI

LVII

LVIII

LIX

LX

LXI

LXII

quinolone (LVIII) and 2-methoxyquinoline (LIX). The 4-hydroxyquinolines also exhibit quinolone spectra and may be written as in (LX). In 7-hydroxyquinoline (LXI) we should expect important contributions from the extended amide form (LXII); this is, in fact, borne out by a comparison of its spectrum with that of the N—Me and O—Me derivatives, all measured in a buffer with pH at least two units away from the pK of the compounds. This avoids superposition of the spectra of two different ionic species, e.g. the neutral molecule and the cation π. 4-Hydroxy-6-methoxyquinoline forms the chromophore of the alkaloid ibogaine (LXIII), the model compound (LXIV) providing confirmation of this assignment of structure. The furoquinolines represent a further variant among the quinolines of natural provenance. For example, dictamnine (No. 7) has λ_{max} 236, 309 and 328 mμ. The apparent model (LXIV) has intense ab-

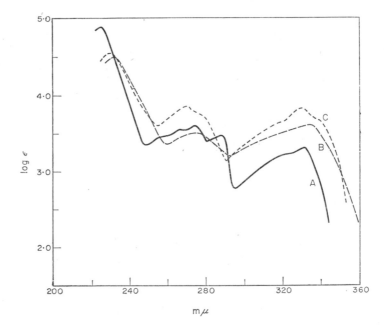

LXIII   LXIV

sorption near 250 mμ and the absence of this band in dictamnine is presumably due to the presence of a 4-methoxyl group, rather than a 4-hydroxyl group, the latter giving rise to the intense absorption associated with quinolone formation.

FIG. 5.1. Absorption spectra of quinolines (in ethanol). A, β-naphthol; B, 6-hydroxy-quinoline; C, 2-hydroxyquinoline. (After G. W. Ewing and E. A. Steck, *J. Amer. Chem. Soc.*, **68**, 2181, 1946.)

In general, the spectra of the quinolines and their derivatives resemble those of the corresponding naphthalenes quite closely, as can be seen by a comparison of the curves of β-naphthol and 6-hydroxyquinoline (Fig. 5.1). In the same figure the curve of 2-hydroxyquinoline is also shown. This has a greater intensity in the 250 mμ region due to quinolone tautomerism.

Isoquinolines (Table 5.6)

The parent nucleus (LXV) has a spectrum very close to that of quinoline, and with the reservations noted for the tautomeric hydroxy- and amino-compounds, the spectra of the isoquinolines may be compared with the corresponding naphthalene derivatives, which they resemble closely. 6-Hydroxy-isoquinoline (LXVI) is in equilibrium with the extended quinone-imine

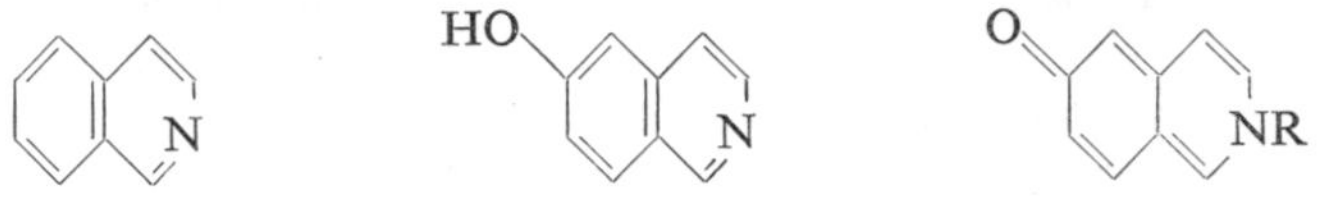

LXV

LXVI

LXVII: R=H
LXVIII: R=Me

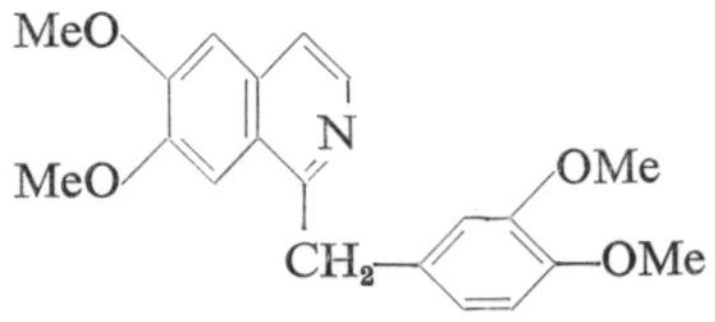

LXIX

form (LXVII). The latter has intense absorption at 263 and 353 mμ (ε 17,200 and 8040) at pH 7·5. The corresponding N−Me derivative (LXVII; R=Me) has λ_{max} 267 and 358 mμ (ε 22,900 and 12,220), indicating the extent of amide tautomer at equilibrium. A typical benzylisoquinoline alkaloid papaverine (LXIX), has λ_{max} 240, 282, 330 mμ (ε 63,000; 8000; 5300).

Acridines (Table 5.6)

The aza-analogue of anthracene, acridine (LXX), has a spectrum resembling that of the parent hydrocarbon, with the long wavelength band at λ 380 mμ (ε 3160). This represents an intensity increase predictable by the spectroscopic moment calculation [equation (1) p. 186]. Substituted acridines resemble the corresponding anthracenes in their absorption spectra. The spectra of many acridines have been recorded and discussed by Albert[40].

Acridone-1,4-quinone (LXXI) is the chromophore of actinomycinol, a degradation product of actinomycin[34].

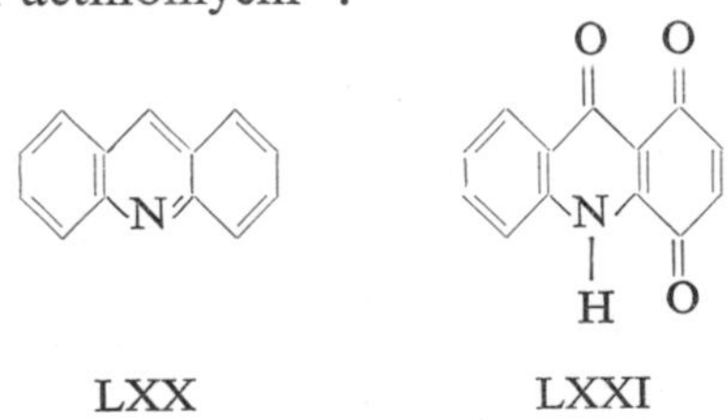

LXX

LXXI

REFERENCES

1. K. BOWDEN and E. A. BRAUDE, *J. Chem. Soc.*, 948 (1946).
2. G. H. COOKSON, *ibid.*, 2789 (1953).
3. U. EISNER and P. H. GORE, *ibid.*, 922 (1958).
4. A. C. JAIN and G. W. KENNER, *ibid.*, 185 (1959).
5. J. R. BARNARD and L. M. JACKMAN, *ibid.*, 1172 (1956).
6. R. A. FRIEDEL and M. ORCHIN, *Ultraviolet Spectra of Aromatic Compounds*, Wiley, New York (1951).
7. G. JONES and T. S. STEVENS, *J. Chem. Soc.*, 2344 (1953).
7a. K. BERNAUER, *Fortschritte der Chemie Organischer Naturstoffe*, **17**, 183 (1959).
8. J. HARLEY–MASON and A. H. JACKSON, *J. Chem. Soc.*, 374 (1955).
9. *Physical Data of Indole Alkaloids*, Lilly Co., Indiana.
10. H. ASMIS, H. SCHMID and P. KARRER, *Helv. Chim. Acta*, **37**, 1983 (1954).
11. J. KEBRLE, H. SCHMID, P. WASER and P. KANER, *ibid.*, **36**, 102 (1953).
12. R. W. BALSIGER, R. W. FRISCHER, R. HIRT and E. GIOVANNINI, *ibid.*, **36**, 708 (1953).
13. R. GOUTAREL, M. M. JANOT, F. MATHYS and V. PRELOG, *Helv. Chim. Acta*, **39**, 742 (1956).
14. V. PRELOG, S. SZPILFOGEL and J. BATTEGAY, *ibid.*, **30**, 366 (1947).
15. V. PRELOG and S. SZPILFOGEL, *ibid.*, **28**, 1669 (1945).
16. P. J. SCHEUER, *J. Amer. Chem. Soc.*, **82**, 192 (1960).
17. B. WITKOP, J. B. PATRICK and H. M. KISSMAN, *Ber. dtsch. chem. Ges.*, **85**, 949 (1952).
18. P. GRAMMATICAKIS, *C. R. Acad. Sci., Paris*, **210**, 569 (1940).
19. B. WITKOP, *Experientia*, **10**, 420 (1954).
20. M. F. BARTLETT, D. F. DICKEL and W. I. TAYLOR, *J. Amer. Chem. Soc.*, **80**, 126 (1958).
21. H. ASMIS, E. BÄCHLI, E. CIESTWECHT, J. KEBRLE, H. SCHMID and P. KARRER, *Helv. Chim. Acta*, **37**, 1968 (1954); H. FRITZ and T. WIELAND, *Liebigs Ann.*, **611**, 268 (1958).
22. A. STOLL, A. HOFMANN and R. BRUNNER, *Helv. Chim. Acta*, **38**, 270 (1955); E. BÄCHLI, C. VAMVACAS, H. SCHMID and P. KARRER, *ibid.*, **40**, 1167 (1957).
23. A. STOLL, A. HOFMANN and F. TROXLER, *ibid.*, **32**, 506 (1949).
24. F. F. HEYROTH and J. R. LOOFBOUROW, *J. Amer. Chem. Soc.*, **56**, 1728 (1934).
25. S. F. MASON, *J. Chem. Soc.*, 1250 (1959).
26. M. L. SWAIN, A. EISNER, C. F. WOODWARD and B. A. BRICE, *J. Amer. Chem. Soc.*, **71**, 1341 (1949); H. V. DAENIKER, *Helv. Chim. Acta*, **35**, 1955 (1952).
27. H. C. BROWN and X. R. MIHM, *J. Amer. Chem. Soc.*, **77**, 1723 (1955).
28. S. F. MASON, *J. Chem. Soc.*, 1253 (1959).
29. S. F. MASON, *ibid.*, 219 (1960).
30. H. H. JAFFÉE, *J. Amer. Chem. Soc.*, **77**, 4451 (1955).
31. A. GARDINER and A. R. KATRITZKY, *J. Chem. Soc.*, 4375 (1957).
32. S. F. MASON, *ibid.*, 5010 (1957).
33. J. IRIARTE, F. A. KINCL, G. ROSENCRANZ and F. SONDHEIMER, *ibid.*, 4170 (1956).
34. W. G. HANGER, W. C. HOWELL and A. W. JOHNSON, *ibid.*, 496 (1958).
35. T. FORSTER, *Z. Elektrochem.*, **45**, 548 (1939).
36. J. R. PLATT, *J. Chem. Phys.*, **25**, 80 (1956).
37. J. R. PLATT, *ibid.*, **19**, 263 (1951).
38. M. J. S. DEWAR, *Steric Effects in Conjugated Systems* (edited by G. W. GRAY), Butterworth, London (1958).
39. E. HEILBRONNER and R. GERDIL, *Helv. Chim. Acta*, **39**, 1996 (1956).
40. A. ALBERT, *The Acridines*, Arnold, London (1951).
41. S. F. MASON, *Quart. Rev.* **15**, 284 (1961).

CHAPTER 6

N-HETEROAROMATIC COMPOUNDS (POLYAZINES)

THE principal effect of the introduction of further nitrogen atoms into the N-heteroaromatic ring is to shift the $n \rightarrow \pi^*$ band to longer wavelengths. Such displacements are dependent on the *position* rather than the *number* of aza-substituents. For example, *sym*-triazine (I) shows the smallest and 3,5,6-tri-methyl-1,2,4-triazine (II) the second largest bathochromic shift of the $n \rightarrow \pi^*$ band. The $n \rightarrow \pi^*$ bands of the polyazines are moved to lower wave-lengths on changing from hydrocarbon to hydroxylic solvent. In the latter solvent-type the hydrogen bonding of the *p*-electrons of nitrogen results in a greater energy requirement for the $n \rightarrow \pi^*$ transition than that obtaining in the promotion of the electron in hydrocarbon solvent. Molecular orbital calculations show that in the 1,2-diazines (as III) ground state interaction between the nitrogen *p*-orbitals becomes an important factor, and the $n \rightarrow \pi^*$ bands are displaced by 6000 cm^{-1} from the position of the pyridine $n \rightarrow \pi^*$ band. In 1,3- and 1,4-diazines such ground-state interaction is less, but the observed shift (relative to pyridine) is 3000 cm^{-1}. This shift has been ascribed by Mason to a lowering of energy of the unoccupied π-orbitals on aza-substitution. M.O. calculations gave agreement to within 1000 cm^{-1} of observed shifts. The spectra of the polyazines in acidic solution show no $n \rightarrow \pi^*$ absorption.

I   II   III   IV

V   VI

The first $\pi \rightarrow \pi^*$ band (i.e., long wavelength $\pi \rightarrow \pi^*$ band) of the polyazines may be compared with the 255 mμ benzene band. The intensity increments for polyaza-substitution when calculated by use of equation (2) (p. 187) give fair agreement with observed values. This method of correlation should be regarded as a useful qualitative working rule, however, which indicates a trend rather than an accurate means of predicting intensity data. Thus, the first $\pi \to \pi^*$ band intensities of pyridazine (III) and pyrimidine (IV) should be equal, and those of pyrazine (V) and s-tetrazine (VI) should also be equal, but the 1,2-diaza member of each pair absorbs with the lower intensity.

Some generalizations are possible within each series as a result of empirical correlations made by investigators seeking confirmation of structural proposals (5). For example, it is found that a pyrimidine has the intensity of the first $\pi \to \pi^*$ band reduced and only slightly shifted towards the red by a carboxyl group at the 2- and 5-positions, whereas the 4-CO_2H group gives a large red shift and intensity increase. 2- and 5-OH or OMe substitution, on the other hand gives rise to increased intensity and a bathochromic shift, the change for 4-substitution by these functions being almost zero. These findings are in harmony with perturbation theory and qualitatively agree with the intensities derivable from the spectroscopic moments of the substituents (see p. 181).

6.1. PYRIMIDINES

Pyrimidine (IV) has maxima at 243 mμ ($\pi \to \pi^*$) and 298 mμ ($n \to \pi^*$) in cyclohexane solution. In hydroxylic solvents the 243 mμ band shows an intensity increase (ε 3000 $\to$ 5000) without positional changes, while the $n \to \pi^*$ band now appears at 271 mμ. The blue shift of 27 mμ for the change from non-polar to polar solvent forms a measure of the electron donating capacity of the azine system. In polar media the p-electrons of nitrogen form hydrogen bonds with the solvent so that the $n \to \pi^*$ transition requires more energy to weaken or break the H-bonds. The $n \to \pi^*$ band of pyrimidine disappears on cation formation. These phenomena are summarized in the data of Table 6.1.

Hydroxypyrimidines may exist as the enol (VII) zwitterion or amide (VIII), cationic (IX) or anionic (X) forms, depending on structural environment (e.g. position of substituent) and on the pH and nature of the solvent. The favoured

VII	VIII	IX	X

XI	XII

side of an equilibrium state of a hydroxy-azine is usually measured by comparison of the spectrum of the tautomeric mixture with that of the corresponding N- and O-methyl derivatives at the appropriate pH (p. 181). However, the

TABLE 6.1. PRINCIPAL ABSORPTION BANDS OF THE PYRIMIDINES

Compound	Band I	Band II	Solvent	Reference
(pyrimidine)	298† (300) 271† (420) —	243 (2030) 243 (3210) 242 (5500)	C W 4 N H_2SO_4	(1) (1) (1)
OH (4-hydroxypyrimidine)	223 (7320)	260 (3740)	pH 6·2	(2)
$O^{\ominus}$	227 (11,100)	263 (3280)	pH 13	(2)
OH, $N^{\oplus}H$	224 (9840)	251 (2920)	5 N H_2SO_4	(2)
O, N—Me	— 229 (10,200)	240 (14,600) 250 sh (2650)	pH 6 pH 0	(2) (1)
O, N—Me	221 (6800) 226 (9080)	269 (3900) 258 (2940)	pH 5 2·5 N HCl	(2) (2)
OMe	— 227 (7700)	247 (3350) 238 sh (6800)	pH 6·95 pH 0	(2)
O, NH, N H, O	—	260 (6300)	A	(3)

† $n \rightarrow \pi^*$ band.

TABLE 6.1—(contd.)

Compound	Band I	Band II	Solvent	Reference
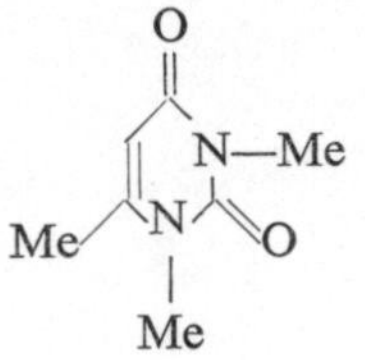 *(structure: N,N'-dimethyl, C-methyl uracil-type)*	—	268 (10,000)	pH 7	(3)
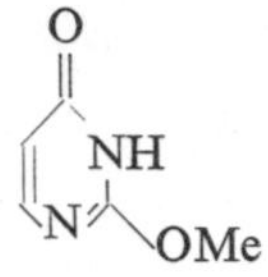 *(structure: 2-methoxypyrimidinone)*	222 (7000)	253 (8000) 263 (7500)	pH 7·6 pH 13	(3)
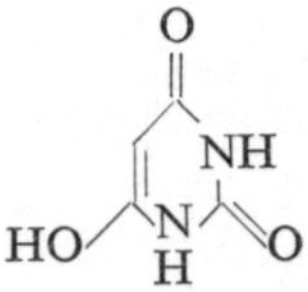 *(structure: 2-hydroxy, 6-hydroxy uracil-type)*	—	256·5 (25,000)	W	(3)
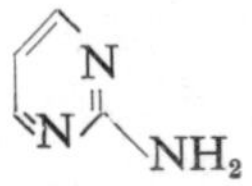 *(structure: 2-aminopyrimidine)*	224 (13,000) 221 (14,800)	292 (3000) 302 (4000)	pH 7 pH 1	(4)
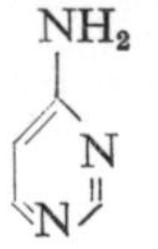 *(structure: 4-aminopyrimidine)*	233 (18,000) 236 (18,500)	268 (5000) —	pH 13 pH 0	(4)
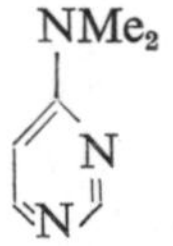 *(structure: 4-dimethylaminopyrimidine)*	250 (16,600) 262 (16,200)	286 (3600) —	pH 9·3 pH 3·15	(4)

interpretation of the electronic spectra of the hydroxydiazines is complicated by the contributions from two zwitterionic and two cationic forms. Both 2- and 5-hydroxypyrimidines (XI and XII, respectively) have unique zwitterions

XIII 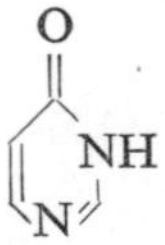　　　XIV 　　　XV 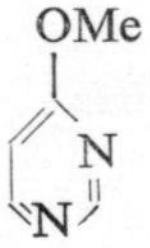　　　XVI

by virtue of their symmetry. 4-Hydroxypyrimidine (XIII) has two amide forms (XIV) and (XV). The difference between the absorption curves of 4-hydroxy-pyrimidine and its O-methyl derivative (XVI) indicates that the compound (XIII) exists as a *lactam*. Comparison of the spectra of the isomeric N–Me derivatives (corresponding to XIV and XV) suggests that the γ-form (XV) is preferred.

Aminopyrimidines

We recall that although 2- and 4-hydroxypyridines prefer to adopt the pyridone structure in solution, the aminopyridines are probably true amines and not imino-pyridones. This phenomenon is also observed in pyrimidine, whose amino derivatives may be considered as having —NH₂ rather than imino functions. Basicity and infrared measurements also support such an assignment.

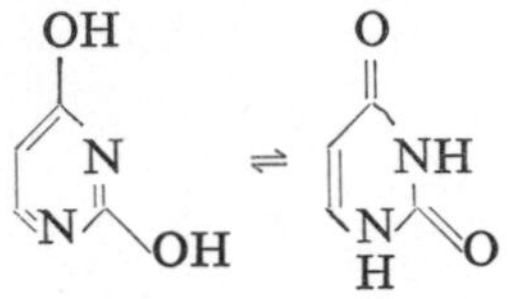

XVII   XVII a   Uracil

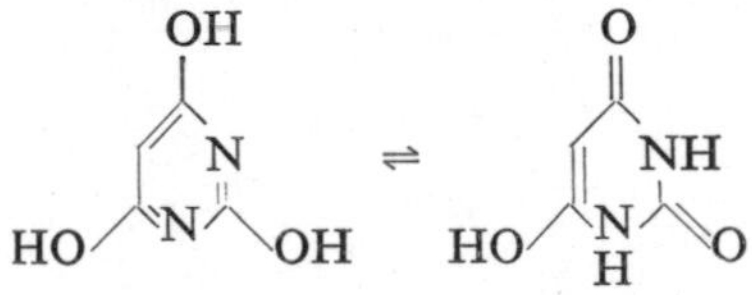

XVIII   XVIII a

Barbituric Acid

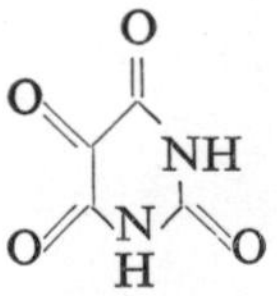

XIX   Alloxan

Biologically important oxygenated pyrimidines include uracil (XVII), bar-bituric acid (XVIII), and alloxan (XIX). The spectroscopic data for these compounds (Table 6.1) indicate substantial contributions from forms (XVIIa) and (XVIIIa).

6.2. PYRAZINES (TABLE 6.2)

Pyrazine (XX) absorbs at 260 mμ (ε, 6000) and at 327 mμ (ε 100) in cyclohexane solution, the first band representing benzenoid absorption intensified by two aza-substituents (π → π*) band and the weak band marking the n → π*

TABLE 6.2. PYRAZINES

Compound	Band I	Band II	Solvent	Reference
	327† (100)	260 (6300)	C	(5)
	221 (8800) 222 (10,400)	317 (5520) 342 (6200)	pH 5 10 N H$_2$SO$_4$	(2)
	234 (6500)	328 (8300)	A	(6)
Aspergillic acid 	—	480 (20,000)	Ch	(7)
	—	500 (12,000)	Ch	(7)
	—	550 (11,000)	Ch	(7)
	250 (120,000)	363 (40,000)	A	(8)

† $n \rightarrow \pi^*$ band.

transition. Hydroxyl substitution produces the expected wavelength shift, e.g. 2-hydroxypyrazine (XXI) has λ_{max} 317 mμ (ε 5500). 2-Hydroxypyrazine N-oxide forms the chromophore of the mould metabolite aspergillic acid (XXII)

XX   XXI   XXII   XXIII

which has λ_{max} 234 and 328 mμ (ε, 6500 and 8300) [cf. 2-hydroxypyridine N-oxide (XXIII), λ_{max} 228 and 305 mμ]. Dibenzopyrazine-N-oxides occur as elaboration products of certain micro-organisms[7]. Some representatives of this class are illustrated in Table 6.2.

6.3. PURINES (TABLE 6.3)

Much of the early work devoted to the measurement of the ultraviolet spectra of hydroxyazines and especially the purines, is rendered inaccurate since inadequate control of solvent pH was maintained. As a result, the exact nature of the ionic species under study was often unknown. This situation has now been clarified by the work of Mason[9], who has measured a large number of purine spectra using buffered solutions with pH values two units above (or below) the pK of the purine. The λ_{max} and intensity values, at appropriate pH, of a selection of purines will be found in Table 6·3.

XXIV   XXV   XXVI

XXVII

The spectrum of purine (XXIV) (in aqueous solution) is reminiscent of that of pyrimidine. Greater similarity is evident when we compare the spectrum of 2-hydroxypurine with that of 2-hydroxy-4,5-diaminopyrimidine or 2-amino-purine (XXV) and 2,4,5-triaminopurine (XXVI). 2-Hydroxy and 2-amino substituents shift the main band at 260 mμ in both purines and 2,4,5-triaminopyrim-

TABLE 6.3. ABSORPTION SPECTRA OF PURINES[9]

Compound	Band I	Band II	pH	Charge of species†
(purine; ring positions numbered 1,2,3,6,7,8,9)	<220 (13,000) <220 (3000) 219 (8300)	260 (6200) 263 (7950) 271 (7600)	0·28 5·7 11	+ 0 −
HO– purine	264 (4700) 238 (2900) 271 (4800)	322 (6500) 315 (4900) 313 (4800)	−0·75 6·05 10·15	+ 0 −
OH (6-hydroxypurine)	248 (10,500) 249 (10,500) 258 (11,000)	—	−0·75 5·18 10·35	+ 0 −
–OH (8-hydroxypurine)	235 (3240) —	280 (10,500) 277 (11,000) 285 (12,900)	0 5·4 10·13	+ 0 −
MeO– purine	246 (2600)	284 (6760) 283 (8100) 283 (7600)	0 6 11·4	+ 0 −
OMe (6-methoxypurine)	254 (10,000) 252 (9800) 261 (9800)	— — —	0·20 5·60 11·3	+ 0 −
H_2N– purine	235 sh (6500) 237 sh (4200) 236 sh (5000) 276 sh (4100)	325 (4200) 314 (4000) 305 (6020) 303 (5750)	−3·5 1·84 7·0 12·0	++ + 0 −
NH_2 (Adenine)	262 (13,200) 260 (13,500) 267 (12,000)	— — —	2·1 7 12	+ 0 −

TABLE 6.3—(contd.)

Compound	Band I	Band II	pH	Charge of species†
Me₂N-substituted purine (N N / N N H)	228 (33,000)	340 (3000)	1·7	+
	223 (26,000)	332 (5000)	6·98	0
	248 (10,500)			
	232 (25,000)	327 (4700)	12·7	−
NMe₂-substituted purine (N N / N N H)	—	276 (15,000)	1·7	+
	—	275 (17,800)	6·98	0
	221 (16,200)	281 (17,800)	13·0	−
OH-substituted purine (N N / HO N N H)	—	267 (7900)	5·05	0
	240 (8000)	277 (8300)	9·99	−
	—	283 (8700)	13·0	=
OH-substituted purine (N N / H₂N N N H)	248 (10,700)	271 (7100)	1·0	+
	246 (10,200)	275 (7700)	6·2	0
	245 (6000)	273 (7400)	10·71	−
	221 (13,000)	274 (8700)	13·0	=

† 0 Neutral molecule.
++ Dication.
+ Cation.
= Dianion.
− Anion.

idines to over 300 mμ with a decrease in intensity from the parent value, whilst 6-hydroxy and -amino groups confer a blue shift and intensity increase relative to purine itself.

The spectra of purines have two broad bands at 260 and below 220 mμ. The 260 mμ band is shifted to longer wavelengths, for a given substituent, in the order $2 > 8 > 6$-substituted purine (Table 6.3a). At the same time, the intensity order for a given substituent is $8 \geqslant 6 \geqslant 2$. Consideration of the available data has led to the view that the 260 mμ absorption is a composite band containing contributions from two transitions involving alternative polarizations within the purine molecule (see XXVII). These polarizations are, respectively, parallel and transverse to the major longitudinal axis. 8-Substituents exert an effect parallel to the main axis and therefore lower the energy of the stronger component of the 260 mμ band. 6-Substituents are transversely dis-

TABLE 6.3a. SUBSTITUTIONAL INCREMENTS FOR THE PURINE NUCLEUS[9]

Substituent	Species	Position in nucleus		
		2	6	8
		shift of 260 mμ band (mμ)		
—NH$_2$	+	54	2	28
	0	42	−3	20
	−	32	−4	19
—NHMe	+	—	7	36
	0	—	3	27
	−	—	2	27
—NMe$_2$	+	80	16	45
	0	69	12	33
	−	56	10	35
—OH	+	62	−12	20
	0	52	−14	14
	−	42	−13	14
—OMe	+	24	−6	—
	0	20	−10	—
	−	14	−10	—
—Me	+	—	5	4
	0	—	−2	3
	−	—	0	3

posed to this axis and affect the weaker component. Substituents at position-2 are disposed at an angle of 30° to the major axis and appear to affect both band components in shifting the entire band to the red. 2-Substituted purines exhibit the following order of magnitude in shifting the 260 mμ band: MeO < MeS ⩽ NH$_2$ < HO < NMe$_2$ < HS. The 6- and 8-derivatives show rather variable effects.

Tautomerism to pyrimidone forms is marked in the hydroxypurines. For

XXVIII   XXIX   XXX

example, the *dissimilarity* of the spectra of 2-hydroxy- and 2-methoxypurines (XXVIII; R=H and Me, respectively) and the *similarity* of the spectra of the amino purine (XXIX) and of its dimethyl derivative (XXX) form suggestive (but not conclusive) evidence that the hydroxy purines may exist in the lactam form; while the amino compounds again may be considered as true —NH$_2$ compounds.

The amino- and hydroxy-purines occur naturally as the bases of the nucleotides. Discussion of structural correlation and diagnosis employing the spectral data of these systems is referred to in Chapter 7 (p. 207).

6.4. PTERIDINES (TABLE 6.4)

Pteridine (XXXI) absorbs at 210, 240, 300 and 384 mμ. The last band (ε 80)

XXXI   XXXII   XXXIII

marks the $n \rightarrow \pi^*$ transition and the remaining absorption is naphthalenoid with intensification caused by aza-nitrogen. Thus the 300 mμ band (ε 7000) is to be compared with the corresponding naphthalene band at 310 mμ (ε 140). The calculated intensity (p. 187) for the 300 mμ band of pteridine is 10,000.

The monohydroxypteridines are conveniently divided into two distinct spectral types. The 4- and 7-hydroxypteridines show three bands in neutral

TABLE 6.4. PTERIDINES

Compound	Band I	Band II	Band III	Solvent	Reference
	—	300 (7080)	384 (80)	C	(5)
	230 (7600) 260 (7000)	307 (6800) —	— 375 (6000)	pH 7 pH 13	(10)
	240 (8200) 236 (7800)	311 (7100) 312 (6500)	— 375 (2300)	pH 7 pH 13	(10)
	230 (9400) 236 (6800)	309 (7800) 271 (4600) 313 (6400)	— 350 (3000)	pH 7 pH 13	(10)
	230 (9600) 242 (17,000) 257 (2700)	265 (3400) — —	310 (6200) 333 (6000) 303 (9000)	pH 5·6 pH 10 pH 2·5	(10)

solution and their curves are reminiscent of those of hydroxynaphthalenes. 4-Hydroxypteridine is mainly in the pteridone form (XXXII) although there is some evidence from infrared data that hydrogen bonding stabilizes the enol form (XXXIII) to a certain extent. This also is borne out by some similarities in the ultraviolet absorption of (XXXIII) and 4-methoxypteridine (XXXIV). The complexity of such data, however, indicates that we have reached the

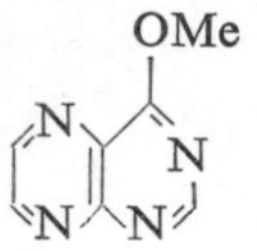

XXXIV 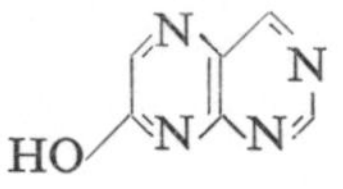   XXXV 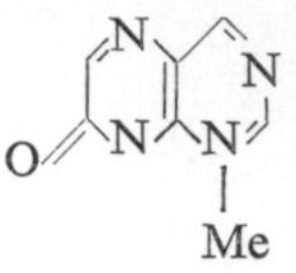   XXXVI

limit of usefulness of the comparison of the spectra of N–Me and O–Me derivatives for purposes of assessing equilibria. The spectrum of 7-hydroxypteridine (XXXV) is, however, so similar to that of the pteridone (XXXVI) that the keto form is almost certainly preferred. It must be mentioned that the infrared spectra of all hydroxypteridines show strong —C=O bands at 1670–90 cm^{-1} in the solid state.

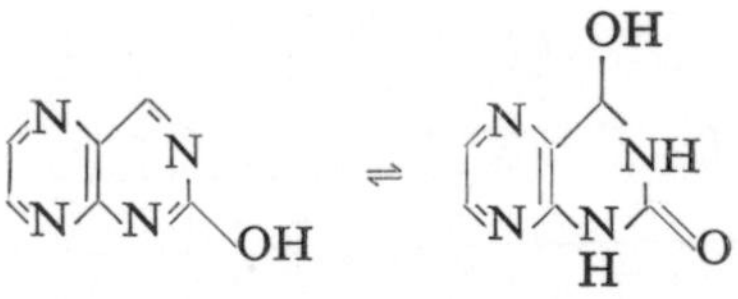

XXXVII   XXXVIII 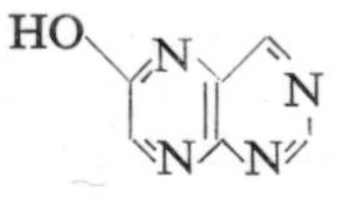   XXXIX

The 2-hydroxypteridines represent another category of pteridine spectra. Their absorption curves are complicated by reversible hydrate formation (XXXVII ⇌ XXXVIII). This is also true for 6-hydroxypteridine (XXXIX) which absorbs in the infrared at 1690 cm^{-1} and, like the 2-isomer, gives a *two* banded spectrum.

Riboflavin (XL) contains the quinomethine chromophore of the pteridine nucleus within a tricyclic framework. The long wavelength band of riboflavin responsible for its colour occurs[11] at 445 mμ (pH 1).

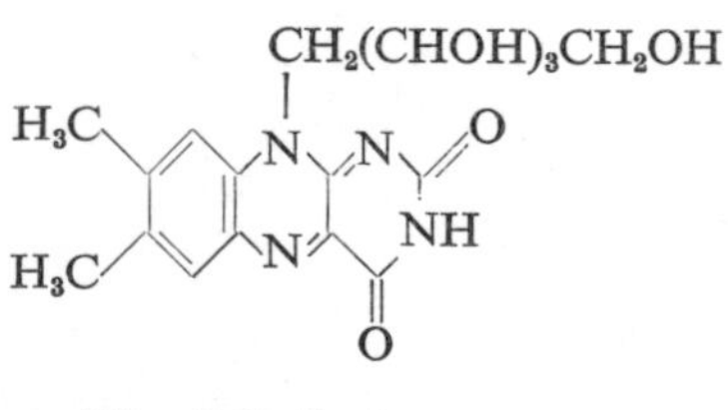

XL   Riboflavin

λ 445 mμ

REFERENCES

1. S. F. MASON, *J. Chem. Soc.*, 1247 (1959).
2. S. F. MASON, *ibid.*, 1253 (1959).
3. J. R. MARSHALL and J. WALKER, *ibid.*, 1004 (1951).
4. D. J. BROWN and L. N. SHORT, *ibid.*, 331 (1953).
5. S. F. MASON, *Chem. Soc. Special Publications*, **3**, 139 (1955).
6. G. DUNN, J. J. GALLAGHER, G. T. NEWBOLD and F. S. SPRING, *J. Chem. Soc.*, 5126 (1949).
7. G. R. CLEMO and H. McILWAIN, *ibid.*, 479 (1938).
8. L. BIRHOFER, *Ber. dtsch. chem. Ges.*, **85**, 1023 (1952).
9. S. F. MASON, *J. Chem. Soc.*, 2071 (1954).
10. D. J. BROWN and S. F. MASON, *ibid.*, 3443 (1956).
11. R. M. CRESSWELL, A. C. HILL and H. C. S. WOOD, *ibid.*, 698 (1959).

CHAPTER 7

SOME APPLICATIONS OF SPECTROPHOTOMETRY
TO THE ANALYSIS OF NATURAL PRODUCTS

THIS chapter deals briefly with miscellaneous applications of ultraviolet and visible spectrophotometry, with particular reference to the analytical estimation of natural products. Any compound characterized by sufficiently well-defined and intense absorption is of course potentially identifiable and estimable by spectrophotometric means. In other cases suitable chromophores may be produced by chemical transformations: thus a great many spectrophotometric methods of analysis have been developed from qualitative colour reactions. Similarly enzymes, coenzymes or substrates are frequently determinable via reactions involving the chromophoric group of an appropriate cofactor. In-homogeneous substances may be estimated, as for example proteins in terms of their content of tyrosine (I) and tryptophan (II), nucleic acids by the absorption due to their purine (III) and pyrimidine (IV) chromophores. The scope of analytical absorption spectrophotometry is chiefly limited by the degree of specificity achievable in the chromogenic reaction (where necessary) and in separating the required absorbing species from extraneous material. Where the difficulties of purification can be overcome, the spectrophotometric methods are generally unmatched for convenience and reliability, and are of adequate sensitivity for the majority of analyses since 1–$10\ \mu$g is a typical measurable

range. Quantities substantially below $1\ \mu$g may require more sensitive techniques (e.g. spectrofluorimetry, gas–liquid chromatography, mass spectrometry or radioactive tracer methods). Thus the firefly luciferins (V)[208] show characteristic and strong absorption but are accessible in such small yield that estimation on this basis is rarely practicable: fortunately the even more intense luminescence affords a sensitive means of determination[1].

Luciferin	Dehydroluciferin
V a	V b
λ_{max} 268 mμ (ε 5000)	λ_{max} 274 mμ (ε 5000)
327 mμ (ε 20,000)	348 mμ (ε 20,000)

The analytical power of spectrophotometry is extensively exploited in studies of reaction equilibria and kinetics. The method may serve to determine both the nature and the concentration of the species present. In solutions containing well-defined components which can be identified and estimated by their light-absorption properties, precise quantitative evaluation of the reaction parameters is frequently possible. In the case of multi-component systems, machine computation may be required[2]. Spectrophotometric data thus permit the determination of pK values[3], stability constants of metal ion complexes[4], etc. Where the light-absorption of the reactants is unsuitable for measurement, indirect procedures, for example the use of a spectrophotometric indicator[5], may be utilized.

In studies of natural products one particular virtue of spectrophotometry is its applicability to labile substances at low concentrations in inhomogeneous preparations. The derived information may be qualitative or even speculative but is an indispensable guide to work with more refined systems. Classical examples from biochemistry are the investigations on the cytochromes[6] and haemocyanins[7]. The availability of purified enzymes[8,9] has prompted many recent studies, largely spectrophotometric, of enzyme–coenzyme interactions[10] and their interpretation with reference to model systems[11].

Determination of the structure of complex natural products is outside the scope of this chapter, but the value of absorption spectra in this respect may be emphasized.

The principal methods used in the spectrophotometric analysis of organic natural products are broadly classifiable as follows.

(1) Those based on existing chromophoric groups.

(2) Transformation by chemical or enzymic methods to yield well-defined products more suited for spectrophotometry.

(3) The formation of derivatives possessing strongly absorbing chromophores.

(4) Colour reactions.

(5) Reactions (chemical or enzymic) in which the formation or destruction of a spectrophotometrically estimable species is observed. These are preferably stoichiometric but not necessarily so.

These methods are illustrated below with reference to a variety of applications, while in the Appendix an attempt has been made to indicate the scope of spectrophotometry as an analytical method in steroid biochemistry. References have been selected arbitrarily from the voluminous literature with the aim of directing attention to the more recent articles and reviews, rather than citing the original investigations. Useful collections of electronic absorption data[12], and of references thereto[13], are available, as are invaluable source books of biochemical data[14,15]. Much information on spectrophotometric procedures is to be found in books devoted to various aspects of natural product analysis[16]. The annual publication, *Methods of Biochemical Analysis*[17] includes well-documented articles dealing with particular spectrophotometric analyses. Many other works on spectroscopy are listed by Gillam and Stern[18]. The classical handbook by Snell and Snell[21], now in its third edition, deserves particular mention: vols. III and IV deal with organic analysis.

7.1. ANALYSIS BASED ON EXISTING CHROMOPHORIC GROUPS

A characteristic absorption band is always a possible basis for estimation, but indirect methods may be preferred on several grounds. Thus conversion of an ultraviolet–absorbing compound into a coloured derivative simplifies the technique of spectrophotometry and generally reduces interference by extraneous absorption. Moreover it may be attended by an increase in absorptivity and thereby in sensitivity. Materials isolated from natural sources often include groups of related compounds showing similar absorption (e.g. porphyrins, carotenoids, adrenocortical hormones) which are estimable only as groups by direct spectrophotometry. A further limitation is that the absorption of a complex substance may be similar to that of its hydrolysis products, as is the case for nucleic acids and their constituent bases.

Among the biologically important compounds determinable by their typical absorption are unsaturated acids[204] (e.g. sorbic acid[95]), uric acid[19], serotonin[20], tryptophan and its metabolites[22], chlorophylls[23], many alkaloids[24], Vitamins A[25], D_2[26] C[27] and B_{12}[28], thiamine[29], β-carotene[30] and the ubiquinones[31]. These are merely illustrative examples – for several of the compounds cited[20,28,29], other methods of estimation may be preferred.

The estimation of haemoglobin[32] may be mentioned in this section, although it may involve transformation of the material, for example to cyanmethaemoglobin by a ferricyanide-cyanide reagent. Oxyhaemoglobin is determined in an aerated ammoniacal solution[33]. The simultaneous estimation of carboxy-, oxy- and met-haemoglobin has been described[34]. The spectrophotometric methods are standardized with respect to the iron content of the haemo-globin.

The ultraviolet absorption of proteins[35, 36] has been extensively studied, both in histological preparations[37] and in solutions. Nearly all proteins show a principal band near 280 mμ, a minimum near 250 mμ, and a steeply rising end absorption below this wavelength. A few show absorption near 250 mμ, of uncertain origin. The absorption in the 220 mμ region is ascribed to the peptide linkage (e.g. glycine has $\varepsilon = 20$ at 210 mμ, glycyl-L-leucine has $\varepsilon = 3000$)[38]. The absorption near 280 mμ arises principally from tyrosine and tryptophan[39] and may be employed for their quantitative determination[40, 41]: the bathochromic shift of the tyrosine band in alkali permits individual estimation of these two amino acids. Other aromatic constituents, such as phenylalanine, may sometimes contribute to the absorption near 280 mμ. Nucleo proteins[42] show additional bands near 260 mμ due to their purine and pyrimidine components (adenosine, λ_{max} 260, $\varepsilon = 14,000$)[38]. Useful tables of spectrophotometric data for nucleic acids, nucleosides and their constituent bases have been compiled[43, 118] and the quantitative determination of these compounds has been reviewed[42, 44]. The ultra-violet absorption of poly-L-glutamic acid has been recorded[45]. The determination of proteins by spectrophotometry in the 210—220 mμ region is preferred by some authors[200] and is of particular value where the content of aromatic amino acids is low, as for example in cottonseed allergens[201].

7.2. ANALYSES INVOLVING TRANSFORMATION TO PRODUCTS SUITABLE FOR SPECTROPHOTOMETRY

Several types of reaction are illustrated in Table 7.1. *Isomerization* of un-saturated fatty acids with spectrophotometry of the conjugated chromophores produced is of importance, though likely to be superseded by chromatographic methods. The characterization of epoxides by isomerization to carbonyl com-pounds and isolation of 2,4-dinitrophenylhydrazones[64] would appear adapt-able to the micro-scale and to spectrophotometric measurement. *Oxidation,* especially with specific reagents, is perhaps most useful when it affords a vol-atile, easily separable product: thus a very wide range of analyses can be effected in terms of liberated formaldehyde. In the determination of corticosteroids by Norymberski's methods[50], on the other hand, volatile products are discarded and the estimation is carried out on the steroid moiety in the oxidation mixture. *Hydrolysis* as applied to proteins and nucleic acids does not greatly alter their absorption characteristics but serves to solubilize them, frequently by selective methods which differentiate between the various constituents. The determination of nucleic acids is often based on the sugars liberated by hydrolysis[52]. *Enzymic oxidation* is of obvious value where a highly specific enzyme such as uricase is applicable. When specificity is in doubt the method merits cautious use: thus xanthine oxidase is stated to affect more than fifty substrates[58]. Among the

TABLE 7.1

Transformation and substance analysed	Reagent	Product	Spectrophotometric method	Reference
Isomerization				
Poly-unsaturated acids	OH⁻	Conjugated acids	U.V. 235–75 mμ	(46)
Hydrolysis				
Nucleic acids	Cl₃C·CO₂H	RNA + DNA soln.	U.V. 260–70 mμ	(52, 53)
	(2) N-HClO₄/18hr./4°	RNA soln.	U.V. of constituent bases or estim. of sugars	(52)
	(2) 0·5 N-HClO₄ 20 min/70°	DNA soln.		
Hydrolytic cleavage				
Glycollic acid	H₂SO₄	CH₂O	Chromotropic acid	(109, 111)
Lactic acid	H₂SO₄	MeCHO	*p*-Hydroxydiphenyl	(111)
Oxidation				
CH₂=C<	HIO₄-KMnO₄	CH₂O	Chromotropic acid	(47)
α-Glycols, α-ketols	HIO₄, Pb(OAc)₄ or NaBiO₃	CH₂O, MeCHO	(See above)	(48, 111)
Hydroxylysine	HIO₄	CH₂O	(See above)	(110)
Glycine; alanine	Ninhydrin	CH₂O; MeCHO	(See above)	(111, 130)
Serine; threonine	HIO₄	CH₂O; MeCHO	(See above)	(49, 111)
Ethanolamine	HIO₄	CH₂O	(See above)	(116)
Corticosteroids	HIO₄ or NaBiO₃	CH₂O, MeCHO	(See above)	(50)
n-C₃H₇CO₂H	Fe, H₂O₂	MeCO·CH₂CO₂H	Nitroprusside	(100)
2-Deoxypentoses	IO₄⁻	Malonaldehyde	2-Thiobarbituric acid, 532 mμ	(112, 113)
Metadrenaline Normetadrenaline	HIO₄	Vanillin	U.V.350 and 360 mμ	(54)
Adrenaline†	I₂	Adrenochrome	Absorption, 529 mμ	(51)
Noradrenaline†	I₂	Noradrenochrome	Absorption, 529 mμ	(51)
17-Hydroxycorticosteroids	NaBiO₃	17-Oxosteroids	Zimmermann	(50)
Hydroxyproline	Cloramine T	Pyrrole	p-Dimethylaminobenz-aldehyde, 560 mμ	(211)

TABLE 7.1—(contd.)

Transformation and substance analysed	Reagent	Product	Spectrophotometric method	Reference
Oxidation—(contd.)				
Creatinine	o-Nitrobenzaldehyde, OH⁻	Me-guanidine	Sakaguchi	(56)
Enzymic oxidation				
Poly-unsaturated acids	O_2/Lipoxidase*	Conjugated diene hydroperoxides	U.V. (e.g. linoleic product 234 mμ)	(61)
Uric acid	Uricase	Allantoin	Fall in absorption 292 mμ	(57, 58)
Hypoxanthine, xanthine	Xanthine oxidase	Uric acid	Changes in absorption 248, 290 mμ	(58)
Adenine	Xanthine oxidase	2,8-Dihydroxyadenine	Absorption of product 305 mμ	(59)
Xanthopterin (VI)	Xanthine oxidase	Leucopterin (VII)	Absn. at isosbestic pt. 371 mμ	(60)
Homogentisic acid (VIII)	Homogentisic acid oxidase	Maleylacetoacetic acid (IX)	Absorption, 330 mμ (ϵ, 13,500)	(197)
Miscellaneous				
α-Amino acids	Ninhydrin	"DYDA"** (X)	"DYDA", 570 mμ (ϵ, 21,600)	(79, 114)
Ergothioneine	KOH	Me₃N	Me₃N picrate, 410 mμ	(63)
Furfural	Aniline, acetic acid	A mesomeric phenylimonium ion	Absorption, 518 mμ	(94)
Acetoacetic acid	p-Nitrobenzene-dia-zonium salt	N, Nʹbis(p-nitrophenyl)-C-acetyl-formazan (XI)	Absorption, 450 mμ (ϵ, 28,500)	(93)
				(93)
Oxaloacetic acid	N_2H_4; HNO_2; KOH	Ion of a C-nitroso pyrazolone-carboxylic acid	Absorption, 430 mμ	(77)

† Reactions not suitable for micro-estimation (> 50 μg required).
* The same reaction serves for assay of the enzyme[62].
** DYDA ~ Dioxohydrindylidenedioxohydrindamine.

miscellaneous reactions listed, attention is drawn to the highly specific methods of estimating acetoacetic acid and furfural.

VI R=H Xanthopterin VIII Homogentisic IX Maleyl-
VII R=OH Leucopterin   acid   acetoacetic acid

X   XI

7.3. FORMATION OF DERIVATIVES POSSESSING STRONGLY ABSORBING CHROMOPHORES

Under this heading are considered simple functional derivatives and also products of other reactions in which the reagent is mainly responsible for the absorption. Where a strongly absorbing chromophore is combined with a comparatively transparent residue the molar extinction coefficient is often sensibly independent of the nature of this residue. Spectrophotometric estimation of molecular weight[65], requiring only a few micrograms of material (subject to accuracy of weighing) is then possible provided that the number of chromophoric groups in the molecule is known. The latter information may sometimes be provided by infrared absorption data. Derivatives suitable for molecular weight determinations (within 1–2%) include naphthylurethanes[66], anilides[66], -dnitrobenzylthiuronium salts[66], 2,4-dinitrophenylhydrazones[66], osazones[67], picrates[68] and styphnates[69]. The method was applied by Spring and co-workers[68] to determine the molecular weight of the metabolic product cordycepin as its picrate. More recently, the molecular weight of the isoprenoid alcohol, dolichol, was estimated from the absorption of its p-phenylazobenzoate and p-nitrobenzoate esters[209].

Water-soluble hydroxylic compounds, including simple alcohols, are seldom estimated as derivatives, because of the difficulty of preparing these from aqueous solutions. (3,5-Dinitrobenzoates (λ_{max} 220 mμ) have been used[99], and are of particular value in the steroid series since the derivatives are well adapted to chromatographic separation). It is usual to oxidize alcohols, and sometimes also acids (e.g. butyric acid)[100] to carbonyl compounds which are more readily isolated as derivatives suitable for spectrophotometry.

In Table 7.2 are listed representative absorption data for some derivatives of a few important carbonyl compounds. Reference should be made to the cited publications for details of solvents, etc. The reagents cited are not specific for the particular compounds given, and are most useful in conjunction with chromatographic or other separation methods. In some cases empirical colour reactions may be preferred (see following section). The sensitivity of analyses based on readily isolated derivatives is limited by their extinction coefficients: for $\varepsilon = 10,000$, an optical density of 0·1 is attainable in a conventional 1 cm cell with a 10 μM solution, i.e. for a final volume of 3 ml approx. 0·03 μmoles of sample are required.

Extensive use is made of 2,4-dinitrophenylhydrazones in microgram-scale analyses, because of the generally quantitative formation and isolation of these derivatives, their separability by paper chromatography[101] and their intense absorption at a wavelength conveniently distant from most extraneous absorption. Attention must be given to the separation of unchanged reagent since its absorption (λ_{max}, 352, $\varepsilon = 14,900$)[92] otherwise interferes. The derivatives may be further transformed by quantitative hydrogenation to amino acids[102] (which are more easily separated by paper chromatography than the corresponding keto acids or their dinitrophenylhydrazones). The ultraviolet-spectrophotometric estimation of dinitrophenylhydrazones has frequently been replaced by colorimetric measurements on alkaline solutions of the derivatives, which show absorption near 500 mμ[104]. Several analyses of α-ketoacids in blood, for example, use this procedure, but where an ultraviolet spectrophotometer is available it is better to dissolve the hydrazone in a neutral solvent: the absorption is then stable, well-defined and characteristic of the hydrazone — which can moreover be recovered. However, one method[106] for simultaneous oxidation of α-oxoglutaric and pyruvic acids depends on measurements on the mixed hydrazones first at 380 mμ and then in alkaline solution at 435 and 520 mμ. Useful reviews of α-ketoacid analyses are given by Neish[107] and by Aspen and Meister[108].

3-Quinolylhydrazine[76] appears to be a promising reagent for estimation of α-ketoacids, on the microgram scale. Simple aldehydes and ketones, as well as β-ketoacids, give unstable products and only transient absorption near 305 mμ. Use of the reagent permitted measurement of the activity of three enzymes (malic, lactic and glutamic dehydrogenase) in 0·5 μg of brain tissue[76]. Of the other reactions illustrated in Table 7.2, the formation of quinoxalines is general for α-dicarbonyl compounds RCO·COR' (where R, R' may be H, Alkyl, OH, OAlkyl) and the formation of benzylidene derivatives is general for α-methylenic ketones. The reaction of formaldehyde with 3-methyl-2-benzothiazolone hydrazone appears to be the most sensitive chemical method yet devised[71] for estimating this aldehyde: however, the well-known colour reaction with chromotropic acid (see following section) is probably still to be preferred for

TABLE 7.2. ANALYTICALLY USEFUL DERIVATIVES OF SIMPLE CARBONYL COMPOUNDS

Compound	Reagent	Derivative	λ_{max}	ε_{max}	References Absorption	References Analyt. use
Formaldehyde	2,4-DNPH†	DNP*	349	18,200	(92)	
	2-Hydrazinobenzothiazole, p-Nitrobenzene-diazonium fluoborate	A mesomeric anion	610	24,000	(70)	(71)
	3-Me-2-benzothiazolone hydrazone	A mesomeric cation	670	65,000	(71)	
Acetaldehyde	Acetylacetone, NH_3	Diacetyldihydrolutidine	412	8000	(72)	(72)
Acetone	2,4-DNPH	DNP	356	21,000	(92)	(98)
Glyoxal	2,4-DNPH	bis-DNP	360	21,100	(92)	(207)
	2,3-Diaminophenazine	A quinoxaline	600		(73)	(73)
Pyruvaldehyde	2,4-DNPH	bis-DNP	{393, 436}		(74)	(97)
Diacetyl	2,4-DNPH, 2NH_2OH; Ni	bis-DNP, Ni dimethylglyoxime				(96)
Glyceraldehyde	Phenylhydrazine	Glycerosazone	{395, 309, 256}	{20,600, 9800, 18,900}	(78)	
Pyruvic acid	2,4-DNPH, Salicylaldehyde/OH^-	DNP, o-Hydroxybenzylidenepyruvic acid	355, 470	22,500		(103), (75)
Oxaloacetic acid	3-Quinolylhydrazine		305	20,500	(76)	

† 2,4-Dinitrophenylhydrazine.
* 2,4-Dinitrophenylhydrazone.

routine purposes. Glycerosazone has been included to indicate the characteristic absorption of sugar osazones: these derivatives are not easily formed quantitatively, but are nevertheless of value in characterizing sugars.

Some derivatives used in the quantitative analysis of amino acids and a few other important compounds are indicated in Table 7.3. As with the carbonyl compounds, separation of the amino acids or their derivatives normally precedes spectrophotometric estimation. The N-2,4-dinitrophenylamino acids are of considerable value both for paper-chromatographic separation and for estimation[80]. The absorption quoted for glycine is typical of most of the common α-amino acids in water or 1% aqueous $NaHCO_3$: in glacial acetic acid[117] λ_{max} is *ca.* 340 mμ. The proline derivative is exceptional in showing λ_{max} about 20 mμ above that for the amino acid derivatives. Glycine is unique in that the absorption of its derivative is changed to 330 mμ in N NaOH ($\varepsilon = 7900$). The

TABLE 7.3. MISCELLANEOUS DERIVATIVES OF ANALYTICAL VALUE

Compound or group	Reagent	Derivative	λ_{max} †	ε_{max}	References
Glycine	2,4-Dinitro-fluorobenzene	N-2,4-dinitro-phenylglycine	361	17,000	(80)
Serine Ethanolamine	1,2-Naphthoquin-one-4-sulphonic acid	A quinone-imine	(480)		(81)
Proline	2,4-Dinitro-fluorobenzene	N-2,4-dinitro-phenylproline	385	19,000	(80)
Histamine	2,4-Dinitro-fluorobenzene	N_α-2,4-dinitro-phenylhistamine	355–60		(82)
Hippuric acid	p-Dimethylamino-benzaldehyde	An azlactone	460	51,000	(83)
Tyrosine	1-Nitroso-2-naph-thol	Condensation	450	~ 3000	(55)
Cysteine	Fluoropyruvic acid	$RSCH_2COCO_2H$ (?)	300	5200	(84)
Glutathione	Fluoropyruvic acid + borate	$RSCH_2COCO_2H$ (?)	(285)		(86)
	Glyoxal + gly-oxalase-I	S-Lactoyl-glutathione	235		(91)
Coenzyme A	Sorbic acid + enzyme	Sorbyl-CoA	300	19,300	(87)
SH groups	p-Chloromercuri-benzoate	Mercaptide	250		(85)
Tocopherols (not α-)	HNO_2	Nitroso-toco-pherols	(410)		(88)
Penicillin	Fe^{3+}, hydroxyl-amine	Fe^{3+}-hydroxam-ate complex	(480)		(89)
Esters Amides	Fe^{3+}, hydroxyl-amine	Fe^{3+}-hydroxam-ate complex	(500–70)		(105) (90)

† Figures in parentheses are not λ_{max} but λ of readings.

mono-dinitrophenyl derivative of histamine may be separated from con-taminants by virtue of the residual basic group[82]. Ethanolamine and serine in phosphatide hydrolysates may be separately determined as their dinitrophenyl derivatives[115,116].

The highly specific estimation of glutathione[87] through its conversion to S-lactoylglutathione, catalysed by glyoxalase-I, is a further example of the potential analytical value of enzymic methods.

7.4. COLOUR REACTIONS

Many successful analytical procedures are based on colour tests in which the reactions occurring are imperfectly understood. The conditions necessary to achieve specificity, reproducibility and sensitivity in the desired analysis tend to emerge gradually from a labyrinth of empirical studies, as for example in the estimation of sugars[123,132] and of cholesterol[50].

Some representative colorimetric methods used or proposed for quantitative determinations are indicated in Table 7.4. It will be appreciated that there is no sharp distinction between some of these reactions and those already discussed. Thus the *p*-bromoaniline method of estimating pentoses may be presumed[132] analogous to the reaction of aniline with furfural (Table 7.1), whilst the thio-barbituric acid reactions doubtless involve condensation of the aldehydes at the 5-position in this compound[212].

Determination of Formaldehyde

Considerable attention has been given to the micro-estimation of this com-pound as a vehicle for analysing a variety of compounds, notably glycols, carbo-hydrates, glycine and corticosteroids. The chromotropic acid reaction is very suitable for most applications, since it is virtually specific and easily performed with readily available reagents, while the final product shows intense absorption which remains stable for many hours. Methanol, acetaldehyde and formic acid when present in the ratio of 10 : 1, do not interfere[130]. (Acetaldehyde may be quantitatively removed[150,111] by aeration in a suitable apparatus and ab-sorption in aqueous bisulphite: formaldehyde remains involatile.) Acetone and benzene inhibit the colour development[151] but may be removed, together with other volatile matter, by mixing the aqueous formaldehyde and chromo-tropic acid solutions and evaporating to dryness: the residue is then treated with sulphuric acid to develop the characteristic chromophore[131]. With per-iodate-oxidized samples it is essential to reduce periodate and iodate, e.g. with bisulphite (if the colour reaction is to be performed directly on the reaction mixture)[49] or with $SnCl_2$ (if the formaldehyde is to be separated by distillation or microdiffusion)[153]. A further practical point is the use of semicarbazide in periodate oxidation to trap formaldehyde, so averting its loss by side reactions

TABLE 7.4. COLOUR REACTIONS

Compound or group	Reagent	λ^*	Remarks	Reference
Formaldehyde	Chromotropic acid H_2SO_4	570	Diacetyl also reacts	(130,111,50)
	Rosaniline	590	MeCHO does not interfere	(101,139)
Acetaldehyde	Piperazine, nitroprusside	560	MeCHO in presence of $HCHO^{140}$	(101,139)
Malonaldehyde (from deoxyribose/IO_4^-)	$CuSO_4$, H_2SO_4; p-Hydroxydiphenyl, OH⁻	560	$\varepsilon \sim 133,000$, cf. Table 7.1	(101,137)
	2-Thiobarbituric acid	532		(112,113)
Diacetyl	Chromotropic acid-H_2SO_4	570		(129,101)
β-Formylpyruvic acid (from sialic acids/IO_4^-)	2-Thiobarbituric acid	549	$\varepsilon \sim 57,000$	(113)
Carbohydrates	Indole-H_2SO_4	470	General reactions giving similar absorption from different classes of sugar. Optical density α conc. of sugar under suitable conditions	(123)
	α-Naphthol-H_2SO_4	550–70		(123)
	Tryptophan-H_2SO_4	480–500	Used for methylated sugars[124]	(123)
	Phenol-H_2SO_4	490	Different absorption produced (at varying rates) by several classes of sugars. Adaptable for differential estimations—see below	(132,134)
	Cysteine-H_2SO_4	—		
Hexoses	Cysteine-H_2SO_4	414, 380	Protein-bound hexose in glyco-proteins	(123)
	Orcinol-H_2SO_4	540	Hexose in glycolipids	(141)
		505	Glucose and fructose in mixtures[129]	(148)
Hexoses in presence of pentoses	Anthrone-H_2SO_4	620–5		(132,136,148)
	Chromotropic acid H_2SO_4	570	CH_2O formed via CH_2OH-furfural from hexoses only. Not quantitative	(132,135)
Ketohexoses	Diphenylamine-AcOH-HCl	635 520–5	Aldohexoses give colours only 2% as intense	(123)
	Resorcinol	515	General reaction of keto sugars	(123)
Aldohexoses	Cysteine-carbazole-H_2SO_4	560		(123)
	Carbazole-H_2SO_4	535	Deoxyribose, hexuronic acids give similar absorption	(123)

TABLE 7.4—(contd.)

Compound or group	Reagent	λ^*	Remarks	Reference
Methyl pentoses	Cysteine-H_2SO_4	{ 400, 430	Detn. in glycoproteins[141]	(123)
Pentoses (e.g. from RNA)	13% HCl; p-Br-$C_6H_4NH_2$	520	cf. Table 7.1 (furfural-aniline) (100 mg glucose, 100 μg xylose)	(132, 133)
Deoxypentoses (e.g. from DNA)	Orcinol-HCl	670–5		(123)
	p-$NO_2C_6H_4NHNH_2$; OH^-	560	via furfuryl alcohol?	(52, 142)
	Ph_2NH-AcOH-H_2SO_4	595–600	Applied directly to DNA	(52, 143)
	Indole-HCl	490	Applied directly to DNA	(52, 144)
Hexuronic acids	Carbazole-H_2SO_4	530–5		(132, 123)
Glucuronic acid	Naphthoresorcinol		Satisfactory for urine but not for acid muco-poly-saccharides[123]	(147)
Hexosamines	Acetylacetone; OH^-; p-$Me_2N\cdot C_6H_4CHO$	530		(125, 127)
	HNO_2; indole-HCl	492		(123)
	H_2SO_4	248, 325		(126)
Sialic acids	p-$Me_2N\cdot C_6H_4\cdot CHO$	565	"Direct" Ehrlich reaction	(127)
	Tryptophan, $HClO_4$	500		(122, 141)
Creatinine	Picric acid, OH^-	525		(56)
Indoles	Fe, glyoxylic acid, H_2SO_4		Characteristic absorption for various indoles	(149)
5-Hydroxyindoles	p-$MeC_6H_4SO_3H$			(119)
	1-Nitroso-2-naphthol, dilute HCl, trace HNO_2	540	More sensitive fluorimetric method available	(20)
Thiamine	p-Acetylbenzene diazonium ion			(120)
Glutathione	Alloxan	305	Suitable for estimation of GSH in 0·05 ml blood	(121)
Vitamin A	$SbCl_3$	550		(25)
Vitamins D	Furfural-H_2SO_4	490, 565		(145)
	Iodine-$(CH_2Cl)_2$	450		(146)

$\lambda^* \sim$ Wavelength of readings, usually also λ_{max}.

without prejudice to the colorimetric estimation[152]. The sensitivity of the chromotropic acid reaction ($\varepsilon \sim 13{,}000$ based on formaldehyde) permits the determination of 1–10 μg, of formaldehyde in conventional apparatus, and 0·1–1 μg by suitable micro-modification. Where greater sensitivity is needed the interesting reagents recently introduced by Sawicki *et al.* (see Table 7.2) may find application. Formaldehyde in gas mixtures may be determined by absorption in chromotropic acid–sulphuric acid[202].

Determination of Acetaldehyde

The *p*-hydroxydiphenyl reagent has been used in several biological analyses: a correction for absorption due to formaldehyde may be applied[154] by estimating the latter on a separate aliquot by the chromotropic acid method. The determination of 17,20-dihydroxysteroids in terms of acetaldehyde is mentioned in the Appendix.

Determination of Carbohydrates

Although some methods of estimating carbohydrates are based on well-defined reactions (periodate oxidation, etc.), for most purposes their quantitative determination depends on empirical reactions, largely adapted from classical colour tests. One group of methods measures the reducing properties of the sugars by titrimetric procedures or, with suitable reagents, by spectrophotometry (see following section). In the second large group of methods the sugars are treated with strong acids, and the degradation products are then subjected to further reactions in order to develop characteristic coloured products. (Some investigators[155] have examined the ultraviolet absorption after the first stage.) Since the latter type of method is applicable both to free sugars and to their combined forms (polysaccharides, nucleic acids, glycoproteins) irrespective of reducing or non-reducing properties, it has been very extensively used. By suitable adjustment of the conditions of the various reactions, differences in absorption produced by various carbohydrate structures can be either enhanced or reduced. The procedures favoured for particular sugars are indicated in Table 4: it is emphasized that the reactions have limited specificity, and that their application in biological assays requires many precautions. Useful reviews are available[123, 132]. The shortcomings of such methods are well exposed by the comparative data presented by Warren[113] for the determination of sialic acids by various procedures. The rational assay[113] by periodic acid oxidation, while affording only 72% of the intensity expected from the results for the model compound, 2-oxo-3-deoxygluconic acid, still represents a tenfold increase in sensitivity as compared with four other methods examined. Moreover the validity of the determination is supported by the similar properties (including identical λ_{max}) of the products formed from N-acetyl-neuraminic acid and 2-oxo-3-deoxygluconic acid.

It should be remarked that most of the colour reactions given for sugars yield excellent results when applied to pure compounds isolated, for example, by paper chromatography[132] or ion-exchange chromatography[156].

7.5. REACTIONS LEADING TO SPECIFIC CHANGES IN ABSORPTION OF ADDED REAGENTS

The methods considered under this heading are of greatest importance in enzyme-catalysed reactions. Before discussing these, some purely chemical processes are briefly mentioned.

The Gibbs reaction, in which 2,6-dichlorobenzoquinone chlorimide (XII) reacts with a phenol lacking a substituent in the *para*-position, has been placed on a reliable footing by spectrophotometric analysis of the absorption of the indophenol (XIII) in the region 500–700 mμ[203]. The appearance of a colour in this test was found to be misleading and not always accompanied by specific absorption in the visible region. This application has been used in deciding between possible isomeric structures for jacareubin, a heartwood constituent.

Estimation of Reducing Substances

Many methods of determining natural products which have reducing properties (sugars corticcsteroids, catechols, catecholamines, ascorbic acid, thiols) employ reagents showing strong absorption either in the oxidised or the reduced form. In general the reactions are not stoichiometric and require careful standardisation when used quantitatively. A few of the more common reagents and their applications are given in Table 7.5.

Miscellaneous Chemical Estimations

(i) Periodate oxidations may be studied by the fall in absorption due to IO_4^- (λ_{max} 222·5 mμ)[157], since the absorption due to IO_3^- is relatively small. The method has been applied to the determination of ribonucleosides[158], but the risk of photochemical disturbances is a limitation[48]. (ii) A method for detecting 1 μmole of hydrogen peroxide depends upon its reaction with a vanadium benzohydroxamic acid chelate complex ($\lambda = 450$ mμ)[159]. (iii) Thiols may be estimated by an ingenious sequence of reactions[160]. S-nitrosation, removal of excess nitrous acid with sulphamic acid, and addition of an acid solution of sulphanilamide and mercuric chloride yields diazotized sulphanilamide in

TABLE 7.5. DETERMINATION OF REDUCING SUBSTANCES

Reagent	Product	λ of readings	Applications	References
2,6-Dichlorophenol-indophenol	3,5-dichloro-4,4′-di-hydroxydiphenyl-amine	525	Ascorbic acid	(168)
$(+p\text{-HgCl}\cdot\text{C}_6\text{H}_4\cdot \text{CO}_2\text{H})$			Ascorbic acid in presence of thiols	(162)
3,4-Dinitrobenzoic acid	3-Nitro-4-hydroxy-aminobenzoic acid	548	Sugars from poly-saccharides	(161)
		415	Ascorbic acid	(163)
3,5-Dinitrosalicyclic acid	3-Amino-5-nitrosali-cylic acid	500, 530	Reducing sugars	(164)
Arsenomolybdic acid	A blue product	690	Adrenaline, nor-adrenaline	(165), (51)
Triphenyltetrazolium chloride, OH⁻	Triphenylformazan (ref. 167)	485 (iso PrOH)	Reducing sugars	(166),(132)
'Blue tetrazolium'	A formazan	525	Corticosteroids	(210)

amount proportional to that of the original thiol. Coupling with a naphthylamine gives an azo-dye of intense absorption suitable for spectrophotometry. (iv) Organic peroxides may be determined by the formation of methylene blue (λ_{max}, 643 mμ) from its leuco-base[206].

Enzymic Spectrophotometric Analyses[198]

A constituent of a well-defined enzymic system may be estimated by reaction with other components leading to a change in absorption. Methods of this type were developed by Warburg[193] and are very extensively used for the assay of enzymes, coenzymes and suitable substrates. In one type of procedure the rate of an enzymic reaction is measured with a rate-limiting concentration of the component to be assayed: this kind of method requires careful control and frequent calibration owing to the sensitivity of enzyme activity to the presence of adventitious substances. The preferred methods aim at stoichiometric conversion of the material to be analysed to a known product, with measurement of a net change in absorption after completed reaction.

Some representative analysis of enzymes, coenzymes and substrates are summarized in Table 7.5a. The first group illustrates reactions which are linked to reduction or oxidation of pyridine nucleotides and measured by the ensuing change in absorption: DPNH and TPNH (XV) have λ_{max} 340 ($\varepsilon = 6220$) while their oxidized forms (XIV) show only low absorption in this region. Where pure enzymes (notably oxidases or dehydrogenases) of good specificity are available these methods have great analytical power. Thus D- and L-xylulose have been determined individually[194], and a sensitive method has been devised to estim-

TABLE 7.5 a. ENZYMIC SPECTROPHOTOMETRIC ANALYSES

Substance assayed	Notes on method	Reference
	1. Based on measurement of oxidation or reduction of DPN or TPN	
L-Lactic acid	$+$ DPN$^+$ (Lactic dehydrogenase), pH 9·7 → pyruvate $+$ DPNH	(205)
L-Aspartic acid in protein hydrolysates	Transamination → oxaloacetate (Malic dehydrogenase) $+$ DPNH → malate $+$ DPN$^+$. Fall in DPNH absorption followed at 366 mμ	(169)
ADP	$+$ Phosphopyruvate (kinase) → pyruvate $+$ ATP; pyruvate $+$ DPNH (lactic dehydrogenase) → lacate $+$ DPN$^+$	(170, 171)
ATP	$+$ Glucose (hexokinase) → glucose–6–phosphate; TPN$^+$ (glucose–6–phosphate dehydrogenase) → TPNH	(172)
Coenzyme A	α–Oxoglutarate (oxidase) $+$ DPN$^+$ → succinyl–CoA $+$ DPNH $+$ H$^+$; succinyl–CoA $+$ H$_2$O (deacylase) → succinate $+$ CoA	(173, 174)
Isocitric dehydrogenase	D-Isocitrate $+$ TPN$^+$ $\xrightarrow[\text{enzyme}]{\text{Mn}^{2+}}$ α-oxoglutarate $+$ TPNH $+$ H$^+$ $+$ CO$_2$	(175)
	2. Based on changes in absorption of various reactants	(mμ)
Formic acid	$+$ Tetrahydrofolic acid, ATP (tetrahydrofolic formylase) → 10-formyltetrahydrofolic acid (XVI) $\xrightarrow{\text{H}^+}$ 5,10-methenyl-tetrahydrofolic acid (XVII)	350 · · · · (199)
Coenzyme A	$+$ Acetate, ATP, p-nitroaniline (enzyme from pigeon liver) → p-nitroacetanilide	420 (fall) · · (176)
Adenylic acid	(deaminase) → inosinic acid	265 · · · · (177)
Inosinic acid	(5-nucleotidase) → inosine phosphate (nucleotide phosphorylase) → hypoxanthine (xanthine oxidase) → uric acid	290 · · · · (171)
Monoamine oxidase	$+$ Kynuramine → (aldehyde) → 4-hydroxyquinoline	360 · · · · (178)
	Benzylamine → benzaldehyde	250 · · · · (179)
Catalase	Decrease in absorption due to H$_2$O$_2$ or ROOH	240 · · · · (180)
Glyoxalase-I	Formation of lactoyl-GSH	235 · · · · (91)
Cytochrome-c oxidase	Rate of oxidation of reduced cytochrome-c	550 · · (181, 187)
Choline esterase	Rate of breakdown of thiocholine chloride esters by fall in thioester band	229 (fall) · · (182)
Succinic dehydrogenase	Succinate $+$ 2 ferricyanide → fumarate $+$ 2 ferrocyanide $+$ 2H$^+$	400 · · · · (183)
Lipoxidase	Formation of conjugated diene hydroperoxides pH 9	234 · · · (62, 184)
Ribonucleases	Change in absorption at 300 mμ on splitting polynucleotides to low-mol.wt. nucleic acids	300 · · · · (185)

TABLE 7.5 a—(contd.)

Substance assayed	Notes on method	(mμ)	Reference
Enolase	2-Phosphoglycerate → 2-phosphoenol-pyruvate	240	(186)
Butyryl-CoA dehydrogenase	2,6-Dichlorophenol-indophenol reduction, pH 7	600 (fall)	(179)
	3. Based on indirect spectrophotometric estimation of various reactants		
ATP + ADP, or ATP, ADP + AMP (if myokinase is added)	ATP + glucose (hexokinase) → ADP + glucose-6-phosphate. Phosphocreatine + ADP (creatine kinase) → creatine + ATP. ATP + AMP (myokinase) → ADP. Creatine estimation using α-naphthol and diacetyl.	520	(192)
Coenzyme A	+ Excess arsenite, catalyses rapid decomp. of acetyl phosphate		(189)
Monoamine oxidase	p-Hydroxyphenylethylamine + O_2 → p-hydroxyphenylacetaldehyde, determined as 2,4-DNP in alkaline soln.	450	(188)
Proteolytic enzymes	Digestion of denatured haemoglobin under standard condns. → hydrolysis products estim. by u.v. or colorimetric methods	280	(190)
Isocitric dehydrogenase	D-Isocitrate + TPN^+ → α-oxoglutarate + TPNH + H^+. Estimation of α-oxoglutarate as 2,4-DNP	390	(191)
Butyryl-coenzyme A dehydrogenase	Incubation (pH 8·2) with substrate + pyocyanine + triphenyltetrazolium chloride. Formazan extracted with organic solvent	485	(179)
Choline esterase	Reduction of indophenol by liberated thiocholine	600 (fall)	(182)

$$\text{XIV} + \text{Substrate·H}_2 \rightleftharpoons \text{XV} + H^+ + \text{Substrate}$$

XIV   XV

XVI   XVII

ate sorbitol[195] in animal tissues. The applications of DPN-linked enzyme reactions have been discussed by Talalay[196] with especial reference to the analysis of steroid hormones. A particular merit of the method is that many different substrates are ultimately measured in terms of the single, well-characterized chromophore of DPNH or TPNH. The second group of analyses in Table 7.5a involve changes in absorption of components other than the pyridine nucleotides, while in the final group the products are not directly measurable but require extraction, and in most cases further reaction, before spectrophotometry is possible. Reference should be made to the papers cited (cf. also Refs. 16(c) and 179) for details of the estimations.

<h1 style="text-align:center">REFERENCES</h1>

1. A. M. CHASE, *Methods of Biochemical Analysis*, **8**, 61 (1960)
2. J. C. STERNBERG, H. S. STILLO and R. H. SCHWENDEMAN, *Analyt. Chem.*, **32**, 84 (1960); J. C. REID and A. W. PRATT, *Biochem. Biophys. Research Comm.*, **3**, 337 (1960).
3. E. A. BRAUDE, *Determination of Organic Structures by Physical Methods*, (edited by E. A. BRAUDE and F. C. NACHOD), Academic Press, New York (1955).
4a. A. E. MARTELL and M. CALVIN, *Chemistry of the Metal Chelate Compounds*, Prentice-Hall, New York (1952); b) S. CHABEREK and A. E. MARTELL, *Organic Sequestering Agents*, Wiley, New York (1959); c) F. J. C. ROSSOTTI and H. ROSSOTTI, *The Determination of Stability Constants*, McGraw-Hill, London (1961).
5. W. R. BRODE, *J. Amer. Chem. Soc.*, **46**, 581, (1924); M. M. DAVIS and H. B. HETZER, *J. Res. Nat. Bur. Stand.*, **60**, 569 (1958).
6. D. KEILIN, *Proc. Roy. Soc.*, **98B**, **312**, (1925), and later papers; *cf.* Ref. (8), p. 412; Ref. (9), vols. 6 and 7.
7. A. C. REDFIELD, *Biol. Rev.*, **9**, 175 (1934).
8. M. DIXON and E. C. WEBB, *Enzymes*, Longmans, London (1958).
9. P. D. BOYER, H. LARDY and K. MYRBÄCK, *The Enzymes*, 2nd. ed., Academic Press, New York (1959–61) (7 vols.).
10. S. SHIFRIN and N. O. KAPLAN, *Advanc. Enzymol.*, **22**, 337 (1960).
11. F. H. WESTHEIMER, Ref. 9, vol. 1, chap. 6.
12a. R. A. FRIEDEL and M. ORCHIN, *Ultraviolet Spectra of Aromatic Compounds*, Wiley, New York (1951); b) *Organic Electronic Spectra Data*, vol. 1, (1946–52), (edited by M. J. KAMLET); vol. 2, (1953–55), (edited by H. E. UNGNADE), *et. seq.*, Interscience, New York (1961).
13. H. M. HERSHENSON, *Ultraviolet and Visible Absorption Spectra*, Index for 1930–1954, Academic Press, New York (1956).
14. H. M. RAUEN (Ed.), *Biochemisches Taschenbuch*, Springer, Berlin (1956).
15. R. M. C. DAWSON, D. C. ELLIOT, W. H. ELLIOT and K. M. JONES, *Data for Biochemical Research*, Oxford (1959); C. LONG (Ed.) *Biochemists' Handbook*, Spon, London (1961).
16. (a) HOPPE-SEYLER THIERFELDER, *Handbuch der physiologisch- und pathologische chemischen Analyse*, 10th ed., B. I-V, Springer, Berlin, (1955–61).
    (b) *Modern Methods of Plant Analysis* (edited by K. PAECH and M. V. TRACEY), 4 vols., Springer, Berlin (1955–6);
    (c) *Methods in Enzymology*, (edited by S. P. COLOWICK and N. O. KAPLAN), 4. vols., Academic Press, New York (1955–7).
17. D. GLICK (Ed.), *Methods of Biochemical Analysis*, Interscience, New York, vols. 1–8 (1952–1960).

18. A. E. Gillam and E. S. Stern, *Electronic Absorption Spectroscopy in Organic Chemistry*, 2nd ed., Arnold, London, (1957).
19. F. Bergmann and S. Dikstein, *Methods of Biochemical Analysis*, **6**, 79 (1958).
20. S. Udenfriend, H. Weissbach and B. B. Brodie, *ibid.*, p. 95.
21. F. D. Snell and C. T. Snell, *Colorimetric Methods of Analysis*, 3rd ed. vols. I–IV, Van Nostrand, New York (1949–1954).
22. E. Boyland and D. C. Williams, *Biochem. J.*, **64**, 578 (1956).
23. J. H. C. Smith and A. Benitez, in Ref. 16 b, vol. IV, 142.
24. A. S. Curry, *Methods of Biochemical Analysis*, **7**, 39 (1959); B. T. Cromwell, in Ref. 16 b vol. IV, 367; C. G. Farmilo, P. M. Oestreicher and L. Levi, *Appl. Spectrosc.* **10**, 15 (1956).
25. N. D. Embree, S. R. Ames, R. W. Lehman and P. L. Harris, *Methods of Biochemical Analysis*, **4**, 43 (1957); T. Moore, *Vitamin A*, Elsevier (1957).
26. D. T. Ewing, T. D. Schlabach, M. J. Powell, J. W. Vaitkus and O. D. Bird, *Analyt. Chem.* **26**, 1406 (1954).
27. C. Daglish, *Biochem. J.*, **49**, 635 (1951); E. J. Hewitt and G. J. Dickes, *ibid.*, **78**, 384 (1961); H. Schmidt and H. Staudinger, *Biochem. Z.*, **326**, 322 (1955).
28. R. A. Fischer, *J. Agr. Food Chem.*, **1**, 951 (1953).
29. J. J. Doherty, N. Cane and F. Wokes, *J. Pharm., Lond.*, **7**, 1053 (1955).
30. T. W. Goodwin, in Ref. 16 (b), vol. III, 272.
31. A. M. Pumphrey and E. R. Redfearn, *Biochem. J.,* **76**, 61 (1960).
32. A. Hainline, *Standard Methods of Clinical Chemistry* (edited by D. Seligson), vol. 2, Academic Press, New York (1958).
33. P. W. Ratcliff and J. Brooks, *J. Sci. Food Agr.,* **10**, 625 (1959).
34. W. G. Zijlstra and C. J. Muller, *Clin. Chim. Acta,* **2**, 237 (1957).
35. G. H. Beaven and E. R. Holiday, *Advanc. Protein Chem.*, **7**, 319 (1952); G. H. Beaven, *Advanc. Spectroscopy*, **2**, 331 (1961).
36. E. Schauenstein, *Acta Histochem.*, **4**, 208 (1957).
37. W. Sandritter, *ibid.*, p. 276.
38. R. B. Setlow and W. R. Guild, *Arch. Biochem. Biophys.*, **34**, 223 (1951).
39. H. Dannenberg, *Angew. Chem.*, **63**, 208 (1951).
40. W. Bencze and K. Schmid, *Analyt. Chem.*, **29**, 1193 (1957).
41. E. R. Holiday, *Biochem. J.*, **30**, 1795 (1936); T. W. Goodwin and R. A. Morton, *ibid.*, **40**, 628 (1946); C. Fromageot and G. Schnek, *Biochim. et Biophys. Acta*, **6**, 113 (1950–1).
42. J. P. Greenstein, *Advanc. Protein Chem.* **3**, (1948); F. Schlenk, *Advanc. Enzymol.*, **9**, 455 (1949).
43. E. Volkin and W. E. Cohn, *Methods of Biochemical Analysis*, **1**, 287 (p. 304–5) (1954).
44. F. G. Fischer and H. Dörfel, in Ref. 16 (a), vol. IV, Part II; R. Markham, in Ref. 16 (b) vol. IV, 246.
45. K. Imahori and J. Tanaka, *J. Mol. Biol.*, **1**, 359 (1959).
46. R. T. Holman, *Methods of Biochemical Analysis*, **4**, 99 (1957).
47. R. U. Lemieux and E. Rudloff, *Canad. J. Chem.*, **33**, 1710 (1955); A. Polgar and J. L. Jungnickel, *Organic Analysis*, **3**, 203 (1956).
48. J. R. Dyer, *Methods of Biochemical Analysis*, **3**, 111 (1956).
49. W. R. Frisell and C. G. Mackenzie, *Methods of Biochemical Analysis*, **6**, 63 (1958).
50. See Appendix.
51. H. Persky, *Methods of Biochemical Analysis*, **2**, 57 (1954); J. H. Gaddum and M. Holzbauer, *Vit. and Horm.*, **15**, 151 (1957).
52. J. M. Webb and H. B. Levy, *Methods of Biochemical Analysis*, 6, 1 (1958); H. S. Loring, *The Nucleic Acids* (edited by E. Chargaff and J. N. Davidsdn), vol. I, Academic Press, New York (1955).
53. J. E. Logan, W. A. Mannell and R. J. Rossiter, *Biochem. J.,* **51**, 480 (1952).
54. J. J. Pisano, *Clin. Chim. Acta,* **5**, 406 (1960).
55. S. Udenfriend and J. R. Cooper, *J. Biol. Chem.*, **196**, 227 (1952).

56. J. F. VAN PILSUM, *Methods of Biochemical Analysis*, **7**, 193 (1959).
57. C. A. DUBBS, F. W. DAVIS and W. S. ADAMS, *J. Biol. Chem.*, **218**, 497 (1956).
58. H. M. KALCKAR, *J. Biol. Chem.*, **167**, 429 (1947); P. PLESNER and H. M. KALCKAR, *Methods of Biochemical Analysis*, **3**, 97 (1956).
59. H. KLENOW, *Biochem. J.*, **50**, 404 (1951).
60. H. M. KALCKAR, N. O. KJELDGAARD and H. KLENOW, *Biochim. et Biophys. Acta*, **5**, 575 (1950).
61. J. MACGEE, *Analyt. Chem.*, **31**, 298 (1959).
62. R. T. HOLMAN, *Methods of Biochemical Analysis*, **2**, 113 (1955).
63. P. C. JOCELYN, *Biochem. J.*, **70**, 656 (1958).
64. A. J. DURBETAKI, *Analyt. Chem.*, **29**, 1666 (1957); J. G. SHAREFKIN and H. E. SCHWARZ, *ibid.*, **33**, 635 (1961).
65. H. H. STRAIN, *J. Biol. Chem.*, **123**, 425 (1938).
66. C. PAQUOT, D. LEFORT, and S. PIEKARSKI, *Chim. Anal.*, **40**, 111 (1958).
67. V. C. BARRY, J. E. MCCORMICK and P. W. D. MITCHELL, *J. Chem. Soc.*, 222 (1955).
68. K. G. CUNNINGHAM, W. DAWSON and F. S. SPRING, *ibid.*, 2305 (1951).
69. V. I. SIELE and J. P. PICARD, *Appl. Spectrosc.*, **12**, 8 (1958).
70. E. SAWICKI and T. W. STANLEY, *Mikrochim. Acta*, 510 (1960).
71. E. SAWICKI, T. R. HAUSER, T. W. STANLEY and W. ELBERT, *Analyt. Chem.*, **33**, 93 (1961).
72. T. NASH, *Nature, Lond.* **170**, 976 (1952).
73. J. M. DECHARY, E. KUN and H. C. PITOT, *Analyt. Chem.*, **26**, 449 (1954).
74. H. REICH and B. K. SAMUELS, *J. Org. Chem.*, **21**, 68 (1956).
75. F. B. STRAUB, *Z. physiol. Chem.*, **244**, 117 (1936); S. BERNTSSON, *Analyt. Chem.*, **27**, 1659 (1955).
76. E. ROBINS, N. R. ROBERTS, K. M. EYDT, O. H. LOWRY and D. E. SMITH, *J. Biol. Chem.*, **218**, 897 (1956).
77. V. BRUCKNER, *Z. physiol. Chem.*, **244**, 127 (1936).
78. J. C. P. SCHWARZ and M. FINNEGAN, *J. Chem. Soc.*, 3979 (1956).
79. E. W. YEMM and E. C. COCKING, *Analyst.* **80**, 209 (1955).
80. H. FRAENKEL-CONRAT, J. I. HARRIS and A. L. LEVY, *Methods of Biochemical Analysis*, **2**, 359 (1955); *cf.* also Ref. (14), p. 190, for values of ε_{max}.
81. E. G. FRAME, J. A. RUSSELL and A. E. WILHELMI, *J. Biol. Chem.*, **149**, 255 (1943).
82. C. F. CODE and F. C. MCINTIRE, *Methods of Biochemical Analysis*, **3**, 49 (1956).
83. G. W. GAFFNEY, K SCHREIER, N. DIFERRANTE and K. I. ALTMAN, *J. Biol. Chem.*, **206**, 695 (1954).
84. Y. AVI-DOR and J. MAGER, *ibid.*, **222**, 249 (1956).
85. P. D. BOYER, *J. Amer. Chem. Soc.*, **76**, 4331 (1954).
86. Y. AVI-DOR and R. LIPKIN, *J. Biol. Chem.*, **233**, 69 (1958).
87. S. J. WAKIL and G. HÜBSCHER, *ibid.*, **235**, 1554 (1960).
88. R. W. LEHMAN, *Methods of Biochemical Analysis*, **2**, 153 (1955).
89. A. O. NIEDERMAYER, F. M. RUSSO–ALESI, C. A. LENDZIAN and J. M. KELLY, *Analyt. Chem.*, **32**, 664 (1960).
90. F. BERGMAN, *Analyt. Chem.*, **24**, 1367 (1952); E. F. HILLENBRAND and C. A. PENTZ, *Organic Analysis*, **3**, 129 (1956).
91. T. WIELAND, K. DOSE and G. PFLEIDERER, *Biochem. Z.*, **326**, 442 (1955).
92. J. D. ROBERTS and C. GREEN, *J. Amer. Chem. Soc.*, **68**, 214 (1946).
93. P. G. WALKER, *Biochem. J.*, **58**, 699 (1954).
94. F. G. ANGELL, *Analyst*, **72**, 178 (1947); A. N. PONOMAREV, *Chem. Abstr.*, **50**, 9234 i (1956).
95. D. C. MORTIMER and M. J. JOHNSON, *J. Amer. Chem. Soc.*, **74**, 4098 (1952).
96. M. HOOREMAN, *Anal. chim. Acta*, **3**, 606 (1949).
97. C. NEUBERG and E. STRAUS, *Arch. Biochem.*, **7**, 211 (1945).
98. G. R. A. JOHNSON and G. SCHOLES, *Analyst*, **79**, 217 (1954).
99. A. D. HOLLEY, and R. W. HOLLEY, *Analyt. Chem.*, **24**, 216 (1952).

100. F. D. SNELL and C. T. SNELL, *Colorimetric Methods of Analysis*, p. 110, Van Nostrand, New York (1937).
101. D. F. MEIGH, in Ref. (16b), p. 428.
102. G. H. N. TOWERS, J. F. THOMPSON and F. C. STEWARD, *J. Amer. Chem. Soc.*, **76**, 2392 (1954).
103. B. McARDLE, *Biochem. J.*, **66**, 144 (1957).
104. G. R. LAPPIN and L. C. CLARK, *Analyt. Chem.*, **23**, 541 (1951).
105. A. R. THOMPSON, *Aust. J. Sci. Res.*, **3**A, 128 (1950).
106. H. J. KOEPSELL and E. S. SHARPE, *Arch. Biochem. Biophys.*, **38**, 443 (1952); *cf.* S. L. BONTING, *ibid.*, **58**, 100 (1955).
107. W. J. P. NEISH, *Methods of Biochemical Analysis*, **5**, 107 (1957).
108. A. J. ASPEN and A. MEISTER, *ibid.*, **6**, 131 (1958).
109. P. FLEURY, J. COURTOIS and R. PERLÈS, *Mikrochim. ver. Mikrochem. Acta*, **36/37**, 863 (1951).
110. P. DESNUELLE and S. ANTONIN, *Biochim. et Biophys. Acta*, **1**, 50 (1947).
111. S. L. TOMPSETT, *Anal. chim. Acta*, **19**, 360 (1958).
112. V. S. WARAVDEKAR and L. D. SASLAW, *Biochim. et Biophys. Acta*, **24**, 439 (1957).
113. L. WARREN, *J. Biol. Chem.*, **234**, 1971 (1959).
114. W. TROLL and R. K. CANNAN, *ibid.*, **200**, 803 (1953).
115. J. AXELROD, J. REICHENTHAL and B. B. BRODIE, *ibid.*, **204**, 903 (1953).
116. J. M. McKIBBIN, *Methods of Biochemical Analysis*, **7**, 111 (1959).
117. W. A. SCHROEDER and J. LeGETTE, *J. Amer. Chem. Soc.*, **75**, 4612 (1953).
118. Ref. (14), pp. 411 and 432.
119. H. G. LEEMANN and H. WELLER, *Helv. Chim. Acta*, **43**, 1359 (1960).
120. O. MICKELSON and R. S. YAMAMOTO, *Methods of Biochemical Analysis*, **6**, 191 (1958).
121. J. W. PATTERSON and A. LAZAROW, *ibid.*, **2**, 259 (1955).
122. M. W. WHITEHOUSE and F. ZILLIKEN, *ibid.*, **8**, 199 (1960).
123. Z. DISCHE, *ibid.*, **2**, 313 (1955).
124. F. SMITH and R. MONTGOMERY, *ibid.*, **3**, 153 (1956).
125. S. GARDELL, *ibid.*, **6**, 289 (1958).
126. J. D. CIPERA, *Analyst*, **85**, 517 (1960).
127. G. R. NOGGLE, *The Carbohydrates* (edited by W. PIGMAN), Academic Press, New York (1957).
128. S. L. BONTING, *Arch. Biochem. Biophys.*, **52**, 272 (1954).
129. J. C. SPECK, *Analyt. Chem.*, **20**, 647 (1948).
130. D. A. MacFADYEN, *J. Biol. Chem.*, **158**, 107 (1945).
131. C. E. BRICKER and W. A. VAIL, *Analyt. Chem.*, **22**, 720 (1950).
132. D. J. BELL, in Ref. (16b), vol. II, pp. 1–54.
133. E. W. RICE, *Analyt. Chem.*, **23**, 1501 (1951).
134. M. DUBOIS, K. A. GILLES, J. K. HAMILTON, P. A. REBERS and F. SMITH, *Nature, Lond.*, **168**, 167 (1951).
135. B. KLEIN and M. WEISSMAN, *Analyt. Chem.*, **25**, 771 (1953).
136. F. A. LOEWUS, *ibid.*, **24**, 219 (1952).
137. E. STOTZ, *J. Biol. Chem.*, **148**, 585 (1943); W. W. WESTERFELD, *J. Lab. Clin. Med.*, **30**, 1076 (1945).
138. C. FROMAGEOT and P. HEITZ, *Mikrochim. Acta*, **3**, 52 (1938).
139. C. L. HOFFPAUIR and R. T. O'CONNOR, *Analyt. Chem.*, **21**, 420 (1949).
140. P. DESNUELLE and M. NAUDET, *Bull. Soc. chim. Fr.*, (5) **12**, 871 (1945).
141. R. J. WINZLER, *Methods of Biochemical Analysis*, **2**, 279 (1955).
142. J. M. WEBB and H. B. LEVY, *J. Biol. Chem.*, **213**, 107 (1955).
143. Z. DISCHE, *The Nucleic Acids* (edited by CHARGAFF and DAVIDSON), vol. I, ch. 9, Academic Press, New York (1955).
144. G. CERIOTTI, *J. Biol. Chem.*, **198**, 297 (1952).

145. D. H. LAUGHLAND and W. E. J. PHILLIPS, *Analyt. Chem.*, **28**, 817 (1956).
146. W. I. LYNESS and F. W. QUACKENBUSH, *ibid.*, **27**, 1978 (1955).
147. H. G. BRAY and W. V. THORPE, *Methods of Biochemical Analysis*, **1**, 27 (1954).
148. N. S. RADIN, *ibid.*, **6**, 163 (1958).
149. H. P. RIEDER and M. BOHMER, *Clin. Chim. Acta*, **5**, 520 (1960).
150. R. I. COX, *Biochem. J.*, **52**, 339 (1952).
151. C. E. BRICKER and K. H. ROBERT, *Analyt. Chem.*, **21**, 1331 (1949).
152. W. R. FRISELL and C. G. MACKENZIE, *J. Biol. Chem.*, **217**, 275 (1955); J. M. JOHNSTON and C. G. MACKENZIE, *ibid.*, **221**, 301 (1956).
153. V. P. HOLLANDER, S. DIMAURO and O. H. PEARSON, *Endocrinology*, **49**, 617 (1951).
154. K. C. KLENDSHOJ and M. FELDSTEIN, *Canad. J. Med. Technol.*, **17**, 74 (1955).
155. M. IKAWA and C. NIEMANN, *J. Biol. Chem.*, **180**, 923 (1949).
156. M. NAKAMURA and K. MORI, *Biochim. et Biophys. Acta*, **34**, 546 (1959).
157. C. E. CROUTHAMEL, A. M. HAYES and D. S. MARTIN, JR., *J. Amer. Chem. Soc.*, **73**, 82 (1951).
158. J. S. DIXON and D. LIPKIN, *Analyt. Chem.*, **26**, 1902 (1954).
159. C. E. MELVAN, M. MAUCK and C. HUFFMANN, *ibid.*, **33**, 104 (1961).
160. E. SAVILLE, *Analyst*, **83**, 670 (1958).
161. E. BOREL and H. DEUEL, *Helv. Chim. Acta*, **36**, 801 (1953).
162. J. A. OWEN and B. IGGO, *Biochem. J.*, **62**, 675 (1956).
163. T. TAKEMOTO, K. DAIGO and T. TAKAI, *J. Pharm. Soc. Japan*, **75**, 1025 (1955).
164. F. HOSTETTLER, E. BOREL and H. DEUEL, *Helv. Chim. Acta.*, **34**, 2132 (1951); E. BOREL, F. HOSTETTLER and H. DEUEL, *ibid.*, **35**, 115 (1952).
165. J. C. WHITEHORN, *J. Biol. Chem.*, **108**, 633 (1935); F. H. SHAW, *Biochem. J.*, **32**, 19 (1938).
166. R. A. FAIRBRIDGE, K. I. WILLIS and R. G. BOOTH, *Biochem. J.*, **49**, 423 (1951); K. WALLENFELS, *Naturwiss.*, **37**, 976 (1950).
167. W. RIED, *Angew. Chem.*, **64**, 391 (1952); B. JAMBOR, *Nature, Lond.*, **173**, 774 (1954).
168. R. E. HUGHES, *Biochem. J.*, **64**, 203 (1956); A. POLK, T. L. FLANAGAN and F. J. VAN LOON, *Clin. Chem.*, **65**, 58 (1960).
169. G. PFLEIDERER, W. GRUBER and T. WIELAND, *Biochem. Z.*, **326**, 446 (1955).
170. A. KORNBERG and W. E. PRICER, *J. Biol. Chem.*, **193**, 481 (1951).
171. W. H. F. MOMMAERTS, *Methods in Medical Research*, vol. 7, (edited by J. V. WARREN), pp. 27–47, Year Book Publishers, Chicago (1958).
172. A. KORNBERG, *J. Biol. Chem.*, **182**, 805 (1950).
173. R. W. VON KORFF, *ibid.*, **200**, 401 (1953).
174. G. D. NOVELLI, *Methods of Biochemical Analysis*, **2**, 189 (1955).
175. S. K. WOLFSON, JR. and H. G. WILLIAMS-ASHMAN, *Proc. Soc. Exp. Biol. Med.*, N. Y., **92**, 231 (1957).
176. H. TABOR, A. H. MEHLER and E. R. STADTMAN, *J. Biol. Chem.*, **204**, 127 (1953).
177. H. M. KALCKAR, *ibid.*, **167**, 445 (1947).
178. H. WEISSBACH, T. E. SMITH, J. W. DALY, B. WITKOP and S. UDENFRIEND, *J. Biol. Chem.*, **235**, 1160 (1960).
179. Ref. (14), pp. 984–94.
180. R. F. BEERS and I. W. SIZER, *J. Biol. Chem.*, **195**, 133 (1952).
181. L. SMITH, *Methods of Biochemical Analysis*, **2**, 427 (1955).
182. E. M. GAL, *Clin. Chim. Acta*, **2**, 316 (1957).
183. T. P. SINGER and E. B. KEARNEY, in *Methods of Biochemical Analysis*, **4**, 307 (1957).
184. A. L. TAPPEL, P. D. BOYER and W. O. LUNDBERG, *J. Biol. Chem.*, **199**, 267 (1952).
185. M. KUNITZ, *ibid.*, **164**, 563 (1946).
186. O. WARBURG and W. CHRISTIAN, *Biochem. Z.*, **310**, 384 (1941).
187. H. R. MAHLER, N. K. SARKAR and L. P. VERNON, *J. Biol. Chem.*, **199**, 585 (1952).
188. A. L. GREEN and T. M. HAUGHTON, *Biochem. J.*, **78**, 172 (1961).
189. E. R. STADTMAN, G. D. NOVELLI and F. LIPMANN, *J. Biol. Chem.*, **191**, 365 (1951).

190. N. C. DAVIS and E. L. SMITH, *Methods of Biochemical Analysis*, **2**, 215 (1955).
191. J. L. BELL and D. N. BARON, *Clin. Chim. Acta*, **5**, 740 (1960).
192. J. B. CHAPPELL and S. V. PERRY, *Biochem. J.*, **57**, 421 (1954).
193. O. WARBURG, *Wasserstoffübertragende Fermente*, Sänger, Berlin (1948).
194. J. HICKMAN and G. ASHWELL, *J. Biol. Chem.*, **234**, 758 (1959); *cf.* S. HOLLMANN and O. TONSTER, *ibid.*, **225**, 87 (1957).
195. S. K. WOLFSON, JR. and H. G. WILLIAMS-ASHMAN, *Proc. Soc. Exp. Biol. Med.*, *N. Y.*, **99**, 761 (1958).
196. P. TALALAY, *Methods of Biochemical Analysis*, **8**, 119 (1960).
197. J. E. SEEGMILLER, V. G. ZANNONI, L. LASTER and B. N. LA DU, *J. Biol. Chem.*, **236**, 774 (1961).
198. J. B. NEILANDS, *Organic Analysis*, **4**, 65 (1960).
199. J. C. RABINOWITZ and W. E. PRICER, *J. Biol. Chem.*, **229**, 321 (1957).
200. W. J. WADDELL, *J. Lab. Clin. Med.*, **48**, 311 (1956); J. B. MURPHY, M. W. KIES, *Biochim. et Biophys. Acta*, **45**, 382 (1960) M. P. TOMBS, F. SOUTER and N. F. MACLAGAN, *Biochem. J.*, **73**, 167 (1959).
201. J. R. SPIES, D. C. CHAMBERS and E. J. COULSON, *Arch. Biochem. Biophys.*, **84**, 286 (1959).
202. A. P. ALTSCHULLER, D. L. MILLER and S. L. SLEVA, *Analyt. Chem.*, **33**, 621 (1961).
203. F. E. KING, T. J. KING and L. C. MANNING, *J. Chem. Soc.*, 563 (1957).
204. J. MITCHELL, JR., B. A. MONTAGUE and R. H. KINSEY, *Organic Analysis*, **3**, 1 (1956): U. V. data, pp. 61–5.
205. G. PFLEIDERER and K. DOSE, *Biochem. Z.*, **326**, 436 (1955); I. M. FRIEDLAND and L. S. DIETRICH, *Analyt. Biochem.* **2**, 390 (1961).
206. A. J. MARTIN, *Organic Analysis*, **4**, 1 (1960); G. SORGE and K. UBERREITER, *Angew. Chem.*, **68**, 352, 486 (1956).
207. T. BANKS, C. VAUGHN and L. M. MARSHALL, *Analyt. Chem.*, **27**, 1348 (1955).
208. F. MCCAPRA, Private communication.
209. J. F. PENNOCK, F. W. HEMMING and R. A. MORTON, *Nature, Lond.* **186**, 470 (1960).
210. G. R. KINGSLEY and G. GETCHELL, *Analyt. Biochem.*, **2**, 1 (1961).
211. D. J. PROCKOP and S. UDENFRIEND, *ibid.*, **1**, 228 (1960).
212. K. TÄUFEL and R. ZIMMERMANN, *Naturwiss.*, **47**, 133 (1960).

CHAPTER 8

APPLICATION OF SPECTRAL DATA
TO INVESTIGATION OF GROSS MOLECULAR
STRUCTURE

In this chapter we shall consider some selected examples illustrating applications of some of the structure–spectral relationships developed in the preceding seven chapters. In a few favourable cases we shall find that it is possible to allocate a substantial proportion of structural environment on the basis of the ultraviolet spectrum, using a minimum of chemical evidence. However, the most common role of the electronic absorption data played during the sequence of isolation, characterization and degradation of a natural product is that of an indispensable member of a set of physical tools, which taken together form a powerful technique whereby the chemist may more easily derive structural information. The *simultaneous* use of ultraviolet, infrared, nuclear magnetic resonance and mass spectrometric data provides a method of attack which should reduce experimentation to a minimum, provided that our interpretation is well founded. Although the ultraviolet data may not provide the rapier-like thrusts of n.m.r. analysis, or the mass of meaningful vibration frequencies of an infrared spectrum, it is often possible to reveal subtleties of structure which other techniques cannot unmask. It is implicit in the ensuing discussion that the molecule whose ultraviolet spectrum is under review displays the appropriate infrared light absorption. We have simplified our arguments by omitting frequency values for the infrared region unless these are germane to the interpretation of the ultraviolet data.

The ultraviolet spectrum may provide a valuable guide during the initial screening and extraction of plant or fungal material. For example the chromophorically active fungal polyacetylenes can be detected by spectroscopy (p. 276) at an early stage in the isolation procedure. During purification of the natural product, the intensity of absorption provides a guide to the progress of separation of mixtures. This application is of great value where minute amounts of labile or difficultly separable materials are being handled, for the combination of such techniques as column, paper and partition chromatography or counter–current distribution with ultraviolet spectroscopy forms a most powerful and convenient analytical tool.

The examples which constitute the material of this and the succeeding chapter have been chosen to illustrate the scope and limitations of the use of the data so far accumulated. It has been necessary to make an arbitrary selection from the enormous number of excellent examples available. We therefore ask the reader's indulgence for the omission of many of his favourite chromophoric arrays. It is our hope that the selected illustrations cover a field sufficiently wide to indicate the operation of certain principles which have general application to many systems excluded either by selection or because they have not yet come to light within the framework of the molecule of a natural product.

The order of the twenty examples which follow is that of increas ng complexity of interpretations rather than of molecular size or number of unsaturated groups in conjugation.

8.1. VITAMIN B₁ (THIAMINE)

The celebrated example of thiamine (I) illustrates the validity of comparison of carefully chosen model spectra with those of the degradation products of a naturally occurring compound.

On cleavage with sodium sulphite thiamine afforded an acidic and a basic fragment which accounted for all the atoms of the vitamin. The base C_6H_9ONS had an ultraviolet spectrum almost identical with that of 4-methyl thiazole (II) and was in fact shown to be 4-methyl-5-(β-hydroxyethyl)thiazole (III). The spectrum of the acidic fragment ($C_6H_9O_3N_3S$) was reminiscent of that of 4-aminopyrimidine (Chapter 6, p. 194). Moreover, the spectrum of the acid on hydrolytic treatment underwent a shift comparable with that obtained by hydrolysis of the model 2,5-dimethyl-6-aminopyrimidine (IV) to the 6-hydroxy base

(V). In support of these spectral considerations, chemical evidence led to structure (VI) for the acidic fragment and thence to expression (I) for thiamine[1].

This first example is an ideal illustration carried out in the pre-infrared era (1937). Apart from the obvious utility of comparisons with model spectra, a concept of some importance to the natural product chemist must be stated at the outset of our discussion, namely the development of a critical and intuitive approach to the interpretation of spectral data. For it is possible to choose a model which may apparently have the required attributes of the suspected structure yet it in fact displays a spectrum quite unlike that of the natural product. Such considerations do not arise in this first ideal case but are illustrated in the next example. The discrepancies between "apparent" model and "real" compound are caused by steric hindrance to coplanarity of contributing chromophores or by increased overlap of chromophores due to structural subtleties.

8.2. β-i-METHYLIONONE

In Chapters 2 and 3 we surveyed the evidence for the effect of steric hindrance on the electron transfer bands of unsaturated carbonyl compounds. Such steric overlap between the side chain- and ring-methyl groups of β-i-methyl-

VII

λ_{max} 278 (ε 4500)

VIII

λ_{max} 281 (ε 20,800)

IX

λ_{max} 296 (ε 10,700)

ionone (VII) lowers the intensity of the dienone band at 278 mμ to 4500, which is about one-quarter of the intensity of the "apparent" model (VIII)[2]. In fact, because of the low intensity, some workers[3] were of the view that the structure (VII) was incorrect, or that the dienone was impure, but β-ionone (IX) absorbs at an intermediate value (H—Me overlap) and there is now ample evidence from this[2] and related studies with ortho-substituted acetophenones that the E.T. band of such compounds may be so suppressed by steric hindrance to coplanarity as to disappear entirely from the spectrum. Such phenomena must also be recalled in the cases of styrene, carbonyl and diene spectra (Chapters 2 and 3) wherever suspiciously low intensity values are obtained.

8.3. CYCLOPENTENONES

The positions of the E.T. bands of acyclic and six-membered α,β-unsaturated ketones may be calculated with accuracy by application of the rules described on p. 58. These rules also apply to exo-unsaturated cyclopentanones (as X). We recall that a parent value of 202 mμ could be used effectively in dealing with the cyclopentenone chromophore (XI) using the Fieser set of increments modified as on p. 58. Close inspection of a number of cyclopentenone spectra, however, reveals certain important deviations from such rules and these are discussed below. At the outset, let us consider a range of chromophores of type (XI) which are "calculable". These are summarized in Table 8.1.

X λ 230 mμ XI λ 218 mμ XII λ 221 mμ

Turning now to the exceptions we find that just as a stereochemical situation may reduce the intensity or cause a wavelength shift of the E.T. band of, for example, cyclohexenones and acetophenones, so cyclopentenones of certain substitution pattern assume conformations which result in absorption spectra reminiscent of the cyclohexenones, i.e. their maxima occur at *longer* wavelengths than those predicted. Fortunately the corresponding infrared frequencies are not affected, so that such phenomena, far from leading to erroneous interpretation, provide evidence as to the environment of the cyclopentenone ring.

XIII λ 231 mμ XIV λ 229 mμ

XV λ 223 mμ XVI λ 221 mμ

TABLE 8.1. CALCULATED AND OBSERVED MAXIMA OF SOME CYCLOPENTENONES (IN mμ)

	λ_{calc}	λ_{obs}	Reference
Cyclopentenone	214	218	(21)
Tetrahydropyrethrolone	236	232	(21)
Dihydrojasmone	236	237	(21)
Isophotosantonic Acid	241	239	(22)
2-Hydroxy-3-methylcyclopentenone	261	258	(23)

We recall that cyclopentenone (XI) absorbs at 218 mμ (*calc.* 214 mμ) while its trialkylated derivatives (XII) have λ_{max} 221 mμ (*calc.* 214 mμ). That such a "discrepancy" provides an indication of the steric situation is supported by the following observations. The maxima of the epimeric steroidal Δ^{15}-17-ones (XIII) and (XIV) occur at 231 and 229 mμ respectively[4] (*calc.* 214 mμ). Now, although it is perhaps surprising that the maximal position of absorption of the cyclopentenone chromophore appears to be independent of the C/D ring fusion in (XIII) and (XIV), even more surprising at first sight is the observation that the 14α- and 14β-oestrone methyl ethers (XV) and (XVI) absorb at 223 and 221 mμ, respectively. These maxima correspond with the position of absorption for the trialkyl compound (XII) so that an apparent return to the "expected" absorption has been made. However, Sondheimer[4] was able to show that the absorption of the anisole component in ring A of XV (λ_{max} 215 and 250 mμ) is superimposed on the E.T. band of the cyclopentenone component, resulting in a net effect of one coalesced band envelope with a maximum at 223 mμ. When the summation of the curves of oestrone methyl ether (ring A chromophore) and

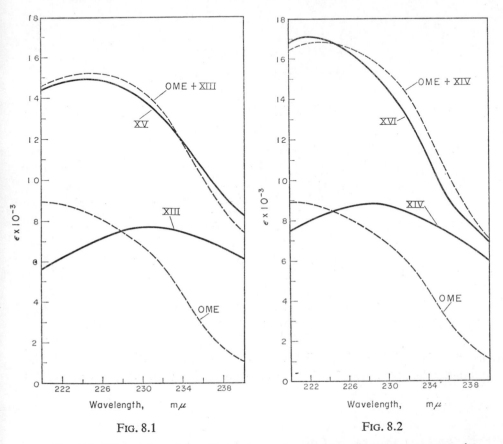

FIG. 8.1   FIG. 8.2

FIG. 8.1. Ultraviolet absorption curves of oestrone methyl ether (OME) Δ^{15}-androsten-3β-ol-17-one (XIII), the summation curve (OME + XIII) and 15-dehydroestrone methyl ether (XV). (Sondheimer, *J. Amer. Chem. Soc.*, **81**, 3213, 1960.)

FIG. 8.2. Ultraviolet absorption curves of oestrone methyl ether (OME), Δ^{15}-14-iso-androsten-3β-ol-17-one (XIV). The summation curve (OME + XIV) and 15-dehydro-14-isoestrone methyl ether (XVI). (Sondheimer, *J. Amer. Chem. Soc.*, **81**, 3213, 1960.)

of the ring A saturated cyclopentenone (XIII) is made, the composite curve shown in Fig. 8.1 is obtained, which closely replicates the spectrum of the 14α-dehydro compound (XV). Similarly, the summation curves of ring A chromophore and cyclopentenone (XIV) afford the spectrum of the 14β-enone (XVI) (Fig. 8.2).

Other examples of cyclopentenone maxima occurring at wavelengths longer than those predicted for such systems may also be noted. For example, photo-γ-tropolone methyl ether (XVII) has λ_{max} 243 mμ (*calc.* 214 mμ)[5]. This effect

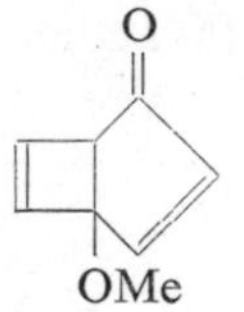

XVII λ 243 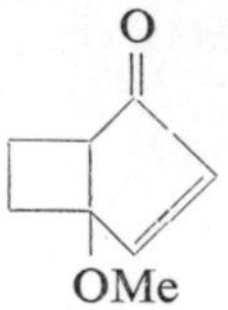   XVIII λ 215

may be attributed to the proximity of the fused cyclobutene ring, for the dihydro-derivative (XVIII) has λ_{max} 215 mμ (*calc.* 214 mμ).

In the sesquiterpenoid perhydroazulene series, the cyclopentenone maxima on the whole follow the predicted trend, e.g. dihydrohelenalin[6] (XIX), tetra-

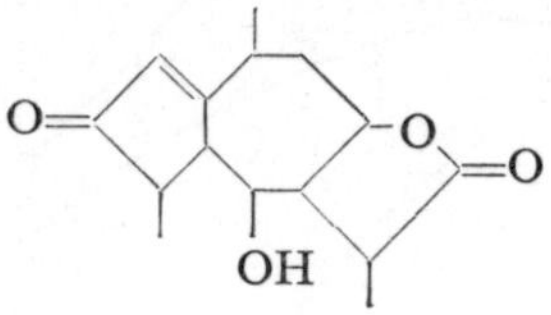

XIX λ 223 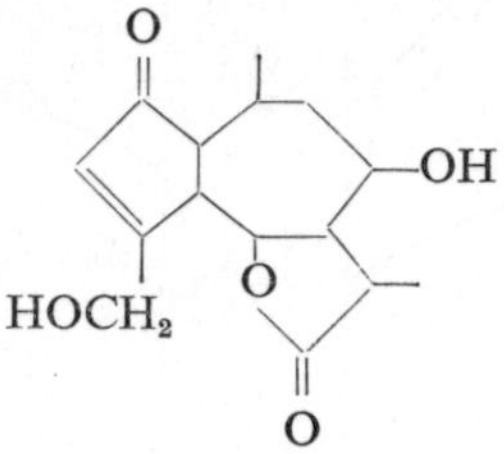   XX λ 227 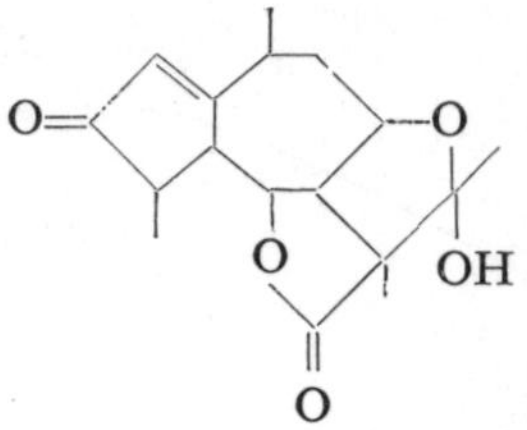   XXI λ 226

hydrolactucin[7] (XX) and tenulin[8] (XXI) all have λ_{max} within 5 mμ of the calculated value. However, it is interesting to note that while the dienone (XXII)

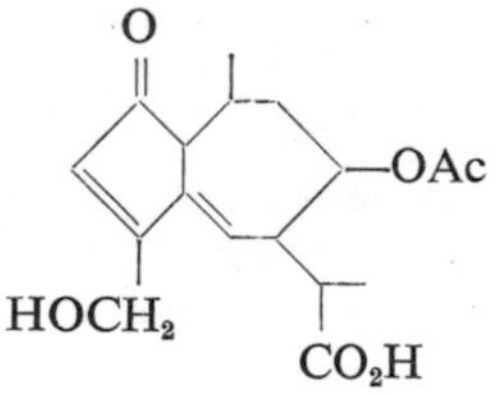

XXII λ 281 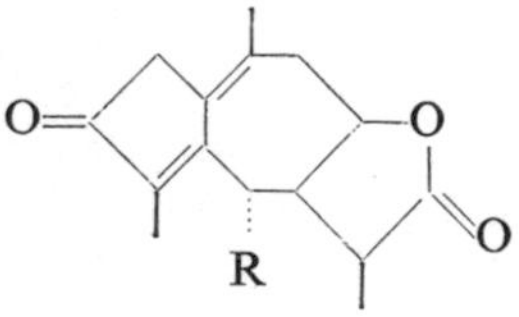   XXIII λ 299

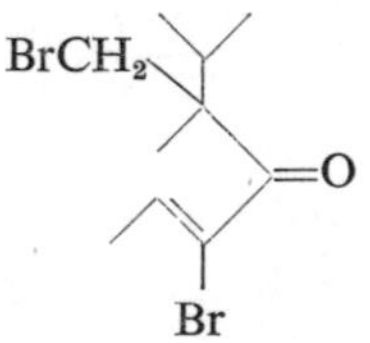

XXIV λ 250

λ_{calc} 251

of the lactucin series has λ_{max} 281 mμ (*calc.* 285 mμ), anhydrogeigerin (XXIII; R=OH) and its acetate (XXIII; R=OAc) have λ_{max} 299 and 303 mμ, respectively[9], some 15 mμ less than the calculated value (318 mμ). Umbellulone dibromide[10] (XXIV) shows absorption at the predicted position.

2-Hydroxycyclopentenones, corresponding to the diosphenols, exhibit pre-

XXV λ 258

dictable absorption maxima, e.g. 3-methylcyclopentane-1,2-dione (XXV) absorbs at 258 mμ (*calc.* 261 mμ) and moreover displays the expected shift on ionization (+ 37 mμ).

8.4. α, β-UNSATURATED LACTONES

The presence of an α,β-unsaturated lactone moiety in a natural product may be inferred most readily by the presence of $-\overset{|}{C}=O$ stretching frequencies in the infrared region, which distinguish the five-membered (butenolide) and six-membered (pentenolide) lactonic functions[11]. However, the information derivable from ultraviolet data, once the presence of such lactone groupings is suspected from infrared and chemical evidence, is of value in deciding both the extent and nature of substitution of such a grouping. The recognition of a

XXVI $\lambda \sim 220$ XXVII λ 215

XXVIII λ 217   XXIX

variety of lactonic arrangements is possible, not by means of a set of well-tried empirical rules, but rather by comparison with the documentation of lactonic absorption, summarized in the form of the set of examples which follow.

(a) *Butenolides* (as XXVI) lacking α- or β-substituents have usually been recorded in the literature as having "end absorption" with, say $\varepsilon_{220} = 8000$.

Several reliable references (12a, b, c), however, give λ_{max} 214 mμ, e.g. (XXVII) has λ_{max} 215 (ε, 8300). Monoalkylated butenolides (as XXVIII) absorb consistently near 217 mμ. Approximately 200 β-substituted steroidal butenolides (cardenolides) have λ_{max} 217 $\pm$ 5 mμ (ε, 10,000–20,000) in ethanol (31). α,β-dialkylbutenolides have λ_{max} 215–30 *dependent on groupings in the γ-positions*. Thus it would appear that α,β-disubstituted unsaturated lactones absorb at slightly lower wavelengths than the mono-alkyl derivatives through thr operation of a steric effect which does not appear to influence the absorption of the closely related dialkylcyclopentenones (as XXIX). In apparent conflict with

XXX λ 222   XXXI λ 227

these observations, the cardenolides (XXX) and (XXXI) have λ_{max} 222 and 227 mμ, respectively[31] in which they show the bathochromic effect to be expected for increasing alkyl substitution.

In addition to the E.T. band near 220 mμ. butenolides display $n \rightarrow \pi^*$ absorption at 260–90 mμ (ε, 30–50). In this connection it is important to note that

XXXII   XXXIII λ 270–275

many cardenolides (as XXXII) show a weak band at 270–5 mμ[31] which is, in fact, due to the presence of dienolide (XXXIII) as impurity (*vide infra*).

A second class of butenolide with an α,β-dialkylation pattern as part of a fused ring system is represented by the sesquiterpenes isodrimenin[13] (XXXIV),

XXXIV λ 217   XXXV λ 217

confertifolin[14] (XXXV) and isoiresin[29] (XXXVI), all of which have λ_{max} 217 mμ [ν_{max} 1770 cm^{-1}]. The isomeric exobutenolide chromophore present in iresin[29] (XXXVII) absorbs at 224 mμ (ε, 13,000).

XXXVI λ 217   XXXVII λ 224

The conjugation of a second double bond in the γ, δ-position contained in the five-membered ring D of the steroid framework (XXXVIII) shifts the E.T. band to 270–3 mμ (ε, 16,000–22,500)† with a second band (partial chromo-

XXXVIII λ 273   XXXIX λ 325

phore?) at 220 mμ (ε, 5000)[31]. Further conjugation as in the ring D diene (XXXIX) effects a red shift to λ_{max} 325 mμ[31]. Again a band at 220 mμ is discernible.

Patulin, $C_7H_6O_4$, a metabolite of *Penicillium patulum*, was erroneously formulated as the ketone (XL) but later work by Woodward[15] demonstrated the incompatibility of this formulation with the ultraviolet spectrum (λ_{max} 276 mμ), a value of not more than 260 mμ being expected for (XL) allowing a (generous) value of 30 mμ for the β—O—CO grouping. The chromophore of a di-unsaturated lactone should absorb near 270 mμ. On the basis of this spectral anomaly

XL   XLI Patulin, λ 276

Woodward concluded that structure (XL) was incorrect and reinterpreted the chemical evidence to arrive at (XLI), a proposal confirmed in every detail by synthesis.

† Range for ten examples.

Oxygenated Butenolides

(a) *Tetronic Acids*[16]. Tetronic acid is the generic name of the β-hydroxy-butenolide grouping (XLII), the favoured tautomer of β-oxobutanolide (XLIII). Tetronic acid itself does not occur naturally, but its spectrum is of interest as

XLII λ 224   XLIII   XLIV   Vitamin C, λ 245

it represents the parental chromophore λ 224 mμ. Like its natural congeners, tetronic acid shows a red shift of the spectrum in base of 20–25 mμ (enol anion absorption). *Vitamin C* (ascorbic acid) (XLIV) is an α-hydroxy-γ-substituted tetronic acid and has λ_{max}, 245 mμ (in water) moving to 265 mμ in sodium acetate (enoliz-

XLV λ 230, 265   XLVI a   R=Me

XLVI b   R=CH$_2$·CO$_2$H

XLVI c

ation). The *mould tetronic acids*, carolinic (XLV), carolic (XLVI a), carlic (XLVI b) and carlosic (XLVI c) acids are α-acyl tetronic acids. They are perhaps best regarded as β-triketones for their spectra are reminiscent of these chromophores (p. 70) in having two maxima of nearly equal intensity near 230 and 265 mμ. The resemblance does not extend to the changes wrought in the spectra of the β-triketones on going from neutral to acidic ethanol. In the latter medium acetyl cyclohexane-1,3-dione retains its maxima at 231 and 276 mμ, whereas the α-acyl tetronic acids lose the lower band entirely and the 260 mμ band is shifted, apparently randomly. Thus carolinic acid (XLV) has λ_{max} 230 and 260 mμ in ethanol, whilst in acidified alcohol a single band at 250 mμ marks the electron-transfer. On the other hand, the 264 mμ band present in the spectrum of (XLVI) in neutral solution moves to 269 mμ in acidic medium.

TABLE 8.2. α-Oxo-γ-Lactones and their Derivatives

No.	Compound	$\lambda_{max}^{EtOH}(\varepsilon)$	$\lambda_{max}^{OH^-}(\varepsilon)$	Reference
1.		226 (4000)	261 (2000)	(24)
2.		232·5 (12,600)	—	(25)
3.		230 (11,000)	—	(25)
4.		230 (15,600)	—	(26)
5.		237 (6310)	270 (7900)	(27)
6.		236 (15,600)	—	(28)
7.		220 (15,000)	—	(28)
8.		238 (11,500)	274 (10,000)	(27)
9.		216·5 (14,000)	—	(27)

TABLE 8.2—(contd.)

No.	Compound	$\lambda^{EtOH}_{max}(\varepsilon)$	$\lambda^{OH^-}_{max}(\varepsilon)$	Reference
10.		233 (7950)	272 (5300)	(29)
11.		240 (7900)	274 (10,700)	(29)
12.		218 (10,500)	—	(29)

That the tautomerism of the tetronic acids favours the enol (XLII) is shown by the spectrum of the enol ether (XLVII) which has λ_{max} 218 mμ (ε 17,000). It is indeed remarkable that the β-hydroxyl group produces an effect of magnitude comparable with that of a β-alkyl substituent. The α-alkyl tetronic acid

XLVII λ 218   XLVIII λ 233   XLIX λ 226

(XLVIII) shows a shift of $+9$ mμ for the α-methyl group. This compound absorbs at 258 mμ in basic solution (shift $+25$ mμ). Penicillic acid (XLIX) has λ_{max} 226 mμ (ε 11,000).

(b) α-oxo-γ-lactones (α-hydroxybutenolides) may be regarded from the point of view of spectral interpretation as lactonic diosphenols, for there are marked resemblances in the spectra of this type of lactone and its derivatives with those of the corresponding diosphenol set. Thus, ozonolysis of iresin[29] (XXXVII) gives the α-oxolactone (L), λ_{max} 240 mμ, shifted in base ($\rightarrow$ LI) to 274 mμ and lowered by acetylation ($\rightarrow$ LII) to 218 mμ. The average base shift is $+35$ mμ

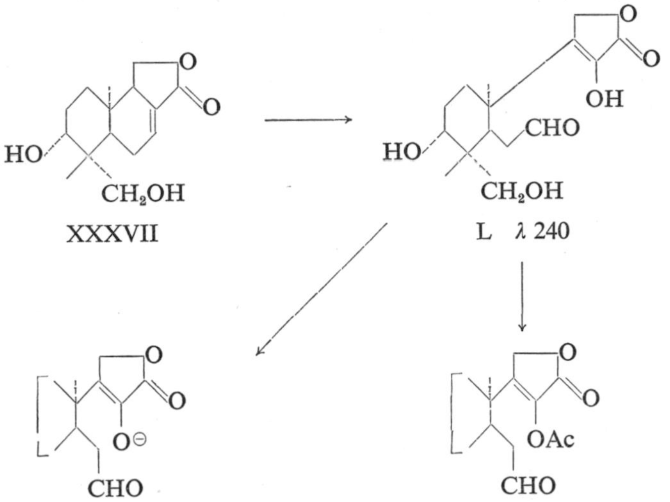

XXXVII

L λ 240

LI λ 274

LII λ 218

provided that lactone opening does not occur under the conditions used for the measurements. As can be seen from the data in Table 8.2, the acetylation shift has not been recorded in many instances, but appears to be close to -20 mμ.

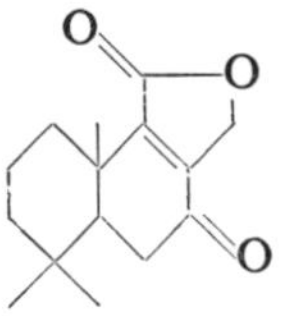

LIII

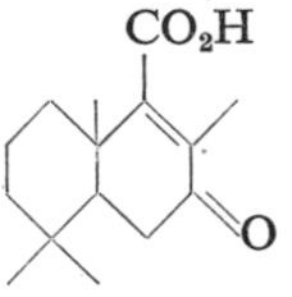

LIV λ 249

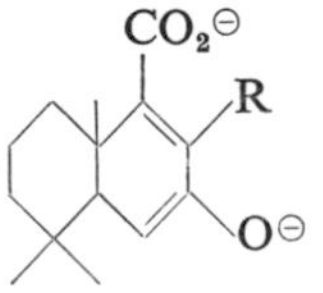

LV λ 261

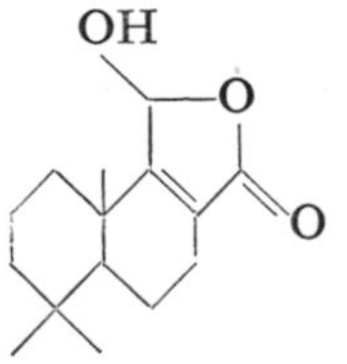

LVa λ* 221 (10,000) valdiviolide
λ^{OH-} 228 (5000) 257 (10,300)

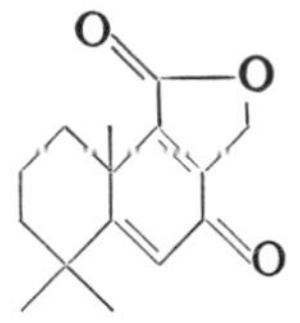

LVI λ 249
λ^{HO-} 249

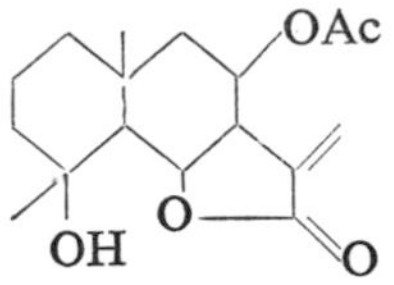

LVII $\lambda\lambda$ $\begin{cases} 206 \ (8100) \\ 210 \ (8000) \\ 220 \ (4000) \\ 230 \ \ (750) \end{cases}$

* The γ-hydroxybutenolides (e.g. LVa) may now be distinguished by basic shift (K. H. Overton, *Priv. comm.*)

(c) *Oxoisodrimenin*[13] (LIII), an oxidation product of the sesquiterpenoid drimenin, has a cross-conjugated enonebutenolide system which has the absorption spectrum (λ_{max} 247 mμ) of the (stronger) enone chromophore (*calc.* 249 mμ) In base, this compound and the related acid (LIV) both show a bathochromic shift of 12 mμ, which is probably due to generation of the enol anion (LV), for the related dienone (LVI), which cannot enolize, undergoes no such shift in alkali.

The "exo" butenolide (LVII) has a multibanded spectrum with the most intense transition near 206 mμ.

(d) *Pentenolides.* α,β-unsaturated-δ-lactones occur with an extra double bond in conjugation as a common chromophore of the cardenolides. The unsubstituted mono-unsaturated pentolide absorption occurs at 205 mμ (Chapter 2,

LVIII λ 300 (ε 5500)   LIX λ 300 (ε 16,600)

p. 82). The diene lactones, i.e. α-pyrones, absorb near 300 mμ (p. 82). γ-Substituted α-pyrone groups occur in the squill glycosides, e.g. (LVIII) and (LIX)[31].

(e) α-*Oxo-δ-lactones (α-hydroxypentenolides).* Two important members of this class are represented by the lactonic chromophores of griseoviridin (LX) and oxolimonin (LXI). Both show bands at 256–7 mμ (ε, 5000) although it is a significant feature of the differing stereochemical environment of these lactones

LX λ 256   LXI λ 257   LXII λ 290

that whereas the griseoviridin lactone is opened in alkali (λ_{max} 256 $\rightarrow$ 246 mμ), the limonin oxolactone is presumably sufficiently stable in alkaline solution to show a shift of $+33$ mμ in this medium (λ_{max} 257 $\rightarrow$ 290 mμ). This absorption may be interpreted as being due to the enol anion (LXII).

8.5. α,β-UNSATURATED ACIDS AND ESTERS

In Chapter 2 we saw that the maxima of acyclic and alicyclic α,β-unsaturated acids and esters may be predicted from the data now resummarized in Table 8.3. The widespread occurrence of these chromophores both in nature and as a

TABLE 8.3. CALCULATION OF MAXIMA OF ACYCLIC AND ALICYCLIC
α,β-UNSATURATED ACIDS AND ESTERS[30]

	$\lambda^{\text{EtOH}}_{\text{max}} \pm 5m\mu$
Alkyl Substitution	
α or β	208
$\alpha\beta$ or $\beta\beta$	217
$\alpha\beta\beta$	225
Increments for each:	
Exocyclic C=C	5
Endocyclic C=C	
in a 5- or 7-membered ring	5
Double bond extending conjugation	30
γ and δ-Alkyl groups	18
α-OH, -OMe, -Br, -Cl	15–20
β-OMe, OAlk	30
β-NMe$_2$	60

direct consequence of degradative operations on natural products prompts us to make some comments on the use of ultraviolet spectra in the diagnosis of structural features of such acids. In addition, we have included in Appendix A the survey made by Nielsen[30], who was responsible for the evolution of the rules for acid absorption. Some selected examples follow:

Acyclic Acids

Table 2.15A includes data for many acyclic α,β-unsaturated acids. The corresponding amides and alkyl esters absorb at essentially the same wavelengths as the acids from which they are derived.

Alicyclic Acids[30]

Table 2.15B contains data for a selection of naturally-occurring and related alicyclic α,β-unsaturated acids. Attention has already been drawn to the dependence of the maxima on the ring size of such acids. We find that

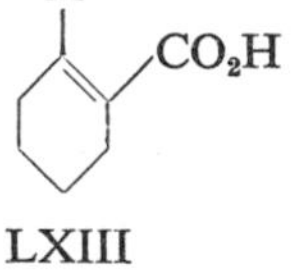

LXIII 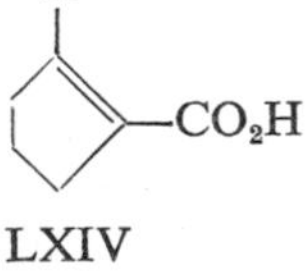   LXIV 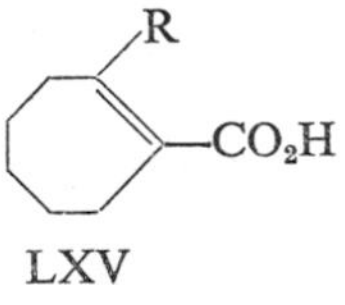   LXV

compared with the unstrained cyclohexene-1-carboxylic acid (LXIII; R=H) λ_{max} 216 mμ, the corresponding five- and seven-membered endocyclic acids

(LXIV, LXV; R=H) both absorb at 222 mμ. The values for the series (LXIII), (LXIV) and (LXV) where R=Me are 224, 230 and 230 mμ. Thus we must add 6 mμ for carrying out calculations of maxima for ring sizes five and seven. Where the double bond is *exo*- to a ring as in (LXVI) an additional 5 mμ must be added.

The effect of steric hindrance to orbital overlap is illustrated for the strained β-cyclogeranic acid (LXVII) which has λ_{calc} 225 mμ (Table 8.3), but in fact

LXVI   LXVII   LXVIII

absorbs at 206 mμ (ε, 3400), a position and intensity comparable with that of the data for 1,2-dimethylcyclohexene (LXVIII) (λ_{max} 208 mμ (ε, 2500)).

LXIX   LXX

The unsubstituted "exo" acids (as LXIX) have maxima near 223 mμ. α-Substituted members of this series (LXX) have λ_{max} 230 mμ. Steric hindrance to coplanarity lowers the ε values for these acids and may depress the wavelength sufficiently to mislead the investigator in assignation of substitution pattern. The increasing use of nuclear magnetic resonance data should provide valuable complementary evidence in this type of problem.

Substituents other than Alkyl[30]

For Cl, Br or OMe placed on the α-carbon atom of the α,β-double bond of the unsaturated acids, a shift of 15–20 mμ together with a slight intensity *de-*

LXXI   LXXII

crease is found. The same groups when placed on the β-carbon atom cause similar shifts with concomitant intensity *increase*. The NMe$_2$ group as usual has an even greater effect ($+ 60$ mμ). Thus the dimethylamino acid (LXXI) absorbs at 285 mμ. The substitution of the double bond at the β-position by oxygen included in the ring as in (LXXII) is a common structural feature in certain classes of alkaloid. This chromophore may be calculated as for —OMe, i.e. 217 (α,β-dialkyl) + 30 (β-OMe) = 247 mμ (*observed* 245 mμ). A list of increments for substitution by groupings other than alkyl or ring residue is given in Table 8.3.

Dienoic Acids[30]

Additional conjugation shifts the E.T. band of an α,β-unsaturated acid by *ca.* 30 mμ. Thus sorbic acid (LXXIII) has λ_{max} 259 mμ (ε, 20,000) (*calc.* 256 mμ)

$$CH_3CH=CH—CH=CH—CO_2H$$

LXXIII

LXXIV λ 229

Cyclopropyl Acids[30]

The conjugative effect of the cyclopropane ring is indicated by the maxima of 3(2-carboxy-3-methylcyclopropyl)propenoic acid (LXXIV) and of chrysanthemum dicarboxylic acid (LXXV).

LXXV λ 236–238   LXXVI   (R=H or Me)

The *non-conjugated dienoic acids*[30] (e.g. LXXVI) show anomalous absorption in having maxima at 200 and 236 mμ. The 200 mμ band presumably is due to the —C=C—CO$_2$H electron transfer while the 236 mμ absorption may be assigned to the π-orbital overlap in the excited state, i.e. a "second-order" E.T. band.

Apart from these notable exceptions, there appear to be few cases where the data of Table 8.3 do not yield satisfactory agreement between calculated and observed values.

Miscellaneous Applications

(i) *Mycolipenic acid,* a dextrorotatory acid from the lipids of tubercle bacilli was shown by Robinson[17] and Cason[18] to have structure (LXXVII).

$$CH_3(CH_2)_{17}CHCH_2CHCH=C—CO_2H$$

LXXVII λ 217

A close study of related model compounds indicated that the compound was in fact an α,β-disubstituted unsaturated acid although Nielsen's generalizations were not available to either group at that time.

(ii) *Tribromohexenoic acids*. Nielsen[30] has employed the generalizations established in the foregoing section to reassign a structure to the tribromo-

$$CH_3CH{=}CBrCH{=}CHCO_2H \rightarrow CH_3CHBrCBr_2CH{=}CHCO_2H$$

LXXVIII   LXXX

↓

$$CH_3CHBrCHBrCH{=}CBrCO_2H$$

LXXIX

acid and obtained by bromination of 4-bromo-2,4-hexadienoic acid (LXXVIII). The suggestion is that the tribromide is in fact the 2,4,5-(LXXIX) rather than the isomeric 4,4,5-compound (LXXX) on the grounds that the maximum of the tribromide is 13 mμ higher than that expected for an acid with only one β-substituent.

(iii) *Tetrahydroindane carboxylic acid*. The structure of the acid obtained as a by-product of Clemmensen reduction of the keto-ester (LXXXI) has λ_{max}

CO$_2$Et   CO$_2$H

LXXXI λ 234 (ε 12,000)

234 mμ (ε, 12,000). For this reason, Nielsen[30] has assigned the trisubstituted structure with the double bond *exo*- to the six and *endo*- to the five-membered ring. λ_{calc} for this acid is 235 mμ.

8.6. ULTRAVIOLET SPECTRA OF SOME STEROIDS[31]

The steroid framework with its rigorous conformational requirements has provided excellent opportunity for the testing of the validity of the rules for diene and enone absorption. Some representative examples were discussed in Chapter 2. In the present section we shall consider the recognition of certain structural features present in steroidal molecules not only from the position of maximal absorption of the chromophore but also from considerations of occurrence of subsidiary maxima. We shall also see how, within this category at least, further refinements and modifications can be made to our sets of values for predicting maxima of $\pi \rightarrow \pi^*$ and electron transfer bands.

(i) *Steroidal Dienes*

Table 8.4 contains average and range values for λ_{max} and ε of hetero- and homo-annular dienes of the steroid group. The wide range of intensity values, especially for the homoannular dienes may be attributed to the difficulty of

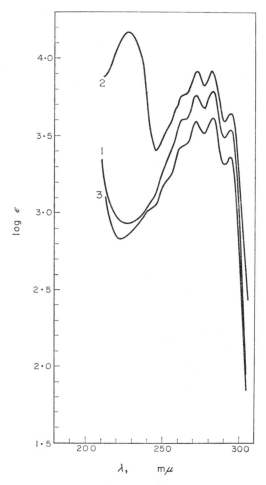

FIG. 8.3. Ultraviolet spectra of $\Delta^{5,7}$-steroidal dienes (in ethanol). Curve 1: Norcholesta-5,7-diene-3β-ol. Curve 2: Norcholesta-5,7-diene-3β-benzoate. Curve 3: Norcholesta-5,7-diene-3β-acetate. (C.G. Alberti, B. Camerino and L. Mamdi, *Helv. Chim. Acta*, **32**, 2038, 1949.)

purification of conjugated olefins. An important feature of the spectrum of the homoannular dienes not implied in any way by the empirical methods[†] of calculating the *strongest* band, is that three peaks are usually present, a maximum appearing *ca.* 10 mμ either side of the principal peak (see Fig. 8.3). This is not

† See Chapter 2.

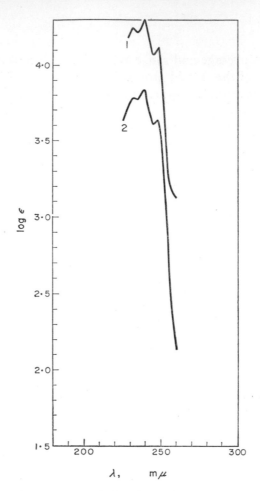

Fig. 8.4. Ultraviolet spectra of $\varDelta^{4,6}$-dienes (in ethanol). Curve 1: Cholesta-4,6-diene-3β-acetate. Curve 2: Norcholesta-4,6-diene-3β-acetate. (G. Alberti, B. Camerino and L. Mamdi, *Helv. Chim. Acta*, **32**, 2038, 1949.)

completely diagnostic for a homoannular diene system, for we note from Table 8.4 that the $\varDelta^{3,5}$, $\varDelta^{4,6}$ and $\varDelta^{7,9(11)}$ *hetero*annular dienes also show such fine structure. However, since the homoannular dienes consistently have absorption bands with ε 10,000–15,000 (or sometimes lower), they may usually be distinguished without

LXXXII

undue difficulty from the *heteroannular* dienes which have λ_{max} 20,000 or more (Fig. 8.4) except in the case of the *cisoid* dienes (as LXXXII).

TABLE 8.4. ULTRAVIOLET ABSORPTION OF CONJUGATED STEROID DIENES

Compound	Average		Range		λ_{max} calculated (mμ)
	λ_{max} (mμ)	ε_{max}	λ_{max} (mμ)	ε_{max}	
$\Delta^{2,4}$	~266 275 ~287			6300–15,000 6300–20,000 13,500	273
CH_2 $\Delta^{3',4}$	233 239	16,200 17,300			239
R $\Delta^{3,5}$ (R = H, CH$_3$COO *)	228 235 243(i)†	18,600 19,000 13,600	228 234–239 243(i)	18,600 16,800–20,000 13,600	234
R $\Delta^{4,6}$ (R = OH, CH$_3$COO)	232 239 248	21,500 23,500 16,000	232 238–240 248	17,800–24,000 20,100–28,200 12,700–19,500	234
$\Delta^{5,7}$	262(i) 271 282 293	7700 11,400 11,900 6900	262(i) 270–273 280–283 292–294	7400–8000 9500–15,500 10,000–15,900 5700–9780	283
$\Delta^{5,7'}$ CH$_2$	236	20,000			239
$\Delta^{6,8 (9)}$	275	5000	275	4700–5300	273
$\Delta^{6,8 (14)}$	253	17,000	245–253		244

† (i) signifies an inflection.
* The bands or inflections at 228 and 243 mμ do not appear when a C$_3$-acetate group or C$_3$-halogen is present.

TABLE 8.4. (contd.)

Compound	Average		Range		λ_{max} calculated (mμ)
	λ_{max} (mμ)	ε_{max}	λ_{max} (mμ)	ε_{max}	
$\Delta^{7,9\,(11)}$	236 243 251	12,800 14,500 10,100	235–236 242–245 250–252	10,000–15,400 10,700–17,000 9000–11,400	244
$\Delta^{7,14}$	242	10,000	242–250	9900–15,000	244
$\Delta^{8,14}$	248	18,500	245–250	16,100–20,000	244
$\Delta^{9,12\,(28)}$	242	19,500			244
$\Delta^{16,20}$	238	15,000			224

An application of the interpretation of the characteristic *shape* of the spectrum of a diene was noted for a triterpene case on p. 51.

(ii) *Trienes*

The observed and calculated maxima for a series of steroidal trienes appears in Table 8.5. We must note that certain crossed chromophoric arrangements of

LXXXIII λ 243, 285

three or more conjugated double bonds are not amenable to the application of the diene–polyene rules. Thus the triene (LXXXIII) has λ_{max} 243 and 285 mμ indicating resolution into partial chromophores, neither of which is, however,

TABLE 8.5. ULTRAVIOLET ABSORPTION OF CONJUGATED STEROID TRIENES

Compound	Average		Range		λ_{max} calculated (mμ)
	λ_{max} (mμ)	ε_{max}	λ_{max} (mμ)	ε_{max}	
$\Delta^{2,4,6}$	296 306 320	14,500	296 304–307 320	12,600–16,600	303
$\Delta^{3,5,7}$ (R=H, CH$_3$COO)	302 315 331	16,800 19,800 13,400	301–305 314–317 330–332	12,500–20,000 15,700–23,400 11,100–17,400	313
$\Delta^{4,6,8,(14)}$	283	33,000			284
$\Delta^{5,7,9(11)}$	312 324 339	10,400 11,800 7400	310–312 322–325 338–340	9100–11,500 10,300–14,500 6400–7950	323
$\Delta^{5,7,14}$	319	16,200	319	15,000–17,500	323
$\Delta^{9,(24),5(11)}$	~243 285	~12,000 9100			

close to the predicted values of diene components of (LXXXIII). It is interesting to find that the placement of an acetoxyl grouping on a diene or triene chromophore often results in the removal of the fine structure to leave only the principal (calculable) maximum.

TABLE 8.6. ULTRAVIOLET ABSORPTION OF $\alpha\beta$-UNSATURATED STEROID KETONES AND RELATED COMPOUNDS

Compound	Average		Range		λ_{max} calculated (mμ)
	λ_{max} (mμ)	ε_{max}	λ_{max} (mμ)	ε_{max}	
Δ^1-3-one	230	10,700	229–232	10,000–12,600	227
Δ^2-2-formyl	235 300	12,600 70			227
Δ^4-3-one	241 306	16,600 94	239–244 295–313	10,500–22,700 70–146	244
Δ^4-6-one	244 310	6300 100	243–244 300–320	6300–6400 85–120	242
Δ^5-4-one	241	5200	240–241	3200–7200	242
Δ^6-7-one	239	12,000	238–240	8900–15,100	244
Δ^7-6-one	252 329	13,400 130	252–253 323–333	13,100–13,600 100–160	244

TABLE 8.6. (contd.)

Compound	Average		Range		λ_{max} calculated $(m\mu)$
	λ_{max} $(m\mu)$	ε_{max}	λ_{max} $(m\mu)$	ε_{max}	
$\Delta^{8(9)}$-7-one	253	11,200	252–254	8300–13,200	249
$\Delta^{8(9)}$-11-one	254	9100	252–255	8700–9600	249
$\Delta^{8(14)}$-7-one	262	9500	260–263	7800–10,800	259
$\Delta^{8(14)}$-15-one	259	13,000	259	12,700–13,300	259
$\Delta^{9(11)}$-12-one	240 318	11,200 85	238–243 311–322	8300–15,800 71–120	244
Δ^{16}-12-one	240 314	10,500 95	239–242 310–318	8000–16,000 64–126	237
Δ^{16}-17-COOH (R = H, CH$_3$)	228	12,600	225–230	12,600	

TABLE 8.6 — (contd.)

Compound	Average		Range		λ_{max} calculated (mμ)
	λ_{max} (mμ)	ε_{max}	λ_{max} (mμ)	ε_{max}	
R = CH$_2$ ... R = C(CH$_3$)$_2$ 16-methylene-17-one	228 250 338	8000 14,800 100			230 254
Δ^{17}-16-one	236	14,800			244
Δ^{17}-21-one	242 310	20,000 120			244
Δ^{17}-21-al	244	26,900	244	26,300–27,500	244
Δ^{17}-21-COOH	222	15,300	222–224	12,600–16,600	224
Δ^{17}-21-nitrile	224	11,600	223–225	10,500–13,800	

TABLE 8.6 a. ULTRAVIOLET ABSORPTION OF STEROID DIENONES

Compound	Average		Range		λ_{max} calculated (mμ)
	λ_{max} (mμ)	ε_{max}	λ_{max} (mμ)	ε_{max}	
$\Delta^{1,4}$-3-one	244	15,000	243–245	10,000–18,600	244
$\Delta^{2,4}$-6-one	315	7000	314–317	6300–7600	316
$\Delta^{3,5}$-2-one	290	12,600			286
$\Delta^{3,5}$-7-one	279	26,400	277–280	24,400–28,000	280
$\Delta^{4,6}$-3-one	284	28,000	281–284	25,000–30,000	280
$\Delta^{7,9}$-12-one	239 292	3700 13,100	238–240 290–293	3700–3800 12,900–13,500	303
$\Delta^{8,14}$-7-one (?)	223 298	15,600 5000	298–300	4800–5300	
$\Delta^{8(14),9}\Delta$-15-one (?)	307	10,000			356

TABLE 8.6 a—(contd.)

Compound	Average		Range		λ_{max} calculated (mμ)
	λ_{max} (mμ)	ε_{max}	λ_{max} (mμ)	ε_{max}	
$\Delta^{14,16}$-17-COOH	295	12,000	292–298	10,500–15,800	
$\Delta^{14,16}$-17-nitrile	286	13,200	286	11,200–14,800	
$\Delta^{14,16}$-20-one	307	17,000			334

(iii) *Unsaturated Steroidal Ketones*

A summary of the rules for the prediction of the E.T. bands of substituted cyclohexenones appears in Chapter 2, while the rather special case of cyclopentenone absorption has been considered in the present chapter. It is felt that the inclusion of a range of α,β-unsaturated steroidal ketone chromophores in this section may provide a reference source helpful in recognizing structural features. Although most of ketones in Table 8.6 may have their maxima predicted to within 5 mμ, certain trends of intensity or wavelength characteristics are discernible which may prove useful in deciding between isomeric structures. Thus, in Δ^4-3-oxosteroids the presence of a —CO$_2$R group at C$_{17}$ apparently causes an intensity drop from 10,700 to 7000.

LXXXIV λ 244, 284, 388
λ_{calc} 384

The various enediones are listed in Table 8.7 and trienones in Table 8.8. Note that all trienones containing a homoannular diene component as (LXXXIV) have *three* absorption bands – the longest (calculable) wavelength band together with bands corresponding to the partial chromophores present.

TABLE 8.7. ULTRAVIOLET ABSORPTION OF STEROID ENEDIONES

Compound	Average		Range		λ_{max} calculated (mμ)
	λ_{max} (mμ)	ε_{max}	λ_{max} (mμ)	ε_{max}	
Δ^4-3,6-dione	253	11,200	252–254	10,800–11,400	244
$\Delta^{8(9)}$-7,11-dione	270	7400	268–272	6300–8700	249
$\Delta^{8(14)}$-7,15-dione	255	5000			259
Δ^{17}-16,22-dione	246	13,500			254

As we noted earlier calculations and predictions of maxima and intensity values must often take account of the geometrical requirements of the chromophores. A particularly apt example is that of the following isomeric pair[74]:

λ 290 (ε 24,000) λ 263 (ε 11,500)

TABLE 8.8. ULTRAVIOLET ABSORPTION OF STEROID TRIENONES

Compound	Average		Range		λ_{max} calculated (mμ)
	λ_{max} (mμ)	ε_{max}	λ_{max} (mμ)	ε_{max}	
$\Delta^{1,4,6}$-3-one	223 256 298	13,500 11,900 15,300	222–224 256–258 296–300	10,700–15,500 9300–13,500 12,300–18,600	280
$\Delta^{1,3,5}$-7-one	230 278 348	18,600 3720 11,000			348
$\Delta^{4,6,8\,(9)}$-3-one	244 284 388	17,800 2190 12,300			384
$\Delta^{4,6,8(14)}$-3-one	348	26,500			356

A useful correlation discernible from the data of the above tables is that the Δ^4-3-and -5-ketones (LXXXV) and (LXXXVI) absorb more intensely and at

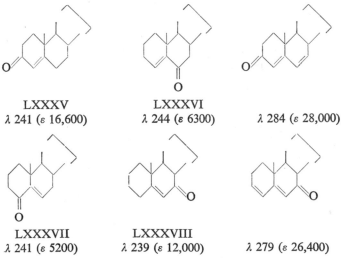

LXXXV
λ 241 (ε 16,600)

LXXXVI
λ 244 (ε 6300)

λ 284 (ε 28,000)

LXXXVII
λ 241 (ε 5200)

LXXXVIII
λ 239 (ε 12,000)

λ 279 (ε 26,400)

Chart I. $\Delta^{4:5}$ and $\Delta^{5,6}$ Steroidal ketones slightly higher wavelengths than the Δ^5-compounds (LXXXVII) and (LXXXVIII) (see Chart I).

The "second-order" effects in (LXXXIX), (XC) and (XCI) are presented without comment in Chart II. Much careful work and the collection of more relevant data are needed before we can make predictions or even interpretations of such phenomena, and there appears to be much scope for further correlation in this area.

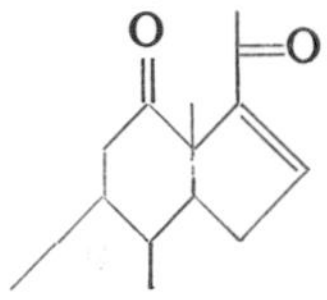

LXXXIX λ 227 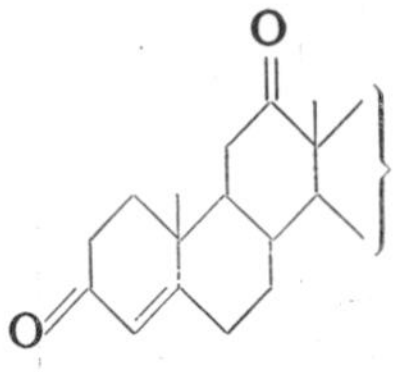   XC λ 236

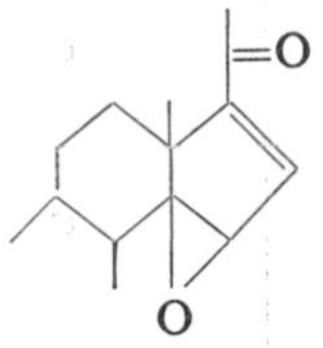

XCI λ 248

Chart II. Steroidal ketones with anomalous absorption

(iv) *Effect of Groupings Adjacent to Enones*

In Chapter 2 we saw that the $n \rightarrow \pi^*$ band of the enone chromophore may be affected by γ-substituents where the p-electrons of such substituents are in conformations propitious for interaction with the π electron system. The general effect on the *major* E.T. bands of the enones has not, in the past, been emphasized, although Dorfman has noted such effects. From the data summarized in Table 8.9 we see that the E.T. band is affected by neighbouring halogen and oxygenated substituents in a manner significant enough to develop incremental (and hyperchromic) values. These effects become increasingly important for polybromo-substitution.

Application of these additional "rules" to some bromoenones can now be made. The increments for the bromo group placed α or β- to an α,β-unsaturated ketone are 25 and 30 mμ, respectively. In Chart III we have listed a number of bromoketones with calculated and observed maxima. The second set of calculated maximum values below those enones which bear *adjacent* bromo groups has been obtained by incorporating the factors in Table 8.9 and provide more reliable values than the first calculated value which has been obtained directly from the Fieser modification of Woodward's rules (p. 58).

The validity of the modified parameters for calculation of new chromophores containing bromo groups is nicely illustrated for the case of the product

TABLE 8.9. EFFECT ON THE E.T. BAND OF SUBSTITUENTS ADJACENT
TO STEROIDAL ENONES[31, 73]

	Conformation	$\Delta\lambda(m\mu)$
A. Δ^4-3-ketones		

	Conformation	$\Delta\lambda(m\mu)$
6α-OH	e	0
6α-OAc	e	0 to -6
6β-OH	a	-3 to -6
6α-OAc	a	-3 to -6
2α-Br	e	$+3$
2α-I	e	$+2$
2,2-DiBr	a,e	$+9$
6α-Br	e	0
6β-Br	a	$+8$

B. Δ^4-6-ketones

	Conformation	$\Delta\lambda(m\mu)$
3β-OH	e	-5
3β-OAc	e	-8

C. $\Delta^{8,9}$-7-ketone

	Conformation	$\Delta\lambda(m\mu)$
	—	$+10$

of bromination of the isodihydroiresin[19] derivative (XCII) to give the dibromide
(XCIII) λ_{max} 262–4 mμ (log ε 4·09) which,

| XCII | XCIII | XCIV |

on the basis of conformation (XCIV) has λ_{calc} 215 (parent) $+10$ (α-methyl)

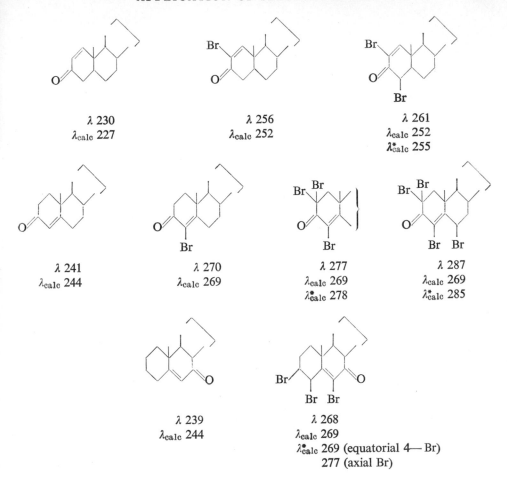

λ 230
λ_{calc} 227

λ 256
λ_{calc} 252

λ 261
λ_{calc} 252
λ^*_{calc} 255

λ 241
λ_{calc} 244

λ 270
λ_{calc} 269

λ 277
λ_{calc} 269
λ^*_{calc} 278

λ 287
λ_{calc} 269
λ^*_{calc} 285

λ 239
λ_{calc} 244

λ 268
λ_{calc} 269
λ^*_{calc} 269 (equatorial 4—Br)
277 (axial Br)

Chart III. Observed and calculated maxima of some steroidal bromoketones

+ 24 (2 × β-ring residues) + 5 (exo C=C) + 3(α-equatorial bromine) + 8(γ-axial bromine) = 265 mμ. Similarly 2α, 6β-dibromo-4-methyltestosterone acetate (partial formula XCV) has λ_{max} 263·5 mμ (*calc*. 265 mμ). Although

XCV

Dorfman has in fact drawn attention to this type of effect in *configurational* terms, the relationship between light absorption and *conformation* of such systems has hitherto been discussed only with a view to finding increments for substituents on $n \rightarrow \pi^*$ transitions of the $-\overset{|}{C}=O$ grouping.† It does not seem too surprising that the E.T. bands should be even more prone to the consequences of steric overlap of p and π-electron systems than the local excitation bands.

(v) *Enol Esters of Unsaturated Ketones*

As a further characterization procedure, the steroidal α,β-unsaturated ketones may be converted to the enol ether or ester which now exhibits the spectrum of a substituted polyene. For example, a $\varDelta^4$-3-oxo steroid gives the corresponding acetate, ether chloride, or thioether (Chart IV) while the $\varDelta^{4,6}$-diene-3-ones give a mixture of the isomeric triene acetates. Ene-diones (as XCVI) may give two diesters (as XCVII, XCVIII).

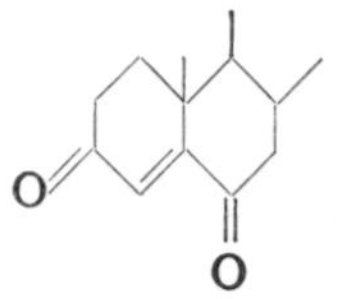

XCVI

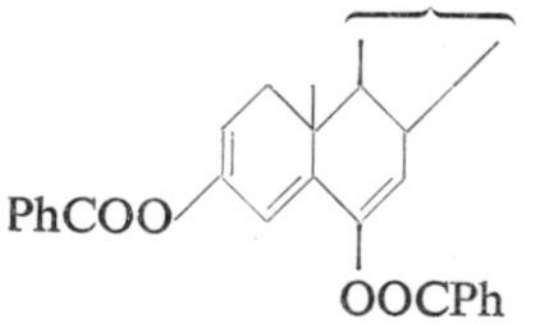

| XCVIII | λ 307 |
| | λ_{calc} 303 |

| XCVII | λ 316 |
| | λ_{calc} 308 |

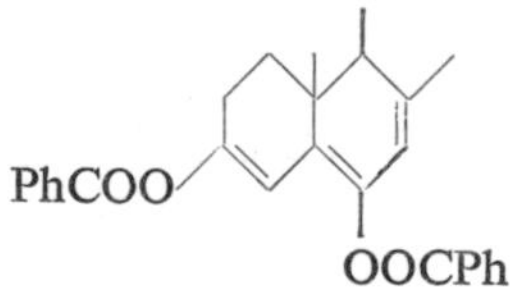

(vi) *Ethylene Mercaptals*

Where these contain a double bond β- to the quaternary spiro carbon atom as in (XCIX), the maximum occurs at 222 mμ (ε 6400). The saturated mercaptals (as C) absorb weakly at 240 mμ (ε 333).

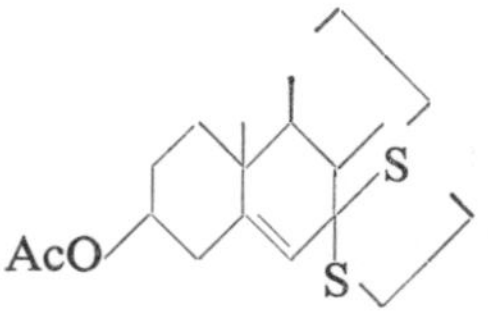

XCIX 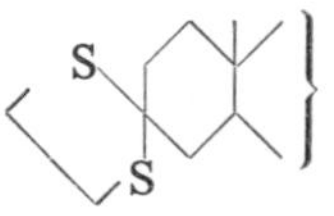   C

† Tables of such increments have recently been published (H.J.Ringold and A.Bowers, *Experientia*, **17**, 65 (1961)).

CHART IV. ULTRAVIOLET ABSORPTION OF ENOL DERIVATIVES OF CONJUGATED STEROID KETONES

Compound	Enol derivative	λ_{max} (mμ)	ε_{max}	Varichromic shift in absorption of conjugated polyene (mμ)
Δ^4-3-one $\varepsilon_{241} \sim 16{,}600$	$\Delta^{3,5}$ R = CH$_3$COO—	235	17,000	
	R = C$_2$H$_5$O—	241	22,600	+ 6
	R = CH$_2$S—	268	22,600	+33
	R = CH$_2$S(=O)—	258	21,400	+23
	R = Cl	238	23,200	+ 3
	R = Br	238	22,700	+ 3
Δ^{16}-20-one $\varepsilon_{240} \sim 10{,}500$	$\Delta^{16,20}$	239	15,100	− 1
$\Delta^{4,7}$-3-one $\varepsilon_{239} \sim 15{,}100$	$\Delta^{3,5,7}$	301	19,300	0
		315	21,300	
		331	17,700	
$\Delta^{4,6}$-3-one $\varepsilon_{234} \sim 28{,}800$	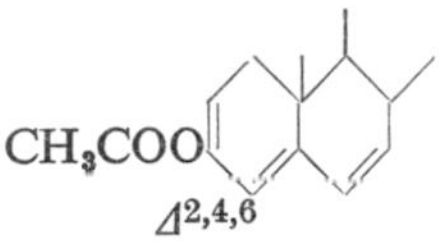 Two forms isolated $\Delta^{2,4,6}$	303	14,600	− 3
$\Delta^{4,7,9}$-3-one $\varepsilon_{243} \sim 32{,}000$	$\Delta^{3,5,7,9}$	338	16,400	
		355	19,700	
		374	14,600	

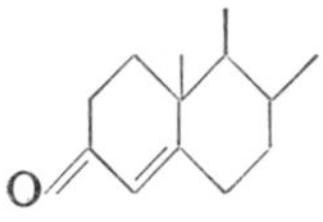

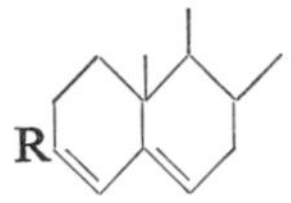

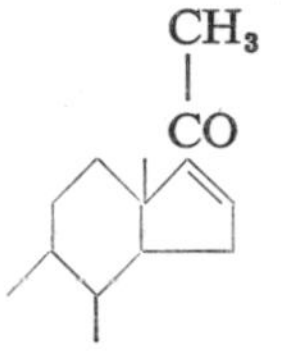

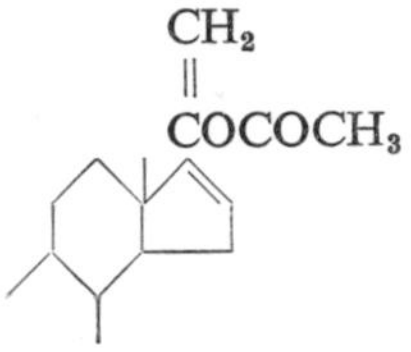

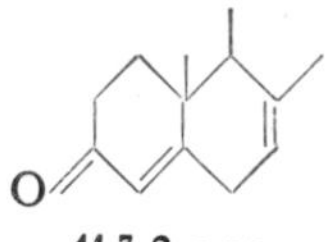

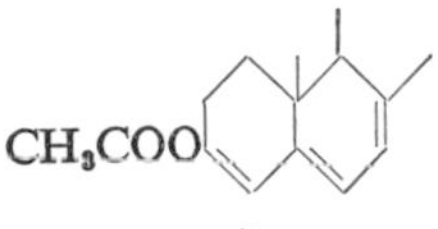

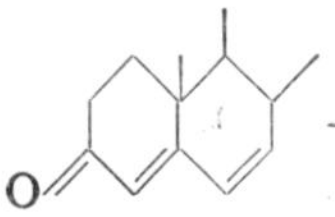

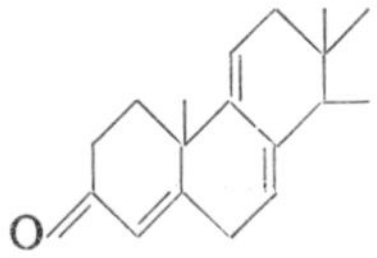

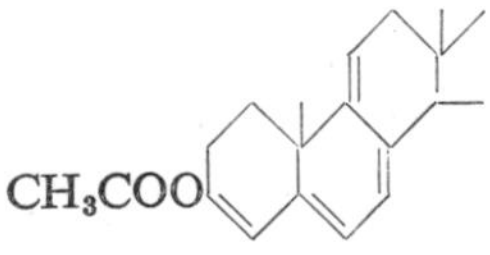

(vii) α-Diketones

The 11,12-diketone (CI) has λ_{max} 279 and 347 mμ (ε 130 and 47) in hexane solution (keto form), the enol (CII) absorbing at 281 mμ (*calc.* 279) in ethanol. The spectral data for a number of steroidal diosphenols and their acetates will be found in Table 8.10 together with the calculated values. The elucidation of

CI   CII

CIII   CIV λ 313   CV

the structures of the enolic forms of diosterol (CIII; cholest-5-ene-3,4-dione) serves as a classical example of the utility of ultraviolet data, although the modifications of the rules as used today were not available to Fieser who deduced the structures in 1948. Diosterol I has λ_{max} 313 (*calc.* for structure CIV 315 mμ). Its benzoate (CV) has bands at 232 mμ (PhCOO E.T. band, *calc.* 230 mμ) and at 287 mμ (dienone, *calc.* 286 mμ). Diosterol II on the other hand has λ_{max} 265 and 300 mμ and is presumably a tautomeric mixture of *enone* (CVI) (*calc.* 262 mμ) and *trienediol* (CVII) (*calc.* 315 mμ). The corresponding acetate (CVIII) has λ_{max} 245 mμ (*calc.* 233 and 242 mμ, respectively) and the benzoate has one intense band at 234 mμ [PhCOO (230 mμ) and enone (233 mμ) bands, superimposed].

CVI   CVII   CVIII

The alkaline shift corresponding to anion formation (CIX) is not always recorded but an average value of + 35 mμ is found through the series and indeed

TABLE 8.10. ULTRAVIOLET ABSORPTION OF ENOLS OF α-DIKETONES

Compound	Enol form	λ_{max} (mμ)	ε_{max}	Bathochromic shift in absorption of parent conjugated ketone (mμ)
2,3-diketo		270	8500	+40
	2-acetate	237	8900	+7
		272	5000	~+42
	3-acetate	238	7400	~+8
3,4-diketo (diketo form also isolated)		280 (CHCl$_3$)	11,500	+39
	4-acetate	248 (CHCl$_3$)	14,500	+8
6,7-diketo	or	275	10,700	~+35
11,12-diketo (diketo form also isolated)		281	~7000	+41
	11-acetate	244	~9500	+4

TABLE 8.10.—(contd.)

Compound	Enol form	λ_{max} (mμ)	ε_{max}	Bathochromic shift in absorption of parent conjugated ketone (mμ)
20-keto-21-al (dicarbonyl form also isolated)	20-acetate	283 246 (ether)	~12,000 14,300	+39 +2
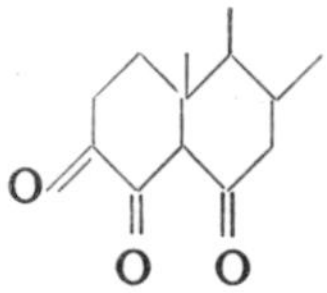 3,4,6-triketo	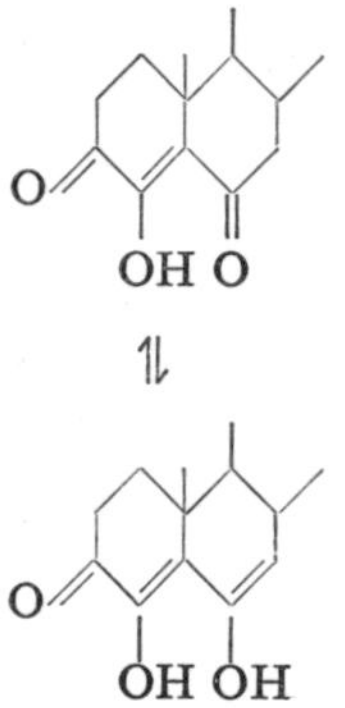	275 (ether) 335	5000 8000	+22 +25

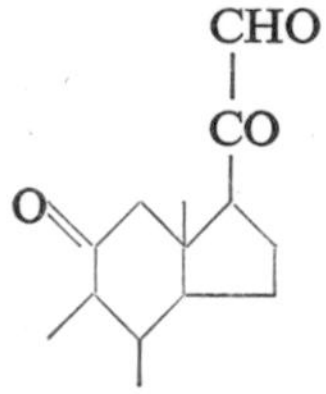

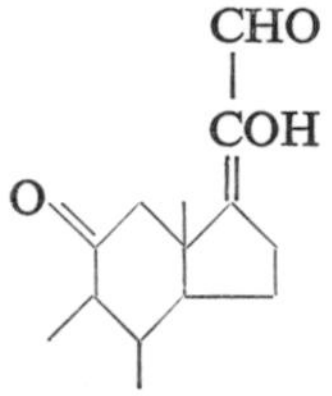

holds for the cyclopentan-1,2-diones (CX), α-oxo-butan- (CXI) and pentanolides (CXII).

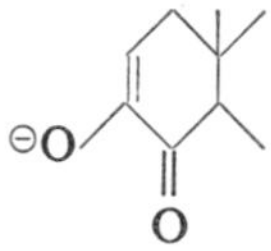

CIX 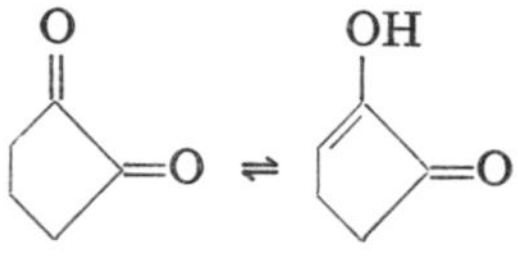   CX

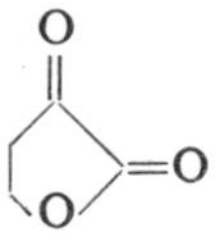

CXI 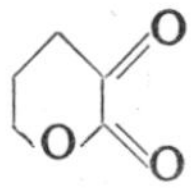   CXII

8.7. β-DIKETONES AND -TRIKETONES (2-ACYL-1,3-DIONES)

The effects of inter- and intra-molecular hydrogen bonding in "flexible" and "trans-fixed" β-diketones has already been mentioned (p. 69). The relevant situations obtaining in appropriate solvents are summarized in Chart V. The maximum for the enolic form of a β-diketone (as CXIII) may be calculated

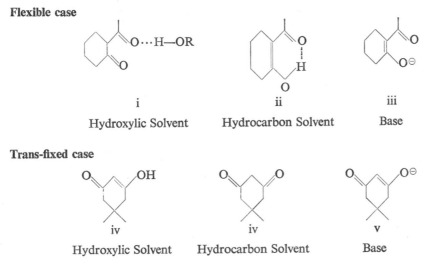

Flexible case

i
Hydroxylic Solvent

ii
Hydrocarbon Solvent

iii
Base

Trans-fixed case

iv
Hydroxylic Solvent

iv
Hydrocarbon Solvent

v
Base

Chart V. Effect of solvent on structure of β-diketones

by using the increment of $+ 30$ mμ for the β-hydroxyl group. It will be noted in several examples, particularly where solvent or dilution is not specified, that the maximum is close to that expected for the enol anion (as CXIV). At high dilution this anion may in fact contribute to the electronic absorption spectrum even in a "neutral" solvent such as ethanol. It should be remembered that the "trans-fixed" β-diketones [as (iv); Chart V] are almost 100% enolized in hydroxylic slovent (intermolecular A-bonding) while in hydrocarbon solvent the diketone form [(v)] is preferred, since intramolecular H-bonding is prohibited. A reversal of this solvent effect on enolization is found in the 2-acylcycloalkanones (as (i)], the keto form being preferred in hydroxylic, the enol in hydrocarbon solvent.

CXIII

CXIV

2-Acylcyclohexan-1,3-diones, which occur in a variety of plants, represent a combination of the fixed and flexible dione cases discussed above. 2-Acetyl-cyclohexane-1,3-dione[20] absorbs at 235 and 275 mμ in ethanol solution. The 275 mμ band may be assigned to contributions from the enols (CXV) and (CXVI) (*calc.* 267 and 272, respectively). The 235 mμ band may represent a

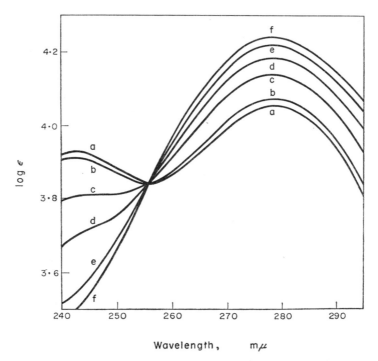

partial chromophore or may in fact indicate a contribution from the dienol form (CXVII). In any event, the relative intensities of the maxima are dependent on the degree of dissociation of the β-triketone. With increasing dilution in ethanol the intensity of the 235 mμ band is *decreased* while the 275 mμ band shows a corresponding increase. Changing to hydrocarbon solvent affords a

FIG. 8.5. Absorption curve of 4,4,6,6-tetramethyl-2-isovalerylcyclohexane-1,3,5-trione at pH, (a) 1·22, (b) 3·38, (c) 4·31, (d) 4·73, (e) 5·41, (f) 13. (Chan and Hassall, *J. Chem. Soc.*, 3497, 1956.)

spectrum almost identical with that observed in acidified ethanol solution. This is good evidence for intramolecular bonding in hydrocarbon solvent. The effect of changing pH on the spectrum of 2-acetyl cyclohexan-1,3-dione is illustrated in Fig. 8.5. There is a sharp isosbestic point at 256 mμ indicating that only two species, the enol (CXV) and its ion (CXVIII) are present.

Although it is not particularly easy to assign absorption bands to contributing species, the conclusion is that the 280 mμ band of β-triketones is associated with both the enol and the ionized species (CXVIII) while the enol itself also contributes to the 240 mμ band. The solution infrared spectrum of the 2 acyl-1,3-diones shows ν_{max} 1650–75 cm^{-1} ($>$C=C—C=O) and has no band above 1700 cm^{-1} in the carbonyl region, indicating that enolization is complete. The chelated C=O absorption occurs at 1540–65 cm^{-1}.

8.8. POLYENES AND CAROTENOIDS

General

The spectra of the all-*trans* polyenes show typical sets of bands spaced at 1450–1500 cm^{-1}, the longest wavelength maximum indicating the extent of conjugation from the Lewis–Calvin equation, $\lambda^2 = kn$ where n is the number of double bonds in conjugation. Bohlmann[32] has pointed out that good agreement with the Lewis–Calvin equation is obtained in the plot λ^2/n provided the *longest* wavelength band is used, whether this represents the most *intense* absorption or not. Thus, the pentaene chromophore of the antibiotic fungi-

CXIX

chromin[36] (CXIX) absorbs at 311, 323, 339 and 357 mμ in accord with expectation, for from data of Table 8.11 which includes the longest bands of some polyene and carotenoid systems we should expect the linear combination of five double bonds with an aldehyde to absorb near the hexaene value (352 mμ).

The naive but useful approach employed in Table 8.11 takes the number of conjugated double bonds of the unsubstituted case as being the effective number, n. This allows certain empirical factors to be added for substitution, e.g. an alkyl group ($\frac{1}{4}$⌐), a terminal ring C=C ($\frac{1}{2}$⌐) and a substituent on the ring C=C ($\frac{1}{8}$⌐). Such good agreement is obtained by this empirical method that in spite of more satisfying theoretical methods† it is the author's opinion that the process described above provides a practical working guide to polyene absorption. As indicated in the case of fungichromin (CXIX), the extension of a

_____

† See p. 52; also a summary of the theoretical treatment of polyenes by the electron gas theory (Ref. 37).

polyene chain by a terminal carbonyl group is equivalent to the effect of adding one double bond. This kind of argument is of value in estimating the effective chromophoric length of a polyene chain, but as we shall now see, many subtleties of stereochemistry can be revealed by a study of the light absorption curve of the carotenoids.

TABLE 8.11. LONGEST WAVELENGTH BANDS AND EFFECTIVE DOUBLE BOND NUMBERS (n) OF SOME POLYENES[32]

Compound	No. of conjugated acyclic double bonds (1 F)	Chain substituents ($\frac{1}{4}$ F)	Ring double bonds ($\frac{1}{2}$ F)	Ring substituents ($\frac{1}{8}$ F)	Effective double bond no. (n)	λ_{max} † (mμ)
$CH_3(CH=CH)_nCH_3$						
$n = 2$	2	—	—	—	2	227
$n = 3$	3	—	—	—	3	263
$n = 4$	4	—	—	—	4	299
$n = 5$	5	—	—	—	5	326
$n = 6$	6	—	—	—	6	352
$n = 8$	8	—	—	—	8	395·5
$n = 9$	9	—	—	—	9	412·5
$C_6H_{13}(CH=CH)_{10}C_6H_{13}$	10	—	—	—	10	432
"C_{30}–KW"	5	2	2	4	7	374
β-Carotene	9	4	2	4	11·5	452
3-dehydro-β-carotene	9	4	3	4	12	461
3,3′-bisdehydro-β-carotene	9	4	4	4	12·5	471
Lycopene ( )	11	6	—	—	12·5	469
Homo-β-carotene ( )	10	4	2	4	12·5	466
Decapreno-β-carotene ( )	13	8	2	4	16·5	498

† in ether or petrol.

Carotenoids

The carotenoid pigments owe their intense colours to their absorption ($\varepsilon \sim 150,000$) in the 400–500 mμ region.† The absorption spectrum of a polyene is conditioned not only by the number and *effective number* of double bonds in conjugation, but also by its *conformation*. Thus, the well-known carotenoids all-*trans* lycopene (CXX) and β-carotene (CXXI) both have eleven conjugated double bonds, although their *effective n* values are 12·5 and 11·5, respectively (Table 8·11). Their longest wavelength bands occur at 469 and 452 mμ, respectively. The effect of alkyl groups on the position of the long wavelength maxi-

† This range is, of course, in the visible, and not the ultraviolet region, but we have widened our spectral horizon at this and certain other points in this monograph to include some account of outstanding work of correlation or interpretation in the visible region.

mum is nicely illustrated by the maximum of 13,13′-desdimethylcarotene (CXXII) which has λ_{max} 10 mμ (2 × $\frac{1}{4}$ ⌐) less than that of β-carotene itself[32].

CXX   All-*trans*   lycopene
λ 469

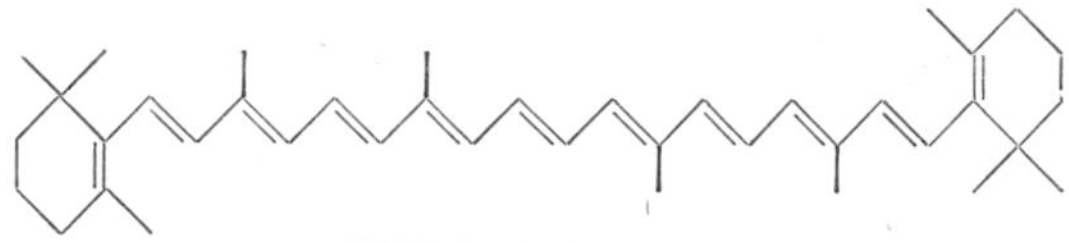

CXXI β-Carotene
λ 452

CXXII   13,13′-Desdimethyl carotene
λ 442

Fine Structure

Inspection of the curves of numerous all-*trans* carotenoids reveals that the principal band may or may not have fine structure. Some classification is possible in that the aliphatic or open chain pigments show much more pronounced fine structure than the hydroaromatic α and β-carotenes. Loss of fine structure is also associated with the introduction of terminal carbonyl groups.

Trans → Cis Isomerization[33]

Perhaps the most meaningful result obtainable from a study of the absorption spectrum of a carotenoid is the information regarding the stereochemistry of the polyene chain. The type of stereoisomerism encountered in carotenoids does not correspond to the adoption of the S-*cis* conformation (CXXIII) associated with the inclusion of a diene moiety within a ring or with a

CXXIII 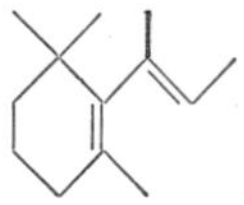   CXXIV

CXXV   CXXVI

CXXVII

sterically overcrowded system (as CXXIV), but rather with geometrical change about the central or double bonds in the molecule represented by (CXXV) → (CXXVI). The experimental observations are as follows. When an all-*trans* carotenoid is converted into a mixture of *cis–trans* isomers of type (CXXVII) by photolytic, catalytic or spontaneous processes, the intensity of the colour of the solution decreases markedly. These changes can be recognized with the aid of the visual spectroscope, but only by following the course of the reaction quantitatively on the spectrophotometer can meaningful interpretation be made. Zechmeister[33] recommends that part of the procedure of character- ization of a new carotenoid should include the recording of the absorption spectrum before and after catalysis by iodine. The wavelength change occasioned by such isomerization then forms an integral part of the description of the polyene and is referred to as the "λ_{max} shift". The results of such measurement are then subjected to the analytical procedure described in the sequel.

CXXVIII   CXXIX

It is found that an all-*trans* carotenoid absorbs at longer wavelength than any of its *cis* isomers. This "rule" is only valid for polyenes of carotenoid di- mension, the lower members showing a reversal of such absorption character- istics. Thus all-*trans* octatetraene (CXXVIII) absorbs at lower wavelength than the all-*cis* isomer (CXXIX). The "λ_{max} shift" values for a series of polyenes are summarized in Table 8.12.

TABLE 8.12. LOCATION OF λ_{max} AND "λ_{max} SHIFTS"
OF SOME POLYCIS LYCOPENES[33]

Name	λ_{max} (hexane)	λ_{max} shift
[All-*trans*]	472–473	0
Neo A	465	7·5
Polycis I	444	28
Prolycopene	438	34·5
Polycis IV	426	46·5

Apart from information derived from the shifts of the long wavelength band during such isomerizations, another generalization is possible for intensity changes occurring simultaneously. Within a given carotenoid set the greatest intensity is shown by the all-*trans* isomer, e.g. (CXXX). Stereoisomers which possess a vertical plane of symmetry (as CXXXI) have a smaller overall length of double bonds in conjugation than the *trans*-isomers. Taking α as 27°22′ it has been found that the $\cos^2\alpha$ law for intensity changes due to steric requirements again applies and we find that the central mono *cis* isomers (as CXXXI) should and in fact do have about 80% of the maximal intensity of the all-*trans* compound, and at a shorter wavelength.

"Cis"-*Peaks*

Because of their bent shape, the second transition or "*cis*-peak" of the central-*cis* carotene (CXXXI) has a dipole moment perpendicular to the straight line joining the ends of the conjugated system. CXXXI would be expected to show the strongest *cis*-peak of the set. Other isomers (e.g. CXXXII) have *cis*-

CXXX all-*trans*

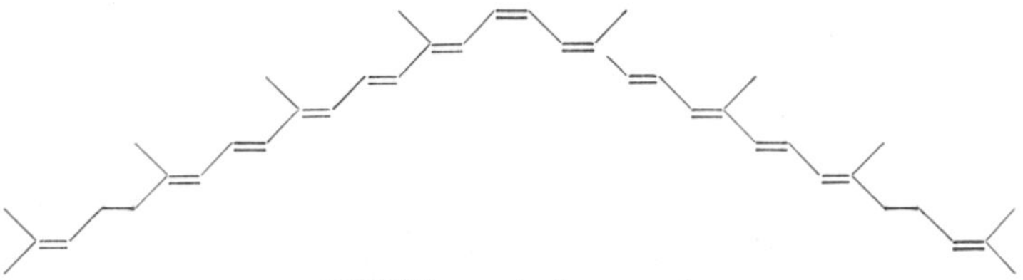

CXXXI central mono*cis*

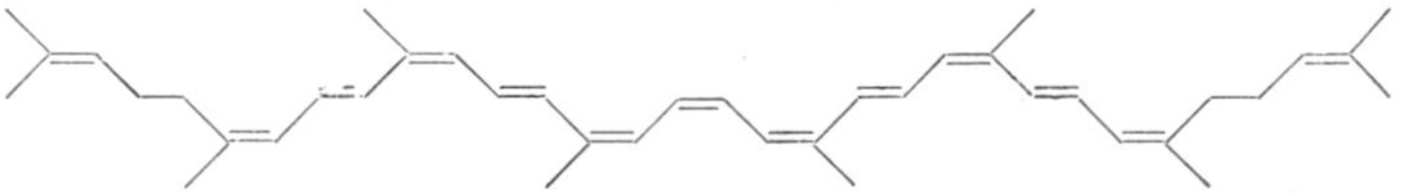

CXXXII hepta-*cis*

peaks of reduced intensity. In the *β*-carotene set 15,15'-di*cis* (CXXXIII) has *no cis* peak, the 15-mono*cis* analogue of (CXXXI) has its strong *cis* peak absorption at 355 m*μ*, the all-*trans* isomer of course showing no *cis* peak. Photoisomerization of the di*cis* carotene (CXXXIII) may be followed by the growth of a

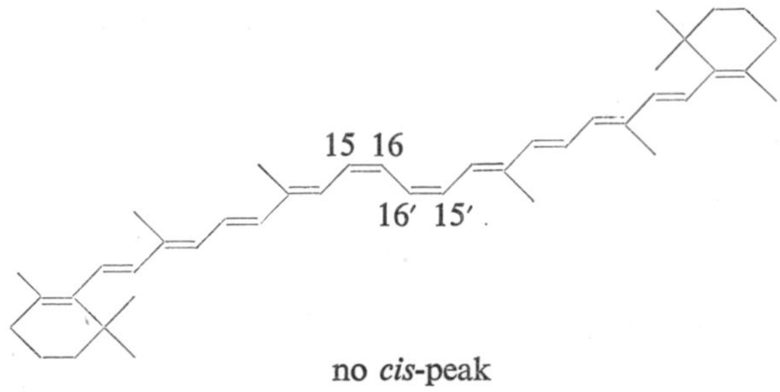

15 16

16' 15'

no *cis*-peak
CXXXIII 16, 16'-di*cis*-*β*-carotene
↓
mono*cis*
↓
all-*trans*

maximum at 355 mμ (di*cis* $\rightarrow$ mono*cis*) while the decay of this peak on pro-
longed irradiation corresponds to the mono*cis* $\rightarrow$ all-*trans* interconversion.
Starting from an all-*trans* isomer of a set irradiation or iodine catalysis usually
gives mono- or di-*cis* isomers which may be respectively identified by the presence or absence of *cis*-peaks. The "λ_{max} shift" values are also helpful because the
fundamental (long wavelength) band is lowered by 5 mμ for mono*cis* and
10 mμ for di*cis* from the all-*trans* position.

Other generalizations which emerge from these studies have been summarized in Table 8.13. These changes are associated with the production of
equilibrium mixtures of the four common classes of stereoisomeric polyene –
all-*trans*, central mono*cis*, peripheral mono*cis*, poly*cis*.

Interpretation of the transitions associated with the *minor* bands of polyene
spectra has been made by Dale[38], whose conclusions may be summarized by the
statement that a minor (or overtone) band of a polyene occurs at a wavelength
(λ_s) near that of the principal (longest wavelength) band of that polyene with
n/s effective double bonds.

For a comprehensive survey of carotenoid spectra the reader is referred to the
review by Zechmeister[33] from whose work the following illustrative example
has been taken. *Methyl bixin* (CXXXIV) is the ester of the naturally occurring
half ester bixin (CXXXV). Several forms of methyl bixin are available for

TABLE 8.13. CONFIGURATIONAL TYPES OF *normal*
CAROTENOIDS AS INDICATED BY SPECTROSCOPIC CHANGES
UPON TREATMENT WITH IODINE[33]

Configuration	Shape of the curve in the *cis*-peak region	Change of the extinction upon iodine catalysis	
		in the *cis*-peak region	in the visible region
All-*trans*	flat	increase	decrease
Central-mono*cis*	high peak	decrease	increase
Peripheral mono*cis*	moderate peak	slight increase	increase
Poly*cis*	flat	increase	strong in-crease

study. These include the natural ester, the all-*trans* isomer, the synthetic central
mono*cis* isomer, and two further isomeric products of iodine catalysis of the
all-*trans* compound, neo A and neo C. The following assignments have been
made on the basis of the spectral data summarized in Table 8.14.

From the λ_{max} shift it is concluded that neo C is a di*cis* isomer ($\Delta\lambda = 10$ mμ)
whereas "natural" and neo A are mono*cis* ($\Delta\lambda = 5$ mμ). At first it was thought
that since neo A had a high *cis*-peak intensity, it must correspond to the central
mono*cis* isomer. However, when it was found that the synthetic central mono*cis*

isomer had an even greater *cis*-peak intensity, neo A was assigned the *next-to-central*, i.e. 8-*cis*-configuration. This leaves the 2,4, and 6-positions for the *cis*-double bond of natural methyl bixin. Now the flatness of the absorption curve in the *cis*-peak region suggests (Table 8.13) that the natural isomer has a peripheral *cis*-configuration. Further, this isomer is not a component of the *trans* → *cis* equilibration of all-*trans* methyl bixin which yields neo A and neo C by iodine catalysis. Natural methyl bixin can be transformed into neo C but not into the all-*trans* isomer. These rather unusual properties suggested that the

TABLE 8.14. λ_{max} SHIFTS OF METHYL BIXINS

Methyl Bixin	$\lambda_{max}^{Benzene}$	λ_{max}^{Petrol}	λ_{max}^{Shift}
All-*trans*	475	458	—
Natural	471	—	4
neo A	470	—	5
neo C	465	—	10
Central mono*cis*	—	455	3

cis-double bond is adjacent to the carbomethoxyl group which confers some stability on the *cis*-form. It was therefore predicted on the basis of these considerations[33] that natural methyl bixin would be the 2-cis-configurational isomer. However, recent evidence from interpretation of the nuclear magnetic resonance spectrum of natural bixin and methyl bixin favours the *cis*-4-configuration[39] (CXXXVI).

CXXXIV; R = Me   CXXXV; R = H

CXXXVI

8.9. NATURALLY OCCURRING ACETYLENES

The spectral properties of poly-yne, poly-yn-ene and polyene-yne chromophores are quite characteristic and considerable use has been made of these data during structural studies. In those systems where triple bonds predominate, the characteristic band spacing of 2000 cm^{-1} forms a reliable guide to the presence of a poly-yne. For mixed poly-yne–polyene chromophores it is often possible to pick out sets of bands spaced at 2000 cm^{-1} [(C≡C)$_n$] and in ad-

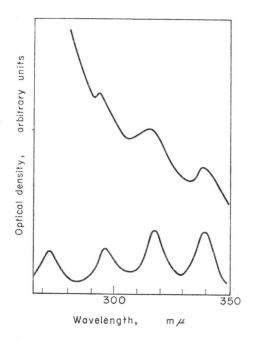

Wavelength,   mμ

FIG. 8.6. Detection of polyacetylenes. Upper curve: absorption spectrum of crude ethanol extract from slope culture of a fungus. Lower curve: absorption spectrum of the acetylenic component after purification. (Bu'Lock, *Quart. Rev.*, **10**, 375, 1956.)

dition the high-intensity–long-wavelength bands of the —(C=C)$_m$— component whose maxima are spaced at 1450–1500 cm^{-1}. Some idea of the ratio of poly-yne to polyene component may be gained by consideration of the intensities and positions of the longest wavelength band of each set.

In some cases, a study of the ultraviolet and infrared spectra followed by reduction of a natural poly-acetylene to a known hydrogenation product have been sufficiently informative uniquely to define the structure, which in this field, has usually been confirmed by synthesis.

Isolation

The course of isolation of poly-acetylenic materials from fungal or plant source is conveniently followed by ultraviolet spectroscopic analysis of crude extracts[40]. In Fig. 8.6 a typical spectrum of such a fungal extract (upper curve) clearly shows the presence of the poly-yne whose spectrum after purification is reproduced in the lower curve.

The following examples indicate the utility of ultraviolet spectra in interpreting the structures of a diversity of acetylenic chromophores.

Mono-ynes

(i) *Carlinoxide and junipal.* These naturally occurring mono-ynes have the acetylenic linkage conjugated with furan and thiophen rings respectively.

CXXXVII   CXXXVIII

Carlinoxide (CXXXVII) has λ_{max} 250 mμ[41], while junipal (CXXXVIII), a constituent of the fungus *Daedalea juniperina*, has λ_{max} 216, 286 and 320 mμ[42] the last of these bands marking the electron transfer between the thiophen-yne and aldehyde groupings.

Enyne

We saw in Chapter 2 that the spectrum of an enyne was closely similar to that of a diene. A shoulder at *ca.* 235 mμ can often be observed in the enyne

$$CH_3(CH_2)_5CH\overset{t}{=}CHC\equiv C(CH_2)_7CO_2H$$

CXXXIX

spectrum which serves as a distinguishing feature, although the distinction is more securely made by reference to infrared and n.m.r. spectra. A natural enyne is represented by ximenynic acid (CXXXIX), λ_{max} 229 mμ[43].

Ene-diynes

The position and spacing of the principal di-yne bands (p. 55) are quite evident in the spectra of such natural products as *cis*-lachnophyllum ester (CXL)[44] and *cis–cis*-matricaria ester (CXLI)[45].

$$CH_3CH_2CH_2(C\equiv C)_2CH\overset{c}{=}CHCO_2Me \qquad CH_3CH\overset{c}{=}CH(C\equiv C)_2CH\overset{c}{=}CHCO_2Me$$

CXL   CXLI

λ^{hexane} 224·5 276   291·5 309·5 mμ λ^{hexane} 232   246   259 314   336

$10^{-3}\varepsilon$ 35·4   9·5 14·4 15·8 $10^{-3}\varepsilon$ 22·2 25·4 23 15·4 12·9

D. *Ene-tri-yne*

$$CH_3(C{\equiv}C)_3CH{\overset{t}{=}}CH{-}CO_2Me \quad CXLII$$

λ 244·7   255   268   283·5   300·8   320·4   343·5

$10^{-3}\,\varepsilon$ 71·8   106·2   8·6   15   32   45   6

In *trans*-dehydromatricaria ester[46] (CXLII) the appearance of the high intensity set of bands which are associated with the $(C{\equiv}C)_n$ chromophore make their appearance in the accessible region of the ultraviolet spectrum. This happens when n is greater than 2. The appearance of the "strong" and "weak" sets of bands in these positions allows of immediate recognition of the type

$$CH_3(C{\equiv}C)_3CH{\overset{t}{=}}CHCH_2CH_2COC_2H_5$$

CXLIII

of absorption and often the extent of conjugation. A second example is provided by the ketone[47] (CXLIII) whose longest wavelength band is at 329 mμ. From this observation it can be concluded that a terminal ester in a tri-yne contributes a bathochromic effect of *ca.* 15 mμ.

E. *Tri-yne Diene*[48, 49]

$$CH_3(C{\equiv}C)_3(CH{=}CH)_2(CH_2)_4CH{=}CH_2$$

Centaur X_3

λ 258   269   288   305   324   347 mμ (petrol)

$10^{-3}\,\varepsilon$ 49·7   101   12·7   25   40   35

$$CH_3(C{\equiv}C)_3CH{=}CHCH{=}O$$

λ 245   258   288   306   326   350 mμ (hexane)

$10^{-3}\,\varepsilon$ 49   87   11·9   27·8   44   36·5

F. *Tetra-yne Diene*[50]

$$CH_3CH{=}CH(C{\equiv}C)_4CH{=}CH_2$$

λ 258   271   278·5   315·5   337   361   390 mμ (hexane)

$10^{-3}\,\varepsilon$ 143   189   143   11·6   17·2   20·9   13·4

G. *Ene-penta-yne*[51]

$$CH_2{=}CH{-}(C{\equiv}C)_5{-}CH_3$$

λ 265 271 286 309 329 352 378 411 mμ (hexane)

$\Delta\nu$ 1930 2600 1960 1990 1900 2170 cm^{-1}

H. *Di-yne Triene*[52]

$$HOCH_2{\cdot}CH_2(C{\equiv}C)_2(CH{=}CH)_3CHOH{\cdot}C_3H_7$$

Cicutoxin

λ 242 252 318 335 mμ

$10^{-3}\,\varepsilon$ 13   22   63·5 65.

We note that the position and intensity of the longest wavelength band corresponds to that of a polyene, *not* a poly-yne. Again the "strong" set of bands associated with poly-yne absorption does not appear in the accessible (215 mμ) region. The isomeric ene-diyne-diene (CXLIV) has the same band spacing, viz. 2230, 2030 and 2080 cm^{-1},

$$HOCH_2(CH{=}CH)(C{\equiv}C)_2(CH{=}CH)_2CH_2{\cdot}CH_2{\cdot}CHOH{\cdot}C_3H_7$$

CXLIV

λ 213 252 267 296 315 337 mμ (EtOH)

$10^{-3}\,\varepsilon$ 17·5 33   17·5 30·5 40   29

and the longest wavelength band appears at 337 mμ although with only half the intensity of that of cicutoxin. The 2000 cm^{-1} spacing is found in all polyen-ynes with at least *two* C$\equiv$C linkages in conjugation.

I. *Cumulene-diyne-diene*

$$CH{\equiv}C{-}C{\equiv}C{-}CH{=}C{=}CH{-}CH{\overset{c}{=}}CH{-}CH{\overset{t}{=}}CH{-}CH_2{\cdot}COOH$$

Mycomycin   CXLV

The antibiotic mycomycin has λ_{max} 256, 267, and 281 mμ ($10^{-3}\,\varepsilon$, 35, 61 and 67)[53]. At first sight it seems surprising that this chromophore should not

$$CH_3(C{\equiv}C)_3(CH{=}CH)_2CH_2COOH$$

CXLVI   Isomycomycin

λ^{Et_2O} 246 257·5 267   287·5 305·5 324   347 mμ

$10^{-3}\,\varepsilon$ 23   58   110   13   27   42   34 exert its full effective length as bands above 300 mμ would be expected in such a highly conjugated system. The allene grouping, however, effectively divides the molecule so that only by transformation into isomycomycin (CXLVI) do we observe a band near 350 mμ. Isomycomycin is easily identified as a diene-tri-yne when we compare the position (267 mμ) and intensity (110,000) of the

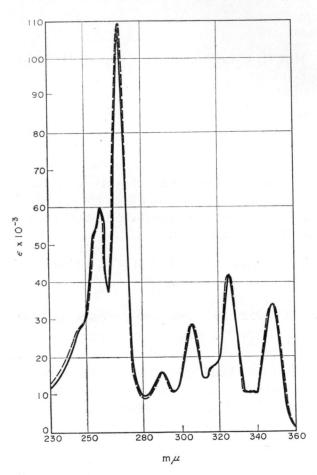

FIG. 8.7. Absorption curves of isomycomycin-methyl esters, natural (——) and synthetic (– – –). (*Chem. Ber.*, **87**, 712, 1954.)

longest wavelength band of the "strong" set with the corresponding data for Centaur X_3 (λ_{max} 269 mμ (ε, 101,000)). Similarly the "weak" set is terminated by a band at 347 mμ (ε, 34,000) in isomycomycin (*cf.* centaur X_3: 347 mμ (ε, 35,000)) (see Fig. 8.7). The structure of isomycomycin led directly to the formulation of the antibiotic as the optically active allene (CXLV). The role played by ultraviolet data was in this case a predominant one. The structure of mycomycin in which the allene separates the diyne and diene components provides a satisfactory explanation of the low λ_{max} value.

J. Nemotin

The structural elucidation of nemotin, a diyne-allene lactone, is a part-icularly good example of the great power of the *combined* use of ultraviolet and infrared data[54]. From the ultraviolet data we find that an ene-diyne chromophore is present (λ_{max} 208, 236, 249, 262 and 278 mμ). In the infrared, nemotin has bands at 3280 (terminal H—C≡C), 2130 (C≡C stretch), 1960 (C=C allene stretch), 1790 (C=O of γ-lactone) and 1150 cm^{-1} (C—O stretch

λ^{EtOH} 208 236 249 262 278 mμ

$$HC≡C-C≡C-CH=C=CH-$$

3280cm^{-1} 2130cm^{-1} 1960cm^{-1}

1790 cm^{-1}

1150 cm^{-1}

CXLVII   Nemotin

$$HC≡C-(C≡C)_2CH=CHCH_2CH_2CO_2H$$

CXLVIII   Nemotin A

λ	204	211	223	230	241	258	272	288	307	328 mμ
$10^{-3}\varepsilon$	26	23	30	59	85	2·8	6	12	15·5	11

of lactone). This information coupled with the observation that nemotin gives undecanoic acid on catalytic hydrogenation defines the structure (CXLVII) beyond reasonable doubt. Additional confirmation comes from the alkaline rearrangement of nemotin to nemotin A (CXLVIII), which is followed in the ultraviolet by the change of chromophore ene-diyne → ene-triyne.

K. Tri-yne Amide[55]

$$HOCH_2 \cdot (C≡C)_3CONH_2$$

λ	215	224	269	280	304	325 mμ
$10^{-3}\varepsilon$	68	86·5	1·75	2·4	3·05	1·95

The spacings (1900–2000 cm^{-1}) and position of the first transition (325 mμ) suggest the presence of (C=C)$_9$. Infrared evidence supplies the information that an unbonded hydroxyl group (ν, 3600 cm^{-1}) and a primary amide grouping (ν, 1670 cm^{-1}) are present.

L. Ene-diyne-amide and Nitrile[55]

The antibiotics diatretyn I and II illustrate the terminal conjugating shift of amide (0 mμ; inferred from section K) and of —C≡N (+ 14 mμ). The parent

$$HO_2C—CH=CH—C\equiv C—C\equiv CH$$

CXLIX

λ 309 mμ

$$HO_2C—CH=CH—(C\equiv C)_2 \, CONH_2$$
Diatretyn I

$$HO_2C—CH=CH—(C\equiv C)_2—CN$$
Diatretyn II

carboxyl ene-diyne chromophore (CXLIX) has λ_{max} 309 mμ for the first transition (longest band) whereas the diatretyns I and II have λ_{max} 309 and 323 mμ, respectively.

M. Aromatic Ene-diyne[50]

$$\langle\bigcirc\rangle—(C\equiv C)_2CH=CH\cdot CH_2OAc$$

λ	222	245	253	263	281	298	317·5 mμ
$10^{-3} \, \varepsilon$	32	37·2	41	15	26	32·5	27·4

From the *position* of the band which indicates the chromophoric length (317·5 mμ) it appears that conjugation of an en-diyne with a phenyl group produces an effect comparable with the addition of a double bond on the acetylene side, e.g. the ene-diyne-ene (CL) has λ_{max} 311 mμ.

$$CH_2=CH(C\equiv C)_2 \, CH=CH_2$$

CL

In Table 8.15 we have listed the major poly-yne and poly-yne-ene parent chromophores[34], together with some polyene-yne examples. The following generalizations emerge:

(1) For a given number of conjugated unsaturated linkages in a straight chain system, the position of the longest wavelength maximum is determined by the number (n) of conjugated —$C\equiv C$— linkages provided $n \geqslant 2$. Thus we have the order: $Me(C\equiv C)_6 Me$ [430 mμ]; $(C=C)(C\equiv C)_5$ [410 mμ]; $(C=C)(C\equiv C)_4(C=C)$ [396 mμ]; $(C=C)_2(C\equiv C)_3(C=C)$ [369 mμ] and $(C=C)_2(C\equiv C)_2(C=C)_2$ [359 mμ].

(2) For values of $A \not> 5$, the chromophores $(C=C)_x(C\equiv C)_n(C=C)_y$ and $(C=C)_x(C=C)_y(C\equiv C)_n$, where $x+y+n = A$, have their longest wavelength bands at the same positions, and where $n = 1$ or 2 close to that of the dimethyl polyene $Me—(C=C)_A—Me$.

TABLE 8.15. MAXIMA OF POLY-YNENES $R(CH=CH)_x(C\equiv C)_n(CH=CH)_y$ R IN mμ; $\varepsilon \times 10^{-3}$ [34]

$x\ n\ y$	Band Group 1					Band Group 2			
1 1 0									223 (15)
1 1 1								266 (20)	275 (16)
0 2 0					230 (2)		230 (0·3)	240 (0·4)	255 (0·2)
1 2 0		230 (31)	235 (30)	244 (23)		238 (5)	251 (10)	264 (14)	280 (11)
1 2 1			252 (33)	267 (29)		261 (8)	276 (14)	292 (20)	311 (17)
2 2 1			242 (13)	252 (22)		281 (17)	296 (30)	316 (40)	337 (29)
3 2 0		254 (28)	276 (34)	290 (33)		287 (17)	303 (39)	319 (63)	336 (65)
2 2 2			264 (32)	274 (27)			312 (32)	334 (45)	359 (43)
3 2 1							310 (36)	330 (57)	284 (42)
3 2 3							355 (51)	374 (60)	405 (55)
4 1 4					326 (47)	342 (47)	379 (74)	400 (76)	435 (65)
0 3 0				210 (150)	240 (0·1)	255 (0·2)	269 (0·2)	286 (0·2)	307 (0·1)
1 3 0		245 (70)	253 (71)	242 (110)	255 (4)	273 (7)	290 (13)	308 (17)	330 (11)
1 3 1	235 (4·5)	246 (27)	258 (60)	266 (59)		289 (11)	308 (20)	328 (27)	353 (19)
2 3 0	235 (49)	242 (66)	273 (96)	268 (110)		289 (10)	305 (28)	325 (42)	348 (34)
2 3 1	245 (50)	260 (70)		289 (81)	309 (20)	320 (30)	330 (20)	342 (39)	369 (29)
0 4 0		215 (90)	228 (200)	238 (280)		287 (0·2)	308 (0·2)	330 (0·2)	355 (0·1)
1 4 0						306 (—)	326 (—)	350 (—)	377 (—)
1 4 1			274 (100)	294 (75)		318 (8)	341 (12)	366 (14)	396 (7)
0 5 0	228 (34)	239 (125)	251 (310)	265 (440)		313 (0·15)	339 (0·25)	364 (0·25)	394 (0·15)
1 5 0			265 (—)	286 (—)	308 (—)	327 (—)	249 (—)	378 (—)	410 (—)
1 5 1	270 (105)	280 (123)	297 (145)	312 (94)		342 (10)	367 (13)	398 (15)	433 (8)
0 6 0	246 (45)	258 (140)	272 (350)	288 (500)	336 (0·9)	360 (1)	367 (0·2)	395 (0·2)	430 (0·1)
0 7 0	263 (50)	277 (160)	292 (395)	310 (530)		357 (0·6)	384 (0·6)	415 (0·6)	453 (0·3)

(3) The effect of terminal substitution on the longest wavelength band of the polyene-ynes may be summarized as follows. In the system

$$R_1—(C=C)_x(C\equiv C)_n(C=C)_y—R_2,$$

replacement of one of the alkyl groups R_1 or R_2 by carboxyl, carbonyl, or amide function gives a bathochromic shift of $+20\ m\mu$. Replacement by a double bond extending conjugation produces a shift of $+25\ m\mu$. Where both R_1 and R_2 are the same chromophore, the shift is not additive (exception: ethylenic groups) but is equal to that found for mono-substitutions. Where $R_1 \neq R_2$, the shift is equal to that produced by the more powerful chromophore.

TABLE 8.16. INTENSITY RATIOS OF BAND SETS IN POLY-YNEENES
$R(CH=CH)_x(C\equiv C)_n(CH=CH)_y.$

x	n	y	$\varepsilon_s/\varepsilon_w$	$n/x+y$
0	3	0	1500	∞
1	3	0	10	3
1	3	1	3	1·5
2	3	0	3	1·5
2	3	1	2·7	1
0	2	0	150	∞
1	2	0	2	2
1	2	1	1·5	1
2	2	1	0·60	0·66
3	2	0	0·50	0·66
3	2	1	0·50	0·50

(4) The ratio $(\varepsilon_s/\varepsilon_w)$ of the intensities of the longest wavelength bands of the "strong" and "weak" sets of *polyene-yne* absorption (Fig. 8.7) indicates the *polyene* character[35]. Thus, for the system $(C=C)_x(C\equiv C)_n(C=C)_y$, the data summarized in Table 8.16 indicate that intensity ratios may be qualitatively related to the "yne/ene" ratios.

In the case of $R(C=C)_3(C\equiv C)_2(C=C)_3R$, $\varepsilon_s/\varepsilon_w$ falls to zero, as the "strong" set does not appear in the accessible region. For examples including $(C\equiv C)_4$ $(n = 4)$, information is meagre but the trend is maintained for $Me(C\equiv C)_4Me$ $(\varepsilon_s/\varepsilon_w = 2800)$ and $Me(CH=CH)\cdot(C\equiv C)_4(CH=CH)Me$ $(\varepsilon_s/\varepsilon_w = 10;$ yne/ene $= 2·0)$.

8.10. BENZOQUINONES AND NAPHTHAQUINONES

Benzoquinone (CLI) is found in bacterial fermentations and may readily be identified by its characteristic ultraviolet $(\lambda_{max}$ 243, 280, 440 $m\mu)$[21] and infrared spectra.

Ubiquinone, a benzoquinone of considerable biological significance, has been isolated from baker's yeast. The proposed structure (CLII) is compatible with the light absorption which is almost identical with that of 2,4,5-trimethoxy-benzoquinone in having bands at 272, 315 (inflection) and 404 mμ[56].

Further examples of benzoquinone spectra are noted on p. 123 (Chapter 3).

CLI   CLII

Vitamin K$_1$. The structural elucidation of this vitamin which contains a substituted naphthaquinone as the chromophorically active centre, was facilitated by comparison of its spectrum with that of several alkylated naphthaquinones.

CLIII

CLIV

The close model, 2,3-dimethylnaphthaquinone, has maxima at 243, 249, 260, 269 and 330 mμ (in hexane). In the same solvent vitamin K$_1$ has λ_{max} 243, 249, 260, 270 and 325 mμ[57]. Chemical evidence for the side chain enabled a final structure (CLIII) to be proposed, although the gross molecular structure of the chromophore was known at a very early stage. Further evidence for the presence of a naphthaquinone was obtained by reduction of vitamin K$_1$ with zinc and acetic acid to a derivative whose spectrum is entirely compatible with that of structure (CLIV).

Hydroxynaphthaquinones[58]. It is possible to discern both quinonoid and Ar—C=O electron transfer bands in the spectra of naphthaquinones. The quinonoid absorption consists of medium and weak intensity bands at 260–76 and 400 mμ, while the Ar—C=O bands appear in the usual regions, viz. 240 mμ (strong) and 330 mμ (medium). For juglone (CLV) we can dissect the spectrum into contributions from *o*-hydroxycarbonyl (249 mμ; *calc.* 253 mμ) and quinon-

oid (262 and 425–95 mμ) chromophores). In isonaphthazarin (CLVI) the domin-
ating feature of the spectrum is the 2,3-dihydroxyquinone absorption at 270 mμ
(cf. ubiquinone, 272 mμ) whereas in naphthazarin (CLVII) the bands at 247 and

CLVI

λ 270

CLVII

λ 247, 254, 298, 338 mμ

CLVIII

CLV

CLIX

λ 249, 262

254 mμ are those expected for the superimposed principal E.T. bands of 2- and
2,5-dihydroxy acetophenone absorption, the subsidiary bands appearing at 298
and 338 mμ (see p. 123–124). The other absorption bands in naphthazarin correspond to quinonoid-type transitions. This type of analysis is, of course, qualitative
and quite empirical in nature, but the validity of such assignments receives some
support when we consider that the 247 and 254 mμ bands are shifted to the
predicted wavelength on acetylation ($\rightarrow$ CLVIII). Again, acetylation of juglone
returns the spectrum to that of an alkylated acetophenone ($\rightarrow$ CLIX).

8.11. ANTHRAQUINONES[58, 59]

The anthraquinone pigments are common metabolic products of fungi and
may be found with a multiplicity of hydroxyl function. By an extension of the
concept of partial contributing chromophores developed above, and using the
parameters available for calculation of E.T. bands of aromatic carbonyl compounds (p. 109), we can carry even further this type of analysis of the spectra
of quinones first adumbrated by Morton. The approach is an over-simplification
and breaks down for complex examples, but it does give an empirical correlative
background to the spectra of natural quinones, at the same time indicating a
link with the spectra of hydroxy-aromatic ketones.

The spectrum of anthraquinone (CLX) may then be regarded as a cross
conjugated acetophenone-benzoquinone system. We designate the transitions
due to acetophenone and quinone chromophores as (a) and (b), respectively.

Thus, for anthraquinone in ethanol, we have λ_{max} 243, 252 (*a* bands) 263, 272 (*b* bands) 325 (*a*) and 405 (*b*) mμ. The 405 mμ quinonoid absorption is susceptible to intensity increase and shifts to longer wavelengths by introduction of nuclear hydroxyl groups.

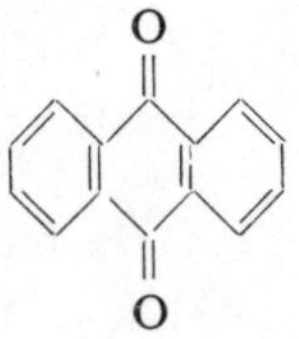

CLX

1-Hydroxyanthraquinone (CLXI)

If our tenet of assignment of partial chromophores is valid, and if the correct assignment has been made, we should predict the following spectrum for 1-hydroxyanthraquinone†: λ_{max} 253, 260–70, 327 and 405 mμ (in ethanol).

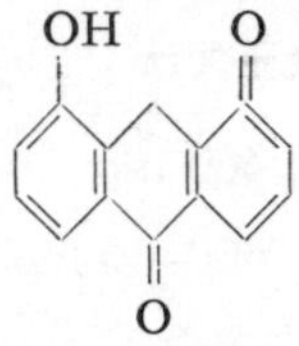

CLXI

Furthermore, by analogy with the secondary E.T. bands of *o*-hydroxyacetophenone we should expect the 327 mμ band to shift to 329 in hexane, to 300 mμ on methylation and to 365 mμ in alkali. The facts are that the compound has λ_{max} 250, 266–76, 322 and 406 mμ in ethanol. The 322 mμ band is unchanged in hexane, but in alkali. no band is evident at 365 mμ. Although the complete analogy is, then, lacking, it is possible to predict the maxima of the neutral molecule in ethanol solution.

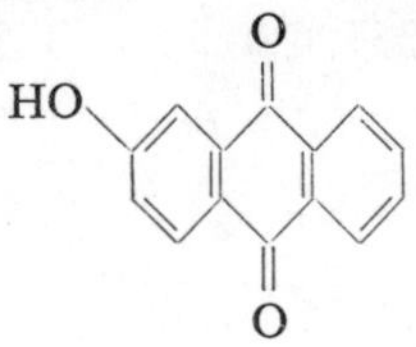

CLXII

For *2-hydroxyanthraquinone* (CLXII) the predicted spectrum is λ_{max} 246 (acetophenone) 271 (*p*-OHArC=O) 270–5 (quinone) 325 (second *a* band) and 400 mμ. The observed maxima are at 241, 271, 283, 330 and 378 mμ.

† The (*a*) bands are calculated from the data on p. 109.

IUS 10a

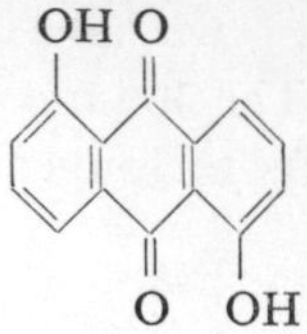

OH O

O OH

CLXIII

1,5-Dihydroxyanthraquinone (CLXIII) has λ_{max} *calc.* 253 (*m*-OHArC=O), 270–275 (quinone), 308, 335 and 400 mμ; λ_{max} *obs.* 253, 276, 287, 330 and 398–418–437 mμ. Other calculations are included below:

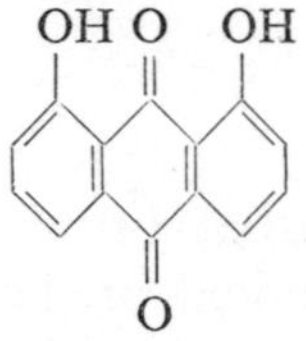

OH O OH

O

CLXIV

1,8-Dihydroxyanthraquinone (CLXIV):

λ_{calc} 253, 300, 400 mμ

λ_{obs} 254, 284, 400–50 mμ.

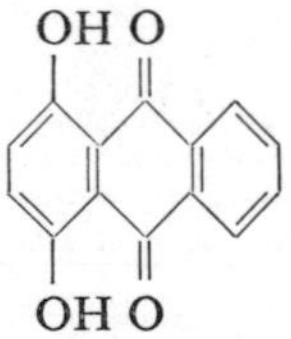

OH O

OH O

CLXV

1,4-Dihydroxynaphthaquinone (CLXV):

λ_{calc} 253, 260, 270–5, 300, 325, 400 mμ

λ_{obs} 250, 257, 280, 291, 325, 450–500 mμ.

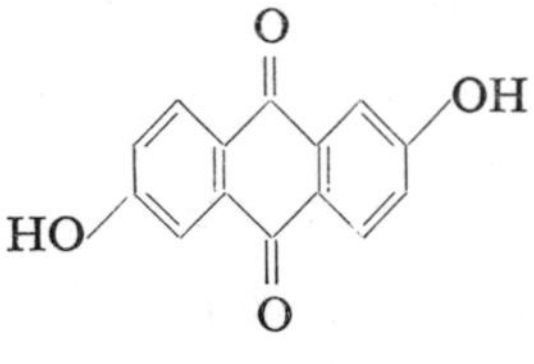

O

OH

HO

O

CLXVI

A particularly relevant case is that of 2,6-dihydroxyanthraquinone (CLXVI) which, unlike the rest of our examples, contains no acetophenone (λ_{calc} 246), or *o*- or *m*-OH acetophenone residue (λ_{calc} 253). Thus we would predict that this should be the only hydroxy anthraquinone which has no band in the

240–250 mμ region and would predict a spectrum of 271 (p-OHArC=O and quinone superimposed), 300, 325 (a bands) with a quinone band near 400 mμ (b band). The observed spectrum has λ_{max}^{EtOH} 274, 301, 349 and 385 mμ.

The ultraviolet absorption data for a number of polyhydroxyanthraquinones are listed in Table 8.17.

Tetracenequinones[60]

A group of antibiotics recently isolated from *Streptomyces* species have been found to contain hydroxyanthraquinone chromophores. Thus rutilantinone†

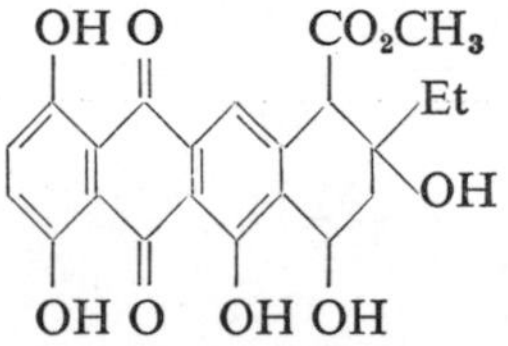

Rutilantinone CLXVII

λEtOH 234 257 293
494 525

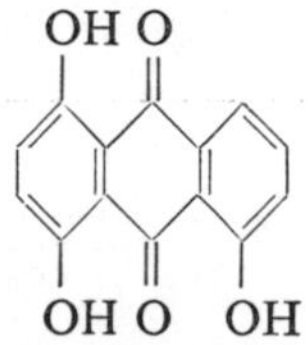

CLXXIV

λ 231 255 289 405
480 490 510 525

↓

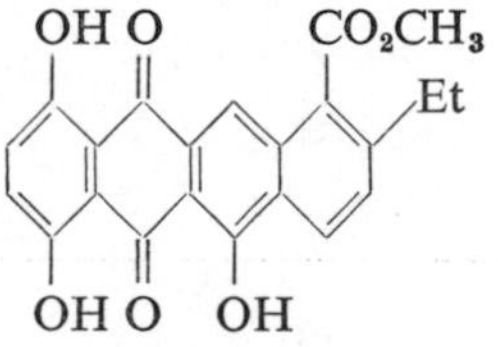

CLXVIII

λCyclohexane 252 275 486
496 508 519 530 mμ

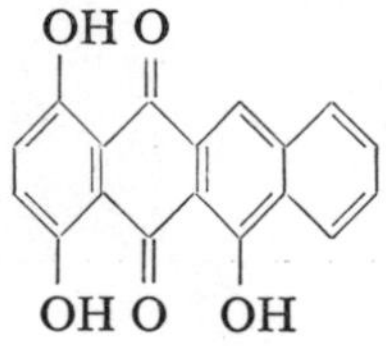

CLXIX

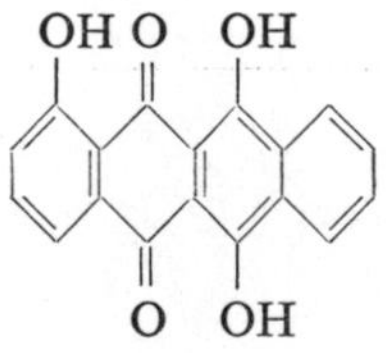

CLXX

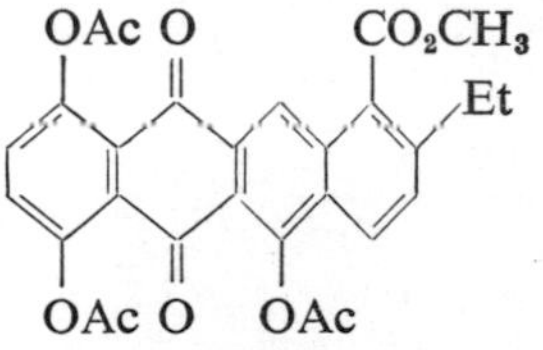

CLXXI

λMeOH 248 299 391 396

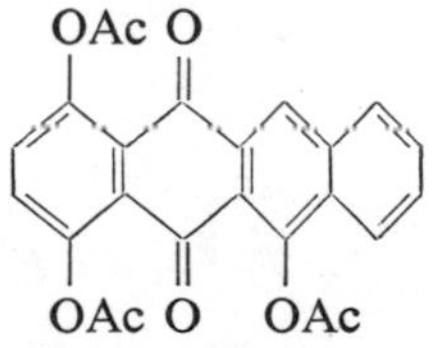

CLXXII

† (= ε-pyrromycinone).

TABLE 8.17. HYDROXYANTHRAQUINONES[59]

Compound	Band 1	Band 2	Band 3	Band 4	Band 5	Band 6	Band 7
Chrysophanol	225	255	277·5	287·5	430	—	—
Emodin	222	252	265	289	437	—	520–30
ω-hydroxyemodin	222·5	250·5	266	289·5	436	—	510–20
Anthragallol	213	241 245	—	287	414	—	—

TABLE 8.17—(contd.)

Compound	Band 1	Band 2	Band 3	Band 4	Band 5	Band 6	Band 7
Islandicin	232	252·5	—	289	390–402 466–70	492 513	527
Helminthosporin	231	255	—	289	405–15	480 490 510	52
Catenarin	231	255	280	298	—	488·5 508	515–255
Cynodontin	221 237·5	—	—	296	—	518	545 558

TABLE 8.17—(contd.)

Compound	Band 1	Band 2	Band 3	Band 4	Band 5	Band 6	Band 7
Rufigallic Acid	213 222	258	—	295	349 438	—	—
Asperthecin	237·5	262·5	—	286·5	318	484 510	545–55

(CLXVII)[60] has the spectral characteristics of a 1,4,5-trihydroxyanthraquinone (CLXXIV), e.g. helminthosporin (Table 8.17). Treatment of rutilantinone with *p*-toluenesulphonic acid gives the bisanhydro compound (CLXVIII)

CLXXIII

whose ultraviolet spectrum is almost identical with that of 1,4,6-trihydro-xytetracenequinone (CLXIX) but quite different from that of 1,6,11-tri-hydroxytetracenequinone (CLXX). Further, bisanhydrorutilantinone triacetate has a spectrum almost superimposable on that of 1,4,6-triacetoxytetracene-quinone (CLXXI). This evidence, together with information derived from Kuhn–Roth, Zeisel and saponification–equivalent experiments, allowed the Bristol group to formulate the partial structure of the bisanhydro compound as (CLXXII). Infrared data and rate of saponification showed (respectively) that a salicylic ester was not present but that the ester was flanked by *two ortho*-substituents. This now leads to structure (CLXXIII) for bisanhydrorutilantinone, a proposal which is also compatible with biogenetic considerations. Placement of the two hydroxyl groups in the hydroaromatic rutilantinone itself could be made on biogenetic grounds. Structure (CLXXIV) followed for the antibiotic. Chemical evidence is in full support of this postulate but the part played by critical use of ultraviolet data in this study cannot be overemphasized. The summarized data in Table 8.17 indicate that certain hydroxyanthraquinones may be classified by means of their ultraviolet spectra.

8.12. HYPERICIN[61]

Hypericin, the photodynamically active plant pigment, has a molecular formula $C_{30}H_{16}O_8$. Kuhn–Roth analysis shows two C—Me groups and benzoyl-ation gives a yellow hexabenzoate. *Reductive benzoylation* of hypericin, on the other hand, affords a *blue octabenzoate*. These observations led Brockmann and his colleagues to the conclusion that hypericin is a hexahydroxyquinone. The fact that zinc dust distillation of hypericin yields meso-anthrodianthrene (CLXXV) without loss of carbon atoms, allows only two possible extended quinonoid systems (CLXXVI) and (CLXXVII) for hypericin. The shift of the ultraviolet spectrum in alkaline solution and the reactivity of the hydroxyl groups suggested the presence of a number of OH groups in the *peri*-positions to the quinone carbonyl functions. Since only two of the six hydroxyl functions are acetylated by keten, the remaining four OH groups were assumed to be in *peri*-positions.

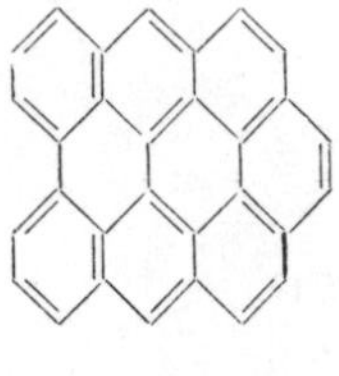

CLXXV

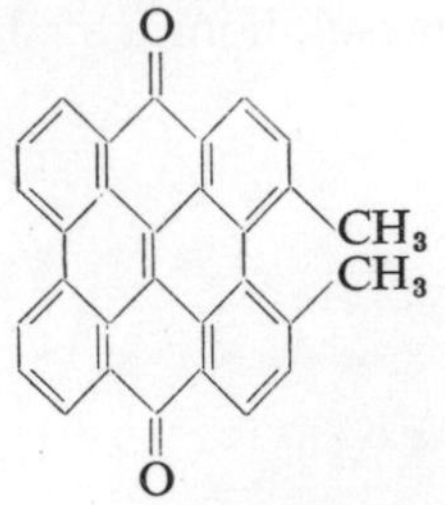

CLXXVI

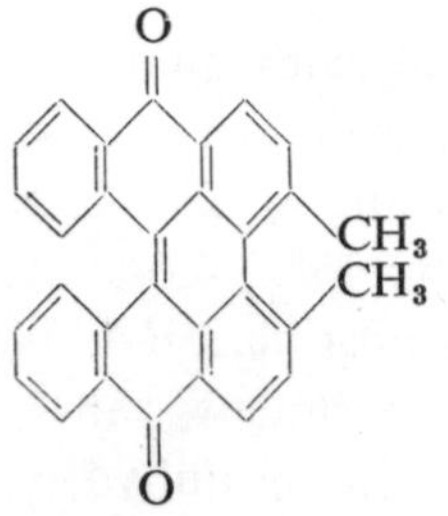

CLXXVII

CLXXVIIIa 2,2′-Dimethylhelianthrene

λ 505, 543 mμ (Red)

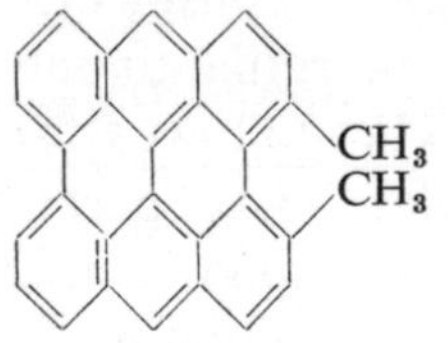

CLXXVIIIb

2,2′-Dimethyl-*meso*-naphthodianthrene

λ 578, 627 mμ (Blue)

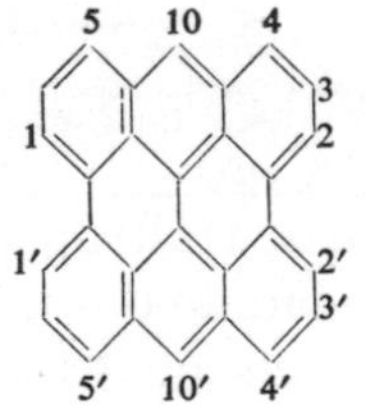

CLXXIX

Meso-Naphthodianthrene

λ 605, 660 mμ

Brockmann[61] next devised a spectroscopic method for the identification of parent hydrocarbons of polycyclic hydroxyquinones. This employed the technique of reductive acetylation to the corresponding polyacetoxy-hydrocarbon, whose spectrum closely resembles that of the parent hydrocarbon in shape and band spacings with the maxima shifted slightly to longer wavelengths by the presence of the acetoxyl groups which correspond roughly to methyl groups in their power of bathochromic displacement. Thus 1,4,5-trihydroxyanthraquinone on reductive acetylation gives 1,4,5,9,10-penta-acetoxyanthracene, the latter having λ_{max} 350, 370, 385, and 410 mμ in dioxan. For comparison, anthracene in this solvent has bands at 325, 340, 360 and 378 mμ, the shapes of these curves being very similar. For strict comparison it would be necessary to have 1,4,5, 9,10-pentamethylanthracene available. Since it is often difficult to obtain reference samples of such complexity, the working rule of a red shift of the entire spectrum of 5 mμ for each acetoxyl group added to the hydrocarbon gives generally adequate agreement.

We now return to the reductive acetylation of hypericin. On the basis of partial structures (CLXXVI) and (CLXXVII) we should expect to be able to distinguish between the parent systems generated by zinc treatment, viz. 2,2-dimethylhelianthrene (CLXXVIIIa) and 2,2′-dimethylmesonaphthodianthrene (CLXXVIIIb). The maxima of these hydrocarbons are sufficiently disparate for such a decision to be made, for the former has its longest band at 543 mμ and is *red*, while the latter absorbs in the visible at 627 mμ and is coloured *blue*. In the event, reductive acetylation of hypericin gives a *blue* hexa-acetate whose spectrum is almost identical with that of (CLXXVIIIb) and whose longest wavelength band is at 625 mμ. Now this is at first sight a surprising result, for we should expect a bathochromic shift of 30 mμ of the spectrum of the hydrocarbon by the introduction of six acetoxyl groups. The desmethyl hydrocarbon (CLXXIX) itself, however, has λ_{max} 605 and 660 mμ in the visible region, the 3,3′-dimethyl derivative λ_{max} 609 and 663 and the 10,10′-diacetate 626 and 678 mμ. The explanation for the correspondence of the absorption maxima of the blue hexa-acetate and of the 2,2′-dimethyl derivative (CLXXVIIIb) is that

CLXXX

CLXXXI

2,2′, 10-Triacetoxy-*meso*-naphthodianthrene
λ 581, 639 mμ

"Blue Hexa-acetate"
λ 578, 625 mμ

steric hindrance to coplanarity of the ring system of the same type as that encountered in the 4,5-disubstituted phenanthrenes (as CLXXX) results in the blue shift of the spectrum of meso-naphthodianthrenes when substituted in the 2,2′ and 7,7′-positions. It is found, for example, that the triacetate (CLXXXI) has λ_{max} 581 and 639 mμ. The acetate groupings may now be placed at the 7,7′-position and the methyls at 2,2′, for any other arrangement would not allow the operation of steric interference with the resonating system. The 7,7′-positions are thus the sites of acetylation in hypericin and since the remaining hydroxyls

must be located in *peri*-positions to the quinone —$\overset{|}{C}$=O functions, the structure of hypericin is uniquely defined as the 4,4′,5,5′,7,7′-hexahydroxy-10,10′-quinone (CLXXXII). This proposal was confirmed in every detail by unambiguous synthesis. The care taken in the selection and study of appropriate model systems and the full use made of the spectroscopic properties during this work indicate the power of analysis by interpretation of electronic spectra.

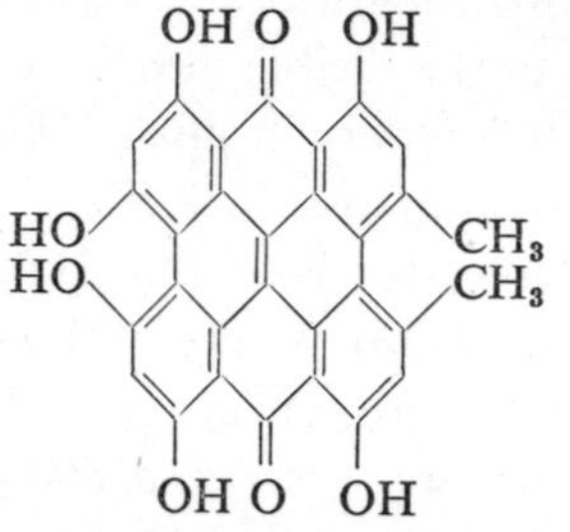

CLXXXII Hypericin

8.13. APHIS PIGMENTS[62]

In a study similar to that of hypericin, the structures of the erythroaphins, a group of deep red colouring matters from certain varieties of aphid were found to be extended quinones of the perylene type. Thus, the spectrum of erythro-

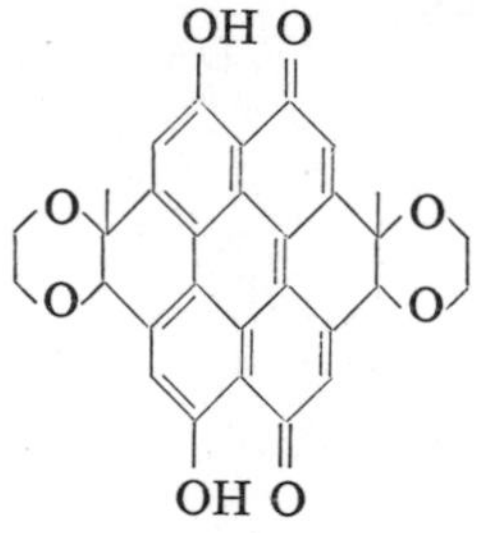

CLXXXIII

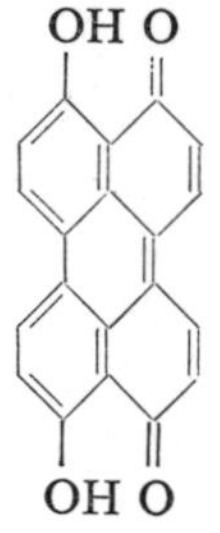

CLXXXIV

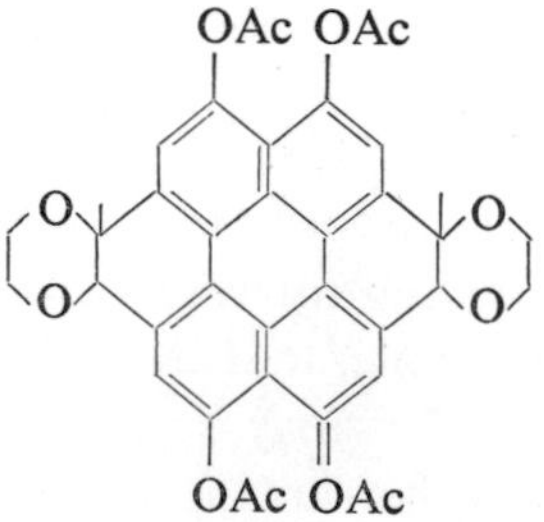

CLXXXV

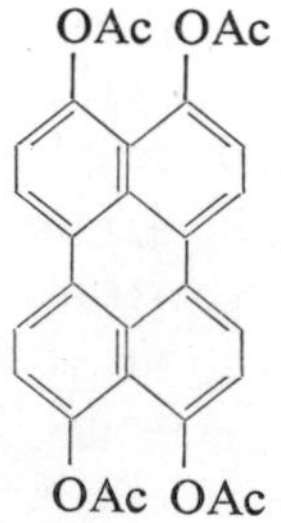

CLXXXVI

aphin-fb (CLXXXIII)[62] (Figs. 8.8a, 8.8b) leaves no doubt as to the gross structure of the principal chromophore when we compare it with the absorption curve of 4,9-dihydroxyperylene-3,10-quinone (CLXXXIV). Similarly, comparison of the spectra of tetra-acetylanhydroerythroaphin fb (CLXXXV) and of

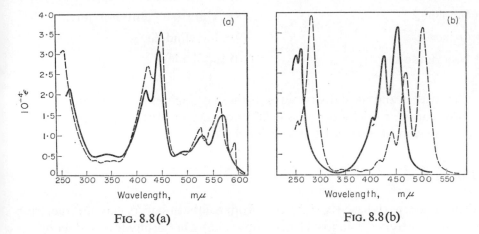

FIG. 8.8(a)   FIG. 8.8(b)

FIG. 8.8(a). Ultraviolet spectra of erythroaphin-fb (– – –) and 4,9-dihydroxy-perylene-3,10-quinone (———) (in tetrachlorethane). (Calderbank, Johnson and Todd, *J. Chem. Soc.*, 1286, 1954.)

FIG. 8.8(b). Tetracetyldihydroerythoaphin-fb (– – –) and 3,4,9,10-tetra-acetoxy-perylene (———) in chloroform (Calderbank, Johnson and Todd, *J. Chem. Soc.*, 1286, 1954.)

3,4,9,10-tetra-acetoxyperylene (CLXXXVI) provided good evidence for the nature of the chromophore, and at the same time allowed the placement of twenty of the thirty carbon atoms with minimum manipulation of precious material.

8.14. INDOLE ALKALOIDS

Correlation between ultraviolet spectra and details of molecular structure have proved to be a most valuable aid in the classification of indole alkaloids[63, 64]†. We have drawn some examples from the *calabash* and *strychnos* group, for they represent an extremely complex family containing a diversity of indolic function. In spite of their complexity (which has only recently been revealed in detail for some members of this family), the ultraviolet spectral data has proved a reliable and informative guide in the hands of the Swiss[63a] and Bristol[63b] workers. The careful correlative studies by Witkop[64] should also be consulted for detailed information on ultraviolet and infrared assignments of indolic functions.

† See also Chapter 5, p. 174.

The main types of chromophore encountered in the indole alkaloids are as follows:

(1) Indole
(2) α-Methylene indoline
(3) Indoline.
(4) Oxindole
(5) N-acylindoline

(6) ψ-Indoxyl
(7) β-Carbolinium
(8) "Curarine" chromophore.
(9) N-acylindole
(10) Indolenine

The spectra and partial structures of these groupings are given in Chart VI. We now consider briefly the classification of certain of the *strychnos* alkaloids by the criterion of ultraviolet absorption.†

C-Fluorocurine

This quaternary base $C_{20}H_{25}O_2N_2{}^+$ from calabash-curare has the spectrum of a 2,2-disubstituted ψ-indoxyl (chromophore 6). On borohydride reduction the carbinol of partial formula (CLXXXVII) is formed (indoline spectrum). Rearrangement of this with acid now gives a 2,3-disubstituted indole (chromo phore 1) (λ_{max} 225, 278 mμ) which was found to be identical with C-mavacurine isolated from the same source. Oxidative rearrangement of C-mavacurine patterned after Witkop's experiments in the tetrahydrocarbazole field now gave a glycol (CLXXXVIII) which could be rearranged to give back C-fluorocurine. Moreover, the foregoing glycol was identical with C-alkaloid-Y previously isolated from a calebash. The structural information derived in this way could therefore be used for all three alkaloids.

Chromophore 6   CLXXXVII (Chromophore 3)

CLXXXVIII (Chromophore 3)   Chromophore 1

† Again it is necessary to point out that the infrared spectrum for each compound discussed was entirely compatible with the assignments suggested by the ultraviolet data.

For a most useful survey of indole alkaloid spectra (ultraviolet and infrared) see ref. 9 on p. 190.

An indication of the ring system present in these alkaloids was given by de-hydrogenation of a tertiary base obtained by pyrolysis of C-mavacurine. This degradation product although obtained in minute yield formed the methiodide

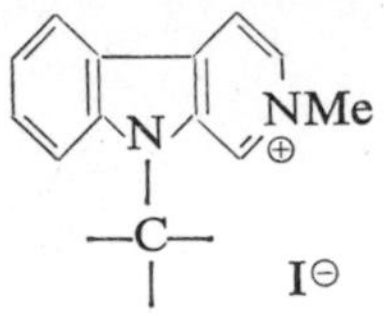

CLXXXIX 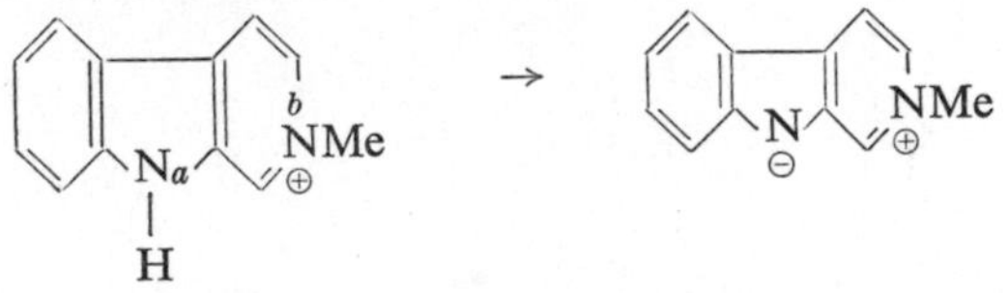   CXC   CXCI

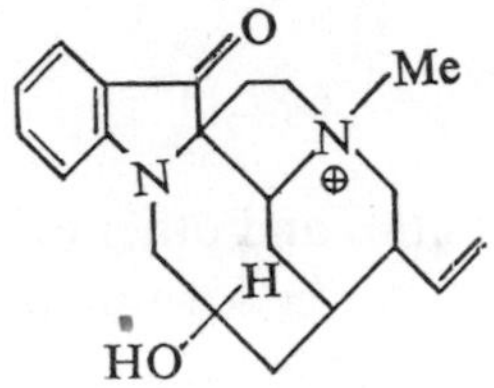

CXCII

(CLXXXIX) which was shown to be a β-carboline (chromophore 7) by its spectrum. Furthermore, since the chromophore was stable to base, the indolic nitrogen N(a) is alkylated. It is a well known property of carboline N(b) meth-iodides of type (CXC) where the N(a) bears a hydrogen atom that the anhydro base (CXCI) is formed in alkaline solution with concomitant spectral change. Further chemical and biogenetic considerations lead to tentative structure (CXCII) for C-fluorocurine.

Alkaloids of Strychnos melinoniana

Degradative work on the eleven melinonines isolated from this species has resulted in structural proposals for four of these compounds. We illustrate the part played in this work by the interpretation of the ultraviolet data.

Melinonine F, $C_{13}H_{13}N_2^+$, can be recognized as a β-carbolinium salt (chromophore 7) and was in fact shown to be N(b)-methoharman (CXCIII).

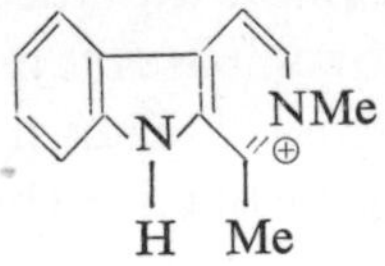

CXCIII

Melinonine G, $C_{17}H_{15}N_2^+$, has an ultraviolet spectrum reminiscent of that of sempervirine (CXCIV). Moreover, vinyl conjugation was excluded by this evid-ence. On catalytic hydrogenation the chromophore (1) of indole was produced.

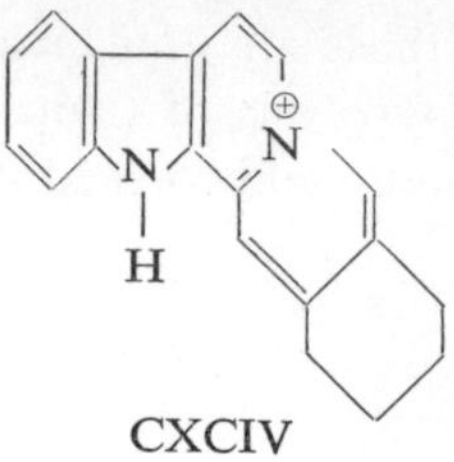

CXCIV

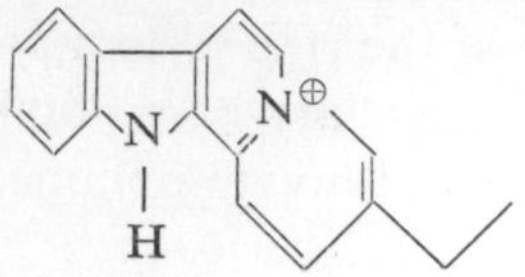

CXCV

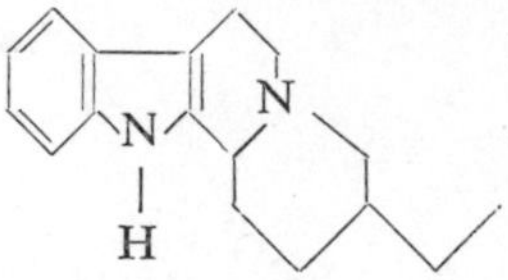

CXCVI

Structure (CXCV) follows from this and other evidence (C–Et group, etc.). The indolic reduction product may then be formulated as (CXCVI).

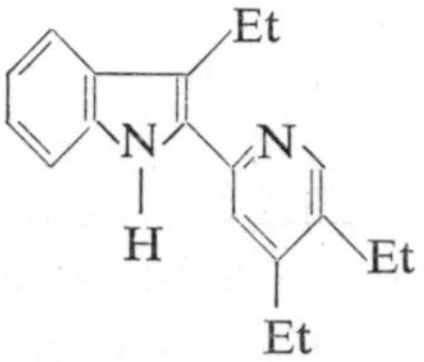

CXCVII

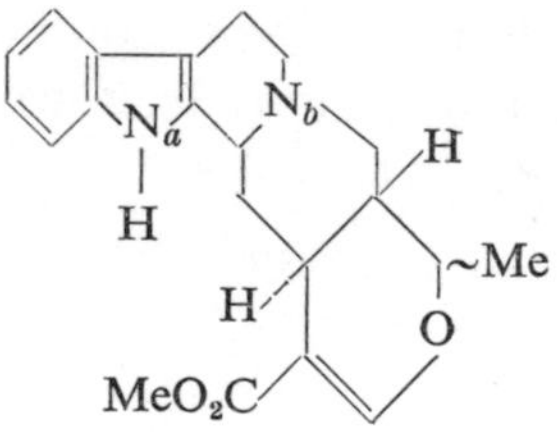

CXCVIII

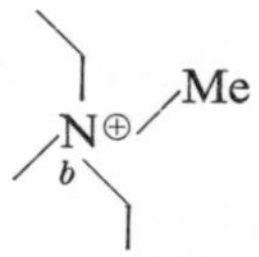

CXCIX

Melinonine A, $C_{22}H_{27}O_3N_2^+$, on pyrolysis gives a tertiary base normelinonine A, $C_{21}H_{24}O_3N_2$. The latter affords alstyrine (CXCVII) on dehydrogenation. The ultraviolet spectrum of normelinonine A is typical of the curve shown by a combination of the indole chromophore with the grouping —O—C=C—CO$_2$Me This fact led Schittler and Hohl to compare the nor-base with tetrahydroalstonine (CXCVIII) with which it was identical. Thus melinonine A is the N(*b*) metho-derivative of base (CXCIX). The distinctive chromophores of (CXCVIII) and alstyrine (which contains the α-pyridyl indole grouping) were thus of great value during this study.

Diaboline, an alkaloid from *Stychnos diaboli*, was shown to be the acetyl derivative (CC) of the Wieland–Gumlich aldehyde (CCI). This assignment follows from the appropriate chemical evidence, and the spectroscopic changes delineated in Chart VII.

Toxiferine I. Without attempting to describe the elegant inter-relative, degradative and synthetic experiments leading to the elucidation of the structures of this and related C_{40} alkaloids by the Zurich and Bristol groups, we note that

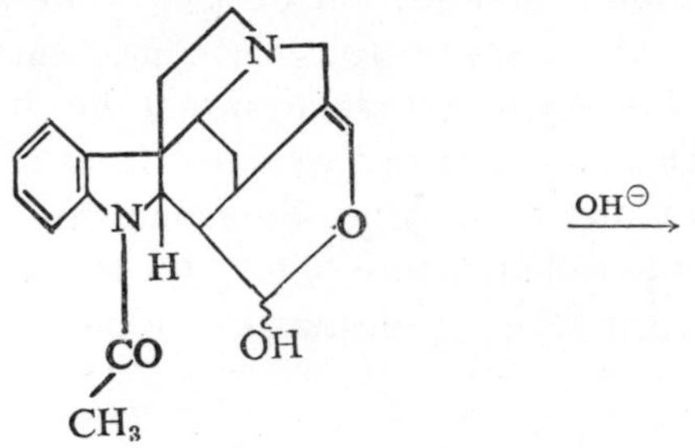

CC Diaboline
Chromophore (5)

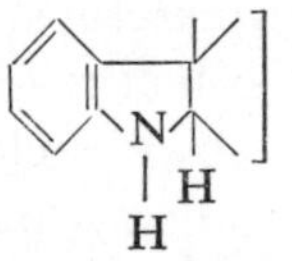

$\xrightarrow{OH^{\ominus}}$

CCI Wieland-Gumlich Aldehyde
Chromophore (3)

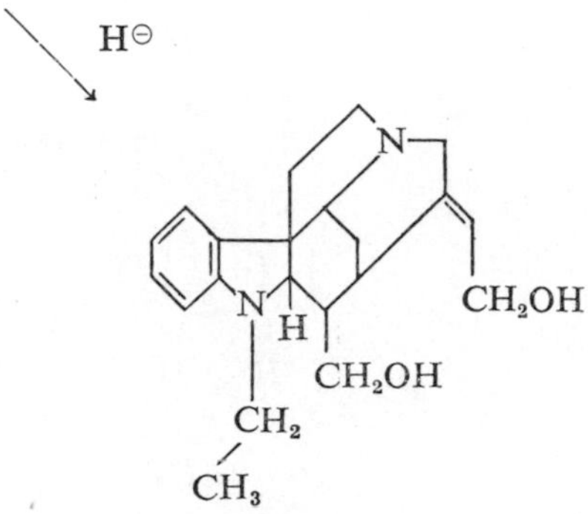

$H^{\ominus}$

Indoline chromophore (3)

Chart VII. Transformation products of diaboline

the pure methylene indoline chromophore is a valuable piece of evidence for the dimeric nature of the proposed structure (CCII). This illustrates quite clearly the validity of the use of spectral assignment even in the most complicated cases.

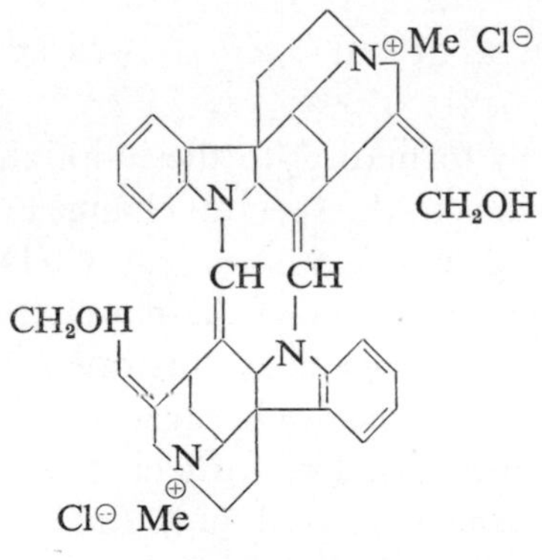

CCII Toxiferine I
λ_{max} 293 mμ

C-Fluorocurarine, a C_{20} alkaloid, has a remarkable chromophore in that its maximum at 358 mμ is reversibly shifted to longer wavelengths in alkali. With dimethyl sulphate the alkaloid gives the N(*a*) methyl derivative having a spectrum almost identical with the parent alkaloid, but now showing no alkaline shift, which must therefore involve the N(*a*) proton. The Zurich workers were able to show by careful studies of borohydride reduction that the chromophore responsible is in fact (CCIII). This was confirmed by a synthesis of the model (CCIV) which absorbs closely to C-fluorocurarine. Biogenetic and correlative chemical studies finally indicated the full structure (CCV) for the alkaloid. The alkaline shift is attributed to the formation of mesomeric anion (CCVI).

CCIII λ 358 mμ CCIV

CCVI   CCV

Indoline absorption. During their studies on toxiferine, Battersby and Hodson noted that many simple indolines (as CCVII) show a return to the spectrum of

CCVII   CCVIII   CCIX

benzene in acid solution by formation to the indolinium cation (CCVIII) in a manner completely analogous to the spectral change aniline → anilinium cation (Chapter 3). In the hexahydro-β-carbolines (e.g. CCIX), however, such a shift is not observed due to the field effect of the closely placed, positively charged N(*b*) nitrogen atom. Here, once again, is illustrated the care required in interpretation of complex cases, this time not because of steric hindrance to coplanarity, but by a field effect which could be difficult to predict.

C-Curarine I and C-Calebassine. Although final structural proposals* have not been made for these C_{40} alkaloids, the Zurich school has found that C-

* see footnote p. 303.

curarine I has a chromophore quite unlike that of the common indole varieties (chromophores 1–7; Chart VII). The compounds C-Alkaloid-G and C-guianine also have this spectrum which may be that of an amino-hemiacetal (CCX). C-calebassine may have chromophore (CCXI) since a shift of 10 mμ in alkali is quite characteristic of this grouping.

Aspidospermine. The 2-methoxy-N-acylindoline chromophore of aspidospermine (CCXII) absorbs at 220 and 258 mμ. The model N-acetyl-1,2,3,4-tetra-hydro-8-methoxycarbazole (CCXIIa) has λ_{max} 217·5 and 256 mμ[65].

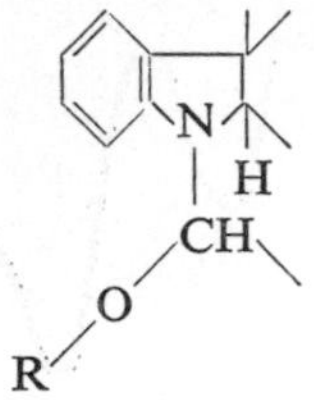

CCX

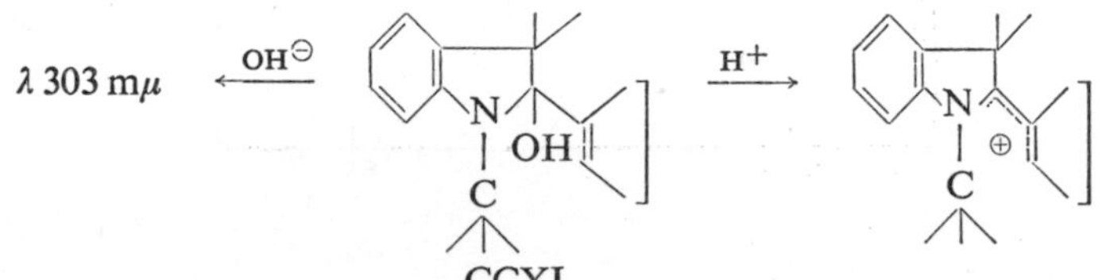

λ 303 mμ $\xleftarrow{\text{OH}^{\ominus}}$ CCXI $\xrightarrow{\text{H}^+}$
λ 293 mμ

λ 320 mμ

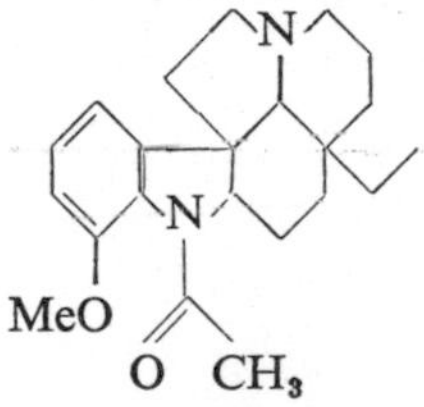

CCXII
λ 220, 258 mμ

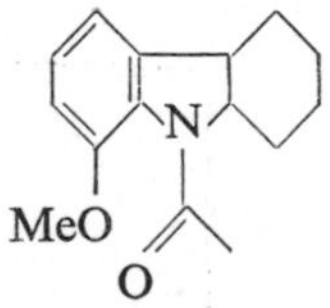

CCXIIa
λ 217·5, 256 mμ

8.15. PYRROLE PIGMENTS

The documentation of the spectra of the porphyrins is largely due to the work of Fischer and Stern[66]. Four main chromophoric types can be recognized and correlated with structural features. The classification is made on the

* Added in proof. C-curarine I and C-calebassine Chromophores are (i) and (ii) respectively; see K. Bernauer [*Helv. Chim. Acta,* **46,** 197 (1963)] for summary.

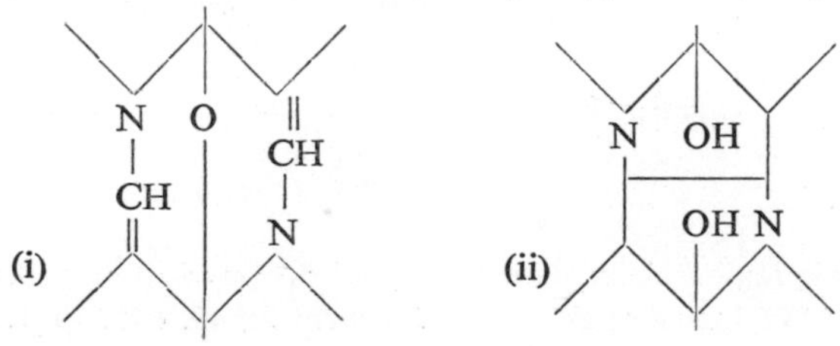

(i)   (ii)

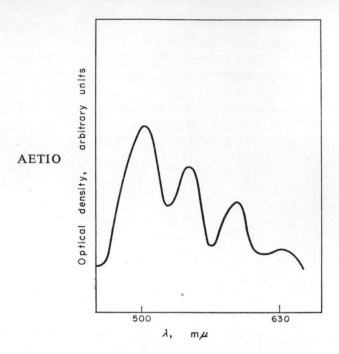

AETIO

FIG. 8.9. Visible region absorption spectra of porphyrin types (neutral solvent). (After Lemberg and Falk, *Biochem.J.*, **49**, 675, 1951.)

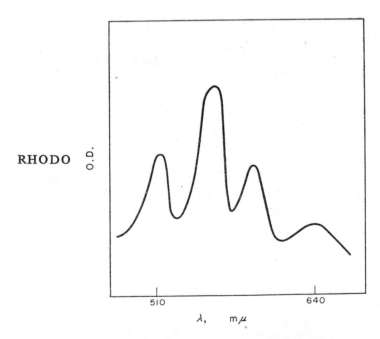

RHODO

FIG. 8.10. Visible region absorption spectra of porphyrin types (neutral solvent). (After Lemberg and Falk, *Biochem.J.*, **49**, 675, 1951.)

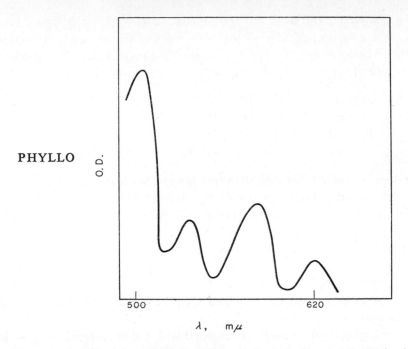

FIG. 8.11. Visible region absorption spectra of porphyrin types (neutral solvent).
(After Lemberg and Falk, *Biochem.J.*, **49**, 675, 1951.)

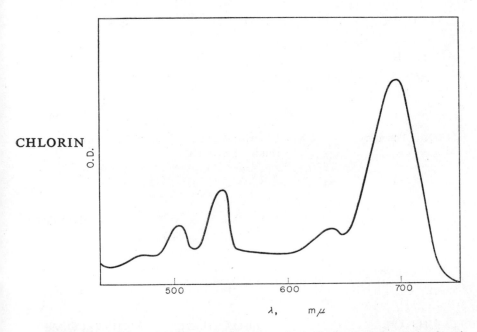

FIG. 8.12. Visible region absorption spectra of porphyrin types (neutral solvent).
(After Lemberg and Falk, *Biochem.J.*, **49**, 675, 1951.)

basis of the relative intensities of the *four longest wavelength bands*. These occur in the visible region in addition to the very intense absorption near 400 mμ (Soret band). The four spectral types, illustrated in Figs. 8.9–8.12, are named as follows, with the four bands in the intensity order indicated:

AETIO: I < II < III < IV
RHODO: I < II < III > IV
PHYLLO: I < II > III < IV
CHLORIN: one very intense long wavelength band.

Correlations of these types with structure may be made in the following way:

Porphyrins include all tetrapyrrolic compounds in which the rings are linked by methine carbon atoms in a closed conjugated system. The naturally occurring members of this class of pigment are found at different oxidation levels. One important group of porphyrins is represented by the *porphins* (as CCXIII), a second group being *chlorins* (as CCXIV) which are dihydroporphins containing one reduced pyrrole ring. A subdivision of chlorins may be made into *phorbins* in which an isocyclic ring joins C—γ and C$_6$ (CCXV) and *rhodins* which are 3-formyl chlorins.

The absence of carbonyl groups conjugated with the main resonating π-electron system (CCXIII) leads to the AETIO spectrum (Fig. 8.9). Examples of com-

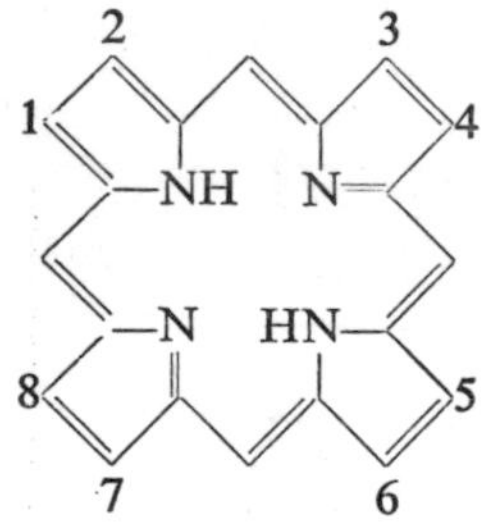

CCXIII-Porphin 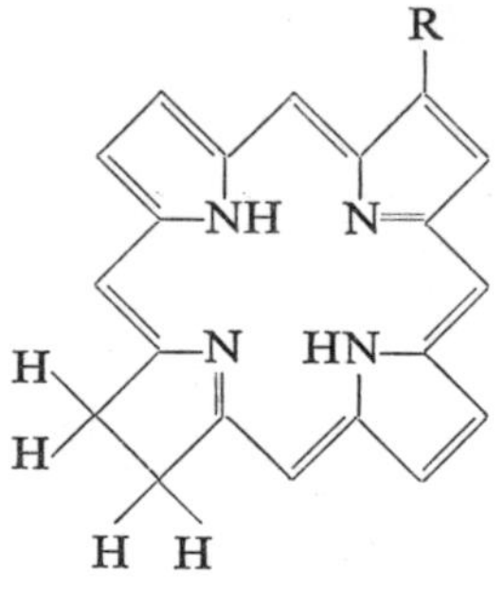   CCXIV-Chlorin: R=H   CCXV-Phorbin
                         rhodin : R=CHO

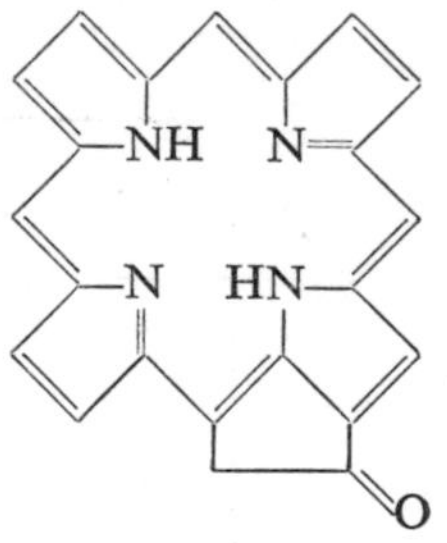

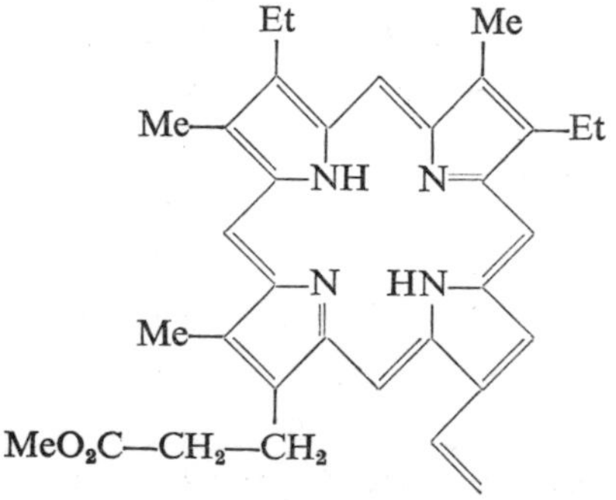

CCXVI 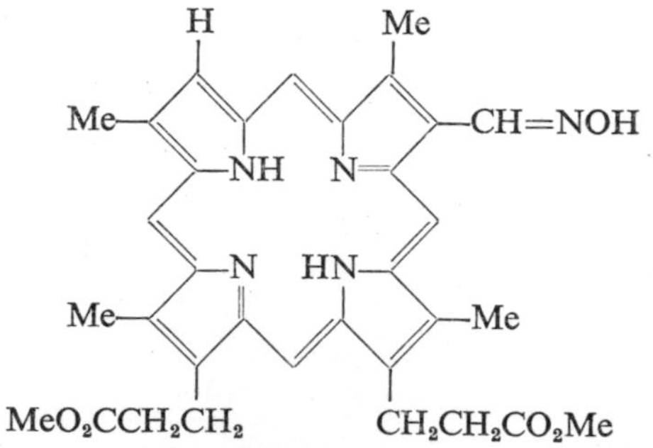   CCXVII

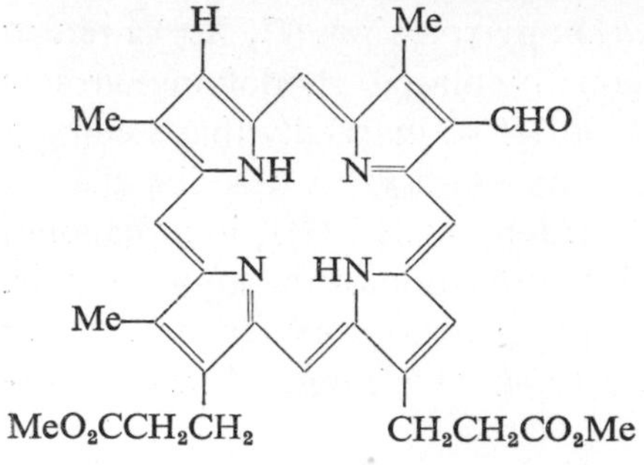

CCXVIII

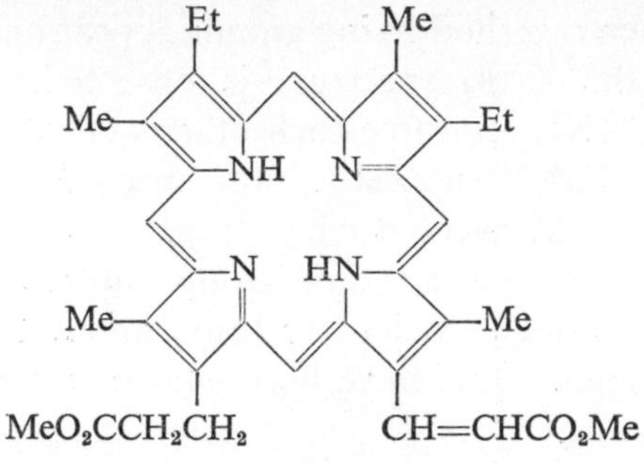

CCXIX

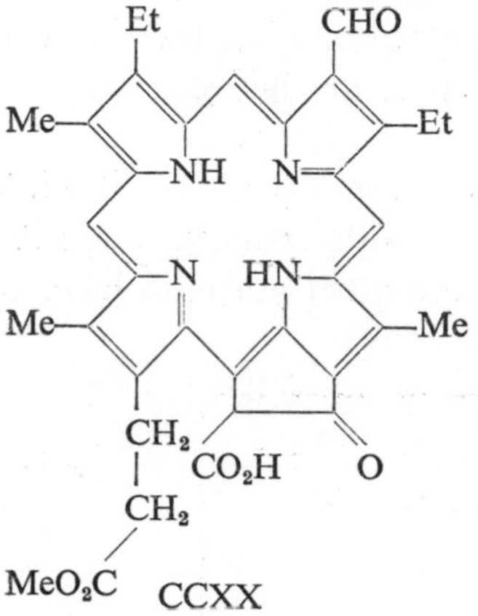

CCXX

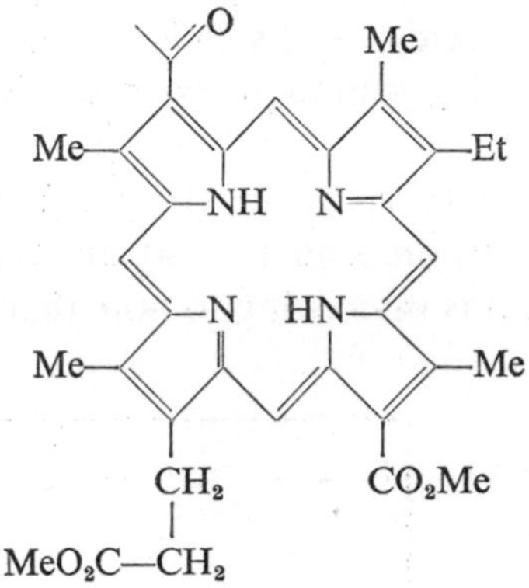

CCXXI

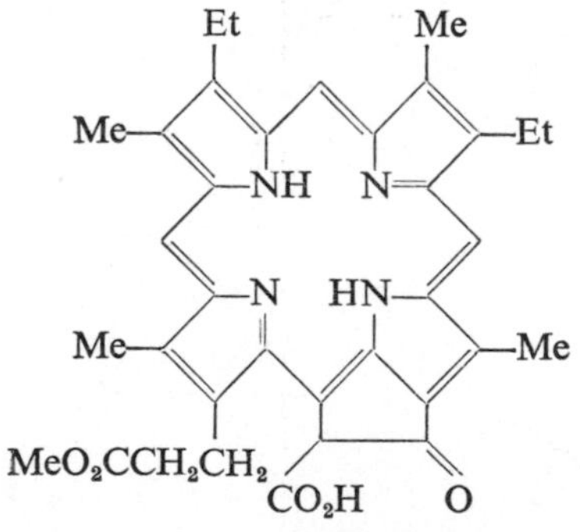

CCXXII

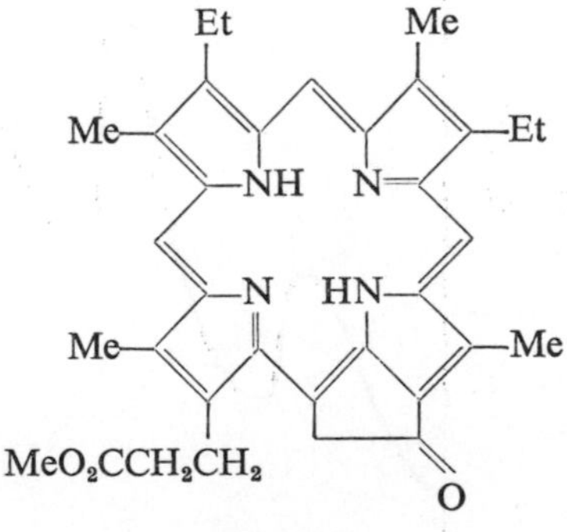

CCXXIII

pounds with this absorption are (CCXVI) and (CCXVII). Introduction of a carbonyl group on the periphery of the ring system moves the entire spectrum to longer wavelengths at the same time intensifying Band III to give a RHODO spectrum. This transition may correspond to the electron transfer from the ring to the carbonyl orbit, for the corresponding oximes show no such intensification of Band III. Thus the carbonyl derivatives (CCXVIII) and (CCXIX) have RHODO spectra (Fig. 8.10). "Rhodofying" groups include —CHO, —COMe,

—CO$_2$Me and —CH=CH·CO$_2$Me, but not —CH=CH$_2$ or —$\overset{|}{C}$=N—R.

When *two* rhodofying groups appear on *adjacent* pyrrole rings (CCXX) a return to the AETIO spectrum is observed. Diagonally placed rhodofying groups (CCXXI) reinforce each other's effect on Band III so markedly that Lemberg and Falk[67] suggest a fifth spectral category OXO-RHODO to describe the resultant absorption curve (Fig. 8.13). A vinyl group —CH=CH$_2$ in a diagonal position to a carbonyl group causes some intensification of the RHODO bands, but is not sufficient to bring about the RHODO → OXO-RHODO change. These generalisations have been shown to be valid for a wide range of simple porphyrins.

The *phorbins* phaeoporphyrin 9$_5$ and phylloerythrin (CCXXII) and (CCXXIII) contain isocyclic OXO groups in conjugation with the ring system. The β-keto acid (CCXXII) has an OXO-RHODO spectrum, while the ring ketone of (CCXXIII), although less rhodofying, has a spectrum between RHODO and OXO-RHODO.

The PHYLLO spectrum (Fig. 8.11) is shown by porphin (CCXIII) itself. This curve corresponds in fact to an AETIO spectrum with reduced intensity of Band III. It is interesting to note that octaethyl- and other porphins have AETIO curves.

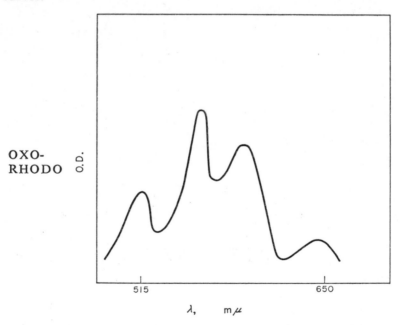

OXO-
RHODO   O.D.

515   650

λ,   mμ

FIG. 8.13. Visible region absorption spectra of porphyrin types (neutral solvent).
(After Lemberg and Falk, *Biochem. J.*, **49**, 675, 1951.)

At the dihydroporphin or *chlorin* (CCXIV) level the energy of transition of Band I is decreased and a single absorption band occurs near 650 mμ. Correlation between symmetry and transition energy of porphyrins has been reached by Jackman in a simplified M.O. treatment of porphin and chlorin spectra.

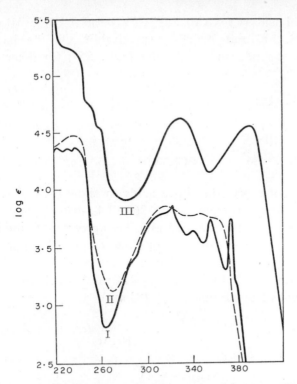

FIG. 8.14. Spectra of tropolone: I, in cyclohexane; II, in water; III, in 0·5 N NaOH.
(Cook, Gibb, Raphael and Somerville, *J. Chem. Soc.*, 508, 1951, Fig. 1.)

Such considerations correctly predict that the longest wavelength bands of these compounds lie in the order D_{2H} tetrahydroporphin > chlorin > porphin > C_{2v} tetrahydroporphin.

8.16. NATURAL TROPOLONES[69]

The ultraviolet spectral curve of tropolone (CCXXIV) can be divided into intense electron transfer absorption near 230 mμ (ε, 22,000) with a second band near 315 mμ (ε, 10,000). The latter band usually appears near 350 mμ in the substituted tropolones which occur naturally. Tropolone itself has not been found in nature. The α,β-and γ-isopropyl derivatives, which have essentially similar spectra, occur in western red cedar *(Thuja plicata)*. These show long wavelength absorption (in hexane) at 350–370 mμ. The presence of carbonyl groups on the

CCXXIV λ 230, 315   CCXXV λ 258   CCXXVI λ 270

ring as in the mould acids (CCXXV), (CCXXVI) and (CCXXVII) gives rise to E.T. bands at 258, 270 and 295 mμ respectively[70]. On the basis of a *m*-hydroxyacetophenone-type band at 253 mμ (*calc.* 253) for β-acetyltropolone

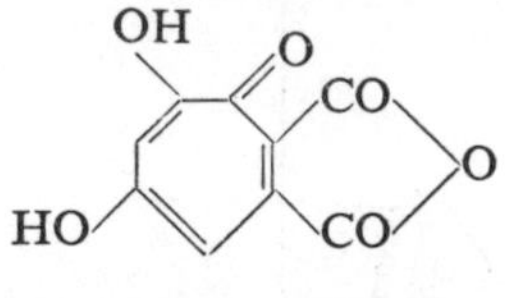

CCXXVII λ 295 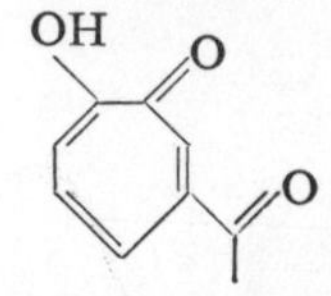   CCXXVIII λ 253 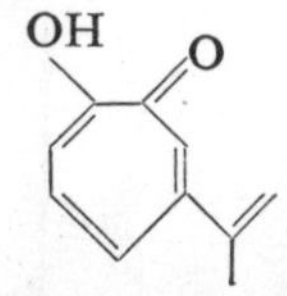   CCXXIX λ 254

(CCXXVIII) we might expect the above acids to show their E.T. absorption at 244 mμ (3,5-dihydroxycarboxylic acid), 269 (3,4,6-trihydroxy acid) and *ca.* 290 mμ (cf. 3,5-dihydroxyphthalic anhydride). The agreement found is indicative of the resemblance of the spectrum of tropolone to that of a phenol, with an addition electron transfer band near 240 mμ. Again we find that β-isopropenyl-tropolone [β-dolabrin (CCXXIX)] has λ_{max} 254 mμ[71] which corresponds with the absorption of *m*-hydroxystyrene (λ_{max} 253 mμ).

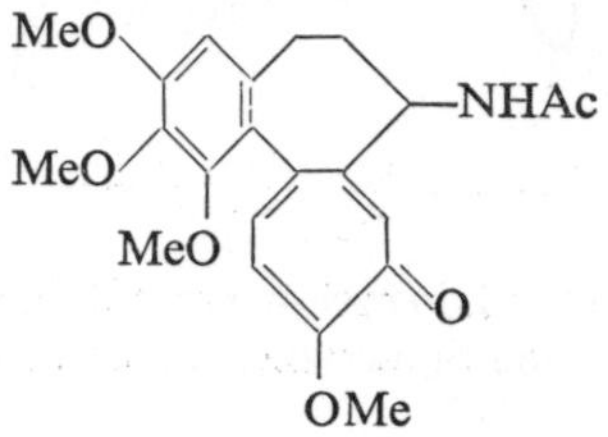

CCXXX λ 243, 355

The spectrum of colchicine (CCXXX) represents the conjugation of tri-methoxyphenyl and tropolone chromophores, the main electron transfer bands occurring at 243 and 355 mμ.

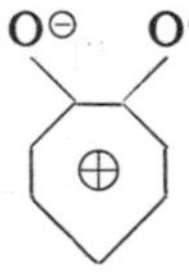

CCXXXI λ 260, 340, 400

The tropolone anion (CCXXXI) absorbs at 260, 340 and 400 mμ.

REFERENCES

1. K. CLIME, R. R. WILLIAMS, A. E. RUEHLE and R. E. WATERMAN, *J. Amer. Chem. Soc.*, **59**, 530 (1937).
2. E. A. BRAUDE, T. BRUUN, B. C. L. WEEDON and R. J. WOODS, *J. Chem. Soc.*, 1419 (1952); and earlier papers in this series.
3. R. M. LUSSKIN and L. WINSTON, *J. Amer. Chem. Soc.*, **71**, 2412 (1949).

4. F. Sondheimer, S. Burstein and R. Mechoulam, *ibid.*, **82**, 3209 (1960).
5. O. L. Chapman and D. J. Pasto, *ibid.*, **80**, 6685 (1958).
6. R. Adams and W. Herz, *ibid.*, **71**, 2546, 2551, 2559 (1949).
7. D. H. R. Barton and C. R. Narayanan, *J. Chem. Soc.*, 963 (1958).
8. D. H. R. Barton and P. de Mayo, *ibid.*, 142 (1956).
9. D. H. R. Barton and J. E. D. Levisalles, *ibid.*, 4518 (1958).
10. R. H. Eastman and A. Oken, *J. Amer. Chem. Soc.*, **75**, 1029 (1953).
11. L. J. Bellamy, *The Infrared Spectra of Complex Molecules*, Methuen, London (1954).
12. (a) U. Eisner, J. A. Elvidge and R. P. Linstead, *J. Chem. Soc.*, 1372 (1953); (b) D. P. Langlois and H. Wolff, *J. Amer. Chem. Soc.*, **70**, 2624 (1948); (c) A. R. Pinder, *J. Chem. Soc.*, 1577 (1956).
13. H. H. Appel and A. Dohr, *Scientia (Chile)*, **25**, 137 (1958).
14. H. H. Appel, J. D. Connolly, K. H. Overton and R. P. M. Bond, *J. Chem. Soc.*, 4685 (1960).
15. R. B. Woodward and G. Singh, *Experientia*, **6**, 238 (1950); *J. Amer. Chem. Soc.*, **72**, 1428, 5357 (1950).
16. L. J. Haynes and J. R. Plimmer, *Quart. Rev.*, **14**, 292 (1960).
17. A. S. Bailey, N. Polgar and R. Robinson, *J. Chem. Soc.*, 3031 (1953).
18. J. Cason and G. Sumrell, *J. Biol. Chem.*, **192**, 405 (1951); *J. Org. Chem.*, **18**, 857 (1953); **19**, 1836 (1959).
19. C. Djerassi and S. Burstein, *J. Amer. Chem. Soc.*, **80**, 2593 (1958).
20. W. R. Chan and C. H. Hassall, *J. Chem. Soc.*, 3495, 4983 (1956).
21. A. E. Gillam and E. S. Stern, *An Introduction to Electronic Absorption Spectroscopy*. Arnold, London (1957).
22. D. H. R. Barton, P. de Mayo and M. Shafiq, *J. Chem. Soc.*, 929 (1957).
23. T. Enkvist, *Acta Chem. Scand.*, **8**, 51 (1954).
24. H. Hift and H. R. Mahler, *J. Biol. Chem.*, **198**, 907 (1952).
25. H. Schinz and M. Hinder, *Helv. Chim. Acta*, **30**, 1349 (1947).
26. A. Rossi and H. Schinz, *ibid.*, **31**, 473 (1948).
27. C. J. W. Brooks, G. Eglinton and D. S. Magrill, *J. Chem. Soc.*, 308 (1961).
28. P. A. Plattner and L. M. Jampolsky, *Helv. Chim. Acta*, **26**, 687 (1943).
29. C. Djerassi and W. Rittel, *J. Amer. Chem. Soc.*, **79**, 3528 (1957).
30. A. T. Nielsen, *J. Org. Chem.*, **22**, 1539 (1957).
31. L. Dorfman, *Chem. Rev.*, **53**, 47 (1953), and refs. cited therein.
32. F. Bohlmann and H. J. Mannhardt, *Chem. Ber.*, **89**, 1307 (1956).
33. L. Zechmeister, *Fort. Chem. Organischer Naturstoffe*, **18**, 223 (1960).
34. F. Bohlmann and H. J. Mannhardt, *ibid.*, **14**, 1 (1957).
35. M. C. Whiting, Private communication.
36. A. C. Cope and H. E. Johnson, *J. Amer. Chem. Soc.*, **80**, 1504 (1958).
37. H. Kuhn, *Helv. Chim. Acta*, **34**, 130 (1951).
38. J. Dale, *Acta Chem. Scand.*, **8**, 1235 (1954).
39. M. S. Barber, L. M. Jackman and B. C. L. Weedon, *Proc. Chem. Soc.*, 23 (1960).
40. J. D. Bu'Lock, *Quart. Rev.*, **10**, 371 (1956).
41. J. Schmidt-Thomé, *Z. Naturf.*, **56**, 409 (1950).
42. J. H. Birkinshaw and P. Chaplen, *Biochem. J.*, **60**, 255 (1955).
43. S. P. Ligthelm and H. M. Schwartz, *J. Amer. Chem. Soc.*, **72**, 1868 (1950).
44. N. A. Sorensen and K. Stavholt, *Acta Chem. Scand.*, **4**, 1080 (1950).
45. R. T. Holman and N. A. Sorensen, *ibid.*, **4**, 416 (1950).
46. J. S. Sorensen, T. Bruun, D. Holme and N. A. Sorensen, *ibid.*, **8**, 26 (1954).
47. F. Bohlmann, H. J. Mannhardt and H. G. Viehe, *Chem. Ber.*, **88**, 361 (1955).
48. F. Bohlmann, E. Inhoffen and P. Herbst, *ibid.*, **90**, 124 (1957).
49. K. Stavholt and N. A. Sorensen, *Acta Chem. Scand.*, **4**, 1567 (1950).
50. J. S. Sorensen and N. A. Sorensen, *ibid.*, **8**, 1741 (1954).

51. J. S. SORENSEN. D. HOLME, E. T. BORLANG and N. A. SORENSEN, *ibid.*, **8**, 1769 (1954).

52. E. F. L. J. ANET, B. LYTHGOE, M. H. SILK and S. TRIPPETT, *J. Chem. Soc.*, 309 (1953).

53. W. O. CELMER and I. A. SOLOMONS, *J. Amer. Chem. Soc.*, **74**, 1870, 2245, 3838 (1952); **75**, 1372 (1953).

54. J. D. BU'LOCK, E. R. H. JONES and P. R. LEEMING, *J. Chem. Soc.*, 4270 (1955).

55. J. D. BU'LOCK, E. R. H. JONES, G. H. MANSFIELD, J. W. THOMPSON and M. C. WHITING, *Chem. Ind.*, 990 (1954).

56. R. A. MORTON, *Biochem. J.*, **73**, 2P (1959).

57. D. T. EWING, J. M. VANDENBELT and D. KAMM, *J. Biol. Chem.*, **13**, 345 (1939); H. DAM, A. GEIGER, J. GLARIND, P. KAMER, W. KAMER, E. ROTHSCHILD and H. SALOMON, *Helv. Chim. Acta*, **22**, 310 (1939); E. A. DOISY, S. B. BINKLEY and S. A. THAYER, *Chem. Rev.*, **28**, 477 (1941).

58. R. A. MORTON and W. T. EARLAM, *J. Chem. Soc.*, 159 (1941).

59. J. H. BIRKINSHAW, *Biochem. J.*, **59**, 485 (1955).

60. W. D. OLLIS, I. O. SUTHERLAND and J. J. GORDON, *Tetrahedron Letters*, No. 16, 17 (1959).

61. H. BROCKMANN, *Fort. Chem. Organischer Naturstoffe*, **14**, 141 (1957), and refs. cited therein.

62. A. CALDERBANK, A. W. JOHNSON and A. R. TODD, *J. Chem. Soc.*, 1285 (1954).

63. (a) K. BERNAUER, *Fort. Chem. Organischer Naturstoffe*, **17**, 183 (1959); (b) A. R. BATTERSBY and H. F. HODSON, *Quart Rev.*, **14**, 77 (1960), and refs. cited therein.

64. B. WITKOP, *J. Amer. Chem. Soc.*, **75**, 3361 (1953), and many other papers.

65. J. R. CHALMERS, H. T. OPENSHAW and G. F. SMITH, *J. Chem. Soc.*, 1115 (1957); H. CONROY, P. R. BROOK and Y. AMIEL, *Tetrahedron Letters*, No. 11, 5 (1959).

66. H. FISCHER and H. ORTH, *Die Chemie des Pyrrols*, vol. II. 2, p. 338, Akademische Verlagsgesellschaft, Leipzig (1940).

67. R. LEMBERG and J. E. FALK, *Biochem. J.*, 674 (1951) and refs. cited therein.

68. R. B. WOODWARD, *Angew. Chem.*, **72**, 651 (1960).

69. T. NOZOE, in *Non-Benzenoid Aromatic Compounds*, (edited by D. GINSBURG), Interscience, New York (1959).

70. G. AULIN-ERDTMAN, *Acta Chem. Scand.*, **5**, 301 (1951).

71. T. NOZOE, K. TAKASE and M. OGATA, *Chem. & Ind.*, 1070 (1957).

72. (a) H. SCHMID and P. KARRER, *Helv. Chim. Acta*, **30**, 2081 (1947);
    (b) E. BACHLI, C. VAMVACAS, H. SCHMID and P. KARRER, *ibid.*, **40**, 1167 (1957).

73. W. BERGMANN and M. B. MEYERS, *Chem. Ber.*, **620**, 46 (1959).

74. M. B. MEYERS, Private communication.

CHAPTER 9

INTERPRETATION OF THE ULTRAVIOLET SPECTRA OF SOME COMPLEX MOLECULES

WE have seen that isolated chromophores may often be detected within a complex molecular environment, provided that this environment displays no selective absorption in the region of the band of the chromophore. We have also provided examples where judicious use of model spectra has been of assistance in the determination of gross molecular structure. The infrared and n.m.r. spectra of a complex molecule usually furnish information (of varying degrees of interpretative difficulty) as to the nature of the functionality of the molecule in the form of well-resolved peaks. The ultraviolet spectrum of such an intact molecule, while providing us with information about the transitions corresponding to the energies appropriate to each wavelength scanned by the spectrophotometer, is in all too many cases a *composite absorption band envelope* containing the unresolved contributions from the chromophoric arrays compressed into a relatively narrow wavelength range. Resolution of a spectrum of such complexity can in most instances only be made by a series of carefully chosen degradative experiments, controlled by spectrophotometric measurement. In cases where a chromophorically active moiety is known to be present from other evidence, subtraction of the spectrum of the known component from the original spectrum provides useful information as to the other contributing species.

These techniques of degradation with spectral control and of constructing difference and summation spectra, when used in conjunction with information from the infrared and n.m.r. regions, lead to structural proposals which may be tested by synthesis or by X-ray crystallographic analysis.

It is our hope that the examples which follow, although strongly influenced by personal choice, will indicate the scope of the methods which have been used in structural work. The original literature should be consulted for mechanistic and experimental details (including infrared and n.m.r. spectra) which obviously cannot be reproduced in the present work.

9.1. TERRAMYCIN

Terramycin, a yellow antibiotic from *Streptomyces rimosus*, is an amphoteric compound $C_{22}H_{24}N_2O_9$. At the outset of the degradational work, the ultraviolet and infrared spectra gave little evidence of specific functions within the molecule, although simple unconjugated carbonyl functions could be excluded by the absence of bands in the infrared carbonyl stretching region above $1665\,cm^{-1}$. The ultraviolet spectrum (Fig.9.7) of terramycin is, *per se*, singularly uninformative.

Alkaline Degradation

An important clue to the structure of rings C and D of terramycin was provided by the isolation of a weakly acidic substance, terranaphthol, $C_{12}H_{12}O_3$, from the treatment of the antibiotic with alkali in the presence of zinc. The

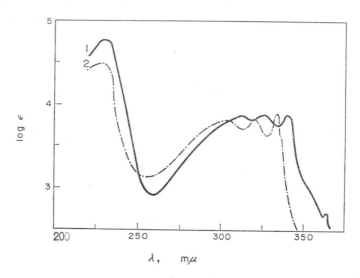

FIG. 9.1. Ultraviolet spectra of (1) terranaphthol; (2) 1,8-dihydroxynaphthalene (in ethanol). (Hochstein *et al.*, *J. Amer. Chem. Soc.*, **75**, 5455, 1953.)

ultraviolet spectrum of terranaphthol clearly showed (Fig. 9.1) that a naphthalene nucleus was present. On the basis of experiments involving acetylation, alkaline fusion and C—Me determination, the partial structure (I) could be written for terranaphthol. The orientation of the phenolic hydroxyl groups as in (II) was indicated by the similarity of the spectra of terranaphthol and 1,8-dihydroxynaphthalene in ethanolic solution (Fig. 9.1). The effect of terranaphthol in increasing the acidity of boric acid solutions confirmed the *peri* relationship of the hydroxyl groups. Partial structure (II) could be proposed on the basis of these results and the isolation of 1-methylnaphthalene on zinc dust distillation of terranaphthol.

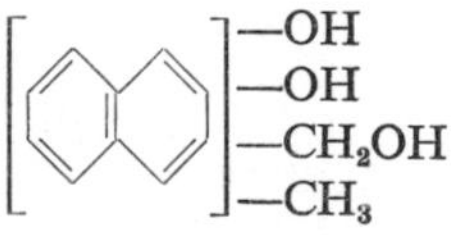

I

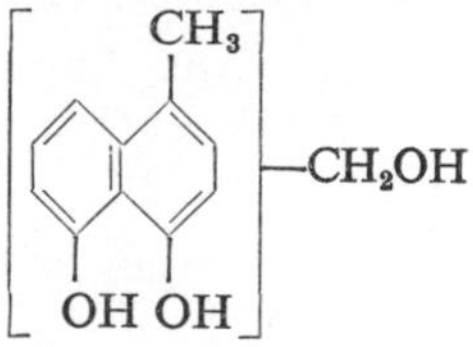

II

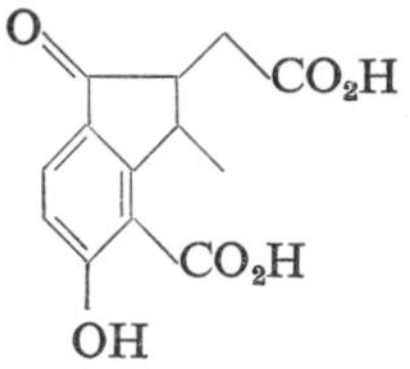

III

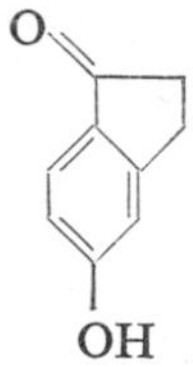

IV

The *major* product of alkaline treatment of terramycin is terracinoic acid (III) whose ultraviolet spectrum is similar to that of 5-hydroxyindanone (IV). A minor product of alkaline treatment whose presence was predicted by consideration of partial structure (V) for terramycin is isodecarboxyterracinoic acid (VI) whose spectrum is close to that of 7-hydroxyindanone (VII) (λ_{calc}, 256 mμ). Interpretation of further chemical evidence led to part-structure (VIII) at the end of the alkaline degradation studies.

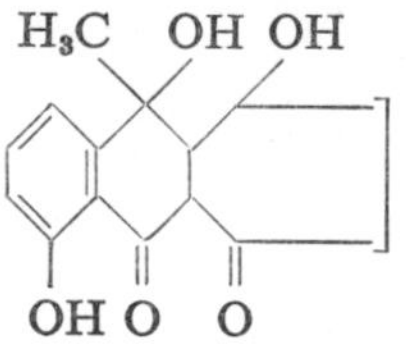

V

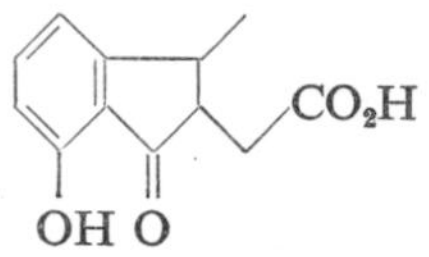

VI

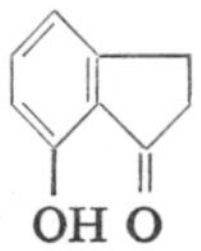

VII

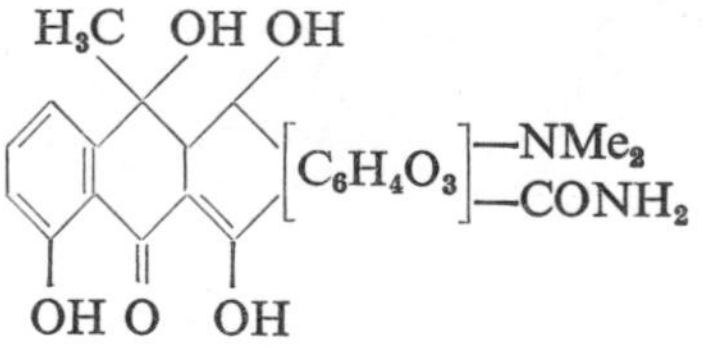

VIII

Acid Degradation

The series of degradation products formed by treatment of terramycin with acid is shown in Table 9.1. Comparison of the spectrum of the first acidic degradation product, anhydroterramycin, with that of the model chromophore

TABLE 9.1. ACID DEGRADATION OF TERRAMYCIN

Terramycin   →   Anhydroterramycin   →   α- and β-Apoterramycin
                        (Fig. 9.2)   (Fig. 9.3)

                                                                      ↓

                   Decarboxamidoterrinolide   ←   Terrinolide
                                                            (Fig. 9.4)

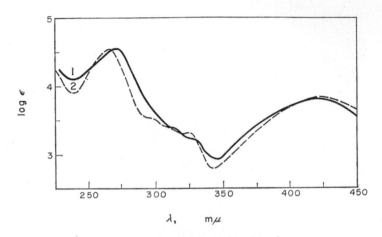

FIG. 9.2. Ultraviolet spectra of (1) anhydroterramycin, (2) 8,9,10-trihydroxy-1-oxo-1,2,3,4-tetrahydroanthracene (IX) (in acid-ethanol). (Hochstein *et al.*, *J. Amer. Chem. Soc.*, **75**, 5455, 1953.)

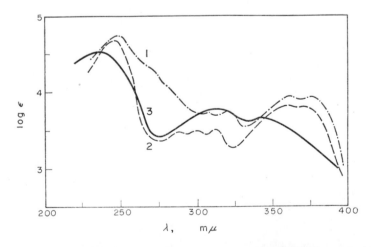

FIG. 9.3. Ultraviolet spectra of (1) β-apoterramycin, (2) 1,8-dihydroxy-7-naphthoic acid (X), and (3) terranaphthoic acid (XI) (in acid-ethanol). (Hochstein *et al.*, *J. Amer. Chem. Soc.*, **75**, 5455, 1953.)

(IX) (Fig. 9.2) provided confirmatory evidence for part-structure (VIII). Further acidic treatment led to a mixture of the isomeric lactones (v 1739 cm^{-1}), α- and β-apoterramycin. These lactones both increased the acidity of boric acid solution and comparison of their spectra with those of the models (X) and (XI) (Fig.9.3) enabled part-structure (XII) to be written for β-apoterramycin. Further, the

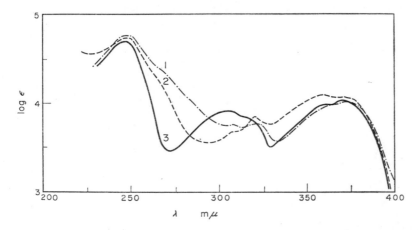

IX X XI

close similarity of the spectra of β-apoterramycin and of its immediate successors terrinolide and decarboxamidoterrinolide suggested that chromophore (XII) was retained in the latter transformation products (Fig. 9.4). Confirmation of

FIG. 9.4. Ultraviolet spectra of (1) β-apoterramycin, (2) terrinolide, (3) decarboxamidoterrinolide (in acid-ethanol). (Hochstein *et al.*, *J. Amer. Chem. Soc.*, **75**, 5455, 1953.)

this view came from infrared and boric acid acidity data and from the result of nitric acid oxidation of both terrinolide and its decarboxamido derivative to an anhydride, $C_{12}H_6O_7$, whose spectrum was reminiscent of that of dimethoxy-pyromellitic anhydride (XIV). Structure (XIII) follows for the anhydride (see Fig. 9.5). Partial structures (XV), (XVI) and (XVII) can now be written for α- and β-apoterramycins, terrinolide and decarboxamidoterrinolide, respectively.

The nature of the moiety $C_6H_5O_3$ in these structures, suggestive of a polyphenol, may now be examined. Compound (XVII) formed a pentamethoxy derivative which could be reduced to a glycol (XVIII). The orientation of the four groups attached to the benzene ring (C_6H_2) of (XVIII) was inferred by

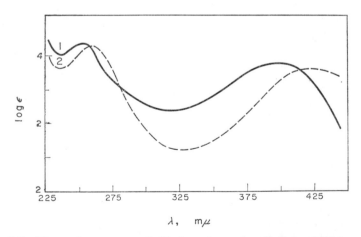

XII

XIII

XIV

XV   Apoterramycin

XVI   Terrinolide

XVII   Decarboxamidoterrinolide

FIG. 9.5. Absorption curves of (1) 3-methoxy-6-methylpyromellitic anhydride, (2) dimethyl pyromellitic anhydride (in conc. H_2SO_4). (Hochstein *et al.*, *J. Amer. Chem. Soc.*, **75**, 5455, 1953.)

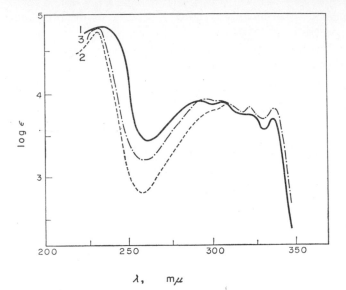

FIG. 9.6. Ultraviolet spectra of (1) The glycol (XVIII); (2) terranaphthol (II); (3) terranaphthol + 1,2,4-trimethoxybenzene (in ethanol). (Hochstein *et al.*, · *J. Amer. Chem. Soc.*, **75**, 5455, 1953.)

ultraviolet spectral analysis. Thus it was argued that since the two chromophores of glycol (XVIII) are insulated, the spectrum should consist of a summation of the curves of the 1,8-dimethoxynaphthalene chromophore (for which terranaph-

CH$_3$ OH

[C$_6$H$_2$(OMe)$_3$]

CH$_2$OH

OH OH

XVIII The Glycol

OH$_3$ H   OH

O

OH OH O   OH   OH

XVIII (a)

H$_3$C OH OH Y   OH

—CONH$_2$

OH O   OH X   O

XIX X or Y = OH or NMe$_2$

thol (II) forms the requisite model) and of a x,y,z-trimethoxybenzene. Only the addition spectrum of 1,2,4-trimethoxybenzene and terranaphthol led to a near identity with the spectrum of the glycol (XVIII) (Fig. 9.6). The displacement of the "synthetic" curve to shorter wavelength than that of the glycol may be ascribed to the lower degree of alkyl substitution of the nucleus in the model compared with that present in the glycol. Subsequent chemical evidence provided complete confirmation of this argument in favour of structural proposal (XVIIIa).

We must now perforce assume the detailed chemical and mechanistic argument leading to part-structure (XIX) for terramycin in order to focus attention on the rôle of ultraviolet spectral analysis in this study.

Reductive Degradation

Treatment of terramycin with zinc and acetic acid afforded desoxydesdimethylaminoterramycin, $C_{20}H_{19}NO_8$, whose spectrum in acidic ethanol (Fig. 9.7) markedly differed from that of terramycin (in the same solvent) in having a

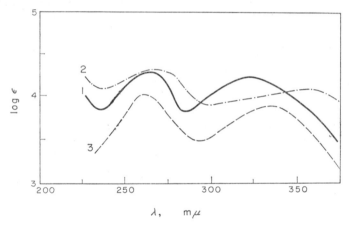

FIG. 9.7. Ultraviolet spectra: (1) desoxydesdimethylaminoterramycin in acid-ethanol; (2) terramycin in acid-ethanol; (3) 8-hydroxy-1-tetralone (XXIII) in acid-ethanol + 3,6-dihydroxy-4-oxo-2,5-cholestadiene (XXV) in CHCl₃. (Hochstein *et al.*, *J. Amer. Chem. Soc.*, **75**, 5455, 1953.)

high intensity band near 320 mμ. The absence of the band above 350 mμ which was assigned to chromophore (XX) in terramycin was indicative that such a hydroxy enolized-β-diketone moiety is absent in the new degradation product. However, it was possible to show by chemical methods that the β-dicarbonyl system (XXI) is *potentially* present in the desoxydesdimethylamino compound. Further, since no carbonyl band appeared above 1660 cm⁻¹ in the infrared spectrum of the latter, it was inferred that enolization had occurred in the alternative sense (XXII) in desoxydimethylaminoterramycin. Confirmation of this

H₃C OH

XX

XXI

H₃C OH

XXII

XXIII

XXIV

XXV

XXVI

XXVII

view comes from a nicely conceived model spectrum. The summation curve of the contributing species was constructed from the absorptions of 8-hydroxy-tetralone (XXIII) and of the unsaturated steroidal diosphenol (XXIV), which

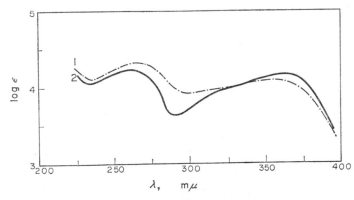

FIG. 9.8. Ultraviolet spectra (1) terramycin, (2) desdimethylaminoterramycin in acid-ethanol. (Hochstein *et al.*, *J. Amer. Chem. Soc.*, **75**, 5455, 1953.)

represents a close approximation for the inaccessible model (XXV). That the resultant synthetic curve reproduced the main features of the spectrum of desoxydesdimethylaminoterramycin represents a satisfying vindication of the additivity principle (Fig. 9.7). In particular, the replication of the high intensity band near 320 mμ indicated that the choice of models had indeed been a happy one.

When the zinc-acetic acid reduction of terramycin was stopped at the des-dimethylamino stage, the resultant product had an absorption spectrum very similar to that of terramycin (Fig. 9.8). It was now possible to expand the formula for terramycin to (XXVI) and thence by exclusion of sterically improbable isomers to (XXVII) as the final structure of the antibiotic.

9.2. PODOPHYLLUM LIGNANS

The formulae and absorption characteristics of the main constituents of *Podophyllum* species are shown in Chart. VIII (p. 234).

The spectrum of podophyllotoxin (XXVIII) represents the simple sum of the insulated contributing species, namely, methylenedioxybenzene (λ_{max} 283mμ

XXVIII   Podophyllotoxin
λ 292 (ε 4500)

XXIX   R=H α-Peltatin λ 210, 274 (ε 29,000, 2570)
          R=Me β-Peltatin λ 210, 273 (ε 58,000, 1820)

(ε 3300)) and 1,2,3-trimethoxybenzene (λ_{max} 270 mμ (ε 650)) with appropriate increments for ring residue substitution ($\sim$10 mμ). This would lead to a predicted maximum at *ca.* 293 mμ ($\varepsilon \sim 4000$). In fact, podophyllotoxin and its congeners absorb at 292–4 mμ (ε 4400–4800). The phenol transfer band (p–π transition) occurs at 210 mμ.

XXX Myristicin
λ 276 (ε 1400)

XXXI Safrole
λ 286 (ε 4000)

The α- and β-peltatins (XXIX; R=H and Me, respectively) have their (displaced) benzenoid bands near 274 mμ, which at first sight seems remarkably low for a ring A oxygenated podophyllotoxin type. We might have predicted λ_{max} 295–300 mμ for the peltatins, but, as Hartwell and Schrecker have pointed out, the spectrum of myristicin (XXX) bears little resemblance to that of safrole (XXXI). The steric situation in (XXX) (as in XXIX) must be responsible for an inhibition of electron transfer leading to reduced intensity and lower wavelength absorption than expected, although the band affected is the displaced benzenoid absorption band rather than the intense phenol band which still appears at 210 mμ.

The isomeric compounds, the α-, β- and γ-apopodophyllins, represent an interesting triad which can be distinguished by virtue of their absorption spectra. The α-isomer (XXXII) contains an oxygenated styrene chromophore and shows evidence of steric hindrance to coplanarity in having the principal styrene absorption as a shoulder (ε 30,000) at 242 mμ and at some 20 mμ lower than the expected maximal position. The 311 mμ band (ε 7590) provides good evidence for the assignment of structure (XXXII) to the α-isomer. The β-compound has a podophyllotoxin spectrum and may be formulated as (XXXIII). This leaves (XXXIV) as the structure for the γ-isomer, and in accord with the chromophore extending over the tri-oxygenated ring, double bond and lactonic functions, this has an intense band at 350 mμ in addition to a partial styrene band at 242 mμ.

The fully aromatic compounds of the series (e.g., XXXV) display typical naphthalenoid absorption.

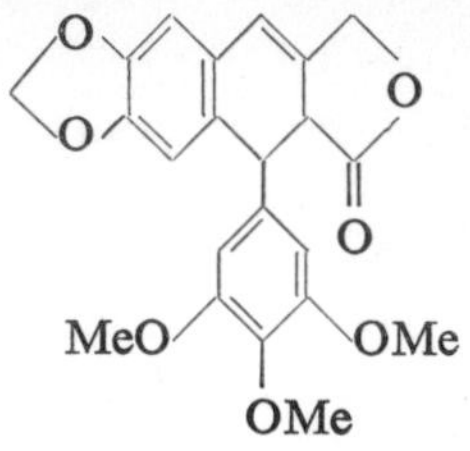

XXXII α-Apopodophyllin
λ 242, 311 (ε 30,000, 7590)

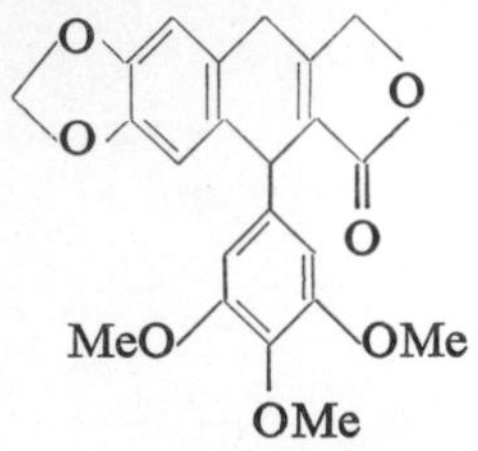

XXXIII β-Apopodophyllin
λ 290 (ε 4570)

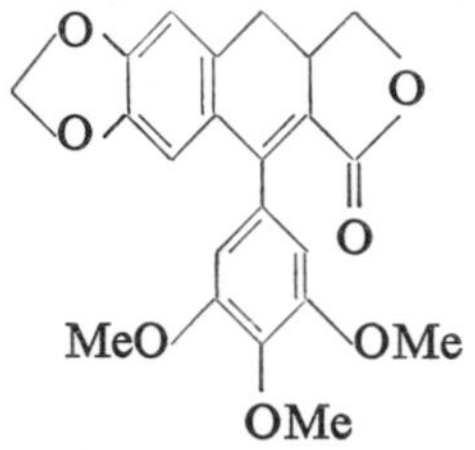

XXXIV γ-Apopodophyllin
λ 245·5, 350 (ε 21,000, 12,600)

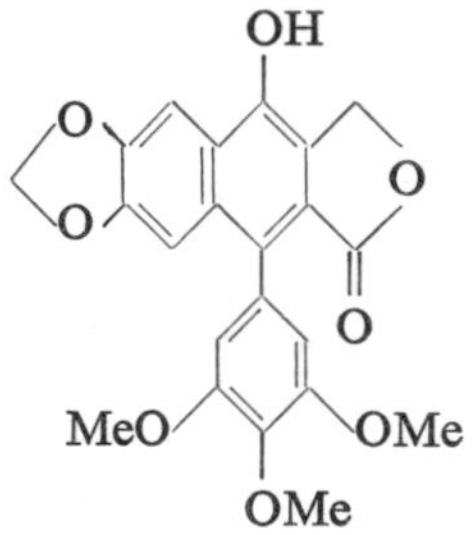

XXXV Dehydropodophyllotoxin
λ 226, 263, 323, 356
(ε 31,000, 42,000, 10,500, 5500)
Chart. VIII

9.3. SHELLOLIC ACID

Recent degradative studies employing information derived from ultraviolet and infrared spectra have resulted in a structural proposal (XXXVI; R=H) for shellolic acid, $C_{13}H_{16}(OH)_2(CO_2H)_2$, a constituent of shellac. The spectrum of the dimethyl ester*, λ_{max} 230 mμ (ε, 6000) shows that a double bond is conjugated with an ester grouping (XXXVI; R=Me). The infrared spectrum shows a broad band at 1700–25 cm⁻¹ (conjugated and unconjugated ester super-

* $n \rightarrow \pi^*$ bands of unsaturated acids, esters and lactones have now been observed e.g. shellolic acid has λ_{infl} at 250 mμ. (U. Weiss, priv. comm.).

imposed) and a peak at 1637 cm^{-1} (C=C stretch). Further, the n.m.r. spectrum indicates that one vinylic hydrogen and one C-methyl group are present. The latter inference was confirmed by Kuhn–Roth oxidation. Oxidation of dimethyl shellolate (XXXVI; R=Me) with manganese dioxide gave a dehydro compound formulated as (XXXVII), since no high intensity absorption appeared above 210 mμ. Oxidation of (XXXVI; R=Me) with selenium dioxide now gave

XXXVI

XXXVII

XXXVIII λ 290, 430 (ε, 40, 12)

XXXIX λ 240

(XXXVIII) whose spectrum [λ_{max} 290 and 430 mμ (ε, 40 and 12, respectively] and further reactions indicated that a non-enolizable α-diketone chromophore was present. When (XXXVI; R=Me) was oxidized with six equivalents of chromium trioxide the resultant acid on esterification had λ_{max} 240 mμ (ε, 8700) in full accord with structure (XXXIX) (cf. LIV, p. 241). Treatment of shellolic acid (XXXVI; R=H) with acetic anhydride–sodium acetate gave a dilactone formulated at (XL) on the basis of its infrared (ν 1770, 1742 cm^{-1}) and ultraviolet spectrum, the latter showing only end absorption indicative of steric hindrance to effective overlap of the π-electrons of the double bond and δ-lactone. Treatment of (XL) with hot water afforded a lactonic acid (XLI), λ_{max} 227 mμ (ε, 5500) in which the strained δ-lactone ring has been opened to reveal the α,β-unsaturated acid chromophore, displaying absorption associated with effective conjugation. We note, however, that the value of 227 mμ for this acid and 230 mμ for shellolic acid itself is higher than might be expected for a cyclohexene carboxylic acid. The γ-oxygen function may well be influencing the position of the E.T. band by participating in charge-transfer absorption (see Chapter 8, p. 260). This observation provides additional evidence for the stereochemical assignment of the hydroxyl group to the quasi-axial conformation.

Fusion of (XXXVI); R=Me) with alkali gave a lactonic diacid (XLII) which retained all the carbon atoms of shellolic acid. This lactone had λ_{max} 237 mμ (ε, 10,000). We should predict 240 mμ for the principal E.T. band of such a substituted benzoic acid on the basis of zero increment for meta −

—O—COR grouping and 10 mμ for the *para*-ring residue added to the parent value of 230 mμ (Chapter 3). Dehydrogenation of (XLII) gave a coumarin

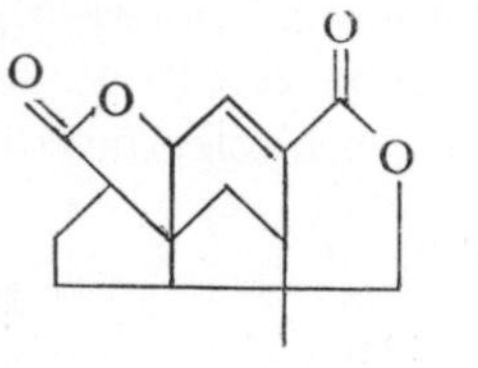

XL End absorption

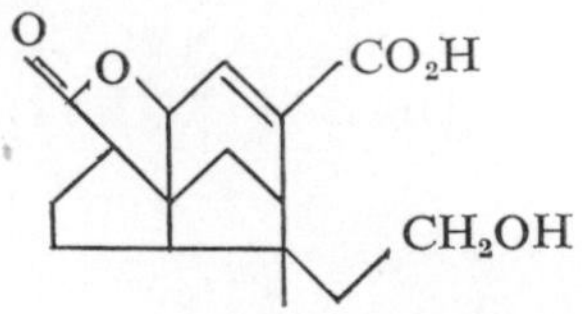

XLI λ 227

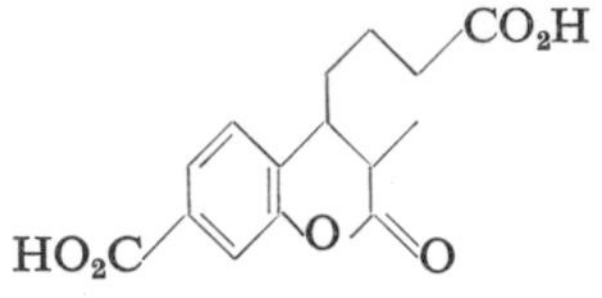

XLII λ 237 λcalc 240

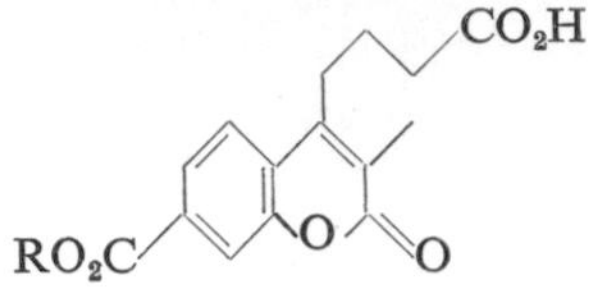

XLIII

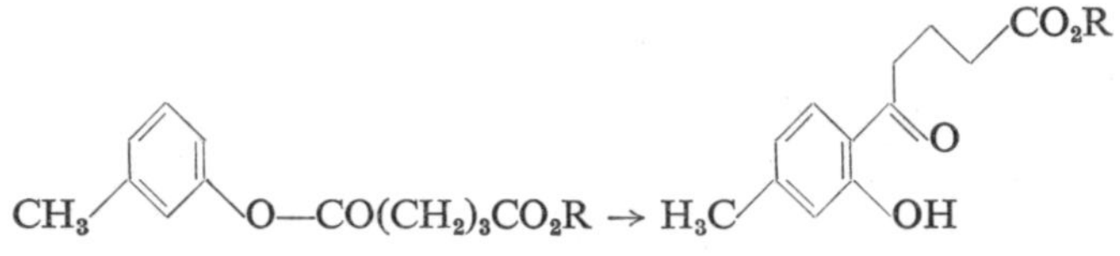

XLIV

XLV λ 262 λcalc 263

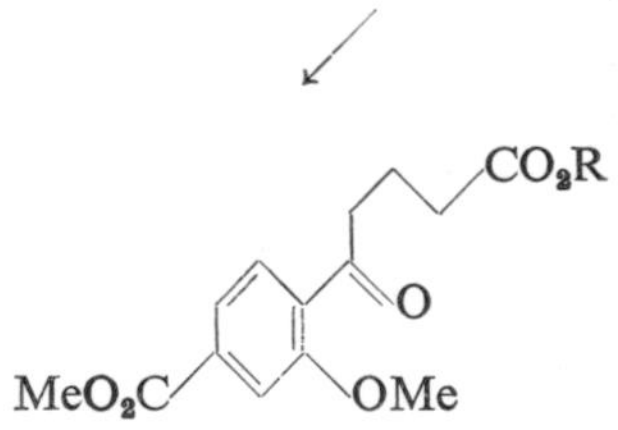

XLVI λ 254 λcalc 253

(XLIII) λ_{max} 275 sh. (13,300), 284 (18,200), 296 (16,200) 315 sh. (7700) 324 (8300) 376 sh. (5300) mμ. This structure of (XLIII) was then proved by synthesis from (XLIV) via (XLV) which had λ_{max} 262 (ε, 13,400) and 325 mμ (ε, 4370). The calculated value of the principal E.T. band of (XLV) is in good agreement with this value (λ_{calc} 263 mμ). Methylation and oxidation of (XLV) now gave the *o*-methoxyacetophenone derivative (XLVI) which had λ_{max} 254 and 320 mμ (ε, 12,800 and 3860) (λ_{calc} 253 mμ with zero increment for *para*-CO$_2$Me). Reformatsky reaction, acidic treatment and methylation then gave (XLIII).

9.4. ACONITUM–DELPHINIUM–GARRYA ALKALOIDS

The successful elucidation of the structures of some of the complex members of this group owes a great deal to the careful interpretation of spectral data made by the investigators at each stage of the degradative work. We shall now consider the ultraviolet data for a number of degradation products of some of these alkaloids.

Delphinine[5,4]

Partial structure (XLVII) for this alkaloid could be deduced on the basis of the following evidence. The degradations now to be described were carried out on the N-formyl alkaloid, α-oxodelphinine, $C_{33}H_{43}O_{10}N$ which, apart from

having $-\overset{|}{N}-CHO$ in place of the $-\overset{|}{N}-CH_3$ of delphinine, is structurally identical with the latter.

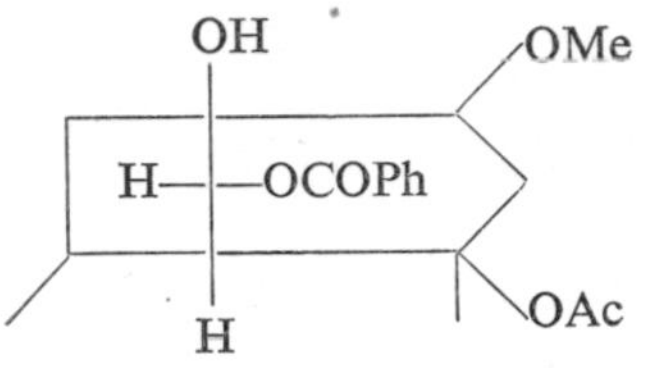

OH   OMe
H——OCOPh
H   OAc
XLVII

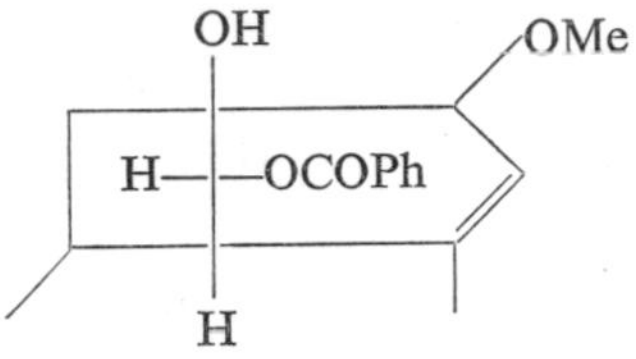

OH   OMe
H——OCOPh
H
XLVIII

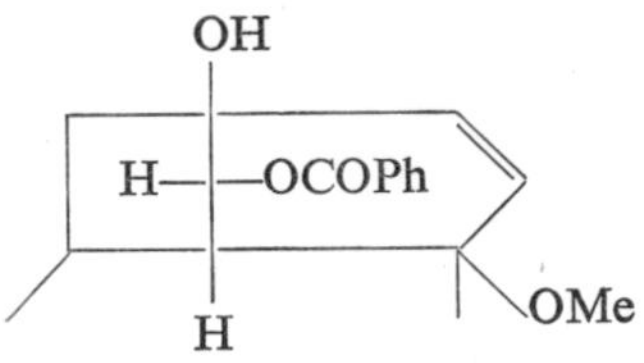

OH
H——OCOPh
H   OMe
XLIX

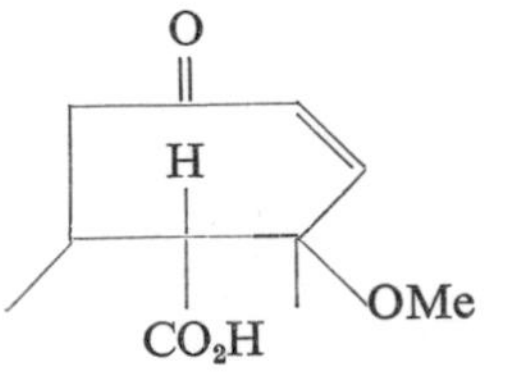

O
H
CO_2H OMe
L $\lambda 235$

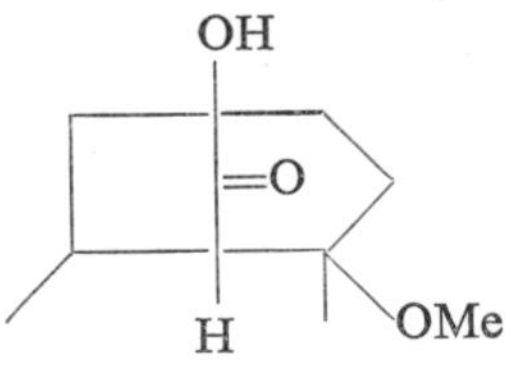

OH
=O
H   OMe
LI

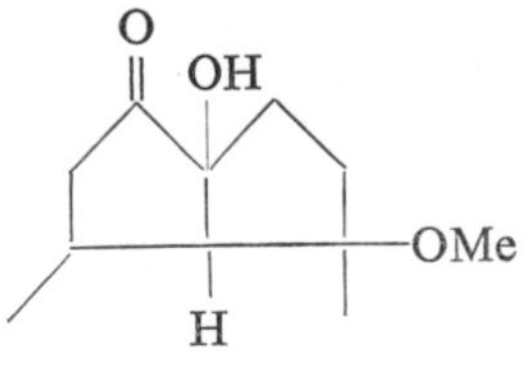

O   OH
——OMe
H
LII

Pyro-α-oxodelphinine (XLVIII) is obtained by pyrolytic loss of acetic acid from (XLVII). The latter compound was isomerized to (XLIX) in methanolic hydrochloric acid, a re-arrangement which involves allylic switch of the methoxyl group. Hydrolysis and oxidation of (XLIX) gave an α,β-unsaturated keto acid, λ_{max} 235 mμ (ε, 9000) which may be represented by (L). This high value (λ_{calc} 227 mμ) may be due to inclusion of the double bond in a seven membered ring or more probably to participation by the γ-methoxyl grouping (see 9.3 and Chapter 8).

Hydrogenation of isopyro-α-oxodelphinine (XLIX) followed by hydrolysis and oxidation gave a ketol (LI) further isomerized with alkali to a ketol for which structure (LII) may be written for the following reasons. (LII) consumes one mole of periodic acid giving a seco keto acid which spontaneously eliminates one mole of methanol yielding an α,β-unsaturated keto acid (LIII), λ_{max} 250 mμ (ε, 10,000). This peak is approximately 10–15 mμ higher than the position expected for a cyclopentenone of such substitution pattern. We recall, however, from Chapter 8 that, under certain steric conditions, cyclopentenones, far from absorbing at wavelengths lower than the corresponding cyclohexenones

LIII λ 250   LIV λ 257

may shown exaltation of λ_{max}. Such an effect is again operative in (LIII). The infrared spectrum confirms the assignment having bands at 1695 (cyclopentenone) and 1730 (—CO$_2$H) cm^{-1}.

The same degradations carried out on α-oxodelphinine (XLVII) gave the methoxy seco acid (LIV), λ_{max} 257 mμ. The presence of the methoxyl group α to the carbonyl function has shifted λ_{max} 7 mμ to the red. This is in contrast to the cyclohexenones where such oxygenated functions produce zero or slight blue shifts (Chapter 8).

LV

The part structure (XLVII) for delphinine could now be incorporated in a complete structural proposal (LV) for the alkaloid, the evidence for the remainder of the molecule coming from degradative results in which chemical, infrared, n.m.r., and biogenetic considerations, played a major role.

Aconitine[6]

This alkaloid, $C_{34}H_{47}O_{11}N$, is the most important and complicated member of the aconitum class. Aconitine, for which structure (LVI) was proposed in 1959, has recently been related to delphinine from which it differs in rings C and D in having an additional hydroxyl group.

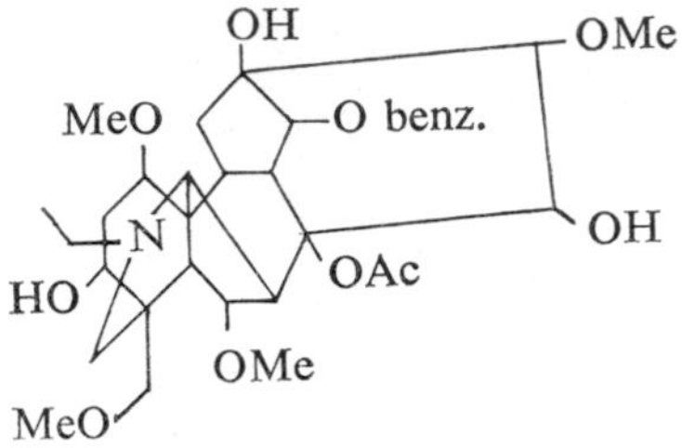

LVI

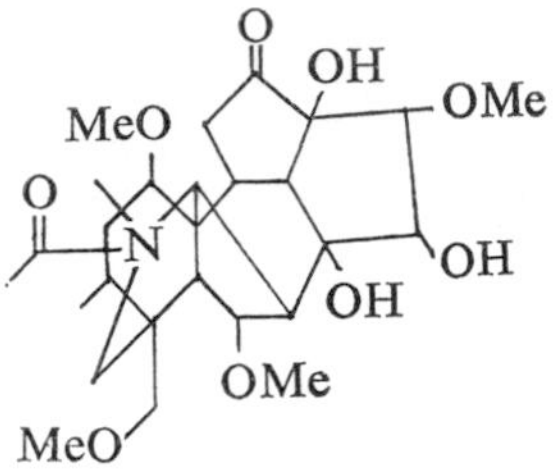

LVII

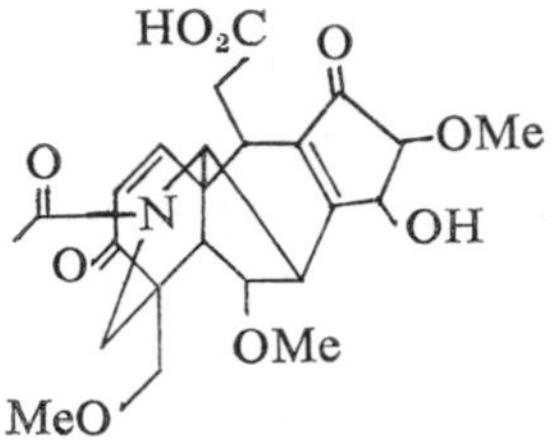

LVIII

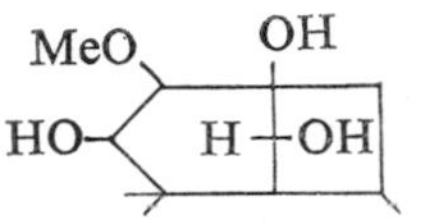

LIX

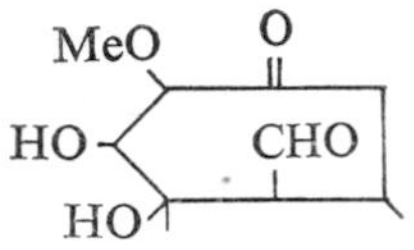

LX

Aconitine was transformed to the N-acetyl derivative (LVII), λ_{max} 295 mμ (ε, 90) which, with lead tetra-acetate, could be cleaved to (LVIII), λ_{max} 230 mμ (shoulder) and 255 mμ. These bands are respectively assigned to the cyclo-hexenone and strained cyclopentenone chromophores (*cf.* delphinine cyclo-pentenone above). Oxidation of oxonine (part structure LIX) with periodic acid and treatment of the crude product (LX) with oxygen in alkaline solution gives a phenol of part structure (LXI) λ_{max} 238, 283 and 315 mμ. These bands

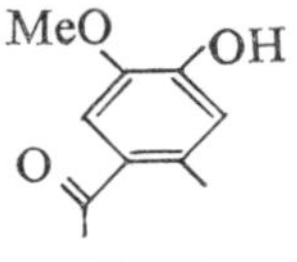

LXI

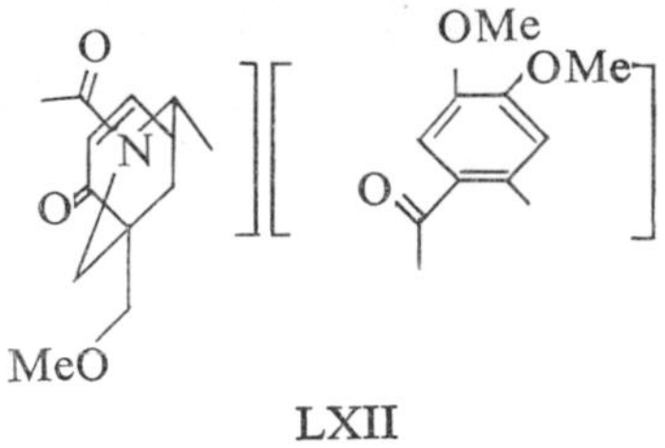

LXII

correspond to the phenol $p - \pi$ transition, and the principal and minor E.T. bands of a substituted acetophenone. The calculated E.T. band for structure (LXI) is at 281 mμ. In base (LXI) has λ_{max} 256 and 353 mμ, the latter value being rather high for the *p*-hydroxy acetophenone anion, which is expected to absorb near 335 mμ. Conversion to (LXII) gave a spectrum representing the summation curve of the cyclohexenone and substituted acetophenone spectra. Similarly, α-oxoisopyrodelphinone (LXIII) may be transformed to (LXIV;

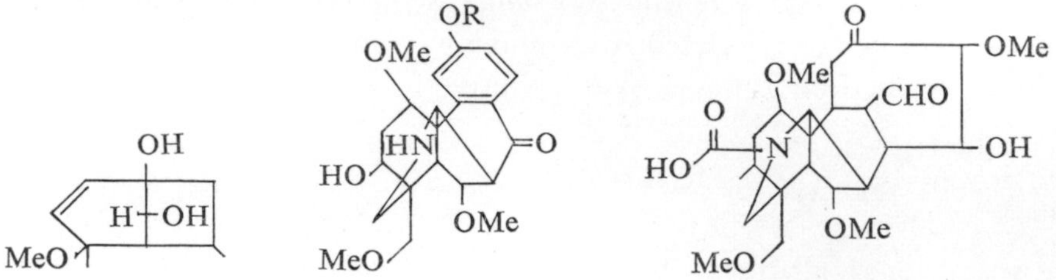

LXIII   LXIV   LXV

R=H) which has λ_{max} 232 and 285 mμ, the latter band being surprisingly high for a 2-alkylated p-hydroxyacetophenone (λ_{calc} 274 mμ). Methylation gave the corresponding ether (LXIV; R=Me) which could be obtained via (LXV) from aconitine. It is interesting to note that (LXV) has the acetophenone band at 280 mμ which is still high ($+ 6$ mμ) but almost within the expected range. Thus, the structures of aconitine and delphinine were directly correlated through a common phenolic degradation product.

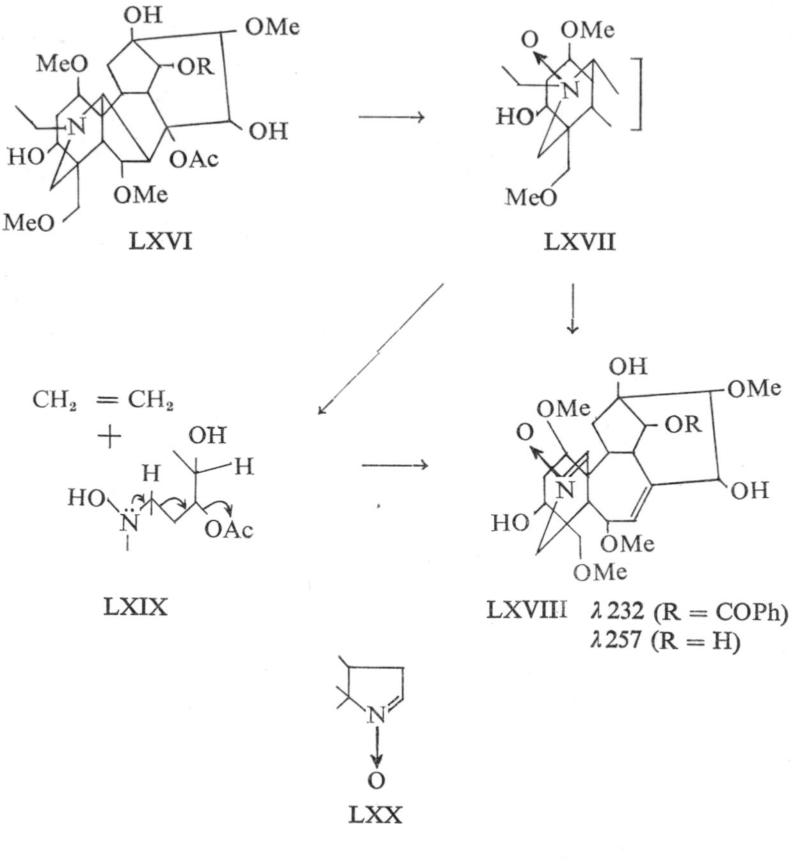

LXVI   LXVII

CH$_2$ = CH$_2$
+

LXIX

LXVIII λ 232 (R = COPh)
         λ 257 (R = H)

LXX

The relationship between the nitrogen atom and the acetoxy group of aconitine (LXVI) was revealed by the following transformations. Aconitine-N-oxide (LXVII) was pyrolysed to (LXVIII) λ_{max} 232 mμ (ε, 18,400) (inflection at 255 mμ) hydrolysed to the desbenzoyl compound (LXVIII; R=H) λ_{max} 257 mμ (ε, 8250), ε_{210}, 6800. These values are in only fair agreement with the absorption maximum of the model (LXX), λ_{max}, 234 (ε, 8800), the maximum at 232 mμ in (LXVIII) being due to the Ph—CO—O chromophore, although steric influence on the spectrum is probably considerable. The change (LXVII) → (LXVIII) can be rationalized in terms of a concerted fragmentation indicated in (LXIX). The correctness of this interpretation was confirmed by regeneration of aconitine (LXVI) from the nitrone (LXVIII). The power of these methods of spectral and mechanistic interpretation is amply illustrated by the establishment of formula (LXVI) for aconitine by X-ray crystallography.

Napellonine[4]

Napellonine (LXXII), an oxidation product of napelline (LXXI), shows carbonyl absorption in the infrared characteristic of a cyclohexanone but has an unusually intense $n \rightarrow \pi^*$ C=O absorption in the ultraviolet at 290 mμ (ε 398).

LXXI Napellonine   LXXII Napellonine

The stereoformula (LXXII) deduced by chemical and stereochemical argument shows that a charge-transfer interaction between the exomethylene and carbonyl π-orbitals is sterically favoured and provides rationalisation for the observed "abnormal" spectrum.

Lycoctonine[4]

The framework of the lycoctonine molecule has been derived by X-ray crystallography of des(oxymethylene)-lycoctonine. The structural proposal

LXXIII

(LXXIII) for the alkaloid itself was a logical extension of this formula based on the known transformations of lycoctonine, some of which are particularly interesting from the point of view of ultraviolet spectral analysis.

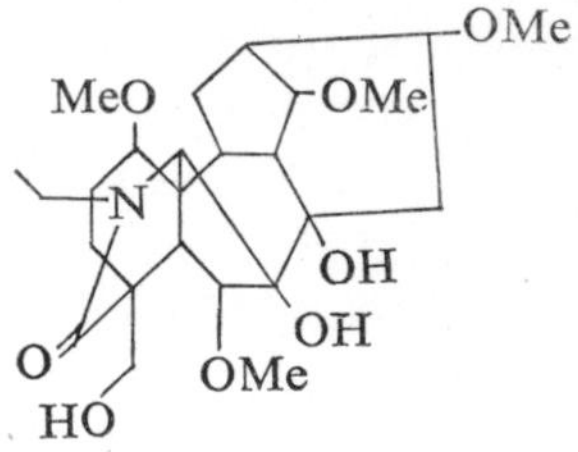

LXXIV

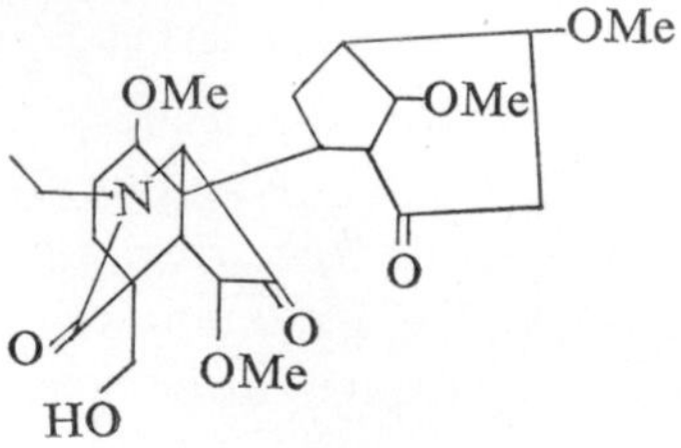

LXXV

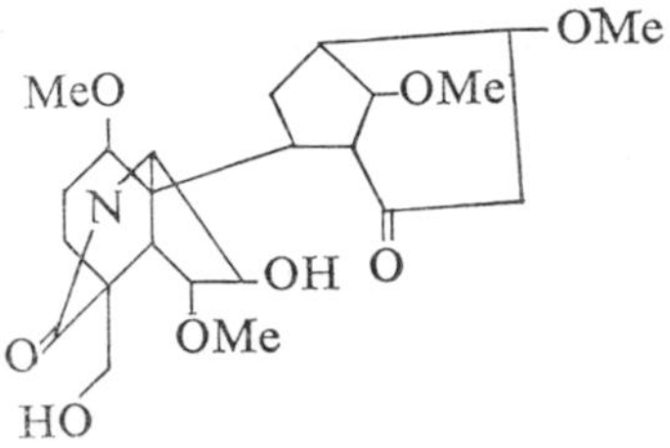

LXXVI

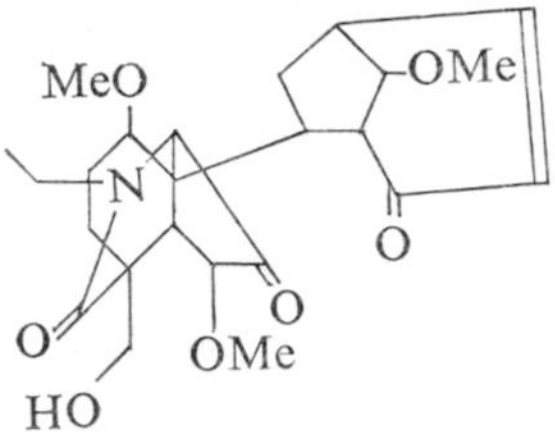

LXXVII

A key oxidation product of lycoctonine is the amide, lycoctonam (LXXIV). When lycoctonam is oxidised with periodic acid the reaction does not proceed beyond a dicarbonyl compound indicating that both alcoholic groups of the vic-glycol are tertiary. This oxidation product, seco-lycoctonam diketone (LXXV) has ν_{max} 1766 (cyclopentanone), 1707 (cyclohexanone) and 1631 (amide) cm^{-1} and λ_{max} 318 mμ^{-1} ε 280). The position and intensity of the $n \to \pi^*$ C=O band indicate that charge transfer is operative between the spatially interactive pair of ketone groups. Reduction of the carbonyl group of the cyclopentanone moiety with sodium borohydride gives a compound with an ultraviolet spectrum compatible with the $n \to \pi^*$ transition of a normal cyclohexanone − λ_{max} 270 mμ (ε 40) − and with expression (LXXVI) for the ketol. Treatment of either the seco diketone (LXXV) or the ketol (LXXVI) with acid or base results in the generation of an α, β-unsaturated cyclohexenone (LXXVII) with loss of the elements of methanol. In accord with this formulation (LXXVII) has ν_{max} 1679 cm^{-1} and λ_{max} 223 (calc. 227 mμ).

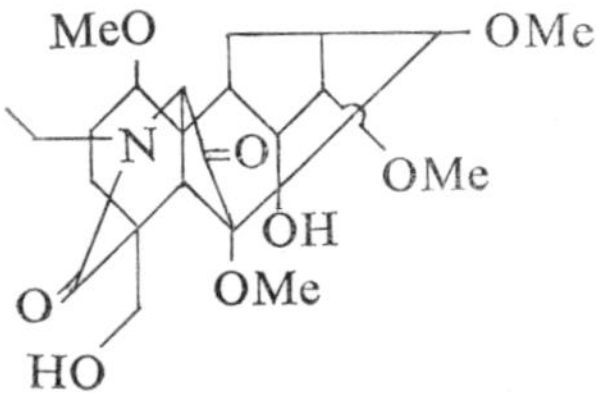

LXXVIII

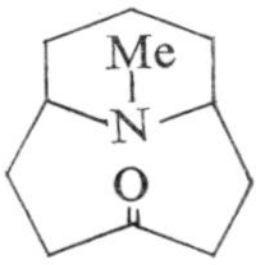

LXXIX

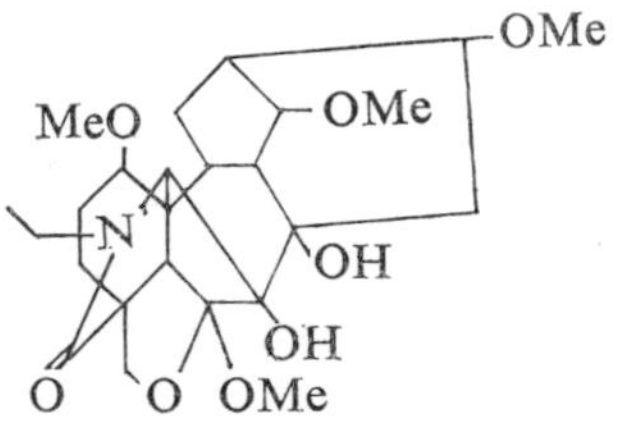

LXXX

Activated alumina or sodium bicarbonate converts the seco diketone (LXXV) to an "iso" compound (LXXVIII) which has normal $-\overset{|}{C}=O$ stretching frequency in the infrared at 1743 cm^{-1}, but λ_{max} 218 and 335 mμ (ε 6600 and 180). These bands may be tentatively assigned to a charge transfer absorption

LXXXI

as a result of the disposition of the tertiary nitrogen with respect to the carbonyl group (cf. LXXIX, λ_{max} 221 (ε 6000)) and to exaltation of the normal $n \rightarrow \pi^*$ absorption by steric overlap of p-electrons or the π-orbital of the amide grouping with the C=O chromophore.

Treatment of the "iso" compound (LXXVIII) with hot mineral acid yields a mixture of the α-iso compound (LXXX) which is transparent to 210 mμ and its further acidic transformation product, the "anhydroiso" compound (LXXXI) whose spectrum (ν_{max} 1763 cm^{-1}; λ_{max} 300 mμ (ε 80)) reflects the environment of the cyclohexanone carbonyl group.

Delpheline[7]

Since this alkaloid has a very low ε value at 210 mμ and its neutral derivatives consume no perbenzoic acid, the molecular formula $C_{25}H_{39}O_6N$ containing three methoxyl, one hydroxyl and a methylenedioxy grouping, must

LXXXII   LXXXIII   LXXXIV

be represented by a saturated heptacyclic structure. Let us now examine the changes wrought by degradation on the ultraviolet spectrum of some members of the delpheline family, in terms of the structural formula (LXXXII) proposed by Cookson and Trevett for the alkaloid. Dehydrodelpheline (LXXXIII) has λ_{max} 269 mμ (ε 160) and its ammonium salt (LXXXIV; R=H) λ_{max} 259 mμ (ε 200), while dehydro-oxodelpheline (LXXXV) has λ_{max} 313 mμ (ε 44). At first it was suspected that the grouping $-\overset{|}{N}-\overset{|}{C}H-CHOH-$ was present in delpheline and that the lowering of the $n \to \pi^*$ CO wavelength in (LXXXIII)

and (LXXXIV) was due to the chromophore $-\overset{|}{N}-\overset{|}{CH}-C-$. However, comparison with model chromophores of amino camphor salts showed that the 280 mμ CO band of camphor was not affected in this way.

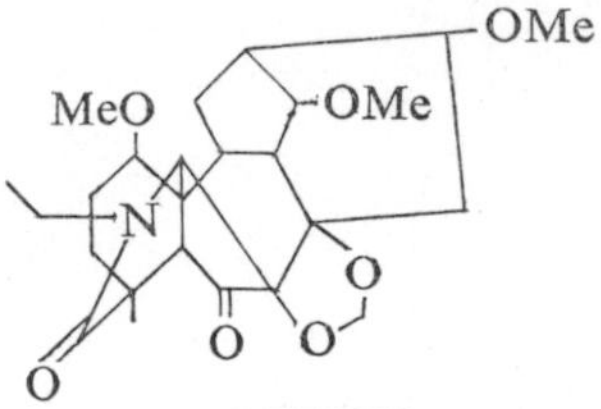

LXXXV

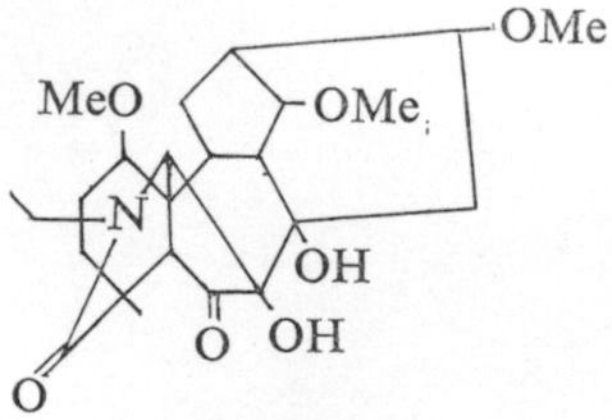

LXXXVI

Oxidation of dehydrodemethylene-oxodelpheline (LXXXVI) with lead tetra-acetate gives a red α-diketone (LXXXVII) with infrared bands at 1775 and 1755 (cyclopentanedione) and 1712 (cyclohexanone) cm^{-1} and λ_{max} 490 mμ (ε, 163).

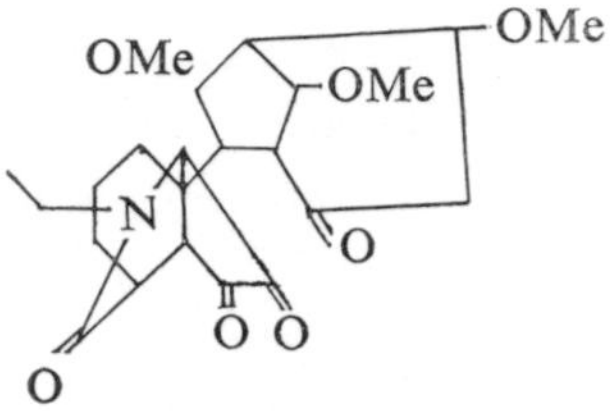

LXXXVII λ 490

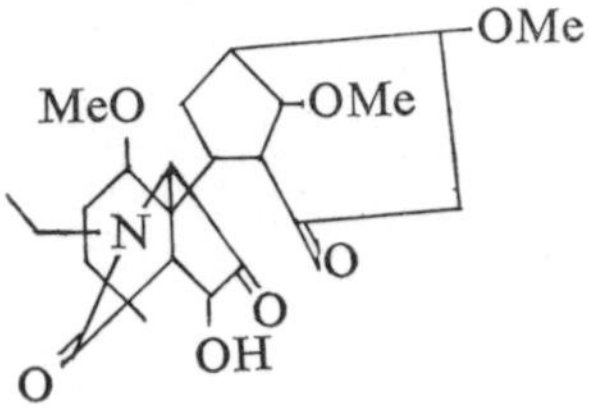

LXXXVIII λ 319 (ε 310)

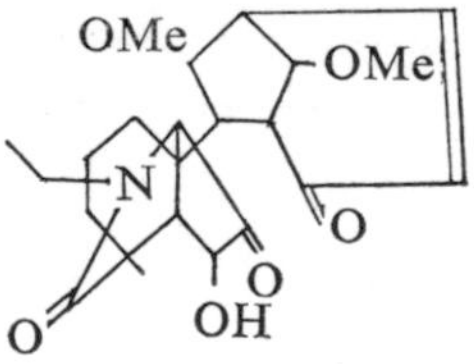

LXXXIX λ 223

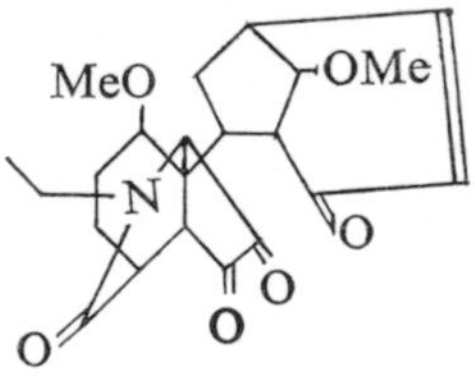

XC λ 223 and 494

Cleavage of (LXXXVI) with one mole of periodic acid gives a seco-diketone (LXXXVIII) with five- and six-membered ring C=O stretching frequencies in the infrared and λ_{max} 319 mμ (ε, 310) indicative of π-orbital interaction. By

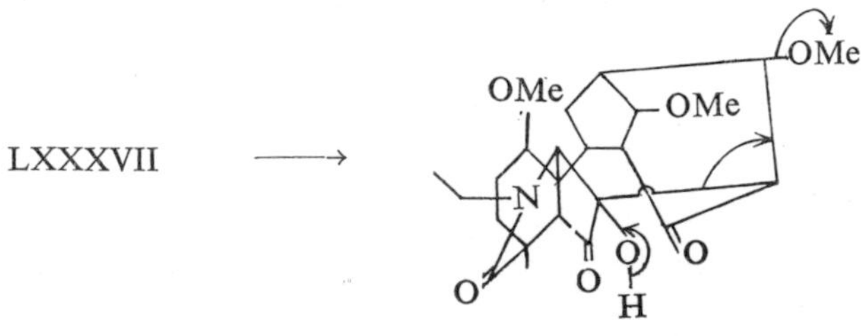

LXXXVII $\longrightarrow$

XCI λ 312 (ε 59)

analogy with lycoctonine chemistry the seco diketone eliminates methanol on treatment with acid to give (LXXXIX) λ_{max}, 225 and 320 mμ (ε, 11,000 and 320). Similarly, the red α-diketone (LXXXVII) gives the unsaturated ketone

XCII

XCIII λ 293 (ε 114)

(XC); λ_{max} 223 and 494 mμ. Treatment of the red α-diketone with alkali gives, first, the colourless aldol (XCI) showing ν_{max} 1755 (five-ring CO) and 1720 (six-ring CO) cm^{-1} and λ_{max} 312 mμ (ε, 59). Further acidic treatment affords the enone (XC).

XCIV λ 420 (ε 53)

When demethylene-oxodelpheline (XCII) is treated with acetyl chloride a dehydrated acetate is formed; recognition as a *ketone* follows from its absorption maximum at 293–4 mμ (ε 114). The infrared evidence is confirmatory but not diagnostic as the acetate and ketonic bands are superimposed at 1738 cm^{-1}. Hydrolysis of this keto-acetate followed by oxidation (CrO$_3$-pyridine) gives a yellow α-diketone with ν_{max} 1758 and 1720 cm^{-1}, λ_{max} 420 mμ (ε, 53). Structures (XCIII) and (XCIV) are proposed for the acetate and the yellow diketone, respectively.

9.5. SOME OXYGEN HETEROCYCLIC MOULD METABOLITES

Griseofulvin[8]

We have reproduced below the ultraviolet data pertaining to some of the products in the degradation and structure proof of the antibiotic griseofulvin, $C_{17}H_{17}O_6Cl$, in terms of the electron-transfer nomenclature developed for aromatic and heterocyclic chromophores in Chapters 3 and 4.

The presence of a β-methoxy-α,β-unsaturated cyclohexenone moiety in ring C of griseofulvin (XCV) is revealed not only by chemical reaction (hydrolysis to a cyclohexan-1,3-dione) and infrared spectrum, but also by subtraction of the ultraviolet spectrum of dihydrogriseofulvin (XCVI) from that of (XCV). This

XCV   XCVI

gives a single maximum at 252 mμ (ε 15,000) in fair agreement with the predicted position of absorption (215 (parent + 12 (β-ring residue) + 30 (β-OMe) = 257 mμ).

XCVII   XCVIII   XCIX

Partial structure (XCVII) which recurs in the majority of the elaboration products of griseofulvin (and in the parent compound itself) has a principal E.T. band calculable from Table 3·4, application of which gives λ_{calc} 285 mμ (246 + 2 × 7 + 25 mμ). The average value of this band in twenty derivatives of griseofulvin covering the range 287–291 mμ is 288 mμ. The secondary E.T. band occurs near 320–330 mμ, while intense absorption in the 220–230 mμ region apparent in many of these compounds, may be assigned to the chloro-phloroglucinol-type E.T. band ($p - \pi$ transition).

One of the key products of alkaline degradation, decarboxygriseofulvic acid, was recognised as a benzofuran by the dramatic change of ultraviolet spectrum from that of chromophore (XCVII) to a curve showing intense absorption at 220, 265 and 295 (sh) mμ. Structure (XCVIII) was assigned to this benzofuran.

C   CI   CII

An isomeric compound (XCIX) was also encountered in which the extended conjugation of a methoxylated ring shifts the main E.T. band to 340 mμ. These changes are summarized in formula (XCV) → (XCVIII) → (XCIX).

When griseofulvin (XCV) is hydrolysed with acid, the dione (C), griseo-fulvic acid, is formed, which can be methylated giving back (XCV) and an iso-mer of the latter, (CI). In addition to the expected absorption at 235 (phenol $p - \pi$ transition) 291 and 326 mμ (E.T. bands of Ar—CO) this has an intense band at 263 mμ (ε, 19,500). Subtraction of chromophore (XCVII) from the spectrum of isogriseofulvin (CI) gives the absorption band of the isomeric ether as 259 mμ. This is unexpected as we should predict λ_{max} 250 mμ for this ether, which has the same substitution pattern as the isomeric griseofulvin ether (λ_{max} (by subtraction) 252 mμ) and as dimedone methyl ether (CII) (λ_{max} 249 mμ). This apparent anomaly has been explained by Grove, Macmillan and their colleagues[8] in terms of $\pi - \pi$ interaction of the C=O chromophores in isogriseofulvin (CI) in a manner reminiscent of the situation

CIII   CIV

found in 1,6-dioxospiro [4:4]-nonane (CIII) which also has an abnormal spec-trum.

Treatment of griseofulvin (XCV) with boiling aqueous alkali hydrolyses the enol ether and *one* of the aryl methoxyl groups to a phenolic function. Ultraviolet data could be used in the following way to predict which ether (4- or 6-) had been hydrolysed. Cram and Cranz had earlier shown that *o*- and *p*-hydroxyacetophenones could be distinguished readily by comparing their ultraviolet spectra in both ionizing and non-ionizing solvent. For *o*-hydroxyaryl ketones the principal E.T. band is shifted *ca.* 5 mμ to the red on changing from non-ionizing to ionizing solvent (1), whereas in the case of the *p*-hydroxy isomers the

(1)

(2)

corresponding solvent change evokes a shift of 50 mμ to longer wavelengths (2). The model hydroxy-coumaranones (Chart IX) show qualitative (but not quantitative) agreement with these two rules of shift and with the rules evolved in the present work (Table 3.4c). The calculated values (from Chapter 3) are

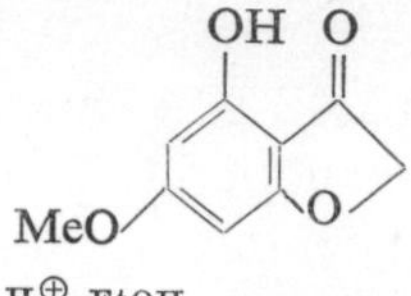

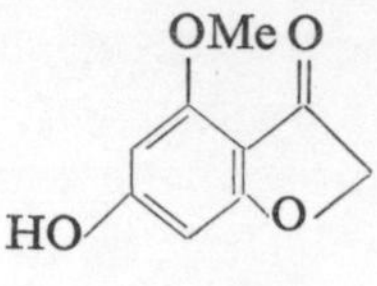

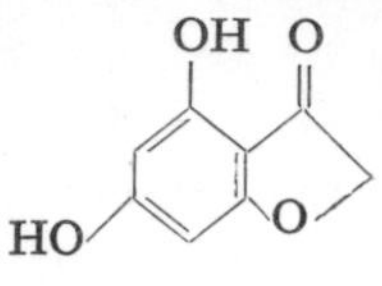

$\lambda^{H\oplus-EtOH}$ 280 (285)†   284 (285)   283 (285)

$\lambda^{OH\ominus}$ 285 (289)   318 (338)   306 (338)

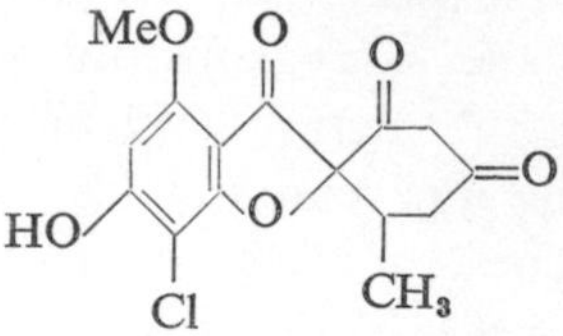

CIV

$\lambda^{H\oplus-EtOH}$ 292 (285)

$\lambda^{OH\ominus}$ 327 (338)

† λ_{calc} in parenthesis.

Chart IX

included in Chart IX and show that although good agreement is obtained in non-ionising media and for *ortho*-hydroxy groups in ionizing solvent, the *para*-hydroxy coumaranones do not suffer a 50 mμ displacement in alkaline solution, but rather a change of 35 mμ. This effect may be of steric origin In the event there was little doubt that it was the 6- and not the 4-methoxyl group which was hydrolysed in griseofulvin, since the desmethyl compound (CIV) showed an alkaline spectrum shift of + 35 mμ. The enolized 1,3-dione chromophore of (CIV) showed concentration dependence in ethanol − in dilute solution the anion absorbed together with the coumaranone band at 285 mμ (*cf.* dimedone anion, λ_{max} 280 mμ) resulting in a broad, intense peak. In concentrated ethanol the trione (CIV) had λ_{max} 267–75 mμ corresponding to the enol (CV), i.e. to the isogriseofulvin system (CI) rather than to the griseofulvin ether type (XCV; λ_{max} 252 mμ).

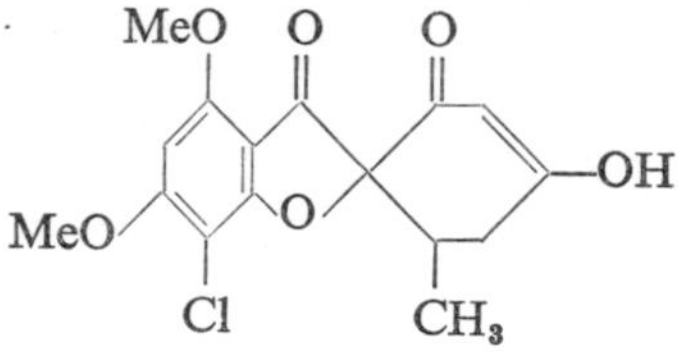

CV 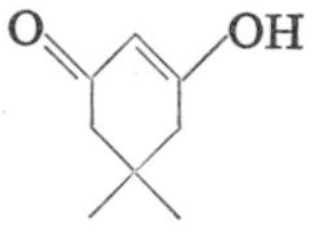   CVI 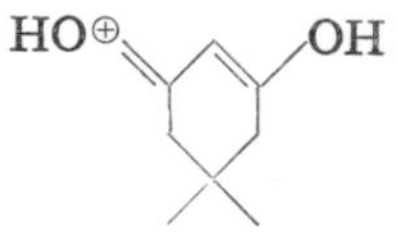   CVII

In acidic methanol griseofulvin (XCV) rapidly developed the spectrum of isogriseofulvin (CI). However, dimedone is not methylated to its enol ether under these conditions. Instead, it has bands at 250 mμ (ε 15,000) (calc. for undissociated enol (CVI) 257 mμ) and at 280 mμ (ε 8000) assigned to the conjugate acid (CVII). Dilution with water gives a single band at 257 mμ corresponding to (CVI).

Geodin[9]

The absorption spectrum of the mould metabolite geodin (CVIII) involves contributions from the insulated coumaranone and cyclohexadienone chromophores. The former grouping (CIX) has λ_{calc} 270 mμ but geodin and its methyl ether in fact display one principal maximum at 280–284 mμ. When the coumaranone curve is subtracted from the spectrum of geodin the resultant differential curve has a maximum at 240–2 mμ. This process was of value in deciding between isomeric formulations (CVIII) and (CX) for geodin. The latter, by analogy with other cyclohexadienones (Chapter 2) should absorb above 320 mμ, and no such band appears in the differential curve or in the spectrum of geodin itself. The subtraction method does not take into account any steric interaction of chromophores within the intact molecule and should be used as a working guide rather than as a definitive technique providing absolute values of λ_{max} or ε. This is illustrated by a similar operation carried out on the spectrum of geodoxin[10] (CXI), a related metabolite, from which the curve of dichloro-*p*-orsellinic acid was subtracted to give λ_{max} 230 and 275 mμ for the chromophore (CXII). This is reminiscent of the value λ_{max} 250 and

CVIII   CIX   CX   CXI   CXII   CXIII   CXIV

278 mμ for the dienone (CXIII). Similarly, subtraction of the curve of orsellinic acid (CXIV) from that of picrolichenic acid[11] (CXV) gives λ_{max} 235 and 280 mμ for the cyclohexadienone (CXVI). This dienone is in fact almost identical with the griseofulvin fragment (CXVII) which by the subtraction tech-

nique using an *intact spiro-model* rather than an aromatic acid model has absorption at 252 mμ, in close agreement with the calculated value (257 mμ). The subtraction technique is thus most useful for qualitative assessment in distin-

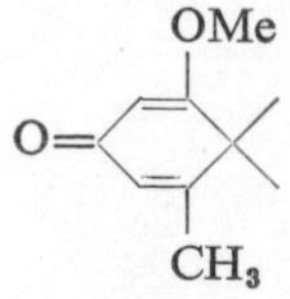

CXVII

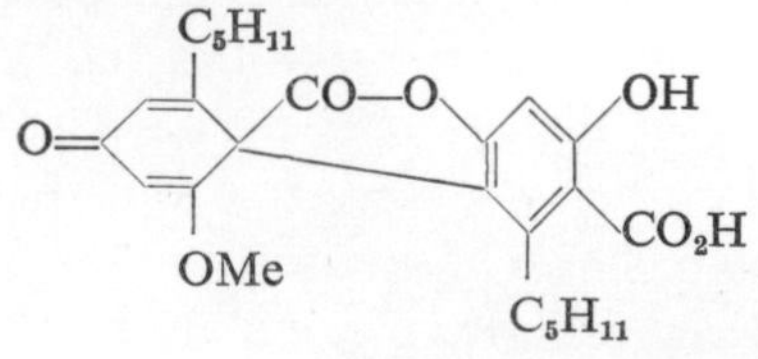

CXV

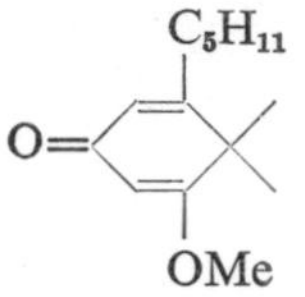

CXVI

guishing between such differently absorbing species as (CVIII) and (CX), but as we have seen in several of our examples, great vigilance is required in the detection of effects of steric overlap, compression and hindrance to coplanarity.

9.6. ATROVENETIN

The constitution of atrovenetin, $C_{19}H_{18}O_6$, a metabolite of *Penicillium atrovenetum*, was recently elucidated by methods which made full use of the ultraviolet spectra of the series of transformation and degradation products of the natural product[12]. The spectrum of atrovenetin (CXVIII) is reminiscent

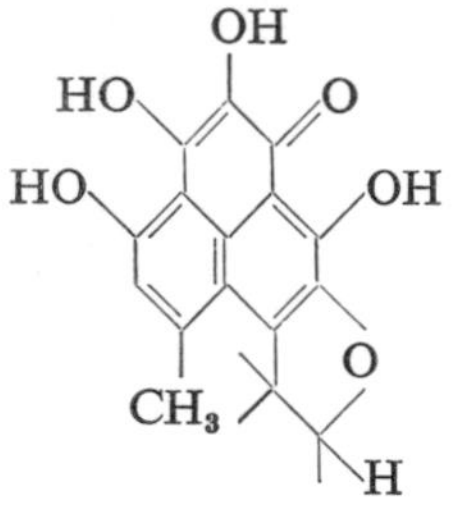

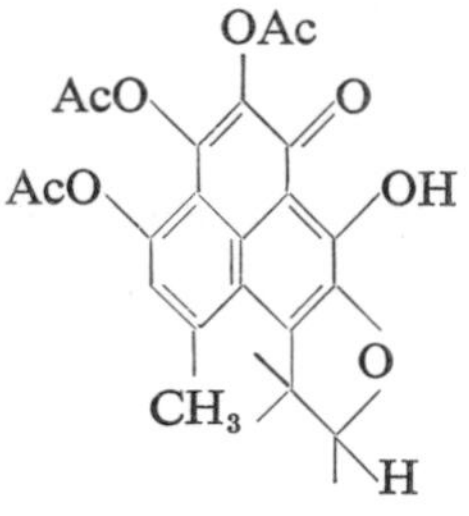

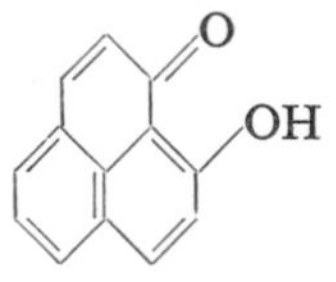

CXVIII	CXX	CXIX
λ_{max}†	λ_{max}	λ_{max}
222	247	235
280–260	275	260
385	347–50	352
410–420 (i)	390 i	395 i
	409	415
	433	438

† ε values 10,000–25,000.

of that of 9-hydroxyperinaphthenone (CXIX), but an even closer resemblance is found between the latter's spectrum and that of atrovenetin triacetate (CXX). This is to be expected on the principle that the spectrum of a phenolic system returns to that of the parent hydrocarbon (with appropriate slight batho-chromic shift) on acetylation. The placement of the hydroxyl groups in atrov-enetin follows from the degradation of a related compound, xanthoherquein, by nitric acid to nitrococussic acid (CXXI). The position of attachment of the ether bridge in (CXVIII) was determined by nitric acid oxidation to a phenolic dilactone $C_{15}H_{14}O_9N_2$, λ_{max} 263 and 344 mμ (ε, 11,750 and 12,300) whose infra-red spectrum and chemical behaviour were compatible with structure (CXXII;

CXXI	CXXII	CXXIII
λ 380–383 (ε 8000)	R=Me; λ 209 (ε 2200)	λ 298–301 (ε 2000)

R=H). Further confirmation comes from the comparison of the spectrum of the methyl ether (CXXII; R=Me) with that of (CXXIII). Both show a shift from the spectrum of the phenol (CXXII; R=H) in having a single band near 300 mμ (ε, 2200), at first sight remarkable for such an apparently

CXXIV

small structural change but adequately explained by steric inhibition of the electron-transfer absorption in the methyl ether, the *ortho*-nitrophenol type absorption (CXXIV) being replaced by the L.E. benzenoid bands of low intensity in the ether.

9.7. AZALEIN[13]

In Chapter 4 we noted that the position of hydroxyl groups attached to the flavone nucleus may sometimes be determined by the shifts of the absorption spectrum engendered by ionization of such groups in basic solution. Careful diagnostic studies by Geissman and by Jurd have led to the development of methods for the facile detection of the presence of certain structural features of polyfunctional flavonoids. The essentials of the approaches used are now presented in the discussion of the structure of azalein, a flavonol glycoside.

Detection of the 3,4'-Dihydroxy Grouping[13]

Although it has been generally considered that the decomposition of flavonols in basic media is not rapid, Jurd and Horowitz were able to show that those flavonols stable to sodium ethoxide solution all have the C_3-hydroxyl (see CXXV) protected by methylation or glycosidation. Such stability is *not*

CXXV   CXXVI

influenced by the number or placement of other hydroxyl groups at the commonly occurring flavonol positions (CXXV) although exceptions to this rule will be found if a pyrogallol grouping is present as the latter group is labile to alkali. Jurd and Horowitz also showed that over a wide range of compounds studied, only those which contained a 4'-OH group *in addition to a free 3-OH* were unstable to alkali. A C_7-OH for example does not produce such instability. Thus while kaempferol (CXXVI; R=H) rapidly decomposes in base the dimethyl ether (CXXVI; R=Me) is quite stable to sodium ethoxide solution. These stability measurements are conveniently made with the ultraviolet spectrophotometer. Compound (CXXVI; R=H) has λ_{max} 266 and 367·5 mμ in ethanol, rapidly changed to a compound with a low intensity band at 315 mμ in base, whilst (CXXVI; R=Me) has λ_{max}^{EtOH} 259 and 375 mμ shifted to 275 and 389 mμ in basic solution.

The 7-Hydroxyl Group[13]

The principle used in the detection of a free hydroxyl group at position 7 of the flavone nucleus is that all phenolic groups (unless subject to severe steric hindrance) are ionized in sodium ethoxide solution, whereas only the strongly acidic phenolic groups are ionized in sodium acetate-ethanol solution. Application of this principle to model 7-oxygenated flavones revealed that the spectra

CXXXVII   CXXXVIII

of the 7-hydroxy flavones are changed in sodium acetate (with respect to ethanolic solution), the principal band at 250–70 mμ moving 8–19 mμ to the red. Flavones with 7-OMe or 7-glycosidoxy groups do not exhibit this shift. The test is sensitive in the presence of hydroxyl groups at positions 3, 5, 8, 3' and 4'. These results provide good evidence for the assignment of the electron-transfer symbolized by (CXXVII) to the 250–70 mμ absorption band in 7-oxygenated flavones. Chelation of the 5-hydroxyl group with the carbonyl function reduces the acidity of the former so that no change in the spectrum is apparent on the addition of sodium acetate. Sodium ethoxide, however, ionizes the 5-OH group in quercitin ether (CXXVIII).

The cross-conjugation present in the flavones does not permit us to predict absolute maximal positions or the magnitude of alkali-induced shifts in the same way as was found possible for the flavanones. It should be noted that the long wavelength band almost always undergoes shift in sodium acetate solution due to partial ionization if 3-,3'- or 4'-hydroxyl groups are present.

The instability of flavonols in sodium ethoxide solution may thus be taken to indicate the presence of a 3,4-dihydroxy grouping, whereas the 7-hydroxyl is revealed by the characteristic ionization shift of the 250–270 mμ band. Exceptions to the latter rule again include the pyrogallol system which is also affected by alkali, and the hydroquinone moiety both of which may be unstable even in sodium acetate solution.

Ortho-dihydroxyl Groups

A catechol may be detected spectroscopically by a shift of 20 mμ of the longest wavelength band in boric acid–sodium acetate medium[14], which increases the acidity of the hydroxyl groups by complex formation, at the same time producing an ionizing-type red shift.

Azalein

The isolation of this glycoside was first reported by Wada, who assigned the probable structure, 3,7,3',4'-tetrahydroxy-5-methoxyflavone-3-rhamnoside (CXXIX) by classical methods. A direct comparison of the aglycone with

CXXIX   CXXX

quercetin-5-methyl ether (CXXX) was not made. Jurd and Horowitz[13] applied the spectrophotometric procedures described above in order to confirm structural proposal (CXXIX). Their data is summarised in Table 9.2. The presence of a free 7-hydroxyl group is confirmed by the 19 mμ shift of the 251 mμ band in sodium acetate solution. Evidence for a 1,2-dihydroxybenzene chromophore comes from the 18 mμ shift of the 339 mμ band in boric acid–sodium acetate. Since azalein is known to be a quercetin derivative the 1,2-dihydroxy groups may be assigned to the 3',4'-position. The methoxyl and gly-

TABLE 9.2. SPECTRAL DATA FOR AZALEIN AND AZALEATIN[13]

Azalein	λmμ	λmμ
Ethanol	251	339
NaOAc	270	363
NaOAc-H$_3$BO$_3$	255	358
0.002 M NaOEt	268	379
NaOEt soln. acidified after 30 min	251	338
Azaleatin		
Ethanol	254	369
0.002 M NaOEt	300	330, 438
NaOEt soln. acidified after 30 min	267	298

cosidoxy groups may now be placed at positions 3 and 5 (not necessarily, respectively). The glycoside, azalein, is stable in 0·002 M sodium ethoxide solution, while the aglycone azaleatin shows a non-reversible change in this medium. Thus the rhamnosido-grouping may be placed at position 3-, and the methoxyl at 5. The originally proposed structure (CXXIX) was thus confirmed by measurements using less than 1 mg of material, although it must be remembered that in this case, it was necessary to know that azalein was a mono-methyl ether of a quercetin glycoside. Other applications of this technique should expedite structural work in the flavone field in the future.

9.8. MAALIOL[15, 16]

The sesquiterpenoid maaliol, C$_{15}$H$_{26}$O, recently formed the subject of a structural investigation which utilized information from a variety of physical methods, not least important of which was the interpretation of relevant ultraviolet data. In the ensuing discussion we have chosen to highlight those degradative and synthetic pathways where the electronic absorption proved particularly helpful in diagnosis of structural detail.

Chemical studies revealed that the oxygen atom of maaliol was present in a tertiary alcoholic grouping and that the skeleton was based on eudesmane. Pyrolysis of maaliol acetate gave a mixture of olefins which could be oxidized

(OsO_4) to the isomeric diols (CXXXI) and (CXXXII). Diol (CXXXI) on cleavage with $Pb(OAc)_4$ gave normaalione (CXXXIII) λ_{max} 280 mμ (ε 24·5), with no C—H aldehyde stretching frequency in the infrared. The 2,4-dinitrophenylhydrazone of this ketone had λ_{max} 364 mμ (ε 21,240) which is to be expected for a cyclohexanone (p. 78). The presence of the grouping

$$-CH_2-CO-\overset{|}{C}H-$$ in this ketone was shown by appropriate deuteration experiments. Oxidation of normaalione (CXXXIII) with perbenzoic acid now

gave a lactone which after base catalysed opening of the ring and oxidation with chromium trioxide in pyridine gave a keto-carboxylic acid (CXXXIV) whose spectrum, λ_{max} 215 mμ (ε, 2680) and ν_{max} 1709 and 1690 cm^{-1} is entirely compatible with the presence of a cyclopropyl ketone of the carone (CXXXV) type rather than of the dihydroumbellulone (CXXXVI) type. The latter distinction could be made on the basis of infrared carbonyl frequencies which are characteristic for these systems. The ultraviolet spectrum is not diagnostic for this type of isomerism.

The isomeric diol (CXXXII) was oxidized with Pb(OAc)$_4$ to give a diketone (CXXXVII) which had λ_{max} 214 mμ (ε 2800) and 280 mμ (ε 68), ν_{max} 1704 (methyl ketone) 1681 (carone cyclopropyl ketone) and 1013 (cyclopropane) cm^{-1}. When maaliol was heated with formic acid a diene was formed having three peaks at 241, 247 and 256 mμ (ε, 19,000, 20,000 and 13,500). The first (241 mμ) band of this triad suggests that structure (CXXXVIII) is preferred to (CXXXIX), the calculated values being 244 and 249 mμ, respectively. More important than the absolute position of the absorption is, however, the fact that neoabietic acid (CXL) has no triple absorption whereas there is good analogy for dienes of type (CXXXVIII) having triple absorption in the 240 mμ region.

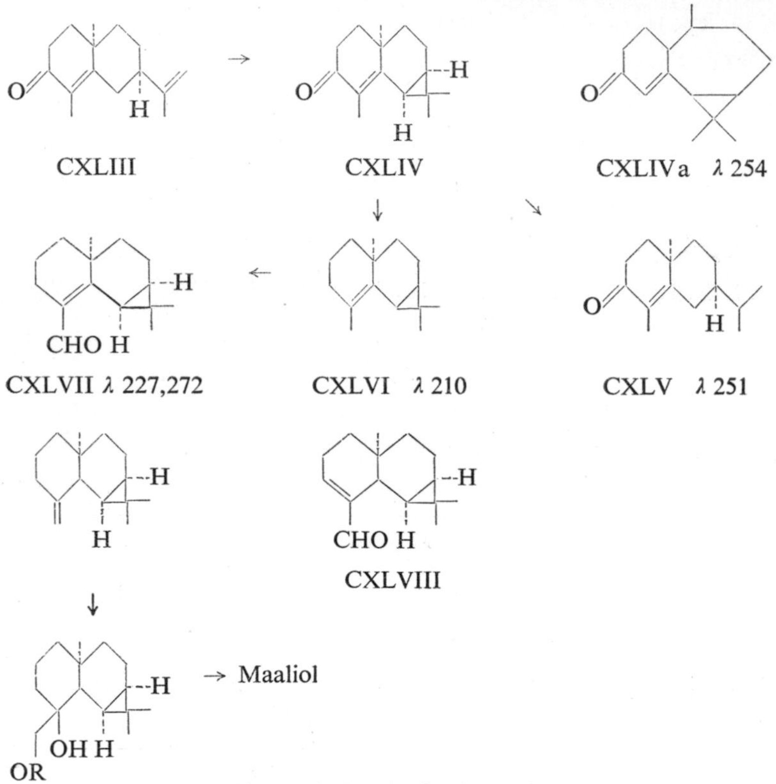

CXLIII   CXLIV   CXLIVa λ 254

CXLVII λ 227,272   CXLVI λ 210   CXLV λ 251

CXLVIII

OR → Maaliol

Chart 9.2. Synthesis of Maaliol

Further chemical and mass-spectrometric evidence was interpreted mechanistically and led to gross structure (CXLI) for maaliol while infrared, optical rotatory dispersion and conformational arguments allowed allocation of stereochemistry depicted in (CXLII).

The structure for maaliol was then confirmed by synthesis, the key intermediates being outlined in Chart 9.2. Starting with *epi-d*-cyperone (CXLIII), bromination and elimination of hydrogen bromide gave the cyclopropyl enone (CXLIV) which has λ_{max} 266 mμ, i.e. an increment of 12 mμ should be added

to the calculated value for a cyclopropyl group extending conjugation. Analogy for this increment is found in ketone (CXLIVa) where this increment is $+10 \, m\mu$.†
Reduction of (CXLIV) with zinc and acetic acid gives (CXLV). The Wolff–Kishner product (CXLVI) (λ_{max} 210 $m\mu$) can be oxidized to the unsaturated aldehyde (CXLVII) whose maxima at 227 and 272 $m\mu$ indicated the presence of (CXLVIII) (*calc.* 227 $m\mu$) as a contaminant of (CXLVII), the peak at 272 $m\mu$ assigned to the latter indicating the powerful conjugative effect of the cyclopropyl group on the enal moiety. Completion of the synthesis as shown above confirmed the structure in complete detail.

9.9. FLAVOTHEBAONE

Reaction of *p*-benzoquinone with thebaine gives the Diels–Alder adduct (CXLIX) readily enolized to the hydroquinone form (CL). Acid treatment of this

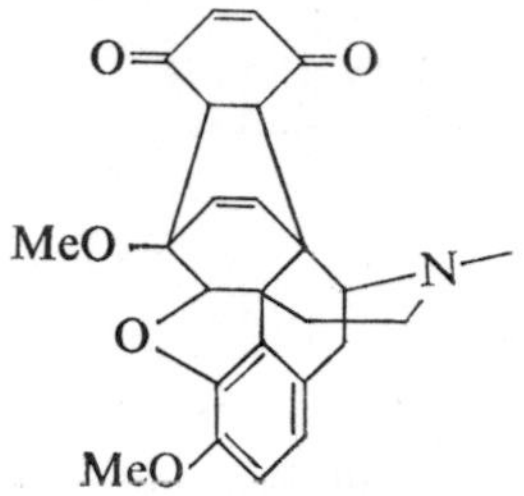

| CXLIX | CL | CLI |

| CLII | CLIII | CLIV |

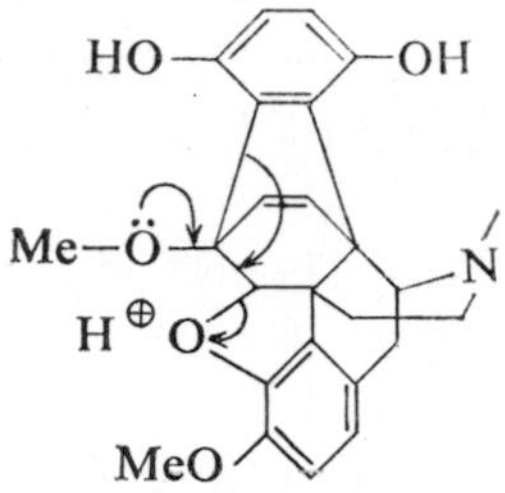

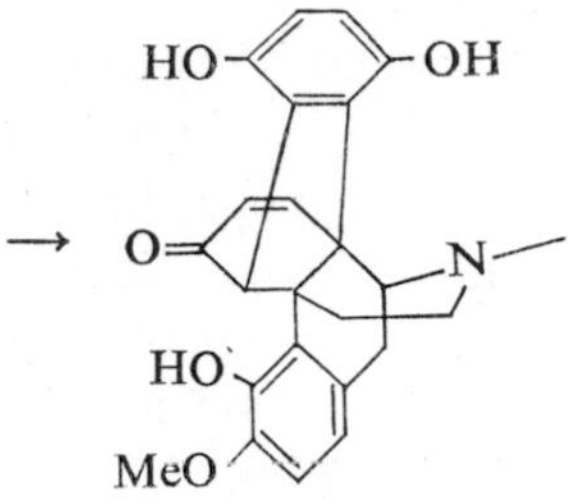

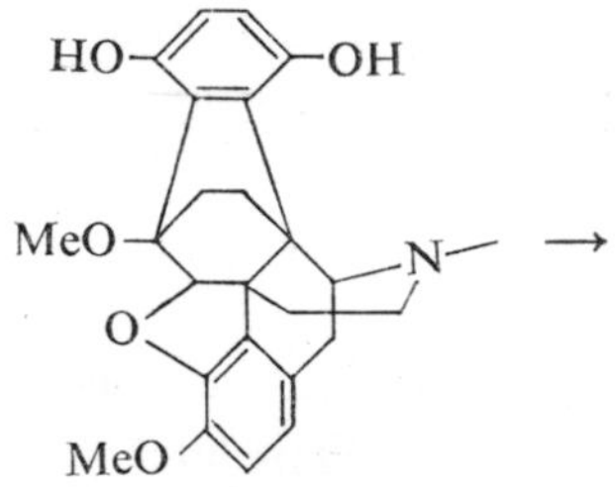

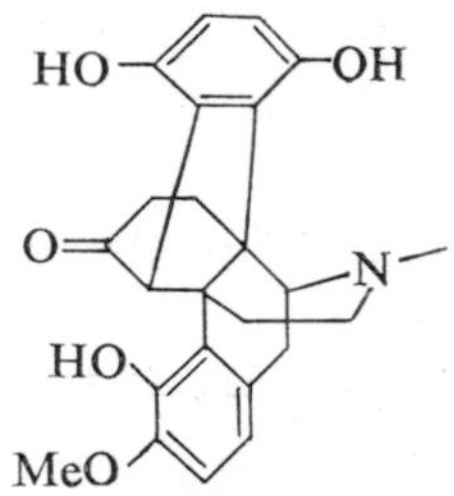

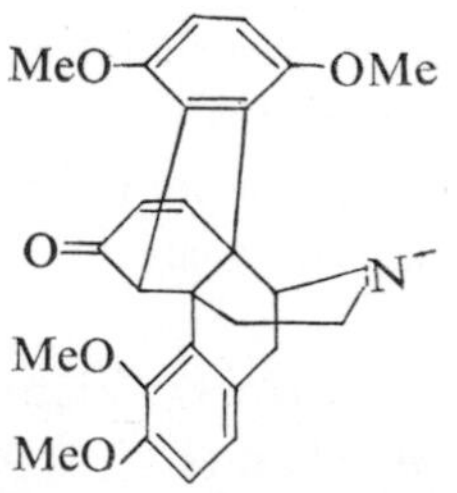

adduct gives flavothebaone, $C_{24}H_{23}O_5N$, which was found by Schopf to contain a new phenolic hydroxyl group, a tertiary nitrogen atom and an α,β-unsaturated

† Note that in the triterpene example (i) such juxtaposition of cyclopropyl and enone chromophores evokes a shift (Δ cyclopropyl) of $+42 \, m\mu$ (Ref. 26).

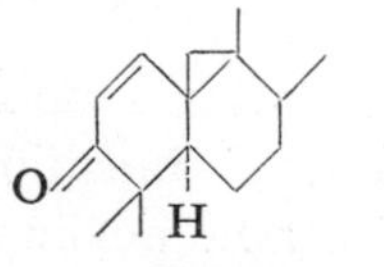

(i) λ_{max} 269 $m\mu$

ketone. A most plausible mechanism attending the acid treatment of (CL) leads by a 1,2-shift of a group of high migratory aptitude followed by demethylation to the structural proposal (CLI) made by Meinwald[17]. Some weight was lent to this conclusion by the success of the parallel transformation on the dihydro compound (CLII) which eliminated several other mechanistic possibilities leading to isomers of (CLI). The dihydrocompound (CLII) had λ_{max} 299 mμ (ε 6200) representing the sum of the contributing 1,4- and 1,2-dioxygenated benzene chromophores. Acid rearrangement (CLII → CLIII) produces a spectrum with λ_{max} 271 and 309 mμ (ε 5400 and 5000) shifted in base to 259 and 303 mμ. These absorption characteristics are entirely compatible with structure (CLIII) when we recall (from Chapter 3) that a shift to shorter wavelengths in alkali is typical of the 1,4-dihydroxybenzene system. The 303 mμ band may be assigned to the phenol anion in the guaicyl residue.

Turning now to the flavothebaone (CLI) series, the trimethyl ether (CLIV) has ν_{max} 1680 cm^{-1} and λ_{max} 266–90 (ε 2700) and 337 mμ (ε 3090). The broad band at 266–90 mμ is assigned to $p - \pi$ phenol ether (E.T.) absorption. The 337 mμ band is discussed below. The 2,4-dinitrophenylhydrazone of (CLIV) has λ_{max} 394 mμ, whilst that of (CLII) has λ_{max} 377 mμ in agreement with the structures proposed.

Flavothebaone itself has λ_{max} 279 and 346 mμ (ε 3250 and 3640). In alkali the spectrum changes to λ_{max} 257 and 298 mμ. On reacidification the spectrum has λ_{max} 285 and 315 mμ, indicating that this reaction, is irreversible at the high dilution required for spectroscopic studies (0·005%). On the basis of structure (CLI) the shifts may be interpreted as being due to the splitting of a (combined) catechol–hydroquinone absorption in base to higher (298 mμ) and lower (257 mμ) wavelengths, respectively (see Table 3.2), there being analogy for the deterioration of hydroquinone spectra in alkali. The 345 mμ band of flavothebaone (337 mμ in the tri- and 344 mμ in the mono-methyl ether) is assigned to a steric overlap transition of the charge-transfer (C.T.) type (see CLV).

The former assignment is supported by the observation that the monomethyl ether (CLVI) has λ_{max} 280 and 344 mμ in acid changed to 293 and

CLV   CLVI   CLVII

404 mμ in base and quantitatively reversed to 280 and 344 mμ on reacidification. The appearance of the $p - \pi$ phenol transition at 293 mμ is in accord with the structural proposals, for we are now dealing with a protected hydroquinone system (CLVII) which behaves "normally" in having longer wavelength ab-

sorption in the anion compared with the phenol. The 60 mμ shift of the C.T. band indicates that as far as crude symbolism will allow, we can designate these transitions as depicted in (CLVIIIa) and (CLVIIIb).

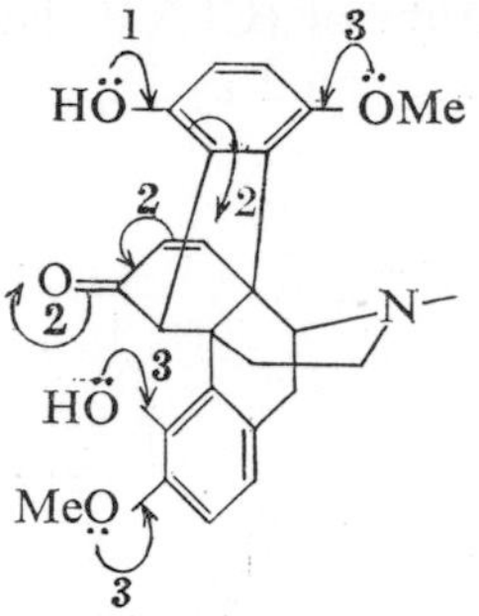

1, 3: 280 mμ
2:    344 mμ

CLVIIIa

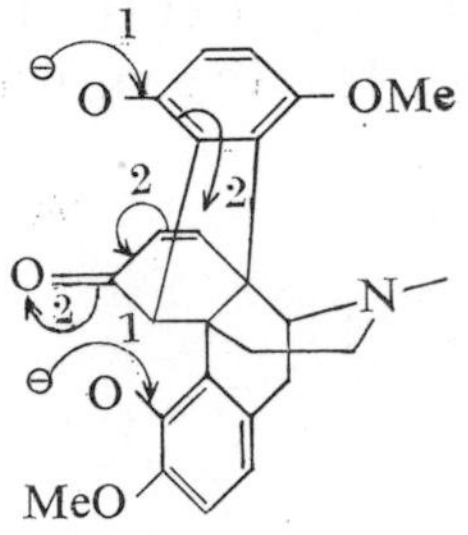

1: 293 mμ
2: 404 mμ

CLVIIIb

9.10. PLUMIERIDE[18]

The bitter principle plumieride is a glycoside whose aglycone has the molecular formula $C_{15}H_{16}O_7$. Plumieride was shown by classical methods to contain methoxy carbonyl, lactonic, and secondary hydroxyl functions, in addition to the hydroxyl group which participates in glycoside formation. The sugar was identified as D-glucose. Stepwise reduction of plumieride (CLIX) proved to be most informative. The natural product itself has broad ill-defined absorption spectrum with maximal intensity at 218–36 mμ. This persists in the dihydro derivative (CLX), whereas the tetrahydrodesoxy compound (CLXI) which has lost the secondary hydroxyl group, has a well-defined selective absorption at 236 mμ compatible with the structural feature

$$-O-CH=\overset{|}{C}-CO_2Me \text{ (p. 81)}.$$ Conversion of plumieride to the bromomethoxy compound (CLXII) reveals the butenolide chromophore, λ_{max} 210 mμ which may be artificially constructed in full detail by subtraction of the spectrum of (CLXI) from that of plumieride (CLIX). Further transformation products of (CLXI) include the tricarboxylic acid (CLXIII) and the diester-

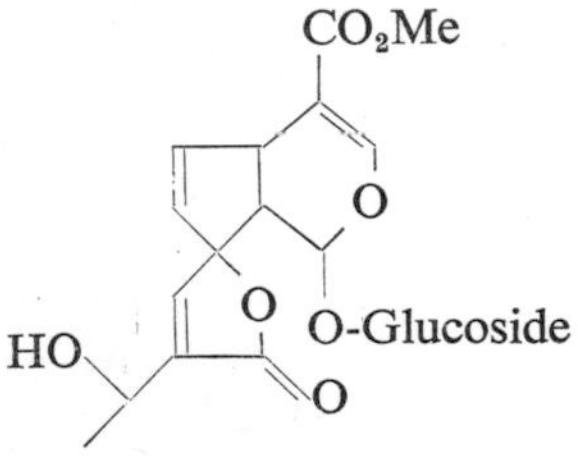

CLIX Plumieride

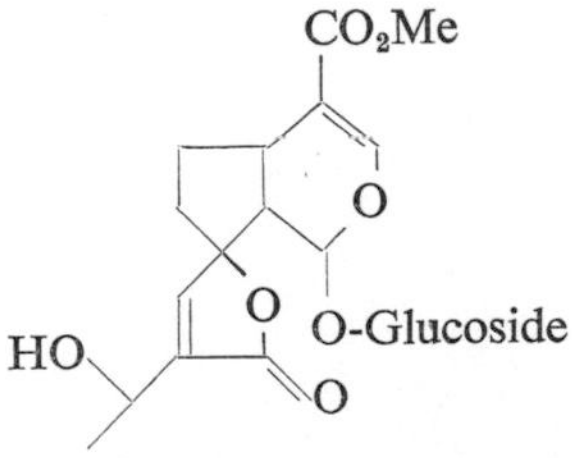

CLX

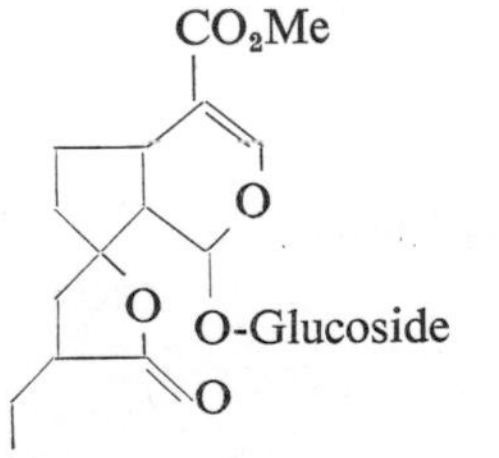

CLXI λ 236 mμ

acid (CLXV) chemically related by lactone (CLXIV). The spectrum of (CLXIII) is not too informative until the spectrum of (CLXV) is subtracted from it giving a difference curve with λ_{max} 207 mμ, the position expected for the acrylic acid chromophore $CH_2\!\!=\!\!\overset{|}{C}\!\!-\!\!CO_2H$. The spectrum of (CLXV) has a well defined peak at 230 mμ (ε, 11,000) assigned to the alkylated cyclopentene-1-carboxylic ester electron-transfer.

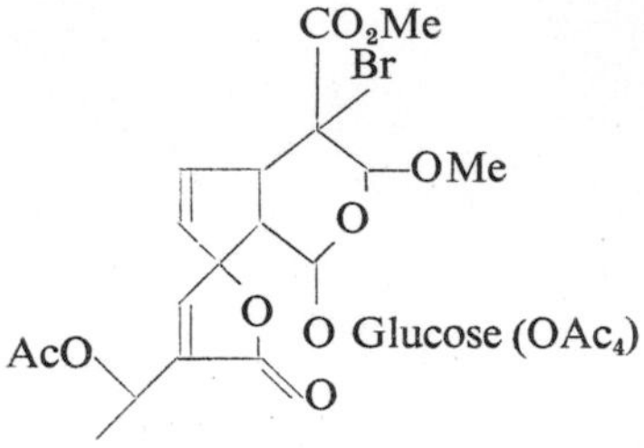

CLXII

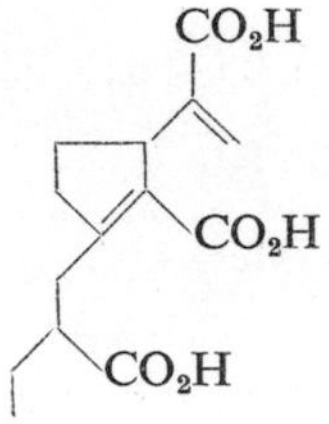

CLXIII

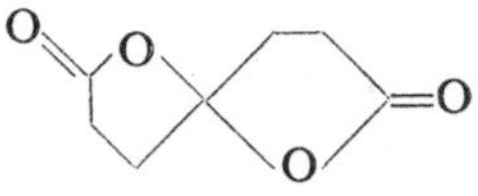

CLXIV

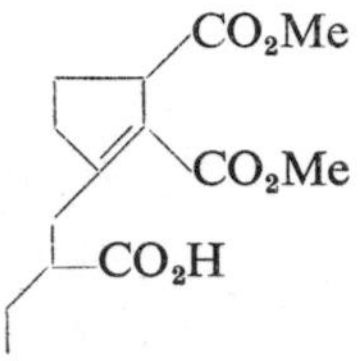

CLXV

9.11. MAGNAMYCIN[19]

This representative of the macrolide antibiotic group is a metabolite of *Streptomyces halstedii* and has the formula $C_{42}H_{67}O_{16}N$. On methanolysis magnamycin gives methyl isovalerylmycaroside (CLXVI) and a basic fragment carimbose (CLXVII) $C_{30}H_{47}O_{12}N$. Magnamycin has λ_{max} 238 and 327 mμ (ε, 15,700 and 76) characteristic of an α,β-unsaturated carbonyl system (E.T. and $n \rightarrow \pi^*$ bands, respectively). Treatment of magnamycin with potassium iodide in acetic acid gives the desoxy compound magnamycin-B, whose spectrum (λ_{max} 278 mμ) is suggestive of an $\alpha,\beta,\gamma,\delta$-unsaturated carbonyl system. This can be rationalized in terms of the presence of the grouping (CLXVIII) in magnamycin.

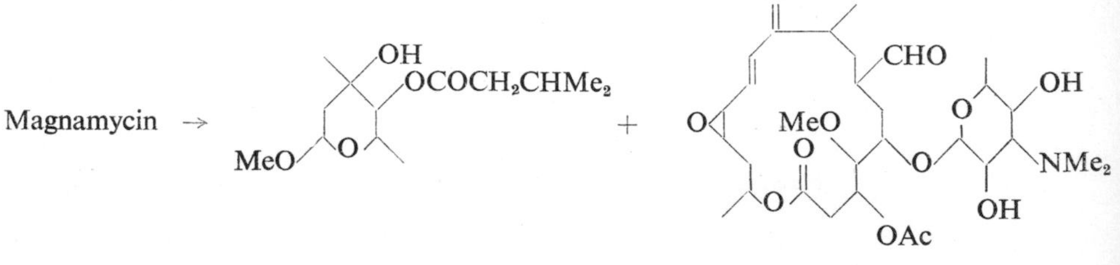

Magnamycin →

CLXVI

CLXVII   Carimbose

When octahydrocarimbose is treated with base, dimethylamine is eliminated to leave an $\alpha,\beta,\gamma,\delta$-unsaturated acid. This change was interpreted as indicated in formulae (CLXIX → CLXX). Treatment of magnamycin, magnamycin-B or carimbose with periodic acid, permanganate and then alkali gave an $\alpha,\beta,\gamma,\delta$-

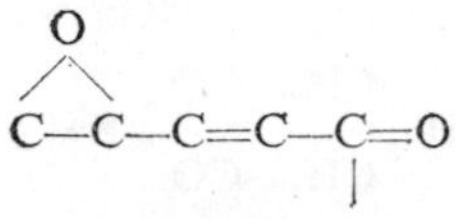

CLXVIII

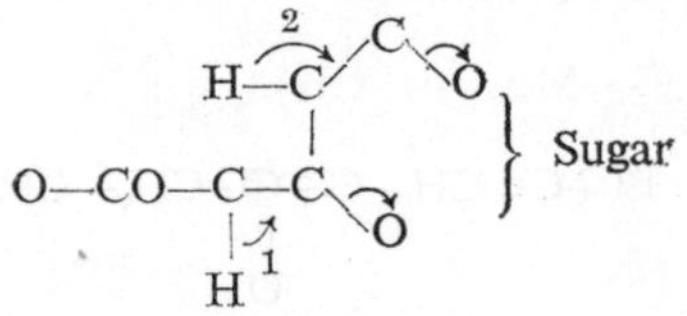

CLXIX

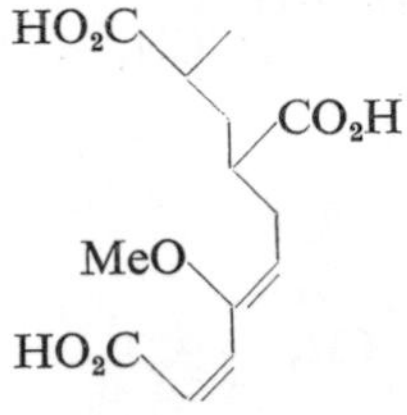

↓

CLXXI

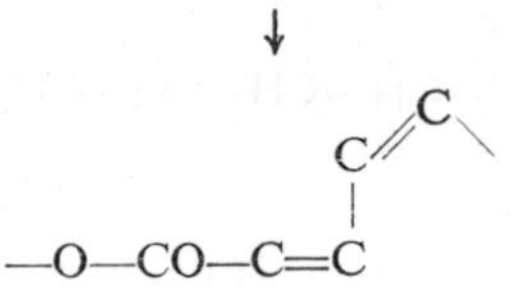

CLXX

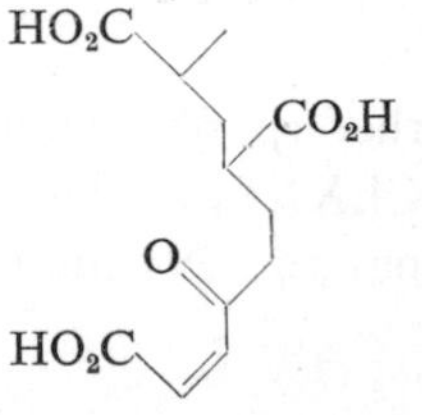

CLXXII

unsaturated acid $C_{13}H_{18}O_7$ (CLXXI), containing a methoxyl group and having λ_{max} 265 mμ (ε 25,900). When this acid was treated with aqueous mineral acid, the methoxyl group was hydrolysed and its relationship to the other functional groups revealed by isolation of the keto acid (CLXXII), λ_{max} 222 mμ. We should expect λ_{max} 225–7 for such an acid where cross-conjugation gives the overall effect of a β-substituted α,β-unsaturated ketone.

9.12. STREPTIMIDONE

In 1959, structure (CLXXIII) was proposed for a new antibiotic, streptimidone, on the basis of chemical and spectroscopic considerations. It later appeared to van Tamelen[20] that the reported chemistry could be interpreted in terms of structure (CLXXIV). Particularly relevant is the base-catalysed conversion of streptimidone to an $\alpha,\beta,\gamma,\delta$-unsaturated ketone (CLXXV) of which formula (CLXXIV) seemed a more likely progenitor. Ketone (CLXXV),

IUS 12a

although certainly a dienone, has an unusually low maximum, λ 279 mμ (*calc.* 291 mμ) for which no explanation is immediately obvious. Although the spectrum of streptimidone itself is superficially compatible with that of a cross-conjugated dienone in having λ_{max} 232 and 291 mμ, the intensity values (23,100 and 790, respectively) are not at all those expected for such a dienone, which by

Me   CH₂
| ‖
Et—C=CH—C—C—CH₂—CHOH—CH〈CH₂—CO〉NH
           ‖   CH₂—CO
           O

CLXXIII

Me   Me
| |
CH₂=CH—C=CH—CH—CO—CH₂—CHOH—CH〈CH₂—CO〉NH
                                  CH₂—CO

CLXXIV

Me   Me
| |
CH₃CH=C—CH=C—C—CH₃
            ‖
            O

CLXXV

analogy with a case cited earlier (p. 65) should have λ_{max} 224 and 290 mμ (ε 8000 and 5000). Formula (CLXXIV) offers a much better alternative, the assignments being 232 mμ (diene) and 291 mμ (β,γ-unsaturated ketone $n \rightarrow \pi^*$ band).

9.13. SOME PHOTOCHEMICAL TRANSFORMATIONS

Intramolecular photochemical transformations, aside from the intriguing structural and mechanistic problems posed by such reactions, have relevance in such topics as the chemistry of vision, photosynthesis, vitamin D chemistry, and biogenesis. Much work remains to be done in elucidating the mechanism of such reactions and we expect this aspect to develop in the next decade. Since such transformations occur through the intermediacy of excited states of the molecule whose absorption characteristics are measured in the electronic spectrum, no treatise, even of the empirical nature of the present work, devoted to the ultraviolet spectra of natural products would be complete without some reference to photochemical transformations. Not only may such reactions be conveniently followed by the ultraviolet spectrum, but the ensuing structural problem is often amenable to treatment by interpretation of ultraviolet data. Two examples follow.

(i) *Carvone–Camphor*

Irradiation of carvone (CLXXVI) with sunlight was observed by Ciamician, one of the pioneers of photochemistry, to give an isomer, $C_{10}H_{14}O$. He proposed structure (CLXXVII) for this product named carvone–camphor. Later, Semagiotto proposed the isomeric structure (CLXXVIII) for the photoisomer. In a recent reinvestigation of the problem, Büchi and Goldman[21]

CLXXVI   CLXXVII   CLXXVIII

CLXXIX   CLXXX   CLXXXI

CLXXVII   CLXXXII   CLXXXIII

CLXXXIV

showed that Ciamician and Silbers' structure (CLXXVII) is, in fact, correct. The salient features of that section of the American authors' argument which employs ultraviolet data are as follows.

Carvone–camphor has 2C-Me groups and a cyclopentanone ring (ν_{max} 1727 cm^{-1}). The low end absorption in the ultraviolet at λ 210 mμ (ε, 1800) excludes —C=C— and >C—C—C— whilst the $n \rightarrow \pi^*$ band is at 301 mμ

(ε 35). Permanganate oxidation of carvone–camphor gives a ketocarboxylic acid, whose ester (CLXXIX) has ν_{max} 1764 cm^{-1} and λ_{max} 210 mμ (ε 112) and

280 mμ (ε 25). This combined spectral information is construed as evidence for the presence of a four- or strained five-ring ketone *not* conjugated with a cyclopropane ring (p. 345). Pyrolysis of carvone–camphor gives another isomer $C_{10}H_{14}O$ formulated as (CLXXX) since it possesses the spectrum of a tetra-substituted cyclopentenone with ν_{max} 1704 cm^{-1} and λ_{max} 237 mμ (ε 11,400) (λ calc 236 mμ). This and other evidence leads to a choice between structures (CLXXVII) and (CLXXXI) for carvone–camphor. The extinction coefficients of the high energy absorptions of carvone–camphor and the keto ester (CLXXIX) at 210 mμ are 1800 and 112, respectively. Examination of models of (CLXXVII) reveals that conjugative overlap of the cyclobutane ring with the carbonyl group is more effective in the former, in complete agreement with the ε values. Also, the positions of the $n \to \pi^*$ bands of these two compounds (301 and 280 mμ, respectively) are in good agreement with the values for cyclopentanone (299 mμ) and cyclobutanone (280 mμ). Differentiation between four- and five-membered ring structures for the ketoester was not without ambiguity on spectral grounds so that the indications derivable from the above argument were confirmed un-ambiguously by chemical methods.

When carvone–camphor (CLXXVII) is oxidized with perbenzoic acid fol-lowed by acidic treatment, the cyclopropane lactone (CLXXXII), ν_{max} 1776 (γ-lactone) 3032, 3064 cm^{-1} (methylene of cyclopropane), can be isolated. This, on reduction and treatment with refluxing pyridine–acetic anhydride, gives the unsaturated acetate (CLXXXIII) whose spectrum λ_{max} 210 (ε 8700) is suggest-ive of the vinylcyclopropane chromophore, $-\text{C}-\text{C}-\text{C}=\text{C}-$. Oxidation of the latter affords a ketone ν 1717 cm^{-1} and λ_{max} 210 mμ (ε 3200) in agree-ment with the assignment of a dihydroumbellulone chromophore as in (CLXXXIV). Additional chemical and physical evidence provides full support for structure (CLXXVII) for carvone–camphor. Since Pyrex flasks were used in the irradiation experiments, Büchi suggests that the intervention of $\overset{+}{\text{C}}-\text{C}=\text{C}-\overset{-}{\text{O}}$, corresponding to the electron-transfer associated with the 250 mμ band of carvone, is fairly remote, and speculations as to the mechanism of genesis of carvone–camphor are couched in terms of radical intermediates.

(ii) *Isophotosantonic Acid and Lumisantonin*[22]

Irradiation of santonin (CLXXXV) in ethanol solution affords lumisantonin (CLXXXVI), which in a dark reaction in acetic acid is converted to isophoto-santonic acid lactone (CLXXXVII), the main product of irradiation of san-tonin in aqueous acetic acid. Lumisantonin (CLXXXVI) has bands in the in-frared at 1785 (γ-lactone) 1703, 1670 cm^{-1} (α,β-unsaturated cyclopentenone) and λ_{max} 239 (ε 5800) (*calc.* for (CLXXXVI) 214 mμ *without* cyclopropane conjugation). The dihydroderivative (CLXXXVIII) has λ_{max} 214 mμ (ε, 4600) characteristic of a conjugated cyclopropane–carbonyl chromophore. Treatment of lumisantonin with HBr–HOAc gives the non-conjugated cyclopentenone (CLXXXIX) which undergoes spontaneous change to the dienone

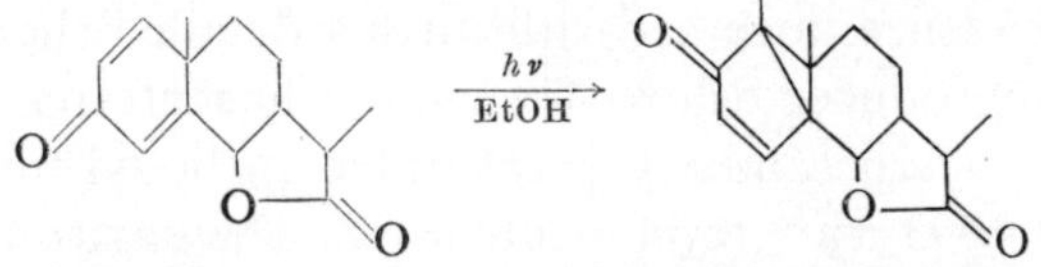

CLXXXV

$\xrightarrow[\text{EtOH}]{h\nu}$

CLXXXVI   λ 239

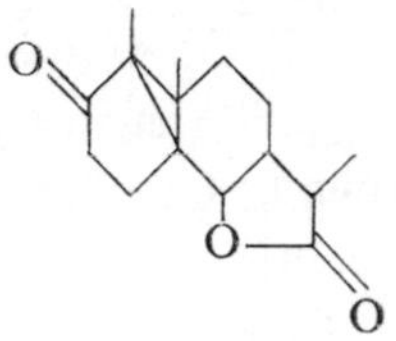

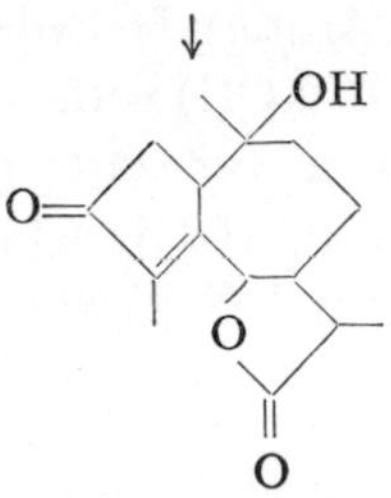

CLXXXVIII

CLXXXVII

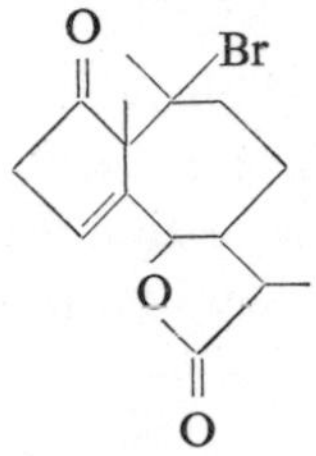

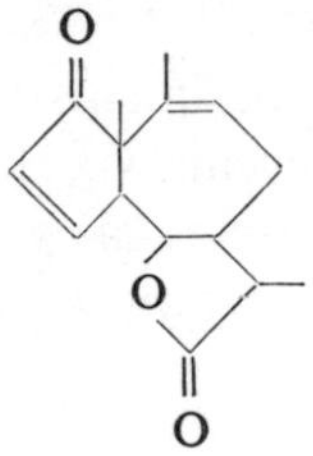

CLXXXIX

CXC   λ 220

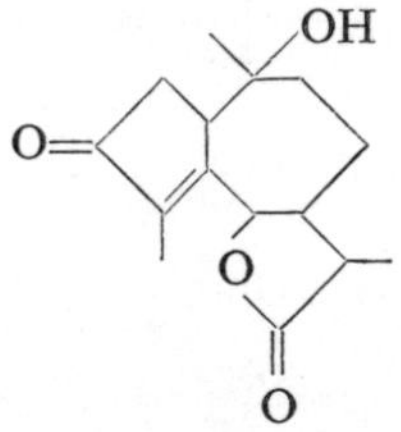

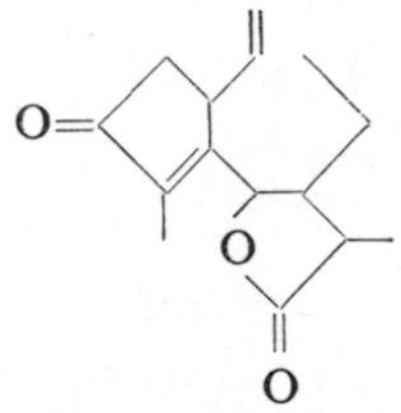

CXCI
λ 239

CXCII

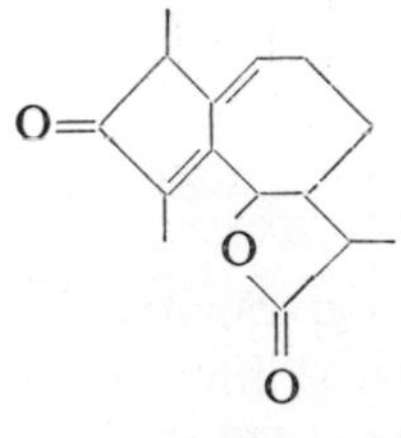

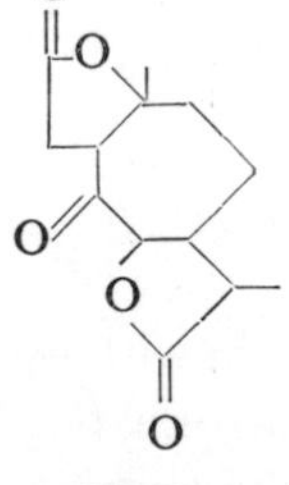

CXCIII
λ 305

CXCIV

(CXC) (spectral change: end absorption → λ_{max} 220 mμ (ε 10,800)). The maximum of the latter at 220 mμ is indicative of a lightly substituted cyclopentenone now without the conjugative influence of the cyclopropane ring.

The structure of isophotosantonic lactone (CXCI) was assigned on the basis of the following evidence, together with further detailed chemical and mechanistic evidence not reproduced below. The lactone has infrared bands corresponding to hydroxyl, γ-lactone and α,β-unsaturated carbonyl functions, the last of these occurring at 1693 cm^{-1} (cyclopentenone). The environment of the cyclopentenone could be inferred from the ultraviolet maximum at 239 mμ (ε 13,000) (calc. for (CXCI), 241 mμ). Dehydration of (CXCI) with pyridine-thionyl chloride gave a dienone (CXCII) with >C=CH_2 (infrared) having essentially the same ultraviolet spectrum as the starting lactone (CXCI). Acidic dehydration gave a conjugated dienone (CXCIII) which had λ_{max} 305 mμ (λ_{calc} 318 mμ). Ozonolysis of (CXCI) gave (CXCIV) which was shown to be a ketone by its absorption spectrum (λ_{max} 294 mμ (ε 50)) and further reactions.

9.14. LIMONIN

The degradative experiments leading of the elucidation of the structure of the bitter principle limonin, $C_{26}H_{30}O_8$ (CXCV) represent the combined efforts of British, Swiss and American groups. In this section we shall discuss the use of ultraviolet data in relation to some of the degradations carried out by Barton's group[23].

CXCV

CXCVI

CXCVII

CXCVIII

Treatment of limonin with hydriodic acid gives, first, deoxylimonin $C_{26}H_{30}O_7$ (CXCVI) and then citrolin ($C_{26}H_{28}O_6$). Deoxylimonin (CXCVI) is an α,β-unsaturated lactone as shown by infrared data (1747 (δ-lactone); 1714 cm^{-1} (α,β-unsaturated-δ-lactone) and by its ultraviolet spectrum, λ_{max} 214 mμ (ε 17,000).

Reduction of deoxylimonin with potassium borohydride gives deoxyepilimonol (CXCVII); λ_{max} 212 (ε 17,300), ν_{max} 1730 and 1706 cm^{-1}.

Catalytic reduction of limonin may be stopped at saturation of the furan ring. The resultant epoxy keto dilactone, tetrahydrolimonin (CXCVIII) on

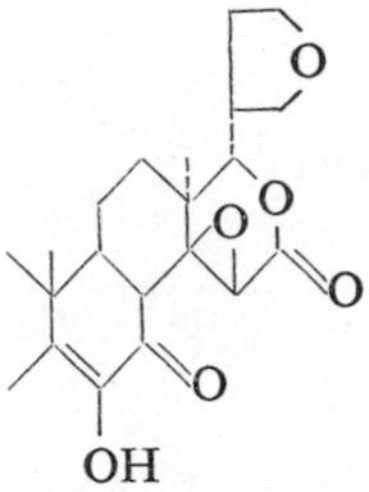

CXCIX 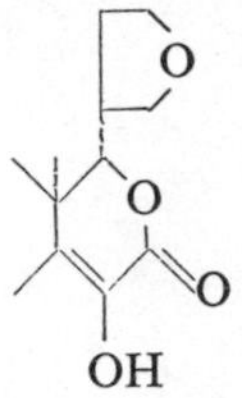   CC

treatment with potassium t-butoxide in an oxygen atmosphere is smoothly transformed to the diosphenol (CXCIX) λ_{max} 278 mμ (ε 11,000) shifted in 0·1 N alkali to 336–40 mμ (ε 6300). Limonin itself also undergoes a corresponding change to a diosphenol exhibiting the expected spectral properties, ferric chloride test etc., and whose acetate shows the expected shift to shorter wavelengths (245 mμ). Similarly, deoxylimonin gives a diosphenol. These results were most important in determining the environment of the ketonic function in limonin. The $n \rightarrow \pi^*$ band of limonin itself occurs at 280 mμ, which suggested

that the grouping $-\overset{|}{C}H-CH_2-\overset{\|}{\underset{O}{C}}-$ was present in which one hydrogen is attached to the β-carbon atom.

Tetrahydrolimonin (CXCVIII) on treatment with HCl-HOAc gives an isomer λ_{max} 256 mμ (ε 5300) changing to λ_{max} 290 mμ (ε 4600) on addition of

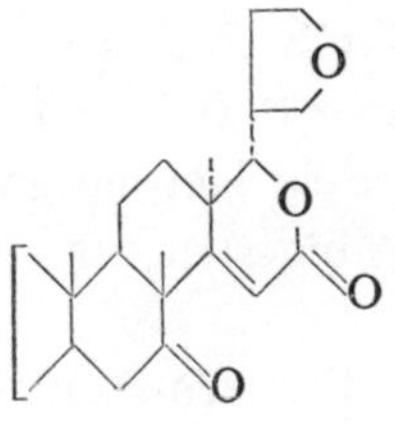

CCI 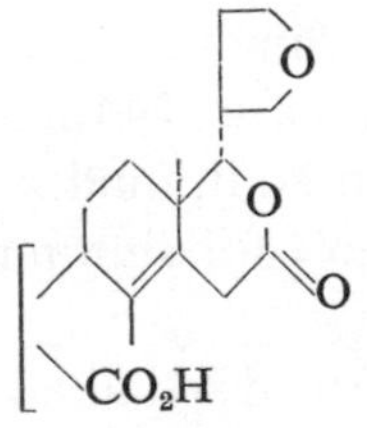   CCII

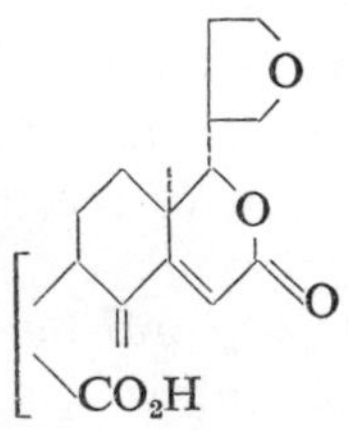

CCIII 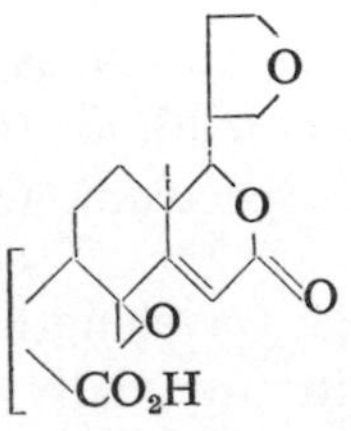 $\rightarrow$ CCIV 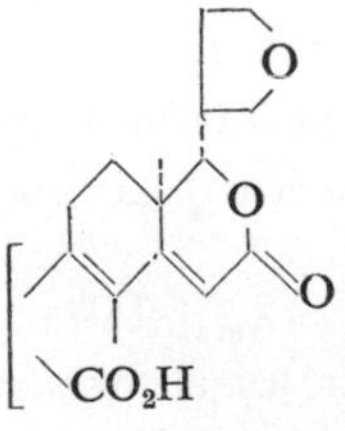   CCV

one drop of alkali. The acetate of this isomer has λ_{max} 218 mμ. This behaviour is entirely compatible with the α-oxolactone formulation (CC) (see p. 82). The presence of such an enolic system was confirmed chemically by ozonolysis and hydrolysis to give oxalic acid.

CCVI   CCVII

The action of base on deoxytetrahydro limonin (CCI) produces (CCII) which has λ_{max} 202 mμ (ε 11,300). Proof of this structure follows from the transformation of (CCII) via a chloro-adduct to *two* diene acids characterized as their methyl esters. The major diene ester has λ_{max} 255 mμ (ε 7800) an intensity characteristic of a *cisoid* diene and therefore assigned structure (CCIII), and further characterized as the epoxide (CCIV) which now showed simple α,β-unsaturated lactone absorption at 217–218 mμ (ε 9,100). The minor diene was the *transoid* isomer (CCV), λ_{max} 230 and 284 mμ (ε 6300 and 16,400). The structures of these lactones were of value in relating the C_7 ketone to the ring D lactone and further demonstrated the presence of a methyl group at C_8 and a hydrogen atom at C_9.

At the outset of this necessarily brief treatment of limonin chemistry we mentioned that citrolin was formed in the reaction leading to deoxylimonin. Early work by Emerson had established that citrolin contains both α,β-unsaturated ketone and α,β-unsaturated lactone functions as well as a furan ring. Subtraction of the spectrum of deoxylimonin (chromophore CXCVI) from that of citrolin gives a curve with maxima at 244 and 215 mμ (ε 14,000 and 18,000) showing that citrolin contains an additional α,β-unsaturated lactone grouping On the basis of structure (CXCV) for limonin, a plausible structure (CCVI) follows for citrolin.

Limonilic acid (CCVII) is formed by alkaline hypoiodite treatment of limonin. Since tetrahydrolimonin (CXCVIII) and hexahydrolimonic acid give limonilic acid analogues, the lactone ring involved in the limonilic acid change must be the A ring. This can be demonstrated by chemical methods. That the environment of the ketone in limonilic acid is quite different from that in limonin is shown not only by chemical methods (no deuterium exchange; no diosphenolation reaction) but by the spectrum, which unlike that of the limonin

$-\overset{|}{C}=O$ (λ_{max} 280 mμ) shows high wavelength absorption (λ_{max} 307 mμ) characteristic of a carbonyl group with an axially oriented ether substituent in the α-position (p. 31).

9.15. MORPHINE ALKALOIDS[24]

Within the framework of the morphine molecule (CCVIII) the course of degradation and transformation may often be conveniently monitored by spectroscopy. In Chart 9.3 we have delineated some transformation products and model compounds in the codeine series. Codeine (CCIX) has the spectrum of a dialkyl catechol, λ_{max} 287 mμ (ε 2700). The isomeric methines, α-(CCX) and β-(CCXI)-codeimethine were assigned structures in agreement with their styrenoid and phenylbutadiene chromophores, respectively. The model compounds

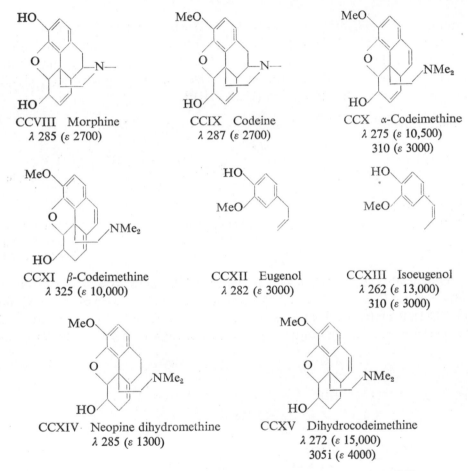

CCVIII   Morphine
λ 285 (ε 2700)

CCIX   Codeine
λ 287 (ε 2700)

CCX α-Codeimethine
λ 275 (ε 10,500)
310 (ε 3000)

CCXI β-Codeimethine
λ 325 (ε 10,000)

CCXII   Eugenol
λ 282 (ε 3000)

CCXIII   Isoeugenol
λ 262 (ε 13,000)
310 (ε 3000)

CCXIV   Neopine dihydromethine
λ 285 (ε 1300)

CCXV   Dihydrocodeimethine
λ 272 (ε 15,000)
305i (ε 4000)

Chart 9.3.   Ultraviolet maxima of some codeine derivatives (in EtOH)

eugenol (CCXII) and isoeugenol (CCXIII) provide useful comparison for the parent chromophore of codeine (CCIX) and of the α-methine (CCX). Similarly neopine dihydromethine (CCXIV) and dihydrocodeine methine (CCXV) were shown to have guaiacol and styrenoid structures.

Thebaine (CCXVI) has λ_{max} 270 mμ (ε 9000) which may be assigned to superimposed homoannular diene absorption with methoxyl increment (λ_{calc}, 269 mμ) and catechol absorptions. Reduction of thebaine with sodium in liquid

CCXVI λ 270 (ε 9000)   CCXVII λ 282 (ε 2000)   CCXVIII λ 284 (ε 11,000)

ammonia gives dihydrothebaine-φ (CCXVII) which is a *non-conjugated* diene and absorbs at 282 mμ (ε 2000). On the other hand lithium aluminium hydride reduction of thebaine gives the isomer (CCXVIII) which although having the same *position* of selective absorption λ_{max} 284 mμ, has an intensity (ε, 11,400) compatible only with formulation (CCXVIII)[25].

CCXIX λ 282 (ε 2000)   CCXX λ 282 (ε 2000)   CCXXI λ 220 (ε 36,000)
                                                    225 (ε 6400)   268 (ε 20,000)
                                                                                          312 (ε 11,200)

Dihydrothebaine-φ (CCXVII) is converted by acid to a β,γ-unsaturated ketone (CCXIX), λ_{max} 282 (ε 2000) which by further steps gives (CCXX) and (CCXXI), the latter having the expected longer wavelength absorption although its spectrum has certain features which do not appear in the spectrum of the

CCXXII   CCXXIII

apparently close models thebainone-B methine (CCXXII) and β-codeimethine (CCXI). No explanation can be offered for the appearance of intense absorption at 268 mμ in (CCXXI). Such absorption in this series is associated with the diphenyl chromophore (CCXXIII) which is present in apomorphine (CCXXIV) morphothebaine (CCXXV) and apocodeine (CCXXVI).

CCXXIV

λ 275 (ε 12,000)

CCXXV

λ 278 (ε 12,000)
305 (ε 9000)
400 (ε 200)

CCXXVI

λ 278 (ε 11,000)
310 (ε 3000)

An interesting example of restricted rotation in this series is provided by α-methyldihydrothebaine (CCXXVII) which displays its diphenyl band at 287 mμ with decreased intensity (ε 4000).

CCXXVII λ 287 (ε 4000)

CCXXVIII Sinomenine

The alkaloid sinomenine CCXXVIII contains the chromophore of an α-methoxy-α,β-unsaturated ketone and the transition is marked by a band at 262 mμ (ε, 4000) (λ_{calc}, 262 mμ).

REFERENCES

1. F. A. HOCHSTEIN, C. R. STEPHENS, L. H. CONOVER, P. P. REGNA, R. PASTERNAK, P. N. GORDON, F. J. PILGRIM, K. J. BRUNINGS and R. B. WOODWARD, J. Amer. Chem. Soc., 75, 5455 (1953).
2. J. L. HARTWELL and A. W. SCHRECKER, Fort. Chem. Organischer Naturstoffe, 15, 84 (1958).
3. P. YATES and G. F. FIELD, J. Amer. Chem. Soc., 82, 5764 (1960).
4. K. WIESNER, F. BICKELHAUPT, D. R. BABIN and M. GOTZ, Tetrahedron Letters, No. 3, 11 (1959); Tetrahedron, 9, 254 (1960).
5. K. WIESNER, D. L. SIMMONS and L. R. FOWLER, Tetrahedron Letters, No. 18, 1 (1959).
6. K. WIESNER, M. GOTZ, D. L. SIMMONS, L. R. FOWLER, F. W. BACHELOR, R. F. C. BROWN and G. BÜCHI, ibid., No. 2, 15 (1959).
7. K. WIESNER and Z. VALENTA, Fort. Chem. Organischer Naturstoffe, 16, 26 (1958).
8. L. A. DUNCANSON, J. F. GROVE, J. MACMILLAN and T. P. C. MULHOLLAND, J. Chem. Soc., 3555 (1957), and previous papers.
9. D. H. R. BARTON and A. I. SCOTT, ibid., 1767 (1958).
10. C. H. HASSALL and T. C. McMORRIS, ibid., 2831 (1959).
11. C. A. WACHTMEISTER, Acta Chem. Scand., 12, 147 (1958).
12. D. H. R. BARTON, P. DE MAYO, G. A. MORRISON and H. RAISTRICK, Tetrahedron, 6, 48 (1959).

13. L. JURD and R. M. HOROWITZ, *J. Org. Chem.*, **22**, 1618 (1957) and refs. cited therein.
14. L. JURD, *Arch. Biochem. and Biophys.*, **63**, 376 (1956).
15. G. BÜCHI, M. S. V. WITTENAU and D. M. WHITE, *J. Amer. Chem. Soc.*, **81**, 1968 (1959).
16. R. B. BATES, G. BÜCHI, T. MATSUURA and R. A. SHAFFER, *ibid.*, **82**, 2327 (1960).
17. J. MEINWALD and G. A. WILEY, *ibid.*, **79**, 2569 (1957).
18. O. HALPERN and H. SCHMID, *Helv. Chim. Acta*, **41**, 1109 (1958).
19. R. B. WOODWARD, *Angew. Chem.*, **69**, 50 (1957).
20. E. E. VAN TAMELEN and V. HAARSTAD, *J. Amer. Chem. Soc.*, **82**, 2974 (1960).
21. G. BÜCHI and I. M. GOLDMAN, *ibid.*, **79**, 4741 (1957).
22. D. H. R. BARTON, P. DE MAYO and M. SHAFIQ, *J. Chem. Soc.*, 140 (1958).
23. D. H. R. BARTON, S. K. PRADHAN, S. STERNHELL and J. F. TEMPLETON, *ibid.*, 255 (1961).
24. K. W. BENTLEY, *The Chemistry of the Morphine Alkaloids*, Oxford, London (1954).
25. G. STORK, *J. Amer. Chem. Soc.*, **74**, 768 (1952).
26. D. S. IRVINE, J. A. HENRY and F. S. SPRING, *J. Chem. Soc.*, 1316 (1955).
27. H. BIRNBAUM, R. C. COOKSON and N. LEWIN, *ibid.*, 1224 (1961).

APPLICATIONS OF SPECTROPHOTOMETRY IN
THE ANALYSIS OF STEROIDS

MANY important steroids, notably among the sterols, bile acids and hormonal metabolites, contain only isolated chromophores and do not lend themselves to direct spectrophotometric analysis. Isolated ethylenic bonds show end-absorption in the 200–20 mμ region which is somewhat characteristic of the degree of substitution and the location of the bond[1,2]. More recently the extension of the practical range of measurement to 190 mμ[3,4] has permitted determination of true maxima, and these observations will be of value in dealing with pure compounds. For routine analysis the 190–220 mμ region is beset with disadvantages, chiefly because of the grave errors ensuing from the presence of extraneous substances.

STEROIDS

Numbering

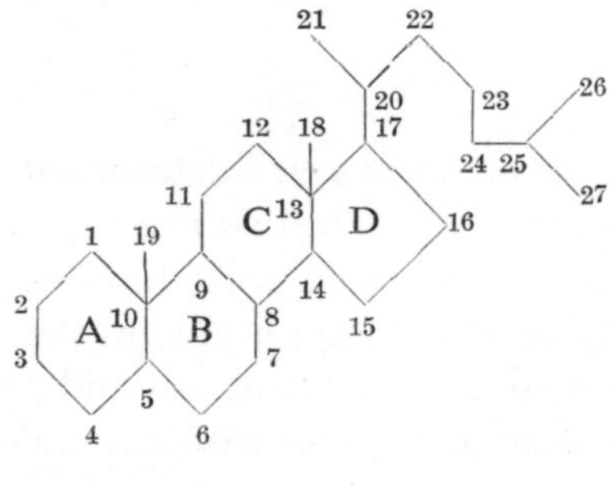

Parent hydrocarbons

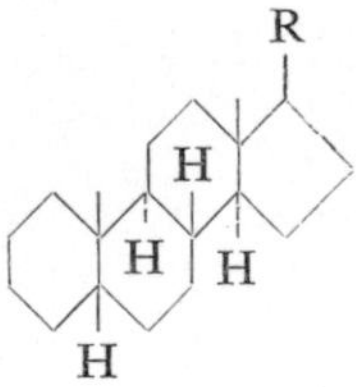

C_{19}	Androstane	R=H
C_{21}	Pregnane	R=CH$_2$CH$_3$
C_{24}	Cholane	R=CHMe(CH$_2$)$_2$CH$_3$
C_{27}	Cholestane	R=CHMe(CH$_2$)$_3$CHMe$_2$
C_{28}	Ergostane	R=CHMe(CH$_2$)$_2$CHMe·CHMe$_2$
C_{29}	Stigmastane	R=CHMe(CH$_2$)$_2$·CHEt·CHMe$_2$
C_{18}	Estrane	R=H; 19—H instead of Me

The commonest conjugated chromophores present in natural steroids are indicated in Table A.1. Their absorption bands are useful in detecting certain steroidal types in extracts of natural products and in characterising the pure compounds. In some cases, e.g. 7-dehydrocholesterol or ergosterol[5], progesterone[6], the ultraviolet absorption may also serve for quantitative estimation. On the other hand the Δ^4-3-ketone structure is common to several hormones, so that their individual determination in mixtures must be based on other structural features. Estrogens are generally assayed by a colour reaction affording a much more intense chromophore. Some tables[7] of maxima of steroids will be found on p. 374 et seq..

TABLE A.1.†

Type		Average values	
		λ_{max}	ε_{max}
$\Delta^{5:7}$-diene	(I)	262	7700
		271	11,400
		282	11,900
		293	6900
Δ^4-3-ketone	(II)	241	16,600
Estrogen	(III)	280	2270
17-cyclobutenolide	(IV)	217	15,400
17-cyclopentadienolide	(V)	300	5450

† Data from Dorfman[7].

The clinical importance attached to the determination of cholesterol (VI) in blood serum has led to an immense literature relating to the analysis of this sterol (for reviews see Refs. 8 and 9). The main procedures depend on the presence of the 3β-hydroxy-Δ^5 grouping and are applicable to the estimation of analogous phytosterols[10]. Most methods involve extraction and partial purification of the sterol followed by application of a colour reaction under carefully defined con-

I

II

III

IV

V

ditions permitting quantitative spectrophotometry. The most satisfactory purification procedure involves isolation of cholesterol digitonide and is considered to be too tedious for routine clinical use, hence many methods have been proposed in which the colour reaction is developed with unpurified extracts, with

VI

the aim of securing a more rapid technique. The problem is thus to devise a sufficiently specific colour reaction to provide reliable results in the presence of contaminants.

Table A.2 gives data for the more important colorimetric procedures applied to cholesterol and its congeners. The colours are attributed to halochromic salts

TABLE A.2. DETERMINATION OF CHOLESTEROL AND RELATED STEROLS

Reagent	Sterol derivative	λ_{max} or λ of measurement	References	Microestimations of serum cholesterol	
				Volume of serum used	References
I. Liebermann–Burchard					
CHCl$_3$, AcOH, H$_2$SO$_4$	Cholesterol digitonide	620	(11; 9, p. 487)	0·04 ml	(12)
	Cholesterol tomatinide	640	(108)		
	Δ^7-Cholestenol	620	(9, p.487)		
	Lanosterol	550	(13)		
	Squalene	400	(14)		
II. Tschugaeff	Cholesterol	528	(15, 16)		
CHCl$_3$, ZnCl$_2$, AcCl					
or AcOH, ZnCl$_2$, AcCl	Δ^7-Cholestenol	395	(15)		
III. Keller–Kiliani	Cholesterol	560	(17)	0·10 ml	(18, 113)
FeCl$_3$, AcOH, H$_2$SO$_4$	Cholesterol esters Cholesterol digitonide			0·05 ml	(19)
IV. FeSO$_4$-AcOH-H$_2$SO$_4$	Cholesterol	490	(20)	0·01 ml	(21)
	Serum lipoprotein cholesterol	490		0·05 ml	(22)
V. Anthrone-H$_2$SO$_4$	Cholesterol digitonide	600	(109)		
+ Thiourea					

of unsaturated hydrocarbons (formed by dehydration) with the strong acid, and the fading generally observed is ascribed to the formation of polymeric unsaturated compounds (*cf.* Refs. (8) and (9) for discussion).

SATURATED HYDROXY- AND OXO-STEROIDS

Compounds such as cholestan-3β-ol, cholic acid, androsterone or pregnane-3α,20α-diol show little or no ultraviolet absorption. When sufficiently purified (e.g. by paper chromatography) they can be determined spectrophotometrically if quantitative reaction affording a chromophoric derivative is possible[23] (see further below).

Recently the analytical application of highly specific enzymes, catalysing the alcohol–ketone interconversion at particular sites on steroid molecules, has been reviewed[24]. By suitable choice of conditions the reaction may be virtually completed in either direction and its course may be followed through the rise or fall in the DPNH band at 340 mμ (ε 6220). Enzymes suitable for estimating 3α- and 3β-hydroxy steroids of the C_{19} and C_{21} series have been described. The specificity of the enzymes appears to permit the analysis of relatively crude extracts.

ESTROGENS

The phenolic absorption (λ_{max} 280 mμ, ε 2000 in neutral solution) is of analytical value only for estrogen concentrations exceeding 10 μg/ml, and in the absence of interfering chromophores[25]. Concentrations of *ca.* 1 μg, in 1–3 ml of solution for measurement require to be determined for clinical purposes, and there is much adventitious absorption near 280 mμ. The only practical spectrophotometric procedures[26, 27] are based on the Kober[28] colour reaction and have been reviewed by their exponents[29, 30]. For very low concentrations of estrogen spectrofluorometric estimation (e.g. 31) may be necessary, but the spectrophotometric method has been adapted to determine estrogens in blood.

In the modified Kober reaction[26, 110] pink colours are developed by the reaction of estrogens with solutions of quinol in aqueous sulphuric acid. The reaction involves two stages: in the first, the optimum acid concentration is 60 %(v/v) for estradiol, 66% for estrone and 76% for estriol, while for the second stage the acid concentration is reduced to about 55%. Elaborate purification of urinary extracts, finally by chromatography (of methylated estrogens) on deactivated alumina[26], or partition chromatography[27], is required to separate the three natural estrogen fractions, which are then submitted individually to the colour reaction under closely controlled conditions. The mechanism of the Kober reaction has been discussed by Brown[32], who associates the pink colour with an oxidation product and suggests that the oxidation–reduction potential of the hydroquinone–quinone system is such as to inhibit further oxidation and fading of the colour. Estriol is assumed to suffer initial dehydration, since the isomeric *cis*-diol, 16-epi-estriol[33] shows more rapid development of maximal colour intensity. With this exception, it is considered[32] that dehydration and sulphonation play little part in the reaction, as the use of more concentrated acid in the first stage gives less intense colour development. The unknown chromophore produced is substantially specific for estrogens and shows maximal absorption at 515–20 mμ (550 mμ for 2-methoxyestrone)[29]. The precise intensity depends on the particular estrogen and on the technique adopted, but it would appear[26, 27, 110] to correspond to an extinction coefficient of the order of 25,000–50,000 based on the estrogen molecular weight, thus offering a large increase in sensitivity compared with direct spectrophotometry. Unfortunately in the urinary analysis, contaminating material produces brown colours showing strong non-specific absorption in the 500 mμ region and necessitating correction of the apparent optical density. It is usual to assume that the background absorption at 515 mμ may be assessed from the mean of the observed optical densities at 515 $\pm$ *ca.* 35 mμ, i.e. the interfering absorption is assumed to be linear[34]. The magnitude of the required correction is a major disadvantage, and the recent publication[35] of a method in which the estrogen colour complex is selectively extracted (by *p*-nitrophenol in chloroform) and determined at 538·5 mμ is of considerable interest. Estimation of *total* estrogens can apparently[35, 86] be performed directly on an aliquot of urine, by this method. Techniques for separating and determining some minor urinary estrogens have been described[51].

17-OXOSTEROIDS (17-KETOSTEROIDS)

Among the steroids occurring in urine are a number of derivatives of 5α- or 5β-androstane, comprising metabolites of androgenic and adrenocortical hormones. The majority of these possess a 17-carbonyl function (Ref. 36, p. 137) and form the group of "neutral 17-ketosteroids" commonly estimated in clinical laboratories. Practically all the methods of estimation (reviewed in Refs. 38, 39, 40) are based on the Zimmermann reaction[37] with *m*-dinitrobenzene and alkali, which under appropriate conditions is remarkably specific for 17-oxosteroids. The reaction requires an unhindered α-methylene group and has been formulated (Ref. 36, p. 140[111]) as

The products from 17-oxosteroids (e.g. androsterone) are violet (λ_{max} 520 mμ): 20-oxosteroids give a similar colour (λ_{max} 490 mμ)[42] but the intensity is only about 15% of that of the 17-oxosteroid product[41, 42] and interference from these compounds is unlikely except in urine of pregnancy. Saturated 3-oxosteroids give, under the usual conditions, about 30% of the absorption (no max.) of androsterone. Non-steroid chromogens may be removed from extracts of blood by chromatography on Florisil and paper[46]. In the absence of serious interfering absorption the principal difficulty in the group estimation is the variation in extinction coefficients among different 17-oxosteroids: thus an 11β-hydroxyl group reduces, an 11-oxo group enhances, the "chromogenic value" of a 17-oxosteroid[41, 44]: the differences are least when the reaction is allowed to proceed to maximal absorption[41]. The use of alcoholic[47] rather than aqueous[48] potassium hydroxide in the reaction has the advantage that there is a linear relation between 17-oxosteroid concentration and optical density over a wider concentration range. A correction is applied[47] for absorption due to extraneous chromogens. Zimmermann[49] prefers to combine use of the aqueous-alcoholic reaction medium with ether extraction to remove interfering chromogens. It has been shown[45] that acidification of the violet complexes affords colourless derivatives extractable with benzene, which may be submitted to chromatography on paper and restored to the violet form by alkali treatment. The Zimmermann reaction has been applied qualitatively to 3-oxotriterpenoids[43].

The method of Pincus[50] in which blue complexes (λ_{max} 610 mμ) of 17-oxosteroids are formed with antimony trichloride in acetic acid–acetic anhydride, has the disadvantage that dehydroepiandrosterone, the principal 17-oxosteroid of human urine, gives only a faint colour.

CORTICOSTEROIDS

The estimation of corticosteroids and their metabolites in biological material has received much attention. The principal corticosteroids of human blood[52] are cortisol (VII) (*ca.* 0·1 μg/ml)[54], corticosterone (VIII) (*ca.* 0·02 μg/ml) and aldosterone (IX) (*ca.* 0·001 μg/ml)[55] and the chief problem in estimating these whether as a group or individually[112], is one of adequate sensitivity, to allow the use of small samples of blood. The determination of urinary corticosteroids is complicated by the variety of compounds present and by their occurrence as water-soluble derivatives (glucosiduronates, sulphates) which cannot be reliably converted into the free steroids.

VII   Cortisol: R=OH
VIII Corticosterone: R=H

Aldosterone (IX)

Dihydroxyacetone Side Chain: Porter–Silber Reaction

A sensitive spectrophotometric determination of 17α-21-dihydroxy-20-oxo-steroids, which is particularly suited to the estimation of blood corticosteroids, is based on their reaction with phenylhydrazine in aqueous sulphuric acid[52] yielding derivatives showing intense absorption ($\varepsilon \sim 25,000$)[58] at 410 mμ. This light absorption resembles that of the sugar osazones which have λ_{max} 395–9, ε_{max} 20,400[56]. On the other hand corticosterone-21-aldehyde (which would be expected to yield an "osazone" with λ_{max} near 365 mμ)[57] produces similar absorption, and the reaction proceeds more rapidly than for cortisone, whence Porter and Silber proposed that the dihydroxyacetone side chain first suffers rearrangement leading to a 20,21-ketal which then reacts at the 21-position, and in the case of cortisone or cortisol also at the 3-position. In connection with this, the authors reported that bis-phenylhydrazones isolated in preparative experiments from cortisone and cortisol showed absorption, in aqueous–ethanolic sulphuric acid, identical with that observed in analytical experiments. These derivatives were presumed to be 3,21-bis-phenylhydrazones as tetrahydrocortisol gave a mono-DNP. The Porter-Silber chromophore has recently been formulated as a protonated 21-mono phenylhydrazone[59], the 20-oxo group remaining unaltacked. 17-Deoxy-20,21-ketols can be estimated by oxidation to 17-glyoxals and application of the Porter–Silber reaction[105].

The specificity of the colour reaction has been discussed[58–60]. The Δ^4-3-oxo-grouping gives rise to maximal absorption near 350 mμ and enhances the intensity of the absorption at 410 mμ slightly in the products from cortisol and cortisone as compared with their tetrahydro-derivatives. Many non-steroids interfere and the analytical specificity achieved depends on the success of the purification. In the methods of Silber and collaborators, which are designed for rapid, routine use, the steroids are isolated by partition between a solvent (methylene chloride[65] or chloroform) and (a) water, (b) 0·1 N NaOH, and (c) the reagent, in sulphuric acid. Alternatively, the washed extract may be evaporated to dryness before the reagent is applied[64]. An adaptation suitable for 2 ml of plasma has been described[63]. More refined procedures incorporating chromatographic purification[61] have also been widely used and are probably more reliable, especially in the lower concentration range[62,63]. Butanol extraction is used by some authors[69]. Individual estimation of cortisol and corticosterone in plasma has been achieved by paper chromatography and fluorimetry[66].

The Porter–Silber reaction has been applied to urinary corticosteroids either by extracting free and "conjugated" steroids with butanol[67] or by enzymic hydrolysis with β-glucuronidase followed by extraction with chloroform[68].

The colour reaction described by Clark[96] using a diphenylamine reagent with which cortisone afforded a violet product, λ_{max} 530 mμ, and cortisol a green product, λ_{max} 630–50 mμ, does not appear to have been applied in corticosteroid analysis.

Selective Analytical Degradation of Corticosteroid Side-chains

Reactions which have been successfully applied for the spectrophotometric determination of corticosteroids are summarized in Table A.3, which depicts the six typical side-chains encountered in these steroids and in their C_{21}-metabolites. All the methods applicable directly to urine are due to Norymberski[71-75] and have the advantage that the acid-labile side-chains are converted to relatively stable 17-oxo (or 17-formyl) compounds before hydrolysis of the conjugates is attempted. (17-Carboxylic acids produced from type (b) are eliminated in working-up.)

Formaldehydogenic Steroids

Analysis of corticosteroids of types (a)–(d) (see Table) by periodate oxidation and estimation of the liberated formaldehyde by the chromotropic acid method was introduced by Lowenstein, Corcoran and Page[77]. The procedure gives good results with pure steroids[44] but is of limited application to urine in view of the difficulty of preparing suitable extracts and of the presence of formaldehyde binding substances[76] therein. The alternative reagent, sodium bismuthate[44,78] is simpler to use, but the same disadvantages remain. The sensitivity of the colour reaction permits the determination of 0·01 μmole of steroid.

"Acetaldehydogenic Steroids"

Oxidation of the 17,20-diols of type (e) with periodate permits their estimation in terms of the liberated acetaldehyde[79,80] and appears to be satisfactory, as compared with other procedures, for the determination of pregnane-3α, 17α,20α-triol in purified extracts of glucuronidase-hydrolysed urine[81]. The acetaldehyde is determined with the p-hydroxydiphenyl reagent[82].

Recently the method has been successfully extended to the determination of individual urinary 17,20-dihydroxysteroids (down to 2 μg) separated on paper chromatograms[103]. Selective estimation of "21-deoxy"-20,17-ketols has been achieved[104] by carrying out the estimation of "acetaldehydogenic steroids" on urine with and without previous treatment with borohydride (see also below).

"17-Ketogenic Steroids"

The estimation of 17,20-dihydroxycorticosteroids by periodate oxidation to 17-ketones and application of the Zimmermann reaction was first effected in 1944[83]. Bismuthate oxidation is a more convenient technique in which the dihydroxyacetone side-chain (d) also yields 17-oxosteroids[44]. However its principal merit is its direct applicability to urine under mild acid conditions (50% acetic acid). The so-called "17-ketogenic steroids" are measured as the increment in 17-oxosteroids produced by bismuthate oxidation[71,72]. By pre-treatment with borohydride[73] all 17-hydroxycorticosteroids may be determined directly from a single spectrophotometric measurement, since the original Zimmermann chromogens are largely removed in the reduction step and the unreactive 17,20-ketols of type (f) are converted to the readily oxidized 17,20-diols of type (e). The value of these procedures has been confirmed[84]. The 17,20-ketols alone are directly estimable by a three-step treatment with bismuthate, borohydride and bismuthate[74]. A third reagent, zinc dust in 50% acetic acid, converts the dihydroxyacetone side chain (d) to products lacking the 17-hydroxyl function (e.g. type (f)) and giving only a weak Zimmermann reaction (largely from the 20-oxo group). Bismuthate oxidation with and without preliminary zinc reduction thus affords a reasonable method of estimating the "steroidal dihydroxy-acetones"[75]. The analytical specificity and convenience of these methods is such that it is unfortunate that their precise quantitative interpretation is impaired by the different chromogenic values of various 17-oxosteroids in the Zimmermann reaction. For routine purposes this limitation is not serious. Where a more refined analysis is desired, the selective transformations indicated may be succeeded by chromatographic fractionation of the mixture of 17-oxosteroids[85] and individual examination of the components. In this respect, gas-liquid chromatography offers great promise. A possible alternative to the Zimmermann reaction would appear to be the use of a specific enzyme. Thus the "β-enzyme" described by Talalay[21], which catalyses, in the presence of DPN, the reversible oxidation of 3β-and 17β-OH groups in the C_{19} steroids, might be applicable to the mixed 17-ketones formed in the two methods (Table A.3) in which other ketones are reduced to alcohols. Since the enzymic reduction of the 17-oxosteroids would be measured by the fall in DPNH absorption, the difficulties of different Zimmermann chromogens would be obviated, as pointed out by Talalay[24].

SPECTROPHOTOMETRY OF STEROIDS DISSOLVED IN STRONG ACIDS

Steroids give rise to characteristic and frequently intense absorption in the 200–500 mμ region when dissolved in concentrated sulphuric[87,88] or phosphoric acid[89]. Several procedures[81,90,91–93] for the determination of pregnane–$3\alpha,17\alpha$, 20α-triol in urine are based on the products formed in sulphuric acid, which show intense and sharp absorption at 440^{81} (435) mμ^{91} ($E_{1cm}^{1\%}$, corrected by subtraction of the mean of the optical densities of 410 and 470 = 458^{81}, thus ε, based on the steroid, $\sim 15,000$). The triol must be liberated from its glucosiduronate (s) by enzymic hydrolysis carried out either on the urine[81,90] or on extracts of the conjugates prepared by ether-ethanol extraction[85] of ammonium sulphate-treated urine[91]. The pregnanediol and pregnanetriol are then separated by chromatography on deactivated alumina and individually estimated.

TABLE A.3. SELECTIVE ANALYTICAL DETERMINATION OF CORTICOSTEROIDS

Reagents	Products suitable for photometric estimation from							Designation of estimated group of steroids
	$21\ CH_2OH$ / $20\ CHOH$ / $17\ CH<$ (a)	CH_2OH / CO / $CH<$ (b)	CH_2OH / $CHOH$ / $C\cdot OH<$ (c)	CH_2OH / CO / $C\cdot OH<$ (d)	CH_3 / $CHOH$ / $C\cdot OH<$ (e)	CH_3 / CO / $C\cdot OH<$ (f)	Other ketones	
Methods Applicable to Urinary Extracts								
IO_4^- or BiO_3^-	CH_2O	CH_2O	CH_2O	CH_2O	MeCHO	—	—	Formaldehydogenic or acetaldehydogenic
IO_4^-	†	—	17 oxo	—	17 oxo	—	other ketones	17:20-Diols* original 17-oxosteroids
Methods Applicable Directly to Urine								
BiO_3^-	†	—	17 oxo	17 oxo	17 oxo	—	other ketones	17-Ketogenic Steroids* ("Total 17-KGS")
(1) BH_4^- (2) BiO_3^-	†	†	17 oxo	17 oxo	17 oxo	17 oxo	—	17-Hydroxycorticosteroids ("Total 17-OHCS")
(1) BiO_3^- (2) BH_4^- (3) BiO_3^-	—	—	—	—	—	17 oxo	—	21-Deoxy-17:20-ketols
(1) Zn-AcOH (2) BiO_3^-	—	—	17 oxo	—	17 oxo	—	other ketones	Zinc-resistant 17-Ketogenic Steroids* ("Zn/Total KGS")

† Aldehydes are formed in these reactions. A modified Angeli–Rimini reaction has been applied to their estimation in suitable extracts[70].

* As applied to urine these methods estimate 17-oxosteroids originally present in addition to those derived by oxidation. The concurrent determination of 17-oxosteroids is thus required.

Zander[94] estimates progesterone in blood (as little as $0.05\,\mu$g per ml, using 50 ml) by extraction, solvent partition, paper chromatography and quantitative spectrophotometry at 240 mμ. The ultraviolet absorption in sulphuric acid is used to characterize the isolated material. Similarly, the absorption of aldosterone in sulphuric or phosphoric acid may be used to characterise and determine this hormone in urine after suitable chromatographic isolation[106]. A convenient method of assaying diosgenin and other 3 β-hydroxy-Δ^5-sapogenins[107] involves treatment with 70% perchloric acid and measurements at 410 mμ on the yellow chromophore so produced.

SPECTROPHOTOMETRY OF STEROID DERIVATIVES

2,4-Dinitrophenylhydrazones

The virtually quantitative formation of these ketonic derivatives, together with their intense absorption, makes them very suitable for spectrophotometric assay. Excess dinitrophenylhydrazine may be destroyed with Benedict's reagent or removed by reaction with pyruvic acid and alkali extraction according to Reich[95]: alternatively it is separable by chromatography, where no hydroxylic or other polar groups are present in the steroid derivative. The derivatives of 3-, 17-, 20- or other saturated oxosteroids absorb at 367–369 mμ (in chloroform), those of Δ^4-3-ketones at 390 mμ, while bis-dinitrophenylhydrazones of steroids having both a saturated and an α,β-unsaturated carbonyl show a single band near 380 mμ. An example of steroid analysis based on chromatography and spectrophotometry of a dinitrophenylhydrazone is afforded by a recent method[97] for estimating progesterone in blood.

Other Ketonic Derivatives

Mention should be made of Girard's reagents which have been employed for separation of ketonic material (e.g. Ref. 51). Among derivatives suitable for spectrophotometry, thiosemicarbazones[98,99], salicyloxylhydrazones[100,101] and isonicotinylhydrazones[102] have been applied analytically, generally to purified ketonic fractions isolated by chromatography.

The determination of steroid hormones by spectrophotometric and other methods has been reviewed in two recent books[114].

On the following pages will be found data for a number of steroids. These consist mainly of Dorfman's tables[7], and are intended to serve both as a reference source and a stimulus to further possible correlations.

TABLE A.4. ULTRAVIOLET ABSORPTION OF CHROMOPHORIC ESTERS OF HYDROXY STEROIDS

Compound	λ_{max} (mμ)	ε_{max}			Solvent†
3β-Acetoxy-17α-benzoxyandrostane	230, 270	12,300,	170		A
5-Androstene-3β,17α-diol					
17-benzoate	229, 272, 280	14,300,	1000,	900	A
3-acetate 17-benzoate	230, 273, 280	14,000,	980,	850	A
3,17-dibenzoate	230, 274, 280	28,600,	1840,	1485	A
3β, 17β-Dibenzoxy-7β-hydroxy-5-androstene	230, 272, 280	28,800,	1700,	1400	A
3β, 7α, 17β-Tribenzoxy-5-androstene	230, 274, 280	43,600,	2690,	2160	A
Cholesterol					
3-benzoate	230, 273, 280	15,300,	970,	760	AC
3-benzoate 7α-bromo	229	24,400			E
3-thioacetate	233	4630			AC
3-thiobenzoate	239, 270	11,500,	8350.		AC
3-(2,4-dinitrophenyl thioether)	228, 270, 340	10,660,	5940,	12,630	AC
7β-(4′-acetaminoanilino) 3-benzoate	229, 275–280	18,110,	21,050		A
7β-anilino	255, 304–306	17,600,	3220		A
3-acetate 7β-anilino	255, 302–305	17,350,	2840		A
7β-anilino 3-benzoate	231, 255, 304	18,000,	18,600,	3200	A
7β-anilino 3-(3,5-dinitrobenzoate)	249, 255, 304	26,400,	27,000,	4130	A
3-benzoate 7β-piperidino	229	14,300			A
7β-(3′-pyridinoamino)	260, 323	21,800,	3720		A
3-benzoate 7β-(3′-pyridinoamino)	230, 259, 322	18,200,	22,900,	3850	A
3-benzoate 7β-(4′-carbethoxypiperazino	230	17,100			A
7α-Hydroxycholesterol					
7-benzoate	230, 272	12,750,	740		A
3,7-dibenzoate	230, 272	24,700,	1590		A
7β-Hydroxycholesterol					
7-benzoate	231, 272	12,500,	705		A
3,7-dibenzoate	229, 270, 280	28,600,	1630,	1410	A
5-Cholestene-3β-methanol					
benzoate	228, 272, 280	13,400,	890	730	A
3,5-dinitrobenzoate	No selective maximum*				AC
5,8-Peroxido-6-cholesten-3β-ol benzoate	230, 274, 280	13,500,	950,	760	A
7-Cholesten-3β-ol benzoate	228, 272, 280	11,560,	1140,	1040	A
Ethyl 12-trimethylammonium-iodide-cholanate	220**	12,600			A

† A = ethanol; AC = sample dissolved in a minimum of chloroform and diluted ethanol
E = ethyl ether.

  * The compound has a strong end absorption, which at 228 mμ is approximately 22,800.

  ** The band at 220 mμ is due to the iodide moiety.

TABLE A. 5.

ULTRAVIOLET ABSORPTION OF STEROIDS CONTAINING ISOLATED DOUBLE BONDS†

Compound	λ_{max}	ε_{max}	ε_{210}	ε_{215}	ε_{220}	ε_{223}
Disubstituted olefinic bonds:*						
Δ^2						
2-Cholestene	203	600	200	—	—	
Δ^6						
6-Cholestene-3β,5α-diol	204	1300	600	100	—	
3-acetate	204	1700	900	350	200	
Δ^{11}						
11-Cholestene-3α,24-diol	203	2500	800	200	—	
3α-Hydroxy-11-cholenic acid	205	2400	1000	350	350	
Trisubstituted olefinic bonds:*						
Δ^4						
4-Cholestene	203	4000	3000	1500	750	
Δ^5						
5-Cholene-3β, 24-diol	203	3000	1800	850	550	
5-Cholestene	204	3700	2700	1400	700	
Cholesterol	203	3400	1600	700	400	
3-acetate	203	2800	1500	800	550	
3-chloride	205	4700	3500	1400	400	
3-bromide	210	—	5600	5100	3500	
β-Sitosterol	203	2800	1600	750	350	
24(28)-Dihydrofucosterol	204	2800	1800	550	400	
Dehydroepiandrosterone	204	3300	1700	650	300	
Pregnenolone	204	3300	1800	600	300	
7α-Hydroxycholesterol	205	3300	1600	500	300	
7α-methoxy	206	4100	3000	1200	500	
7β-Hydroxycholesterol	205	3700	2400	600	200	
Δ^7						
7-Ergostene	207	4200	4000	2900	1500	
7-Ergosten-3β-ol	207	4500	4300	3000	1500	
3-acetate	208	4900	4700	3500	1800	
Δ^9						
Methyl 9-cholenate	206	3400	2900	1400	500	
9-Cholen-24-ol	206	3700	2400	1500	500	
Δ^{14}						
Dihydroxycholanic acid	205	3600	2600	1000	300	
methyl ester	205	3500	2500	900	200	
14-Ergosten-3β-ol	204	4100	2400	800	100	
3-acetate	204	4100	2800	1000	300	
Tetrasubstituted olefinic bonds:						
$\Delta^{8(9)}$						
8-Cholestene	207	4600	4400	3900	3400	2800
8-Cholesten-3β-ol	207	4700	4500	4000	3500	2900
8-Cholesten-3-one	207	4700	4400	4000	3500	2800

TABLE A. 5 — (contd.)

Compound	λ_{max}	ε_{max}	ε_{210}	ε_{215}	ε_{220}	ε_{223}
$\Delta^{8(14)}$						
3β-Acetoxy-8-pregnen-20-one	205	10,500	—	6700	—	—
8-Ergostene	208	10,400	10,100	8400	5700	3500
8-Ergosten-3β-ol	208	9800	9500	8100	6000	3400
3-acetate	209	10,600	10,500	9200	7000	4400
8-Ergosten-3-one	208	9700	9500	7500	5300	3000
8-Cholesten-3β-ol	208	10,000	9900	8300	6000	3600
3-acetate	208	10,000	9800	8600	6700	4500
3β-Acetoxy-22-iso-8-allospiro-stene	203	7700	—	4050	—	—
Apocholic acid	208	7000	6500	4700	3100	
methylester	208	9000	8600	6300	3900	
$\Delta^{9(19)}$						
Westphalen's diol	205	9300	770	4700	1900	
diacetate	206	10,000	8400	5100	5100	
Westphalen's diketone	205	7800	6300	5000	4000	
Isolated dienes:						
Stigmasterol ($\Delta^{5,22}$)	204	3800	1800	600	200	
Fucosterol ($\Delta^{5,24(28)}$)	203	4300	2200	1000	600	
Zymosterol ($\Delta^{8(9),24}$)	205	6700	5600	4800	4000	
Zymostadienone ($\Delta^{8(9),24}$)	205	6800	6000	4800	3700	
7,22-Ergostadiene	205	5400	4900	3500	1700	
7,22-Ergostadien-3β-ol	205	5700	4800	3300	1700	
3-acetate	206	6100	5400	3900	2000	
5,17-Pregnadiene-3β, 21-diol	205	6000	4800	1600	300	

† The extinction coefficients at 210, 215, 220, and 223 mμ indicate the slope of the absorption curve and are not specific bands.

* See also Chapter 2.

TABLE A.6 ULTRAVIOLET ABSORPTION OF STEROIDS CONTAINING ISOLATED KETONE GROUP

Compound	λ_{max} (mμ)	ε_{max}	Solvent†
Monoketones			
3-keto:			
17α-Hexahydrobenzoxyandrostan-3-one	281	31	A
17β-Hydroxyalloandrostan-3-one	281	28	A
3-(2,4-dinitrophenylhydrazone) 17-hexahydrobenzoate	367	25,800	C
4-bromo-17-hexahydrobenzoate 2-iodo	258	910	
17-Hydroxy-19-nor-5(10)-androsten-3-one	272–294(i)*	51	A
3-Ketoetioallocholanic acid			
2-iodo methyl ester	256	980	A
3-(2,4-dinitrophenylhydrazone)	243, 366	9800, 17,400	C
3-Cholestanone	∼ 286	∼ 16	
2-iodo	258	810	A
3-(2,4-dinitrophenylhydrazone)	367	25,700	C
3-(ᵣ-methyl 2,4-dinitrophenylhydrazone)	245, 387	10,700, 17,800	C
5α, 6β-dichloro 3-(2,4-dinitrophenylhydrazone)	366	25,400	C
3-ethylene mercaptol	240	333	A
2-Hydroxycholestan-3-one			
2-methyl sulfonate	226	9300	A
2-acetate 3-(2,4-dinitrophenylhydrazone)	247, 360	11,600, 24,500	C
5α-Hydroxycholestan-3-one			
3-(2,4-dinitrophenylhydrazone) 6β-chloro	366	27,200	C
3-Sitostanone			
3-(2,4-dinitrophenylhydrazone)	255, 281, 291, 368	18,000, 14,000, 10,000, 25,500	C
6-keto:			
3,5-Cyclocholestan-6-one	∼ 280	∼ 25	
3-Acetoxycholestan-6-one	280	40	
5-bromo	308	125	
7β-bromo	310	160	
5,7β-dibromo	340	160	
5′,7β-dibromo	305	125	
5α-Hydroxycholestan-6-one			
6-semicarbazone	228	13,000	A
2-Cholesten-6-one	285–300	50	
5α-Hydroxy-2-cholesten-6-one			
6-semicarbazone	226	12,100	A
7-keto:			
3β,11α,20β-Trihydroxyallopregnan-7-one	No selective maximum		
3β,20β-Diacetoxy-9α,11α-oxidoallopregnan-7-one	No selective maximum		
7-Cholestanone	292	40	A

TABLE A.6 — (contd.)

Compound	λ_{max} (mμ)	ε_{max}	Solvent†
Monoketones— (contd.)			
7-keto: — (contd.)			
3β-Acetoxycholestan-7-one	287	40	A
6α-bromo	282	40	A
6β-bromo	313	160	A
5,6β-dibromo	314	160	A
3β-Acetoxy-8,9-oxido-22-ergosten-7-one	No selective maximum above 230 mμ		
3β-Acetoxy-8,14-oxidoergostan-7-one	No selective maximum above 230 mμ		
3β-Acetoxy-8,14-oxido-22-ergosten-7-one	No selective maximum above 230 mμ		
11-keto:			
Methyl 3α-acetoxy-11-ketocholanate	No selective maximum above 220 mμ		A
3β-Acetoxyergostan-11-one	290	50	A
3β-Acetoxy-22-ergosten-11-one	280–290	107	A
12-keto:			A
12-Ketocholanic acid	~288	~70	A
methyl ester	No selective maximum		
Kammogenin	286	30	A
3β-Hydroxy-5-solaniden-12-one	~282	~80	A
15-keto:			
3β-Acetoxy-8,14-oxidoergostan-15-one	No selective maximum above 230 mμ		
16-keto:			
3α,12α-Dihydroxyetiocholan-16-one	No selective maximum from 225 to 350 mμ		
3β,20β-Diacetoxyallopregnan-16-one	267	35	A
17-keto:			
Androsterone	294	48	A
3-acetate	293	45	A
3-acetate 17-(2,4-dinitrophenylhydrazone)	366	25,680	C
Epiandrosterone			
3-acetate	294	48	A
3-acetate 17-(2,4-dinitrophenylhydrazone)	372	110,000**	C
3-acetate 16-sulfonic acid	300	98	A
9,11-Oxidoepiandrosterone	225††	1260	A
3β-Hydroxyetiocholan-17-one			
17-(2,4-dinitrophenylhydrazone)	370	112,000**	C
	400		AA

TABLE A.6 — (contd.)

Compound	λ_{max} (mμ)	ε_{max}	Solvent†
	Monoketones— *(contd.)*		
17-keto: —(contd.)			
Dehydroepiandrosterone	292	45	A
3-benzoate	229, 273, 280	14,300, 990, 790	AC
3-acid succinate	230, 290	871, 66	A
3-chlorocarbonate	290	60	A
17-(2,4-dinitrophenylhydrazone)	370	105,000**	C
	395		AA
3-mercaptan	No selective maximum from 220 to 310 mμ		AC
3-thioacetate	233	4670	AC
3-ethyl thioether	295	54	A
3-thiobenzoate	239, 270	12,100, 9150	AC
3-(2,4-dinitrophenyl)thioether	268(i), 339	6300, 13,500	A
3-ethyl sulfone	293	53	A
3-disulfide	246	559	A
3β-Acetoxy-5,14-androstadien-17-one	285	50	A
3β-Acetate-13-iso-5,14-androstadien-17-one	~ 275	~ 230	A
20-keto:			
3β-Hydroxyallopregnan-20-one	284	50	
3-acetate 20-(2,4-dinitrophenylhydrazone	370	21,400	C
3β-Hydroxy-5-pregnen-20-one	285	50	A
3-acetate	285	40	A
20-(2,4-dinitrophenylhydrazone)	245, 372	14,700, 30,400	C
3-mercaptan	280	65	A
3-thioacetate	234	4620	A
3-acetate 20-enol acetate	No selective maximum from 215 to 300 mμ		A A
3β-Hydroxy-7-allopregnen-20-one	282	60	A
3-acetate	284	50	A
3β-Acetoxy-9-allopregnen-20-one	280	78	A
3β-Acetoxy-16-(β-benzoxyethylmercapto)-5-pregnen-20-one	230	15,100	A
3β-Acetoxy-16-(γ-methyl-5-acetoxyvalerate)-7-allopregnen-20-one	276	42	A
3β-Acetoxy-17α-hydroxy-5-pregnen-20-one	295	~ 50	A
3β-Acetoxy-17β-hydroxy-5-pregnen-20-one	294	~ 60	A
3β-Acetoxy-17-iso-14,15β-oxidoallopregnan-20-one	284	69	
3β-Acetoxy-16,17-oxidoallopregnan-20-one	299	40	
3β-Acetoxy-21-phenoxy-5-pregnen-20-one	272§	1780	
21-Acetoxy-3α,12α-dihydroxypregnan-20-one	285	76	A

TABLE A.6—(contd.)

Compound	λ_{max} (mμ)	ε_{max}	Solvent†
Monoketones—(contd.)			
20-keto: — (contd.)			
3β,21-Diacetoxy-16,17-oxidoallopregnan-20-one	290	45	
3α-Acetoxy-21-diazopregnan-20-one	240–290(p)*	10,000	
	380	32	
3β-Acetoxy-16,17-methylene-5-pregnen-20-one	~275	~60	A
3β-Acetoxy-21-diazo-16,17-pyrazole-5-pregnen-20-one	275, 330(i)*	10,400, 310	A
Diketones			
3,11-diketo:			
Methyl 3,11-diketocholanate	No selective maximum		A
12α-bromo 3-(2,4-dinitrophenylhydrazone)	367	25,000	C
4,12α-dibromo 3-(2,4-dinitrophenylhydrazone)	364	24,500	C
Methyl 12α-bromo-3,11-diketo-4-methoxycholanate			
3-semicarbazone	230	13,600	M
3-(2,4-dinitrophenylhydrazone)	370	26,500	C
3,12-diketo:			
3,12-Diketocholanic acid	~288	~70	A
3,12-Solanidanedione	282	70	A
3,17-diketo:			
3,17-Androstanedione	290	61	A
2-iodo	256	710	A
3,20-diketo:			
21-Acetoxy-14-pregnene-3,20-dione	229**	1580	A
6,17-diketo:			
2-Androstene-6,17-dione	285–300	110	A
7,11-diketo:			
Methyl 3α-acetoxy-7,11-diketocholanate	290	100	A
3β-Acetoxy-22-ergostene-7,11-dione	290	100	A
11,20-diketo:			
3α,21-Dihydroxypregnane-11,20-dione 20-(2,4-dinitrophenylhydrazone)	367	22,700	C
	371	24,400	B

TABLE A.6—(contd.)

Compound	λ_{max} (mμ)	ε_{max}	Solvent†
Diketones — *(contd.)*			
11,20-diketo: — (contd.)			
12α-bromo 20-(2,4-dinitrophenylhydrazone)	366	23,100	C
	369	24,000	B
3-acetate 12α-bromo 20-(2,4-dinitro- phenylhydrazone)	363	23,100	C
	366	24,500	B
21-acetate 12α-bromo 20-(2,4-dinitro- phenylhydrazone)	359	24,200	C
	363	24,600	B
3,21-diacetate 20-(2,4-dinitrophenyl- hydrazone)	360	24,000	C
	364	24,400	B
3,21-diacetate 12α-bromo 20-(2,4-dinitro- phenylhydrazone)	359	24,600	C
	362	24,000	B
3,21-diacetate 12α,21-dibromo 20-(2,4- dinitrophenylhydrazone)	362	22,400	C
3α-Acetoxy-12α-bromo-11,20-diketo-21- pregnanoic acid			
20-(2,4-dinitrophenylhydrazone)	364	24,900	C
	376	25,500	B
20-(2,4-dinitrophenylhydrazone)methyl ester	364	26,600	C
	367	27,000	B
16,22-diketo:			
Dihydrokryptogenin	283	70	A
Kryptogenin	285	65	A
Triketones			
3,11,20-triketo:			
21-Acetoxy-12α-bromopregnane-3,11,20- trione			
20-(2,4-dinitrophenylhydrazone)	359	24,100	C
	362	24,700	B
2,21-Diacetoxy-17α-hydroxypregnane- 3,11,20-trione	No selective maximum from 220 to 330 mμ		
3-(2,4-dinitrophenylhydrazone)	365	25,600	C
4,21-Diacetoxy-17α-hydroxypregnane- 3,11,20-trione			
3-(2,4-dinitrophenylhydrazone)	358	22,000	C

† A = ethanol; AA = alkaline ethanol, usually 0·1 N; AC = sample dissolved in a minimum of chloroform and diluted with ethanol; B = acetone; C = chloroform; M = methanol.

* (i) signifies an inflection; (p) signifies a plateau.

** The extinction coefficient is too high.

†† A high-absorbing impurity is present.

§ The band is due to the benzoyl group.

TABLE A. 6—(contd.)

Compound	λ_{max}	Δ_{ax}	Δ_{eq}
α–Hydroxy and Acetoxy Ketones			
Cyclohexanones (in EtOH)			
12-ketone	290		
11β–OH	307	+17	
11α–OH	278		−12
11-ketone	299		
12α–OH	313	+14	
12β–OH	290	−9	
12x–OAc	310	+11	
12β–OAc	293		−6
6-ketone	280		
5α–OH	299,5	+19,5	
5α–OAc	290	+10	

Compound	λ_{max}	$\Delta\lambda$	
Cyclopentanones (in Dioxan)			
16-ketone	298		
17α–OAc	314	+16	
17β–OAc	298	0	
17-ketone	295,5		
16α–OAc	305	+9,5	
16β–OAc	307,5	+12	

TABLE A.7 ULTRAVIOLET ABSORPTION OF STEROIDS CONTAINING ISOLATED ALDEHYDE
GROUPS

Compounds	λ_{max} (mμ)	ε_{max}	Solvent†
10-Aldehyde:			
Dianhydrodihydrostrophanthidin	303	126	A
Monoanhydrodihydrostrophanthidin	303	25	A
21-Aldehyde:			
3,20-Dihydroxy-21-dimethylacetal-5-pregnene	No selective maximum		A

† A = ethanol.

TABLE A.8 ULTRAVIOLET ABSORPTION OF CONJUGATED OLEFINS

Compound	λ_{max} (mμ)	ε_{max}	Solvent[a]
Dienes			
$\Delta^{2,4}$			
2,4-Cholestadiene	267, 275	6300, 6300	
α-Cholesterylene (bis- $\Delta^{2,4}$)	$\sim$ 266, 275, $\sim$ 287	$\sim$ 30,000 $\sim$ 39,000 $\sim$ 27,000	
$\Delta^{3,4}$			
3-Methylene-4-cholestene	233, 239	16,230, 17,260	CH
$\Delta^{3,5(b)}$			
Testosterone			
3-enol acetate 17-acetate	239	15,500	C
3-enol acetate 17-pro- pionate	235	18,900	A
3-(β-benzoxyethyl) thio- enol ether 17-benzoate	230, 268	37,200, 16,600	A
3-benzylthioenol ether	268	24,000	A
3-benzylthioenol ether 17- benzoate	228, 268	28,800, 20,900	A
3-pyridinium chloride 17-propoxy	330	10,000	C
3,5-Androstadien-17-one	220(i), 234, 243(p)[c]	–, 18,000, –	E
4-chloro	238	23,200	E
3-bromo	238	22,700	E
4-Androstene-3,17-dione			
3-enol ethyl ether	241, 280–300	19,700, 64	A
3-(β-hydroxyethyl) thio- enol ether	268	25,700	A
3-(β-hydroxyethyl) hemithioketal[d]	238	20,000	A
3-benzylthioenol ether	268	24,600	A
3-benzylsulfoxidoenol ether	258	22,400	A
Methyl 19-acetoxymethyl- 3,5,14-etiocholatrienate	232	26,300[e]	A
3,5,20-Pregnatriene	228, 235, 243	–, 25,100[e], –	A
20β-Hydroxy-4-pregnen-3- one			
3-benzylthioenol ether	268	25,700	A
17α,20β-Dihydroxy-4- pregnen-3-one			
3-benzylthioenol ether	268	25,100	A
3,5-Pregnadien-20-one	228, 234	18,600, 20,000	A
20-semicarbazone	232	30,900	A
Progesterone			
3-enol acetate	235	17,500	A

TABLE A. 8—(contd.)

Compound	λ_{max} (mμ)	ε_{max}	Solvent[a]
	Dienes—*(contd.)*		
$\varDelta^{3,5}$[b] — *(contd.)*			
3,20-dienol diacetate			
($\varDelta^{3,5,20}$)	~ 235	~ 19,500	A
3-benzylthioenol ether	268	22,900	A
3-benzylsulfoxidoenol			
ether	258	20,900	A
16α-Hydroxyprogesterone			
3-benzylthioenol ether			
16-thiobenzyl	268	23,400	A
20-semicarbazone	268	23,400	A
17α-Hydroxyprogesterone			
3-benzylthioenol ether	268	24,000	A
21-Acetoxy-3,5-pregnadien-			
20-one	228, 234	10,200, 10,700[f]	A
Desoxycorticosterone			
acetate			
3-benzylthioenol ether	268	20,000	A
3-benzylsulfoxidoenol			
ether	258	20,900	A
16-Isopropylidene-3,5-			
androstadiene	235	19,100	
21-Acetoxy-16,17-oxido-4-			
pregnene-3,20-dione			
3-enol ethyl ether	241	21,900	M
21-Acetoxy-17α-hydroxy-4-			
pregnene-3,11,20-trione			
3-enol ethyl ether	242	26,300	M
3,5-Cholestadiene	~ 229, 235, 244 (i)[c]	~ 18,000, 19,700, ~ 13,600	IA
4-Cholesten-3-one			
3-enol acetate	238	16,800	C
4,6-dibromo 3-enol	245		A
acetate	245		A
3-ethylthioenol ether	272	26,000	E
3-benzylthioenol ether	268	20,500	A
22-Iso-3,5-spirostadiene	228, 234	18,600, 20,000	A
22-Iso-4-spirosten-3-one			
3-benzylthioenol ether	268	20,400	A
3-Methyl-3,5-cholestadiene	231, 239	21,500, 22,700	CH
$\varDelta^{4,6}$			
4,6-Androstadiene-3β,17β-			
diol	232, 240, 248	21,900, 23,400, 19,500	A
3β-Hydroxy-4,6-androsta-			
dien-17-one	232, 238	21,700, 23,600	A

TABLE A.8—(contd.)

Compound	λ_{max} (mμ)	ε_{max}	Solvent[a]
		Dienes—(contd.)	
$\Delta^{4,6}$—(contd.)			
3β-Hydroxy-4,6-pregna-dien-20-one	232, 240, 248	37,200, 39,900, 26,300[e]	A
4,6-Choladienic acid	235	17,200	
3β-Acetoxy-4,6-norchol-estadiene	232, 239, 248	6180, 6950, 4370[f]	A
4,6-Cholestadiene	238	24,000	E
4,6-Cholestadien-3β-ol			
3-acetate	232, 239, 248	17,800, 20,100, 12,700	A
3-benzoate	239, 280	38,200, 1100	A
3-thiobenzoate	245, 272	29,800, 13,700	AC
4,6-Cholestadienyl-7-ether (bis-$\Delta^{4,6}$)	243, 249 (i)[c]	54,000, 48,000	E
22-Iso-4,6-spirostadien-3β-ol	232, 240, 248	24,000, 25,700, 16,600	A
3-acetate	232, 238, 248	21,900, 24,000, 15,100	A
3-benzoate	240	42,700	A
3-(p-nitrobenzoate)	250	29,500	A
3β-Acetoxy-4,6,22-ergosta-triene	$\sim$ 232, 240, $\sim$ 247	$\sim$ 24,600, $\sim$ 27,000, $\sim$ 18,000	E
$\Delta^{5,7}$			
5,7-Androstadiene-3,-7β-diol	271, 282, 293	11,200, 11,750, 6800	A
3,17-diacetate	271, 281, 292	10,800, 11,300, 6400	A
3-acetate 17-benzoate	229, 271, 281, 293	14,850, 12,450, 12,700 7000	A
17-benzoate	229, 271, 281, 293	12,300, 10,800, 11,150, 5000	A
3,17-dibenzoate	229, 271, 281, 293	25,900, 14,000, 14,200, 7250	A
3β-Hydroxy-5,7-androsta-dien-17-one	271, 282, 293	10,410, 10,900, 6250	A
3-acetate	271, 281, 293	11,300, 11,850, 6700	A
3-benzoate	229, 271, 281, 293	13,500, 12,600, 12,800, 7000	A
3β-Hydroxy-5,7-pregna-dien-20-one	272, 282, 294	19,100 20,400, 12,300[e]	A
3-acetate	272, 282, 294	11,600, 12,200, 7000	A
3-benzoate	229, 272, 282, 294	13,000, 12,350, 12,700 7225	A
3β-21-Dihydroxy-5,7-preg-nadien-20-one	272, 282, 294	11,400, 11,950, 7180	A
21-acetate	272, 282, 294	12,030, 12,800, 7650	A

TABLE A.8— (contd.)

Compound	λ_{max} (mμ)	ε_{max}	Solvent[a]
	Dienes— *(contd.)*		
$\Delta^{5,7}$ — *(contd.)*			
3,21-diacetate	272, 282, 294	10,400, 11,100, 6450	A
3,21-dibenzoate	229, 272, 282, 294	31,800, 13,400, 13,850, 7460	A
3β-Hydroxy-5,7-chol-adienic acid	271, 281, 294	10,200, 10,500, 6300	
5,7-Norcholestadien-3β-ol	$\sim$ 270, 281, $\sim$ 290	$\sim$ 5000, 6210, $\sim$ 3100[f]	A
3-acetate	$\sim$ 270, 281, $\sim$ 290	$\sim$ 4000, 4200, $\sim$ 2000[f]	A
3-benzoate	$\sim$ 230, $\sim$ 270, 281, $\sim$ 290	$\sim$ 15,900, $\sim$ 6310, 8450, $\sim$ 4000[f]	A
5,7-Cholestadiene	$\sim$ 273, 280, $\sim$ 295(i)[c]	—, 11,100, —	
3-chloro	263, 273, 283, 295	9250, 12,070, 12,600, 7700	AC
3-bromo	235, 274, 285, 297	3050, 12,710, 13,550, 8040	AC
7-Dehydrocholesterol	272, 282, 293	11,250, 11,900, 6650	A
3-acetate	271, 282, 293	11,500, 12,160, 6820	A
3-methyl ether	272, 282, 294	9900, 10,600, 5950	A
3-benzoate	230, 272, 282, 294	14,200, 13,360, 13,510 7290	A
3-(p-nitrobenzoate)	271, 282	22,940, 19,600	A
3-(3,5-dinitrobenzoate)	271, 282, 293	16,650, 14,940, 8750	A
3-mercaptan	273, 283, 295	12,800, 13,550, 7800	AC
3-thiocetate	232(i), 265(i)[c], 274, 284, 296	5490, 9000, 12,800, 13,800, 7950	AC
3-thiobenzoate	239, 274, 284, 295	13,000, 21,400, 20,750, 12,400	AC
3-disulfide	273, 284, 296	24,460, 26,460, 15,510	AC
3-rhodanide	274, 285, 297	12,090, 13,410, 8050	A
3-bromo	275, 285, 297	13,000, 13,500, 9000	CH
22-Iso-5,7-spirostadien-3β-ol	270, 282, 292	14,500, 15,100, 9120	A
3-acetate	270, 280, 292	15,500, 15,900, 9780	A
3-benzoate	228, 270, 282, 292	14,800, 13,800, 13,800, 7760	A
3-(p-nitrobenzoate)	270, 282	31,600, 27,600	A
3-(2,4-dinitrobenzoate)	260, 270, 280, 292	15,100, 15,100, 13,500, 8130	A
5,7-Cholestadiene-3β-methanol	271, 282, 293	11,260, 11,970, 6850	A
3-acetate	271, 282, 293	11,720, 12,400, 7050	A
3-benzoate	228, 271, 282, 293	14,180, 12,320, 12,760, 7090	A
3-(3,5-dinitrobenzoate)	260, 270, 282, 293	15,080 14,310, 13,140, 7810	AC

TABLE A.8—(contd.)

Compound	λ_{max} (mμ)	ε_{max}	Solvent[a]
	Dienes—*(contd.)*		

Δ^{5,7}—*(contd.)*

Compound	λ_{max} (mμ)	ε_{max}	Solvent[a]
Methy 5,7-cholestadiene-3-carboxylate	271, 282, 293	11,670, 12,250, 6930	A
5,7,22-Ergostatriene	271, ~ 281, ~ 297		
Ergosterol	271, 282, 293	11,450, 11,990, 6880	A
4-acetate	271, 282, 293	11,970, 12,450, 7000	A
3-benzoate	225, 260, 271, 280, 293		
3-cinnamate	280		
3-diphenylacetate	260, 270, 280		
3-(4-nitrobenzoate)	261, 270, 281, 293(i)[c]	20,100, 20,000, 16,000, 9100	H
3-(3-nitro-4-methyl-benzoate)	~ 261, ~ 271, ~ 282, ~ 294	~ 11,000, ~ 12,000, ~ 11,900, ~ 7800	H
3-(3,5-dinitrobenzoate)	~ 260, ~ 271, ~ 282, ~ 293	~ 12,100, ~ 12,100, ~ 12,000, ~ 7500	H
	~ 253, ~ 258, ~ 271, ~ 282, ~ 294	~ 15,800, ~ 14,500, ~ 13,700, 12,100, 7,500	A
3-(3,5-dinitro-4-methyl-benzoate)	~ 261, ~ 271, ~ 281, ~ 293	~ 10,500, ~ 12,500, ~ 12,800, ~ 9000	
22-Dihydroergosterol	270, 280		
7-Dehydrocampesterol	272, 282	−, 10,600	
Lumisterol	270, 280	−, 8500	
3-acetate	270, 280	12,000, 11,500[g]	
Epilumisterol	274, ~ 280, ~ 295	9900, ~ 9100, ~ 4500[g]	A
Pyrocalciferol	274, 294		
Isopyrocalciferol	262, 280		
7-Dehydrositosterol	270, 280	−, 11,700	E
7-Dehydrostigmasterol	270, 280		E
Dihydrotachysterol	242, 261		E

Δ$^{5,7'}$

Compound	λ_{max} (mμ)	ε_{max}	Solvent[a]
7-Methylenechoesterol	236	20,000	

Δ$^{6,8(9)}$

Compound	λ_{max} (mμ)	ε_{max}	Solvent[a]
Isodehydrocholesterol	275	5300	E
6,8-Coprostadien-3β-ol	275	4700	

Δ$^{6,8(14)}$

Compound	λ_{max} (mμ)	ε_{max}	Solvent[a]
6,8-Cholestadiene[d]	245		A
6,8-Cholestadiene-3β,9-diol	248		
3-acetate	245	28,700[e]	
3,5-Cyclo-6,22-ergosta-triene[i]	261	26,800	A

TABLE A. 8—(contd.)

Compound	λ_{max} (mμ)	ε_{max}	Solvent[a]
	Dienes— *(contd.)*		
$\varDelta^{6,8(14)}$ — *(contd.)*			
6,8,22-Ergostatrien-3β-ol	248		E
(ergosterol-B$_2$)	253	17,000	A
3-acetate	253	17,000	A
3-benzoate	234, 252	23,000, 21,500	A
3,5-Cyclo-22α-6,8-spirosta-			
diene	256		A
$\varDelta^{7,9(11)}$			
7,9-Androstadiene-3β,17β-			
diol	236, 243, 250	12,100, 13,800, 9000	A
3,17-diacetate	235, 242, 250	13,100, 14,900, 9600	A
3,17-dibenzoate	232, 250(i)[c], 273, 280	36,200, 10,300, 4150, 3300	A
7,9-Allopregnadiene-			
3β,20β-diol	235, 242	12,300, 13,500	A
3,20-diacetate	236, 242	12,900, 13,800	A
3β-Hydroxy-7,9-allopreg-			
nadien-20-one	236, 242	12,000 13,500	A
3-acetate	236, 242	10,000, 10,700[f]	A
3-acetate 16α,17α-oxido	234, 242	13,500, 14,800	A
Methyl-3α-acetoxy-7,9-			
choladienate	244	17,400	
Methyl 7,9-lithochola-			
dienate	245	15,900	A
3-acetate	245	15,900	A
7,9-Cholestadiene[h]	243		A
7,9-Cholestadien-3β-ol	236, 243, 252	14,100, 16,100, 10,600	A
3-acetate	236, 243, 251	15,400, 17,000, 11,400	A
3-benzoate	234, 250, 273, 281	26,600, 12,500, 1100, 900	A
7,9-Coprostadien-3β-ol(co-			
prostadienol D)	240		
3β,6α-Diacetoxy-7,9-chole-			
stadiene	242	19,500	A
7,9-Cholestadiene-3β,6β-			
diol	248	15,000	E
3,6-diacetate	245	18,300	A
22-Iso-7,9-spirostadien-3α-			
ol	236, 244	13,800, 14,800	A
22-Iso-7,9-spirostadien-			
3β-ol	236, 242	13,200, 14,500	A
3-acetate	236, 242	13,500, 14,800	A
7,9,22-Ergostatriene			
(ergostatriene-D)	235, 243, 252		

TABLE A. 8—(contd.)

Compound	λ_{max} (mμ)	ε_{max}	Solvent[a]
Dienes — (contd.)			
$\Delta^{7,9(11)}$ — (contd.)			
7,9,22-Ergostratrien-3β-ol			
(ergosterol-D)	236, 243, 251	14,200, 15,700, 10,600	A
3-acetate	236, 242	11,700, 13,200	A
3β-Acetoxy-7,9-ergo-			
stadiene	235, 242	13,400, 13,400	A
Ergosterol-F[h]	235, 242		
Ergostatrienone-D	235, 243, 252		
7,9-Ergostadiene-3,5-diol	240	13,800	E
$\Delta^{7,14}$			
3α,12β-Dihydroxy-7,14-			
choladienic acid	241–248		
3,12-diacetate methyl			
ester	242	12,000	
7,14-Cholestadiene[h]	242, 250		A
Cholesterol-B$_3$	248		
3-acetate	248	15,100	E
Ergosterol-B$_2$	242	10,100	C
acetate	242	9900	A
$\Delta^{8(9),14}$			
8,14-Androstadiene-3β,			
17β-diol			
3,17-diacetate	247	16,100	A
3,17-dibenzoate	232, 280	34,400, 1820	A
3α-12β-Dihydroxy-8,14-			
choladienic acid[a]	249		A
3,12-diacetate methyl			
ester	244[j]	17,800	
8,14-Cholestadiene	245[j]		A
8,14-Cholestadien-3β-ol			
(cholestadienol-D)	250	20,000	A
3-acetate	245[j]	11,700[f]	E
8,14-Coprostadien-3β-ol	248		
3β-Acetoxy-8,14-ergosta-			
diene	248	19,800	A
Ergosterol-B$_1$ $\Delta^{(8,24,22)}$	250	19,400	A
3-acetate	249	18,100	A
Ergosteryl-B$_1$ chloride	248	18,300	A
$\Delta^{9(11),12(23)}$			
9,12-Dehydronorchola-			E
diene	242	19,500	

TABLE A.8—(contd.)

Compound	λ_{max} (mμ)	ε_{max}	Solvent[a]
	Dienes — *(contd.)*		
$\Delta^{16,20(21)}$			
3α-Acetoxy-16,20-pregna-dien-11-one	238	15,000	A
3β-Acetoxy-16-allopreg-nen-20-one 20-enol acetate	~ 239	~ 14,500	A
3β-Acetoxy-5,16-pregna-dien-20-one 20-enol acetate	~ 239	~ 15,800	A
3β-Acetoxy-21,21-di-methyl-5,16,20-pregna-triene	240	~ 8900	H
$\Delta^{16,20(22)}$			
5,16,20-Furostatriene-5β, 26-diol	226	13,200	A
3,26-diacetate	226	14,500	A
$\Delta^{22,24(22)}$			
3β-Acetoxy-5,22,24-stigma-statriene	238	15,800	A
Miscellaneous:			
3,5-Cyclo-6-cholestene	~ 210	~ 8000	
	Trienes		
$\Delta^{2,4,6}$			
17-Propionyloxy-2,4,6-androstatriene[k]	304	12,600	D
2,4,6-Cholestatriene[l]	298(i)[e], 307	—, 15,200	CH
	306	15,700	E
	307		A
4-Cholestene-3,6-dione 3-benzoate 3-enol ethyl ether,	308	13,200	A
3,6-dienol dibenzoate	230, 307	48,400, 18,200	AC
4,6-Cholestadien-3-one 3-enol acetate	302	12,600	A
22-Iso-2,4,6-spirostatriene	296, 306, 320	18,600, 21,400, 14,100[e]	A
4,6-Ergostadien-3-one 3-enol acetate	304	16,600	A
$\Delta^{3,5,7}$			
3,5,7-Cholestatriene[m]	303, 315, 330	12,540, 15,700, 11,100	IA
4-Cholestene-3,6-dione 3,6-dienol dibenzoate	230, 316	37,600, 20,200	AC

TABLE A.8—(contd.)

Compound	λ_{max} (mμ)	ε_{max}	Solvent[a]
Trienes — (contd.)			
$\Delta^{3,5,7}$— (contd.)			
4,6-Choleastadien-3-one			
3-enol acetate	305, 316, 330	—, 20,000, —	A
22-Iso-4,7-spirostadien-3-one			
3-enol acetate	302, 314, 330	20,000, 23,400, 17,400	A
3,5,7,22-Ergostatetraene	302, 316, 332	~ 16,000, 19,000, ~ 14,000	A
4,7,22-Ergostatrien-3-one			
3-enol acetate	301, 317, 331	~ 18,500, 21,400, ~ 18,000	A
Lumistatetraene	314		
4,7,22-Lumistatrien-3-one			
3-enol acetate	301(i), 315, 331(i)[c]	—, 19,100, —	A
$\Delta^{4,6,8(14)}$			
$\Delta^{4,6,8,22}$-Ergostatetraene	283	33,000	A
$\Delta^{5,7,9(11)}$			
5,7,9-Androstatriene-3β,			
17β-diol	312, 324, 339	11,230, 12,680, 7905	A
3,17-diacetate	212, 324, 339	9900, 10,300, 6400	A
3,17-dibenzoate	229, 312, 324	30,250, 11,300, 12,700,	
	340	8100	A
3β-Hydroxy-5,7,9-andro-			
stastrien-17-one	311(i), 322, 339(i)[c]	9650, 10,800, 6800	A
3-acetate	312(i), 323, 339(i)	990, 11,100, 6900	A
3-benzoate	227, 311, 323,	17,350, 11,600, 12,850,	A
	336	8100	
3β-Hydroxy-5,7,9-pregna-			
trien-20-one	312(i), 323, 339(i)	10,200, 11,550, 7400	AC
3-acetate	312, 324, 339	11,500, 12,800, 770	A
3-benzoate	228, 312, 324, 339	16,900, 11,450, 12,900,	
		8000	A
3β-21-Dihydroxy-5,7,9-			
pregnatrien-20-one	311, 324, 339	9300, 10,700, 6660	A
3,21-diacetate	312, 325, 339(p)[c]	10,500, 11,900, 7400	A
5,7,9-Cholestatrien-3β-ol	312, 325, 339	10,100, 12,800, 7950	A
3-acetate	311, 325, 340	10,300, 11,900, 7450	A
3-benzoate	228, 282, 310,	13,700, 4700, 9500,	AC
	325, 340	10,900, 7000	
22-Iso-5,7,9-spirostatrien-			
3β-ol	310, 324, 338	13,200, 14,500, 8900	A
3-acetate	210, 324, 338	15,100, 17,000, 10,500[e]	A
5,7,9,22-Ergostatetraen-3β-			
ol (dehydroergosterol)	325, 340	11,100, —	A
3-acetate	311, 325, 341	10,500, 12,100, 7500	A
Dehydrolumisterol	320	7500[f]	
3-acetate	315	11,700	E
	318		

TABLE A.8—(contd.)

Compound	λ_{max} (mμ)	ε_{max}	Solvent[a]
Trienes — (contd.)			
$\Delta^{5,7,14}$			
5,7,14,22-Ergostatetraen-3β-ol (14-dehydroergosterol)	319	17,500	A
3-acetate	319	15,000	A
3-benzoate	319	16,000	A
$\Delta^{6,8(14),9(11)}$			
3β-Acetoxy-6,8,9-cholestatriene	~ 243, 285	~ 12,000, 9100	E
Tetraenes			
$\Delta^{3,5,7,9(11)}$			
22-Iso-4,7,9-spirostatrien-3-one 3-enol acetate	336, 354, 372	17,800, 21,900, 16,200	A
4,7,9,22-Ergostatetraen-3-one 3-enol acetate	339, 356, 375	~ 15,000, 17,400, ~ 13,000	A
$\Delta^{4,6,8(9),11}$			
4,6,8,11-Cholestatetraen-3β-ol	355	13,500	E
$\Delta^{3,5,3',5'}$			
17,17'-Dipropionyloxy-3,3'-bis-3,5-androstadiene	298, 313	37,000, 53,000	C
3,3'-bis-3,5-cholestadiene	280, 293, 305, 321	38,900, 53,700, 63,100, 45,700	E
	298, 312, 323	47,900, 63,100, 46,800	C

(a) A = ethanol; AC = sample dissolved in a minimum of chloroform and diluted with ethanol; C = chloroform; CH = cyclohexane; D = dioxane; E = ethyl ether; H = hexane, IA = isopropyl alcohol; M = methanol.

(b) The bands or inflections at 228 and 244 mμ do not appear when a C_3-acetate or C_3-halogen is present.

(c) (i) signifies an inflection; (p) signifies a plateau.

(d) The hemithioketal is at the C_{17}-position.

(e) The extinction coefficient is too high.

(f) The extinction coefficient is too low.

(g) The extinction coefficient at 280 mμ should be the highest.

(h) The chemical individuality is questioned.

(i) It has been shown that a cyclopropane ring has chromophoric powers approaching that of an ethylenic bond. Thus it was expected that a cyclopropane ring would have a bathochromic effect of approximately 15 mμ when in conjugation with a conjugated diene.

(j) The absorption band should appear at 248–250 mμ.

(k) A $\Delta^{3,5,7}$-triene was proposed by the authors.

(l) The compound was previously described as a $\Delta^{3,5,7}$-triene.

(m) The compound was previously described as a $\Delta^{2,4,6}$-triene.

TABLE A. 9 ULTRAVIOLET ABSORPTION OF CONJUGATED STEROID KETONES

Compound	λ_{max} (mμ)	ε_{max}	Solvent[a]
Enones			
Δ^1-3-one:			
17β-Hydroxy-1-alloandrosten-3-one	230	10,000	A
17-hexahydrobenzoate	232	6800	A
2-bromo 17-hexahydrobenzoate	255	7600	A
	254	7700	E
2,4-dibromo 17-hexahydrobenzoate	261	6600	A
1-Alloandrostene-3,17-dione	230	10,200	A
2-bromo	256	6990	A
3-Keto-1-etioallocholenic acid	231	7950	A
methyl ester	232	6170	A
2-bromo methyl ester	257	7080	A
3-(2,4-dinitrophenylhydrazone)			
methyl ester	257, 383	17,300, 30,000	C
3-(α-methyl-2.4-dinitrophenyl-			
hydrazone) methyl ester	245, 393	20,800, 21,600	C
1-Allopregnene-3, 20-dione	230	12,600	A
17α-Hydroxy-1-allopregnene-3,20-			
dione	230	11,300	A
21-Acetoxy-1-allopregnene-3,20-dione	229	12,000	A
21-Acetoxy-17α-hydroxy-allopreg-			
nene-3,20-dione	230	11,000	A
21-Acetoxy-17α-hydroxy-1-allopreg-			
nene-3,11,20-trione	227	10,000	A
21-Acetoxy-17α-hydroxy-1-pregnene-			
3,11,20-trione	225	9130	M
3-(2,4-dinitrophenylhydrazone)	381	28,300	C
21-Diazo-1-pregnene-3,20-dione	233, 240	17,100, 19,900	A
3-Keto-1-bisnorallocholenic acid	240		
Methyl 12α-acetoxy-3-keto-1-cholenate	231	7200	A
2-bromo	256	880	M
Methyl 12α-bromo-3,11-diketo-1-			
cholenate	224	9890	M
3-(2,4-dinitrophenylhydrazone)	381	29,200	C
1-Cholesten-3-one	231	9770	A
2-bromo	256	8500	A
3-(2,4-dinitrophenylhydrazone)	257, 384	16,400, 27,100	C
3-(α-methyl-2,4-dinitrophenyl-			
hydrazone	248, 293	18,000, 20,000	C
2-bromo 3-(α-methyl-2,4-dinitro-			
phenylhydrazone)	245, 392	15,300, 16,700	C
3-semicarbazone	266	25,800	C
1-Coprosten-3-one	230	10,200	A
2-bromo	256	7400	M
3-semicarbazone	270	9670	C
1-Cholestene-3,6-dione	228	8150	IA
2-bromo	257	7450	IA

TABLE A.9—(contd.)

Compound	λ_{max} (mμ)	ε_{max}	Solvent[a]
	Enones — *(contd.)*		
Δ²-2-formyl:			
2-Formyl-2-cholestene	235, 300	12,600, 71	A
2′oxime	233	20,000	A
Δ⁴-3-one:			
19-Nortestosterone	241, 308	17,000, 93	A
4,16-Androstadien-3-one	240	17,800	
Testosterone	241	15,800	A
	241	15,400	M
	240		C
	236	15,200	D
	234	15,600	E
	230	15,100	H
17-propionate	241	16,900	A
17-methoxyacetate	241	16,800	A
17-ethoxyacetate	241	17,100	A
17-n-propoxyacetate	240	17,000	A
17-isopropoxyacetate	241	16,500	A
17-n-butoxyacetate	240	15,600	A
17-methoxypropionate	241	17,000	A
17-hexahydrobenzoate	241	13,200	A
17-undecylenate	240	16,000	A
17-phenylacetate	240	16,000	A
17-phenylmercaptoacetate	240	22,700	A
17-benzylmercaptoacetate	240	18,200	A
17-methylmercaptopropionate	240	16,900	A
17-(2′-methylmercapto) propionate	241	17,700	A
17-(2′-ethylmercapto) propionate	241	17,300	A
17-methylmercaptobutyrate	241	16,800	A
17-(2′-methylmercapto) butyrate	241	17,900	A
2-bromo 17-hexahydrobenzoate	245	12,000	A
	~ 240	~ 13,500	E
2,6α-dibromo 17-acetate	240	12,600	A
2,6β-dibromo 17-acetate	248	12,900	A
2-iodo 17-hexahydrobenzoate	242	17,400	A
17-sodium sulfonate	241	17,700	A
	249	20,300	W
Epitestosterone	238	17,400	
17-Acetoxy-14-allo-17-epitestosterone	240	15,400	
16-Hydroxytestosterone	241	16,700	M
	250	16,400	W
16,17-acetonide	234	17,400	E
4-Androstene-3,17-dione	240, 295	17,170, 146	A
2-bromo	244	11,800	A
4-bromo (?)[b]	248	14,400	E
6α-bromo	240	17,000	A

TABLE A. 9 — (contd.)

Compound	λ_{max} (mμ)	ε_{max}	Solvent[a]
		Enones — (contd.)	
Δ^4-3-one:— (contd.)			
6β-bromo	245	10,300	
2,4-dibromo	297(?)	10,300	
2,6-dibromo	240	15,500	A
	248		
2-iodo	242	14,800	A
3-semicarbazone	265	35,000	C
17-(β-hydroxyethyl) hemithioketal	238	20,000	A
17-(β-benzoxyethyl) thioenol ether	232	24,000	A
4,7-Androstadiene-3,17-dione	237	14,800	A
4,11-Androstadiene-3,17-dione	238	16,600	A
4,14-Androstadiene-3,17-dione	237	16,800	A
4-Androstene-3,11,17-trione	239	13,800	A
disemicarbazone[c]	233, 271	~ 48,000, ~ 55,000	
17α-Methyltestosterone 3-(2,4-dinitrophenylhydrazone)	395	178,000[d]	C
Methyl 3-keto-14-iso-17-iso-19-nor-4-etiocholenate	240	14,100	A
ethyl ester	239	19,860	A
Methyl 3-keto-4-etiocholenate			
2-bromo	244	11,000	A
6β-bromo	248	14,800	A
2-iodo	244	20,000	A
6α-Hydroxy-3-keto-4-etiocholenic acid	239	17,060	A
6β-Hydroxy-3-keto-4-etiocholenic acid	238	12,250	A
Methyl 12α-hydroxy-3-keto-4-etiocholenate	241	14,940	A
Ethyl 19-hydroxy-3-keto-4-etiocholenate	243	14,860	A
19-acetate	239	15,470	A
3,11-Diketo-4-etiocholenic acid	238	20,200	
Ethyl 3-keto-8,19-oxido-4-etiocholenate	243	13,610	A
Ethyl 8-hydroxy-3-keto-17-iso-21-nor-4-pregnene-19-carboxy-19→8-lactone-20-carboxylate	244	13,130	A
19-Norprogesterone	240	22,900[d]	A
3,20-di(2,4-dinitrophenylhydrazone	380	60,300	C
17α-Ethyltestosterone	243	14,300	C
17β-Hydroxy-4,20-pregnadien-3-one	242	16,000	C
17α-Ethylnyltestosterone	240, 310	16,400, 85	A
17α-Ethynyltestosterone-20,21-C^{14}	241		A
20-Hydroxy-19-nor-4-pregnen-3-one	240	22,400[d]	A

Compound	λ_{max} (mμ)	ε_{max}	Solvent[a]
		Enones — *(contd.)*	
*Δ*⁴*-3-one:* — *(contd.)*			
20β-Hydroxy-4-pregnen-3-one	242	20,400[d]	A
17α-Hydroxy-20,21-oxido-4-pregnen-3-one	240	12,600	A
16α-20α-Diacetoxy-4-pregnen-3-one	241	17,000	
17α,20β-Dihydroxy-4-pregnen-3-one	240	19,500[d]	A
Progesterone	241	17,000	A
	234	17,300	E
2,6,17-tribromo	250	16,200	A
20-ethylene hemithioketal	242	20,400	A
3,20-di(2,4-dinitrophenylhydrazone)	283	53,000	C
14-Allo-17-isoprogesterone	242, 305	16,600, 100	
7-Dehydroprogesterone	238	14,600	A
11-Dehydroprogesterone	238	21,900[d]	A
12α-Hydroxyprogesterone	242	10,500	A
12-acetate	240	13,800	A
16α-Hydroxyprogesterone			
16-methoxy	241	16,000	M
16α or β-(β-hydroxyethylmercapto)	240	20,400	A
16α or β-(β-benzoxyethylmercapto)	234	38,000	A
16α- or β-thiobenzyl	240	19,500	A
3-semicarbazone 16-thiobenzyl	268	47,900	A
17α-Hydroxyprogesterone	242	16,500	A
2-iodo	244	14,100	A
17β-Hydroxyprogesterone	241	15,800	A
21-Acetoxy-17,20-oxido-4-pregnen-3-one	240	11,200	A
	240	11,200	A
20α-21-Diacetoxy-17α-hydroxy-4-pregnen-3-one	241	17,400	M
20β,21-Diacetoxy-4-pregnene-3,11-dione	238	15,370	
11β,17α,20β,21-Tetrahydroxy-4-pregnen-3-one	240		
20,21-diacetate	241	20,000	M
20β,21-Diacetoxy-17β-hydroxy-4-pregnen-3,11-dione	239	28,300[d]	A
Desoxycorticosterone	240	19,000[d]	A
21-acetate	240	∼ 17,400	A
14-Allo-17-isodesoxycorticosterone acetate	241	17,000	A
17-Isodesoxycorticosterone acetate	244	15,200	A
21-Acetoxy-4,7-pregnadiene-3,20-dione	237	13,600	A
21-Acetoxy-4,9-pregnadiene-3,20-dione	240	∼ 12,600	A

TABLE A. 9 — (contd.)

Compound	λ_{max} (mμ)	ε_{max}	Solvent[a]
		Enones — *(contd.)*	
Δ⁴-3-one: — (contd.)			
21-Acetoxy-4,11-pregnadiene-3,20-dione	240	17,000	A
6α-Hydroxydesoxycorticosterone	240	15,230	A
6,21-diacetate	238	15,910	A
6β-Hydroxydesoxycorticosterone	235	13,730	A
6,21-diacetate	236	15,950	A
Corticosterone	240	20,000[d]	A
12β,21-Dihydroxy-4-pregnene-3,20-dione			
21-acetate	244	13,200	A
12,21-diacetate	244	14,100	A
21-Acetoxy-14-hydroxy-14-iso-4-pregnene-3,20-dione	240	16,600	A
17α-Hydroxydesoxycorticosterone	240	16,600	A
21-acetate	241	17,400	A
11-Dehydrocorticosterone acetate	238	13,300	M
12α-bromo	238 ·	16,400	M
12α-bromo 3-(2,4-dinitrophenyl-hydrazone)	387	31,200	C
21-Acetoxy-4-pregnene-3,12,20-trione	240	17,800	A
17α-Hydroxycorticosterone	241	13,800	A
21-acetate	243	15,370	A
17α,21-Dihydroxy-4-pregnene-3,11,20-trione	238	16,000	A
21-acetate	238	15,800	A
3-(2,4-dinitrophenylhydrazone) 21-acetate	387	30,500	C
21-Diethylmercaptol-4-pregnene-3,20-dione	242	15,900	A
21-Al-20-hydroxy-4-pregnen-3-one			
21-dimethylacetal	~225–245, 305	~15,900, 100	A
20-acetate 21-dimethylacetal	242	14,500	A
17β-Hydroxy-17α-propargyl-4-androsten-3-one	240	15,800	A
16-Methylprogesterone	236	36,300[d]	A
16,17-Methyleneprogesterone	240	21,000	A
17-Methylprogesterone	242	17,800	A
17-Methylprogesterone-B	242	17,400	A
3-Keto-4-bisnorcholenic acid	240	21,000[d]	C
Methyl 12α-hydroxy-3-keto-4-bis-norcholenate	241, ~300	14,000, ~100	A
17-(17²-Oxopropyl)-4-androsten-3-one	240, 296(p)[e]	20,000[d], 105	A
Methyl-12α-hydroxy-3-keto-4-nor-cholenate	242	16,320	A

TABLE A.9 — (contd.)

Compound	λ_{max} (mμ)	ε_{max}	Solvent[a]
		Enones — *(contd.)*	
Δ⁴-3-one: — (contd.)			
17α-Hydroxy-3-keto-4-norcholenic			
acid lactone	238	15,800	A
3-Keto-4-cholenic acid	240	19,000	A
methyl ester	241	16,800	A
Methyl 12α-hydroxy-3-keto-4-			
cholenate	242	14,500	A
3-(2,4-dinitrophenylhydrazone)	259, 390	18,300, 30,700	C
2,2,4,6-tetrabromo 12-acetate	285	14,500	A
Methyl 12β-acetoxy-3-keto-4-cho-			
lenate	240	10,700	A
Methyl-12α-bromo-3, 11-diketo-4-			
cholenate	238	16,600	M
3-(2,4-dinitrophenylhydrazone)	387	30,200	C
3-oxime (*N*- or *O*-acetyl)	250	9,740	C
3-phenylhydrazone	323	24,600	MC
3-semicarbazone	269	32,200	M
3,12-Diketo-4-cholenic acid	236	15,800	A
4-Cholesten-3-one	241, 312	11,800, 100	A
	234	16,400	E
6α-chloro	239	19,604	A
6β-chloro	241	15,100	A
2α-bromo	243	14,100	A
4-bromo[b]	261·5	12,000	E
6α-bromo	238	15,800	A
6β-bromo	244	13,700	E
2,2,6β-tribromo	260	12,000	A
2α,6β-dibromo[b]	248	14,400	E
2,2,4-tribromo	277	13,150	A
2,2,6β-tribromo[b]	260	11,900	E
2,2,4,6-tetrabromo	290	12,100	A
3-acetimino	270	26,100	E
3-(2,4-dinitrophenylhydrazone)	256, 281,	21,500, 16,000,	C
	292, 393	11,500, 29,500	
3-oxime	240	23,000	A
3-semicarbazone	271	26,000	C
6-sulfonic acid	237	13,000	
22-Iso-4-spirosten-3-one			
6α-bromo	238	18,200	A
2,6β-dibromo	250	16,600	A
Pennogenone	~ 240	~16,000	A
4,7-Cholestadien-3-one	238	15,500	A
22-Iso-4,7-spirostadien-3-one	238	19,500[d]	A
6α-Hydroxy-4-cholesten-3-one			
6-acetate	242	14,500	
4-bromo 6″α″-methoxy(?)[b]	237	11,000	E

TABLE A.9 — (contd.)

Compound	λ_{max} (mμ)	ε_{max}	Solvent[a]
		Enones — *(contd.)*	
Δ^4-3-one: — *(contd.)*			
3-(2,4-dinitrophenylhydrazone)			
6''α''-methoxy	309, 405	18,600, 37,100	C
6β-Acetoxy-2,2-dibromo-4-cho-			
lesten-3-one	250	9430	IA
7β-Hydroxy-4-cholesten-3-one	243, 311	15,500, 85	A
7-acetate	238, 312	16,100, 60	A
7-benzoate	235, 280, 314	27,700, 820, 70	A
4,22-Ergostadien-3-one	242	18,200	A
4,7,22-Ergostatrien-3-one	239	15,100	A
3-semicarbazone	267	36,830	C
4,7,22-Lumistatrien-3-one	229(?)	17,000	A
4,24(28)-Fucostadien-3-one	240, 310	17,000, 70	A
3-(2,4-dinitrophenylhydrazone)	392	32,000	C
3-oxime	241	23,000	A
3-semicarbazone	272	27,000	C
4,22-Stigmastadien-3-one	241, 308	17,000, 75	A
3-(2,4-dinitrophenylhydrazone)	242, 265, 280,	21,500, 23,000, 18,500,	C
	293, 393	17,000, 31,000	
3-oxime	240	22,000	A
3-semicarbazone	271	29,000	C
4-β-Sitosten-3-one	241, 307	17,000, 75	A
3-(2,4-dinitrophenylhydrazone)	259, 282, 292,	21,500, 16,000, 14,000,	C
	395	31,500	
3-oxime	240	20,000	A
3-semicarbazone	272	25,000	C
Δ^4-3-one (miscellaneous):			
17α-Methyl-4,17-D-homoandrosta-			
dien-3-one	240	18,200	A
D-Homotestosterone	243	16,600	
17-benzoate	238	31,700	A
D-Homoisotestosterone	243	19,100	
4-D-Homoandrosten-3,17-dione	244	23,400	
Testolactone	238	17,000	A
Testolactam	240	22,900	A
3-Keto-4-oxazolidine	242	24,000	A
N-acetyl	242	24,000	A
Koster's ketone	239	15,300	A
Δ^4-6-one:			
4-Androstene-6,17-dione	244, 300	6300, 120	A
4-Cholesten-6-one	243	6360	A
6-(2,4-dinitrophenylhydrazone)	257, 377	12,300, 24,900	C
6-semicarbazone	253	7050	A
3β-Hydroxy-4-cholesten-6-one	239, 319	6300, 85	A
3-acetate	236, 320	6300, 89	A

TABLE A. 9 — (contd.)

Compound	λ_{max} (mμ)	ε_{max}	Solvent[a]
	Enones — (contd.)		
Δ^4-6-one — (contd.)			
3-acetate 4-bromo (?)[b]	245, 335	8000, 120	A
7-bromo	238–243	15,900	A
3-acetate-6-semicarbazone	258	9980	A
Δ^5-4-one:			
17β-Hydroxy-5-androsten-4-one	240	3200[g]	C
5-Cholesten-4-one	241	7200	
Δ^5-6-nor-7-carboxylic acid:			
3β-Hydroxy-6-nor-5-cholestene-7-carboxylic acid			
ethyl ester	230	10,000	A
3-acetate	228	7900	
3-acetate ethyl ester	230	8000	A
Δ^5-7-one:			
3β-Acetoxy-5-androstene-7-one	234	11,200	A
3β,17β-Dihydroxy-5-androstene-7-one	240	15,100	A
3,17-diacetate	237	14,100	A
3-acetate 17-benzoate 7-ethylene-	228		A
mercaptol	228	20,800	A
3β-Acetoxy-5-androstene-7,17-dione	235	12,300	
3β-Acetoxy-5-pregnene-7,17-dione	235, 290	18,200, 71	
7-Keto-5-cholenic acid	239		
3β-Hydroxy-7-keto-5-cholenic acid	238	8900	A
3,4,6-Tribromo-5-cholesten-7-one	~ 268	~ 10,000	A
3β-Hydroxy-5-cholesten-7-one			
3-acetate	235	12,050	A
	234	14,200	E
3-ethylmercapto	234	15,500	E
3-ethylsulfonyl	229	12,000	E
3-acetate 7-ethylenemercaptol	222	6430	A
3-benzoate 7-ethylenemercaptol	230	19,400	A
7-oxime	238	14,200	E
3β,4β-Dihydroxy-5-cholesten-7-one	235	9300	A
3-acetate	235	11,000	A
3,4-diacetate	231	9300	A
3,4-dibenzoate	232	37,100	A
Δ^7-6-one:			
7-Bromo-7-cholestene-3,6-dione (?)[b]	256	8000	C
5-Hydroxy-7-ergostene-3,6-dione	252, 333	13,500, 160	C
3β-Acetoxy-5-hydroxy-7,22-ergosta-dien-6-one	252, 333	13,600, 155	C
3-Acetoxy-5-hydroxy-7,22-lumista-dien-6-one	252, 323	13,100, 105	C
5-Hydroxy-7,22-lumistadiene-3,6-dione	253, 25	13,500, 100	

TABLE A. 9 — (contd.)

Compound	λ_{max} (mμ)	ε_{max}	Solvent[a]
Enones — *(contd.)*			
$\Delta^{8(9)}$-7-one:			
3β,11α,20β-Trihydroxy-8-allopreg-nen-7-one	254	12,900	A
3β-Hydroxy-8-allopregnene-7,20-dione	252	12,600	A
3β,11α-Dihydroxy-8-allopregnene-7,20-dione			
3-acetate	252	13,200	A
3,11-diacetate	252	11,700	A
Methyl 3α-hydroxy-7-keto-8-cho-lenate			
3-acetate	254	11,000	A
3-formate	255	7100	A
3β-Acetoxy-8-zymosten-7-one	252	10,000	A
3β-Hydroxy-8-cholesten-7-one			
3-acetate	254	9680	A
3-benzoate	252	6300	A
3β-Acetoxy-14-hydroxy-8-cholestene-7,15-dione	254	10,400	A
3β-Acetoxy-8,22-ergostadien-7-one	253	12,600	A
3β-Acetoxy-8,22-stigmastadien-7-one	252	8300	A
$\Delta^{8(9)}$-11-one:			
Methyl 3α-acetoxy-11-keto-8-cho-lenate	254	8700	A
Methyl 3β-acetoxy-11-keto-8-cho-lenate	255	8900	A
3β-Acetoxy-8,22-ergostadien-11-one	253	9550	A
$\Delta^{8(14)}$-7-one:			
3β-Acetoxy-8-cholesten-7-one	263	9500	A
3β-Acetoxy-8-ergosten-7-one	262	10,000	A
5-Hydroxy-8-ergostene-3,7-dione	254	10,800	E
3β-Acetoxy-8-stigmasten-7-one	260	7800	A
$\Delta^{8(14)}$-15-one:			
3β-Acetoxy-8-cholesten-15-one	259	12,750	A
3β-Acetoxy-8-ergosten-15-one	259	13,300	A
$\Delta^{9(11)}$-12-one:			
3β-Acetoxy-9-androstene-12,17-dione	238	15,800	A
Methyl 3α-acetoxy-12-keto-9-etio-cholenate	240	10,000	A
9-Pregnene-3,12,20-trione	239	10,000	A
Methyl 3α-acetoxy-12-keto-9-nor-cholenate	240	8500	A
Methyl 12-keto-9-cholenate	235	11,800	H

Compound	λ_{max} (mμ)	ε_{max}	Solvent[a]
	Enones — (contd.)		
$\Delta^{9(11)}$-12-one: — (contd.)			
3α-Hydroxy-12-keto-9-cholenic acid	240	10,700	A
methyl ester	240	12,000	
3-acetate	241	9000	A
3-acetate methyl ester	241	11,500	A
Methyl 3α-carbethoxy-12-keto-8-			
lithocholenate	239	12,600	A
3,12-Diketo-9-cholenic acid	243	12,200	A
methyl ester	238	8300	A
3α,7α-Dihydroxy-12-keto-9-cholenic			
acid	240	9770	A
7-acetate methyl ester	238	10,000	A
3,7-diacetate methyl ester	237	11,500	A
3β-Hydroxy-22-iso-9-allospirosten-			A
12-one	240, 322	13,500, 71	A
3-acetate	238, 322	14,800, 64	A
3-acetate 23-bromo	240, 311	11,500, 120	A
9-Dehydromanogenic acid	240	10,000	A
$\Delta^{12(23)}$-22-one:			
12-Dehydronorcholen-22-one	234	15,500	E
Δ^{16}-17-carboxylic acid:			
Methyl 3β-acetoxy-16-etiocholenate	225	12,600	A
3β-Hydroxy-5,16-etiocholadienic acid;	230	12,600	
Methyl 3β-acetoxy-14,15-oxido-			
16-alloetiocholenate	233	7200	
Methyl 3β-acetoxy-5α,6β-dihydroxy-			
14,15β-oxido-16-alloetiocholenate	236	6600	A
Methyl 3β-acetoxy-16-methyl-5,16-			
etiocholadiene	233	12,600	
Δ^{16}-20-one:			
3α-Acetoxy-16-allopregnen-20-one			
20-semicarbazone	267	24,400	C
3α-Hydroxy-16-pregnen-20-one 20-			
semicarbazone	267	24,000	C
3β-Acetoxy-16-allopregnen-20-one	240, 310	10,200, 150	A
3β-Acetoxy-14,15β-oxido-16-allo-			
pregnen-20-one	248, 327	11,200, 71	
16-Pregnene-3,20-dione	239	9800	A
3β-Hydroxy-5,16-pregnadien-20-one	241	8000	A
	234	9300	E
3-acetate	239	9100	A
	234	9600	E
20-semicarbazone	267	24,000	C
3-acetate 20-semicarbazone	267	24,000	C

TABLE A. 9—(contd.)

Compound	λ_{max} (mμ)	ε_{max}	Solvent[a]
Enones — *(contd.)*			
Δ^{16}-*20-one: — (contd.)*	266	22,900	A
3-acetate 20-(2,4-dinitrophenyl-hydrazone)	384	26,800	C
3β-Acetoxy-7,16-allopregnadien-20-one	238	12,900	A
3β-Acetoxy-8(14),16-allopregnadien-20-one	230	11,700	A
3β-Acetoxy-9, 16-allopregnadien-20-one	238	11,700	A
2,3β-Dihydroxy-5, 16-pregnadien-20-one	~240	~7000	A
3α,12α-Diacetoxy-16-pregnen-20-one	238, 315	11,600, 105	A
3α-Hydroxy-16-pregnene-11,20-dione	235	7400	M
3β-Acetoxy-16-allopregnene-11,20-dione	235	9050	A
3β-Acetoxy-16-allopregnene-12,20-dione	227–230	8510	A
16-Pregnene-3,11,20-trione	235	8900	M
3β-21-Diacetoxy-16-allopregnen-20-one	~242, ~310	~11,200, ~64	
3α,21-Diacetoxy-16-pregnene-11,20-dione			
12α-bromo	235	8700	M
	231	8700	E
12α,15α-dibromo	237	11,000	M
	235	11,000	E
12α,15β-dibromo	235	9800	E
12α,15,21-tribromo	251	8700	E
12α,15,21-tribromo (epimer)	251	8600	E
12α-bromo 15α-iodo	243	13,000	E
12α-Bromo-3α,15,21-triacetoxy-16-pregnene-11,20-dione	229	9800	E
3α-Acetoxy-12α,15-dibromo-21,21-dihydroxy-16-pregnene-11,20-dione	241	10,500	E
3β,21-Diacetoxy-14,15β-oxido-16-allopregnen-20-one	248	7100	
3β,12-Diacetoxy-16-methyl-16-pregnen-20-one	248	10,000	A
3β-Hydroxy-16-methyl-5,16-pregnadien-20-one			
3-acetate	250	11,500	A
3-semicarbazone	268	~15,800	
$\Delta^{16'}$-*17-one:*			
3β-Acetoxy-5-androsten-17-one			

TABLE A. 9 — (contd.)

Compound	λ_{max} (mμ)	ε_{max}	Solvent[a]
	Enones — *(contd.)*		
$\Delta^{16'}$-*17-one:* — *(contd.)*			
16-methylene	228	7940	A
16-isopropylidene	250, 338	14,800, 100	A
16-isobutylidene	245	12,800	E
16-benzylidene	223, 295	8220, 24,000	A
$\Delta^{16'}$-*22-one:*			
Fesogenin	245	13,700	A
5-Dihydrofesogenin	~ 245	~ 14,000	A
Δ^{17}-*16-one:*			
3β,22-Dihydroxy-22(26)-oxido-5,17-cholestadien-16-one	236	14,800	A
hydrazine product	238, 256	20,000, 19,500	A
3-acetate hydrazine product	238, 256	21,900, 19,500	A
Δ^{17}-*20-al, carboxylic acid, or cyano:*			
3β-Hydroxy-5,17-pregnadien-20-al	244	26,300	A
3-acetate	244	27,500	A
Methyl 3β-acetoxy-17-allopregnene-20-carboxylate	224	16,600	
3β-Hydroxy-5,17-pregnadiene-20-carboxylic acid	222	12,600	A
ethyl ester	222	16,600	A
3-acetate ethyl ester	222	25,100[d]	A
4,21-Diacetoxy-5-hydroxy-3-keto-17-pregnene-20-cyano	225	10,500	A
3β,21-Diacetoxy-5,17-pregnadiene-20-cyano	224	10,500	A
11β,21-Dihydroxy-3-keto-17-pregnene-20-cyano	223	13,800	M
Δ^{17}-*21-one:*			
3β-Acetoxy-17(17^2-oxopropylidene)-5-androstene	242, 310	20,000, 120	A
$\Delta^{20(22)}$-*22-carboxylic acid:*			
Methyl 3β-hydroxy-20-norallocholenate	231	15,800	
3-acetate	230	20,000	
Methyl 3β-acetoxy-5,20-norcholadienate	230	20,000	
3α,12β,21-Trihydroxy-20-norcholenic acid	229	12,600	
$\Delta^{20(22)}$-*22-cyano:*			
3β-Hydroxy-5,20-bisnorcholadiene-22-cyano			

TABLE A. 9 — (contd.)

Compound	λ_{max} (mμ)	ε_{max}	Solvent[a]
Enones — *(contd.)*			
$\Delta^{20\,(22)}$-*22-cyano:* — *(contd.)*			
"*trans*"	226	12,300	A
"*cis*"	223	16,600	A
Δ^4-*3,6-dione:*			
17β-Acetoxy-4-androstene-3,6-dione	252	11,400	C
4-Androstene-3,6,17-trione	252	10,800	C
3,6-Diketo-4-etiocholenic acid	248	13,060	A
4-Cholestene-3,6-dione	252	11,400	C
4,7-dibromo(?)[b]	254	9100	C
4,7,7-tribromo(?)[b]	257	10,200	C
4,22-Ergostadiene-3,6-dione	254		E
4-Stigmastene-3,6-dione	254		A
Δ^5-*3,4-dione:*			
5-Cholestene-3,4-dione (Diosterol, enol forms)			
Diosterol I (4-hydroxy-4,6-cholestadien-3-one)	313·5	4680	A
4-enol benzoate	232, 287	15,500, 25,700	A
Diosterol II (3-hydroxy-2,5-cholestadien-4-one)	265, 300	5130, 5370	A
3-enol acetate	245	14,800	A
3-enol benzoate	234	20,000	A
Δ^5-*3,7-dione:*			
5-Cholestene-3,7-dione, enol, (3-hydroxy-3,5-cholestadien-7-one)	320	24,300	A
	393	62,200	AA
enol acetate	283	22,500	A
enol methyl ether	308	27,600	A
enol ethyl ether	~ 310	~ 12,600[g]	A
$\Delta^{8\,(9)}$-*7,11-dione:*			
3β-Acetoxy-8-allopregnene-7,11,20-trione	268	6600	A
Methyl 3α-acetoxy-7,11-diketo-8-cholenate	272	8100	A
3β-Benzoxy-8-cholestene-7,11-dione	269	6300	A
3β-Acetoxy-8,22-ergostadiene-7,11-dione	266	9300	IO
	270	8700	A
$\Delta^{8\,(14)}$-*7,15-dione:*			
3β-Acetoxy-8-ergostene-7,15-dione	255	5000	A
7,15-pyridazine	262	1800	A

TABLE A. 9—(contd.)

Compound	λ_{max} (mμ)	ε_{max}	Solvent[a]
	Enones — *(contd.)*		
Δ^{17}-*16,22-dione:*			
3β,26-Dihydroxy-5,17-cholestadiene-16,22-dione			
3,26-diacetate	246	13,500	A
16,22-pyridazine	258, 296	2140, 470	A
3,26-diacetate 16,22-pyridazine	258, 294	2000, 410	A
	Dienones		
$\Delta^{1,4}$-*3-one:*			
17α-Hydroxy-1,4-androstadien-3-one	244	15,800	A
	236	~ 16,000	E
2-bromo 17-hexahydrobenzoate	255	11,500	A
17-acetate 6-bromo	248	20,900	A
17-acetate 3-semicarbazone	~ 298	~ 22,000	C
1,4-Androstadiene-3,17-dione	244	17,000	A
6-bromo	250	21,900	A
3-Keto-1,4-etiocholadienic acid	245	18,600	A
methyl ester	245	13,200	A
3-(2,4-dinitrophenylhydrazone) methyl ester	250, 301, 401	16,200, 7600, 34,200	C
17α-Hydroxy-1,4-pregnadiene-3,20-dione	244	13,800	A
21-Acetoxy-17α-hydroxy-1,4-pregnadiene-3,20-dione	244	18,200	A
Methyl 3-keto-1,4-choladienate	236	15,100	
3-semicarbazone	298	24,200	
Methyl 12α-acetoxy-3-keto-1,4-choladienate	243	14,000	M
Methyl 12α-bromo-3,11-diketo-1,4-choladienate	240	13,200	
1,4-Cholestadien-3-one	245	14,500	M
6-bromo	250	17,400	
2,6β-dibromo[b]	253	17,800	A
4,6-dibromo(?)	254	14,500	A
2,4,6-tribromo	274	10,600	A
3-(2,4-dinitrophenylhydrazone)	258, 400	17,900, 34,700	C
3-semicarbazone	302	18,800	C
6β-Hydroxy-1,4-cholestadien-3-one			
2-bromo	255	14,560	IA
6-acetate 2-bromo	253	12,880	IA
1,4-Cholestadiene-3,6-dione			
2-bromo	255	11,130	IA

TABLE A. 9—(contd.)

Compound	λ_{max} (mμ)	ε_{max}	Solvent[a]
	Dienones — *(contd.)*		
$\Delta^{2,4}$-6-*one:*			
2,4-Cholestadien-6-one	314	7620	A
6-(2,4-dinitrophenylhydrazone)	257, 320, 408	11,660, 7830, 25,120	C
3-Acetoxy-2,4-cholestadien-6-one	317	6300	A
7-Methoxy-2,4-7-cholestatrien-6-one(?)	315	15,800[d]	A
$\Delta^{2(2'),4}$-3-*one:*			
2-Hydroxymethylene-4-cholesten-3-one	250, 310	12,600, 6300	
$\Delta^{2,5}$-4-*one:*			
3-Hydroxy-2,5-chol stadien-4-one (Diosterol II enol)	265, 300	5130, 5370	A
3-acetate	245	14,800	A
3-benzoate	234	20,000	A
$\Delta^{3,5}$-2-*one:*			
3,5-Cholestadien-2-one	290	12,600	
$\Delta^{3,5}$-7-*one:*			
17-Hydroxy-3,5-androstadien-7-one	280	28,000	C
17-acetate	280	27,800	C
Methyl 7-keto-3,5-etiocholadienate	279	25,120	A
Methyl 12α-acetoxy-7-keto-3,5-etio-choladienate	278	26,900	
3,5-Cholestadien-7-one	277	24,400	A
2-bromo	280		
6-bromo(?)[b]	288, 344	$\sim$ 20,000, $\sim$ 159	A
4,6-dibromo(?)[b]	303	11,200	A
3-Hydroxy-3,5-cholestadien-7-one	320	24,300	A
(Enol of 5-cholestene-3,7-dione)	393	62,200	AA
3-enol acetate	283	22,500	A
3-methoxy	308	27,600	A
3-ethoxy	$\sim$ 310	$\sim$ 12,600	A
$\Delta^{4,6}$-3-*one:*			
17β-Hydroxy-4,6-androstadien-3-one	284	29,500	A
17-acetate	284	33,900[d]	A
3-(α-methyl-2,4-dinitrophenyl-hydrazone) 17-hexahydro-benzoate	266, 309, 404	14,100, 12,700, 30,900	A
4,6-Androstadiene-3,17-dione	282	33,100[d]	A
	273	26,500	E
Methyl 3-keto-4,6-etiocholadienate	283	30,500	A
3-(2,4-dinitrophenylhydrazone)	270, 310, 402	17,700, 13,900, 39,600	C

TABLE A. 9—(contd.)

Compound	λ_{max} (mμ)	ε_{max}	Solvent[a]
Dienones — *(contd.)*			
$\Delta^{4,6}$-*3-one:* — *(contd.)*			
3-(α-methyl-2,4-dinitrophenyl-hydrazone)	272, 308, 398	16,900, 15,600, 37,200	C
6-Dehydroprogesterone	282	~ 25,100	A
6-Dehydrodesoxycorticosterone acetate	283	33,900[d]	A
Methyl 12α-bromo-3,11-diketo-4,6-choladienate	281	25,900	M
3-(2,4-dinitrophenylhydrazone)	308, 398	13,200, 36,200	C
4,6-Cholestadien-3-one	284	26,300	A
	283		D
2,4-dibromo	293	14,590	IA
2α,6-dibromo[b]	296	19,400	C
2,2,6-tribromo[b]	313	17,400	C
3-(2,4-dinitrophenylhydrazone)	309, 405	18,600, 37,100	C
3-(α-methyl-2,4-dinitrophenyl-hydrazone)	270, 310, 404	17,100, 14,100, 37,700	C
3-oxime	280	18,100	C
3-semicarbazone	300	43,700	D
4-Hydroxy-4,6-cholestadien-3-one (Diosterol I enol)	314	4680	A
4-benzoate	232, 287	15,500, 25,700	A
6-ethoxy	295	16,800	E
22-Iso-4,6-spirostadien-3-one	284	30,200[d]	A
4,6-Ergostadien-3-one (isoergosterone)	284	26,400	A
	281, 335	33,100, —	A
3-(2,4-dinitrophenylhydrazone)	308, 400	16,700, 35,900	C
3-semicarbazone	304	46,700	A
6-Ethoxy-4,6-ergostadien-3-one	297		A
$\Delta^{5,7(7')}$-*7'-carboxylic acid:*			
3β-Acetoxy-5-cholestenylidene-7-acetic acid	268	14,500	
$\Delta^{7,9(11)}$-*12-one:*			
3α-Hydroxy-12-keto-7,9-choladienic acid	240, 293	3700, 12,900	A
methyl ester	238, 290	3800, 13,500	A
$\Delta^{8(9),14}$-*7-one:*[h]			
3β-Acetoxy-8,14-cholestadien-7-one	223, 298	15,630, 4800	A
7-(2,4-dinitrophenylhydrazone)	261, 393	18,760, 23,681	C
$\Delta^{8(14),9(11)}$-*7-one:*			
3α-Acetoxy-8,9-ergostadien-7-one(?)	298[i]	5100	A

TABLE A. 9— (contd.)

Compound	λ_{max} (mμ)	ε_{max}	Solvent[a]
Dienones — (contd.)			
$\Delta^{8(14),9(11)}$-7-one: — (contd.)			
3β-Aetoxy-8,9,22-ergostatrien-7-one(?)	300[i]	5000	A
3β-Acetoxy-8,9,22-stigmastatrien-7-one(?)	299	5300	A
$\Delta^{8(14),9(11)}$-15-one:			
3β-Acetoxy-8,9-ergostadien-15-one (?)[j]	307[k]	10,000	
$\Delta^{14,16}$-17-carboxylic acid or nitrile:			
Methyl 3β-acetoxy-14,16-alloetio-choladienate	292	15,800	A
Methyl 3β-acetoxy-14,16-etiochola dienate	295	11,000	A
Methyl 3β-acetoxy-5,14,16-etio-cholatrienate	295	11,700	
Methyl 3β-acetoxy-5,6α-oxido-14,16-alloetiocholadienate	295	11,000	
Methyl 3β-acetoxy-5α,6β-dihydroxy-14,16-etiocholadienate	298	10,500	
3β-Acetoxy-14,16-alloetiochola-dienic acid nitrile	286	13,500	A
3β-Acetoxy-14,16-etiocholadienic acid nitrile	286	14,800	A
3β-Acetoxy-5,14,16-etiocholatrienic acid nitrile	286	11,200	A
$\Delta^{14,16}$-20-one:			
3β-Acetoxy-14,16-allopregnadien-20-one	309	12,600	
3β-Hydroxy-5,14,16-pregnatrien-20-one	307	17,000	
3β,21-Diacetoxy-14,16-allopregna-dien-20-one	233, 310[l]	2500, 15,800	
12α-Bromo-3α,21-diacetoxy-14,16-pregnadiene-11,20-dione	305	9000	E
Trienones			
$\Delta^{1,4,6}$-3-one:			
17β-Acetoxy-1,4,6-androstatrien-3-one	222, 256, 298	15,500, 13,500, 18,600	A
1,4,6-Androstatriene-3,17-dione	222, 256, 298	15,500, 13,500, 18,600	A
Methyl 12α-acetoxy-3-keto-1,4,6-cholatrienate			
2,4-dibromo	228(i)[e], 238,	13,420, 14,100,	A

TABLE A. 9 — (contd.)

Compound	λ_{max} (mμ)	ε_{max}	Solvent[a]
Trienones — *(contd.)*			
$\Delta^{1,4,6}$-3-one: — (contd.)			
	278, 322	9270, 11,100	
1,4,6-Cholestatrien-3-one	224, 258, 300	10,700, 9300, 12,900	A
2,4-dibromo	267, 298	12,200, 10,200	E
2-bromo [b]	267, 298	12,200, 9300	E
2,6-dibromo[b]	228, 280, 326,	14,800, 10,400, 12,800	A
3-semicarbazone	~ 309	32,000	
22-Iso-1,4,6-spirostatrien-3-one	222, 256, 296	13,500, 12,300, 14,130	A
$\Delta^{1,3,5}$-7-one:			
1,3,5-Cholestatrien-7-one	230, 278, 348	18,600, 3720, 11,000	A
$\Delta^{4,6,8(9)}$-3-one:			
22-Iso-4,6,8-spirostatrien-3-one	244, 284, 388	17,780, 2190, 12,300	A
$\Delta^{4,6,8(14)}$-3-one:			
4,6,8-Ergostatrien-3-one	348	26,500	A
3-(2,4-dinitrophenylhydrazone)	427	41,000	C

[a] A = ethanol; AA = alkaline ethanol, usually 0·1 N; C = chloroform; D = dioxane; E = ethyl ether; H = hexane; IA = isopropyl alcohol; IO = isoöctane; M = methanol; MC = sample dissolved in a minimum of chloroform and diluted with methanol; W = water.

[b] See Fieser and Fieser, *Steroids*, p. 294, Reinhold (1959)

[c] The band at 233 mμ is due to the C_{17}-semicarbazone.

[d] The extinction coefficient is too high.

[e] (p) signifies a plateau; (i) signifies an inflection.

[f] The compound is a 2,6β-dibromo derivative.

[g] The extinction coefficient is too low.

[h] Two alternate structures were proposed for the compounds in this group (see text).

[i] There is indication of a band below 220–230 mμ.

[j] The structure and homogeneity of the dienone are in doubt.

[k] A high-absorbing impurity is present.

[l] The spectra indicates the presence of the starting material, Δ^{16}-en-20-one.

[m] The compound is believed to be a $\Delta^{1,4,6}$-trien-3-one with a bromine atom on one of the double bonds.

TABLE A.10. ULTRAVIOLET ABSORPTION OF STEROID α-DIKETONES AND THEIR ENOLS

Compound	λ_{max} (mμ)	ε_{max}	Solvent†
2,3-Diketones:			
2,3,17-Androstanetrione, enol (Δ^3-3-ol-2-one)	272	9550	A
3-enol acetate	236, 296	13,500, 79	A
3-enol tosylate	228, 294	20,000, 89	A
2,3-Cholestanedione, enol form "A"			A
(Δ^3-3-ol-2-one)	272	5000	A
3-enol acetate	238	7400	A
2,3-Cholestanedione, enol form "B"			
(Δ^1-2-ol-3-one)	270	8500	A
	268	10,400	E
2-enol acetate	237	8900	A
2,3-Cholestanedione, enol form "A + B"	320	3700	AA
3,4-Diketones:			
3,4-Cholestanedione, enol (Δ^4-4-ol-3-one)	280	11,500	C
4-enol acetate	248	14.500	C
3,4,6-Cholestanetrione, enol (Δ^4-4-al-3,6-dione + $\Delta^{4,6}$-4,6-diol-3-one)	275, 385	5000, 8000	C
6,7-Diketone:			
3β-Acetoxy-6,7-cholestanedione enol (Δ^6-6-ol-7-one or Δ^7-7-ol-6-one)	275	10,700	A
11,12-Diketones:			
11,12-Diketocholanic acid	~ 226, 279, 347	~ 130, 87, 47	H
enol (Δ^9-11-ol-12-one)	281	8700	A
Methyl 3,9-epoxy-11,12-diketocholanate	295, 376	104, 39	A
3β-Hydroxy-22-isoallospriostane-11,12-dione			
enol (Δ^9-11-ol-12-one)	282	1900*	A
3-acetate 11-enol acetate	244	11,200	A
3α-Hydroxy-11,12-diketocholanic acid			
3-acid succinate methyl ester	284	140	A
11,12-dihydrazone	301	238	A
enol (Δ^9-11-ol-12-one)	281	7000	A
enol (Δ^9-11-ol-13-one) methyl ester	280	5200	A
3α-acetate 11-enol acetate methyl ester	243	7800	A
20-Keto-21-aldehydes:			
21-Al-3β-hydroxy-5-pregnen-20-one 21-dimethyl acetal	~ 305	~ 63	A

TABLE A. 10—(contd.)

Compound	λ_{max} (mμ)	ε_{max}	Solvent†
20-Keto-21-aldehydes: — *(contd.)*			
21-Al-3α-hydroxy-11,20-pregnane-dione			
3-acetate 12α-bromo	440	20	A
3-acetate 12α-bromo 20-(2,4-di-nitrophenylhydrazone)	370, 401	20,500, 22,200	C
	373, 380–392	22,200, 22,000	B
	365	24,700	M
12α-bromo-21,21-dimethoxy 20-(2,4-dinitrophenylhydrazone)	366	25,300	C
3,21,21-triacetate 12α-bromo 20-(2,4-dinitrophenylhydrazone)	358	24,500	C
	359	24,400	B
3-Acetate 12α-bromo 21-(2,4-dinitrophenylhydrazone)	351	24,400	C
	360	24,800	B
	358	24,300	M
3-acetate 12α,17α-dibromo 21-(2,4-dinitrophenylhydrazone)	354	24,600	C
	378	26,700	B
	380	25,700	M
3-acetate 12α-bromo 20,21-bis-(2,4-dinitrophenylhydrazone)	349, 395, 450	31,200, 22,000, 21,000	C
	354, 398, 440	31,900 24,200, 21,200	B
12α-bromo enol (Δ^{17}-21-al-20-ol)	284	10,900	M
3-acetate 12α-bromo	282	12,500	M
enol (Δ^{17}21-al-20-ol)	284	13,700	C
20-enol acetate	246	14,300	E
3-Acetate, 12α-bromo 21-(2,4-dinitrophenylhydrazone) enol (Δ^{17}-21-al-20-ol)	268, 305, 379	13,000, 9,960, 26,400	C
	388	27,900	B
20-enol-acetate	262, 289, 373	14,100, 8,600, 30,900	C
	381	30,700	B
21-Al-3,11,20-pregnanetrione 12α-bromo 20-(2,4-dinitrophenyl-hydrazone	371, 400	20,400, 22,200	C
	374, 380–392	22,600, 22,400	B
12α-bromo 21,21-dimethoxy 20-(2,4-dinitrophenylhydrazone)	365	22,500	C
3β-Acetoxy-14-hydroxy-21-glyoxyl-oxy-20-keto-14-isopregnane	273	282	A

† A = ethanol; AA = alkaline ethanol, usually 0·1 N; B = acetone; C = chloroform; E = ethyl ether; M = methanol.

* The low extinction coefficient indicates that in solution the keto-enol equilibrium is in favour of the α-diketone.

TABLE A.11. ULTRAVIOLET ABSORPTION OF STEROID β-DIKETONE AND ITS ENOL

Compound	λ_{max} (mμ)	ε_{max}	Solvent†
16,20-Diketone:			
3α,12α-Dihydroxy-16,20-pregnanedione 3,12-diacetate 20-enol acetate (Δ^{17}-16-one-20-acetate)	249	11,200	A

† A = ethanol.

TABLE A.12. ULTRAVIOLET ABSORPTION OF STEROIDS CONTAINING TWO CHROMOPHORIC
SYSTEMS

Compound	λ_{max} (mμ)	ε_{max}	Solvent†
Diene + α,β-conjugated ketone:			
3,5,16-Pregnatrien-20-one	234, 318	30,200, 56	A
16-Isopropylidene-3,5-androsta-dien-17-one	~ 235, ~ 248, ~ 338	~ 30,200, ~ 25,100, ~ 63	
4,7,9-Androstatriene-3,17-dione	236(i), 242, 249(i)*	24,700, 27,200, 22,400	A
4,7,9-Pregnatriene-3,20-dione	243	27,200	A
22-Iso-4,7,9-spirostatrien-3-one	242	32,400	A
4,7,9,22-Ergostatetraen-3-one	242	31,600	A
4,16,20-Pregnatrien-3-one	238	31,500	A
ω-Homo-4,17,21-pregnatrien-3-one	241, 310	28,000, 80	A
	236	42,100	E
Two α,β-conjugated ketones:			
4,7-Cholestadiene-3,6-dione			
7-bromo(?)**	259	11,700	C
4,7-dibromo(?)**	259	11,000	C
16-Dehydroprogesterone	234	26,100	E
3-benzylthioenol ether	242, 268	18,600, 22,900	A
16-Methyl-16-dehydroprogesterone	250, 310	27,500, 260	
17-(17²-Oxopropylidene)-4-andro-sten-3-one	242, 314	28,200, 220	A
α,β-Conjugated ketone + α,β-conjugated nitrile:			
20-Cyano-21-hydroxy-4,17-pregnadien-3-one	236	47,900	A
α,β-Conjugated ketone + dienone:			
1,4,16-Pregnatriene-3,20-dione	241	14,800	A
α,β-Conjugated ketone + trienone:			
1,4,6,16-Pregnatetraen-3,20-dione	234, 298	21,900, 15,500	A
Diene + cyclobutenolide:			
Anhydroadynerigenin	247	12,600	
α,β-Conjugated ketone + cyclobutenolide:			
3-Keto-21-oxy-4,20(23)-norcholadienic acid lactone	241, 310	21,900, 69	
α,β-Conjugated ketone + cyclopentenolide:			
Anhydrotelocinobufagon	240, 300	17,000, 5250	A

TABLE A.12—(contd.)

Compound	λ_{max} (mμ)	ε_{max}	Solvent†
α,β-Conjugated ketone + benzenoid ring A:			
3-Methoxy-1,3,5,14-estratetraen-16-one	227, 280	18,600, 2510	A
17-Acetyl-3-hydroxy-1,3,5,16-estra-			A
tetraene	230, 280	15,800, 2950	A
20-semicarbazone	266	28,800	C
17-Acetyl-3-hydroxy-1-methyl-			
1,3,5,6,16-estrapentaene	228, 266, 306	33,900, 8130, 1780	A
α,β-Conjugated ketone + phenylketone			
24-Phenyl-4-cholene-3,24-dione	240, 280(i)*	25,100, 1400	A

† A = ethanol; C = chloroform; E = ethyl ether.
* (i) signifies an inflection.
** Since a bromine atom on the double bond should cause a large bathochromic shift, it is unlikely that the structural assignment is correct.

TABLE A.13. ULTRAVIOLET ABSORPTION OF STEROIDS CONTAINING A CONJUGATED
LACTONE RING

Compound	λ_{max} (mμ)	ε_{max}	Solvent[a]
Cyclobutenolides			
17-Cyclobutenolides:			
Acolongifloroside-E	217	15,100	A
Acolongifloroside-G	217	16,200	A
Acolongifloroside-H acetate	217	17,000	A
Acolongifloroside-J	217	15,500	A
Acolongifloroside-K acetate	217	16,200	A
Acovenoside-A	217	15,800	A
diacetate	217	~ 19,100	A
Acovenoside-B	217	~ 15,800	A
Acovenoside-C diacetate	217	17,800	A
Acovenosigenin-A diacetate	217	17,400	A
Adonitoxigenin	218	12,900	A
Al-dihydro-α-antiarin	217	10,500	A
3β-Acetoxy-17α-hydroxy-20-allopreg- nene-21-acid lactone	215	8300	A
Allouzarigenin-3 acetate	210	35,500[b]	
α-Anhydrogenin acetate	217	16,200	A
α-Antiarin	217, 305[c]	12,000, 32	A
Corchortoxin	217		A
Courmontoside-A acetate	217, 280–290(i)[d]	15,900, ~ 79	A
Courmontoside-B acetate	217	15,500	A
Courmontoside-C	217 280–300(p)[d]	15,500, ~ 500	A
Cryptograndoside-A	215, ~ 270[e]	13,500, ~ 500	A
Cryptograndoside-B	215, 270[e]	13,500, 2200	A
16-acetate	215, 270[e]	14,100, 580	A
Cryptograndoside-C acetate	116, 275[e]	16,600, 850	A
Dehydroacovenoside-A diacetate	215, 292	17,400, 21	A
Desglucodigitalinum verum aus Adenium honghel	218	15,100	A
Digitalinum verum hexaacetate aus Adenium honghel	217	13,200	A
Desglucodigitalinum verum aus Adenium multiflorum	217	16,200	A
Digitoxigenin	216	16,600	A
β'-(3β,5α-Dihydroxyetioallocholanyl- 17-$\Delta^{x',\beta}$-butenolide 3-acetate	219	20,000	
3α,12β-Diacetoxy-21-oxy-20(22)-nor- cholenic acid lactone	220	20,000	
3α,21-Diacetoxy-12β-oxy-20(22)-nor- cholenic acid lactone (23→12)	221	7100	
Emicymarin	217	16,200	A

TABLE A.13 — (contd.)

Compound	λ_{max} (mμ)	ε_{max}		Solvent[a]
Cyclobutenolides — *(contd.)*				
17-Cyclobutenolides: — (contd.)				
Gofruside	217	10,000		
Hongheloside-A	217, ~ 280(i)[d]	14,100,	~ 60	A
Hongheloside-C	217	14,100		A
acetate	216, ~ 280(i)	14,800,	~ 60	A
Hongheloside-D	217	14,100		A
Hongheloside-E	215	13,500		A
Hongheloside-G	217	15,800		A
β'-(Δ^5-3β-Acetatenorcholenyl-23)- $\Delta^{\alpha',\beta'}$-butenolide	217	11,200		
α'-methyl	222	20,000		
3β-Acetoxy-21-oxy-20(22)-norallo-cholenic acid lactone	220	25,100		A
3α-Hydroxy-21-oxy-20(22)-norcho-lenic acid lactone	221	22,400		
3-acetate	220	25,100		
3β-Acetoxy-21-oxy-5,20(22)-nor-choladienic acid lactone	~ 222	$\sim 25,100$		
β'-(3β-Acetoxy-5-ctiocholenyl-17)-α'-methyl-$\Delta^{\alpha',\beta'}$-butenolide	227	22,400		
Monoanhydroconvallatoxigenin benzoate	270, 280			C
Neriifolin	217	10,200		A
Odorigenone-B	217, 280–290(i)	15,500,	43	A
Oleandrigenin	216, 270(i)	14,000,	—	A
Oleandrigenone	216, 270–290(i)	14,500,	—	A
Ouabagenin-A acetate	217, 260(i)	14,100,	—	A
Ouabagenin-B acetate	217, 305	14,100,	45	A
Pantroside acetate	215, 270–280(i)	17,400,	75	A
Periplogenin	218	$\sim 15,800$		A
acetate	~ 219	$\sim 12,600$		A
Sarmentogenin 3β,11α-diacetate	218	$\sim 20,000$		
Sarmentoside-A acetate	217	18,200		A
Sarmentoside-A acetate acid methyl ester	217	16,600		A
Sarveroside	216, 280(i)	16,600,	80	A
Strophanthidin	216,			
	290–310(i)[e]	17,000,	~ 80	A
Strophanthidol	217	15,500		A
Trianhydroperiplogen	285[f]	~ 400		C
Trianhydrostrophanthidin	279[f]	~ 400		A
β'-3α,2α,12α-Trihydroxyetiochol-anyl-17)-$\Delta^{\alpha',\beta'}$-butenolide	223	12,600		
β'-(3α,7α,12β-Trihydroxynorcholanyl-23)-$\Delta^{\alpha',\beta'}$-butenolide-7,12-diacetate	217	12,600		

TABLE A.13—(contd.)

Compound	λ_{max} (mμ)	ε_{max}	Solvent[a]
Cyclobutenolides—(contd.)			
17-Cyclobutenolides: —(contd.)			
Xysmalobigenin acetate	217	12,600	A
Xysmalobin	215	18,200	A
Conjugated cyclobutenolides			
Δ^{16}-*17-Cyclobutenolides:*			
Anhydroadynerigenin	280	25,100	
16-Anhydrodesglucodigitalinum			
verum diacetate	270	18,600	A
16-Anhydrodigitalinum verum	272	17,000	A
16-Anhydrogitoxigenin acetate	271	18,600	A
Desacetylanhydrocryptograndoside-A	220, 277[g]	5000, 17,800	A
16-Desacetylanhydroöleandrin	~ 220, 270[g]	~ 5000, 17,400	A
acetate	~ 220, 270[g]	~ 5000, 17,000	A
16-Desacetylanhydrocryptogrando-side-B	~ 220, 270[g]	~ 5000, 16,200	A
Desacetylanhydrohongheloside-A	~ 220, 270[g]	~ 5000, 16,600	A
Hongheloside-F	~ 220, 270[g]	~ 5000, 16,600	A
β'-(3β-Acetoxy-16-etioallocholenyl-17)- $\Delta^{\alpha',\beta}$-butenolide	273	22,400	
$\Delta^{14,16}$-*17-Cyclobutenolides:*			
Anhydro-16-dehydrodigoxigenin di-acetate	332,	17,800	
14,16-Dianhydrogitoxigenin	223, 338	11,500, 20,400	A
β'-(3β-Acetoxy-14,16-etioallochola-dienyl-17)- $\Delta^{\alpha',\beta}$-butenolide	332	22,400	
Dianhydroöleandrigenone	337	~ 50,000[d]	A
Cyclopentenolides			
17-Cyclopentenolides:[f]			
Bufotalin	303	5900	
Cinobufagin	293		C
Cinobufotalin	295		
Desglucohellebrin acid acetate methyl ester	308	5020	
γ-Bufogenin	300		
Hellebrigenol 3-acetate	300	7080	A
Hellebrin	300	6300	A
Marinobufagin	300		C
14-Monoanhydrobufotalin acetate	296	5100	A
Scillaren-A	300	~ 11,000	A
Scillarenin	300	5250	A
Scillarenone	240, 300[h]	17,800, 5500	A
Scillaridin-A	230, 300[i]	17,000, 5010	A

TABLE A.13 — (contd.)

Compound	λ_{max} (mμ)	ε_{max}	Solvent[a]
Cyclopentenolides — (contd.)			
17-Cyclopentenolides[f]: — (*contd.*)			
Scilliroside	300	~ 6300	A
tetraacetate	300	3980	A
Scillirosidin	~ 300	~ 6300	A
Tetraacetylanhydrodehydroscilliro-side	~ 287[j]	~ 15,800	A
Tetraacetyldehydroscilliroside	300	5000	AC
$\Delta^{14,16}$-17-Cyclopentenolides:			
Bufotalien	300		
Bufotalienone	300		
16-Desacetyl-14,16-bufotalin acetate	300[k]	16,600	A

[a] A = ethanol; AC = sample dissolved in a minimum of chloroform and diluted with ethanol; C = chloroform.

[b] The extinction coefficient is too high.

[c] The band at 305 mμ can probably be attributed to an aldehyde group.

[d] (i) signifies an inflection; (p) signifies a plateau.

[e] The band at 270–275 mμ is due to the presence of a small amount of the C_{16}-anhydro compound.

[f] There is indication of a band below 220–230 mμ.

[g] The band at 220 mμ indicates the presence of starting material, a non-conjugated cyclobutenolide.

[h] The band at 240 mμ is due to the presence of a Δ^4-en-3-one component.

[i] The broad band at 230 mμ is due to the presence of a $\Delta^{3,5}$-diene component.

[j] The band at approximately 287 mμ is a composite curve of two isolated chromophoric systems of which one is the cyclopentenolide and the second must be a conjugated system that absorbs at 270–280 mμ.

[k] The band at 300 mμ is quite broad, continuing in a shallow decline from 340 to 380 mμ.

TABLE A.14. ULTRAVIOLET ABSORPTION OF STEROIDS CONTAINING BENZENOID RINGS

Compound	λ_{max} (mμ)	ε_{max}	Solvent†
Benzenoid ring A*			
17-Desoxyestrone	280	2510	
1,3,5,16-Estratetraen-3-ol	280	2510	
17α-Estradiol	280	2000	A
17β-Estradiol	280	2000	A
	300		AA
17-acetate	280	2640	A
3,17-diacetate	268	700	A
3,17-dibenzoate	230, 265(i)**	17,400, —	A
"α"-Dihydroequilin	281, 290(i)	1960, ∼1800	A
3-Hydroxy-1,3,5-estratrien-16-one	281	2190	A
Estrone	280	2300	A
	300		AA
3-acetate	260	1040	A
3-methoxy	280		A
3-sodium sulphonate	272	850	M
17-ethylene hemithioketal	282	1950	A
Equilin	280	2000	A
16-Epiestriol (isoestriol-A)	280	2300	A
Estriol (theelol)	280	2300	A
	300		AA
17-Ethynylestradiol	280	2140	A
3-acetate	268	850	A
3-methoxy	280	2280	A
3-Hydroxy-1,3,5-estratriene-17-carboxylic acid	280	2120	A
17-methyl ester	280	2460	A
17-ethyl ester	282	2075	A
3-methoxy 17-methyl ester	280	2290	A
17-Acetyl-3-hydroxy-1,3,5,estratriene	222, 280	6610, 2510	A
17-Acetyl-3-hydroxy-16-methoxy-1,3,5-estratriene	280	2140	A
17-Acetyl-3,17α-dihydroxy-1,3,5-estratriene	280	1950	A
17-(β-Acetoxyacetyl)-3-methoxy-1,3,5-estratriene	220(i),** 278	—, 2450	A
19-Nor-1,3,5-cholestatrien-3-ol	284	1590	A
3-acetate	265	430	A
1-Methyl-1,3,5-cholestatrien-7-one	285		A
Doisynolic acid	281	1820	A
methyl ester	282	2050	
Marianolic acid dimethyl ester	282	1580	
1-Methyldoisynolic acid (?)***	285	1410	A
1-Methylestradiol	284	1910	A
17-acetate (?)***	282	2300	A
3,17-diacetate	268	340	A
3,17-dipropionate	268	340	A

TABLE A.14 — (contd.)

Compound	λ_{max} (mμ)	ε_{max}	Solvent†
Benzenoid ring A* — (contd.)			
1 Methylestradiol — (contd.)			
2-bromo (?)***	289	2630	A
2-bromo 3-17-diacetate (?)***	273	470	A
1-Methylestrone	282	1820	A
3-acetate	268	330	A
3-Hydroxy-1-methyl-1,3,5-estratriene-			
17-carboxylic acid (?)***	283	2340	A
3-acetate 17-methyl ester (?)***	267	301	A
3-methoxy (?)***	278–84	2040	A
17-Acetyl-3-hydroxy-1-methyl-			
1,3,5-estratriene	284	2040	A
3-acetate	268	390	A
17-(β-Acetoxyacetyl)-3-methoxy-			
1-methyl-1,3,5-estratriene (?)***	278–84	2140	A
1-Hydroxy-4-methyl-19-nor-1,3,5-			
cholatrienic acid***	283	2400	
1-Hydroxy-4-methyl-19-nor-1,3,5-chol-			
estatriene***	284	2000	A
Conjugated benzenoid ring A			
Δ^6			
6-Dehydroestradiol	262, 302	10,000, 2950	A
17-acetate	222, 262,	28,800, 8510,	A
	$\sim$ 270, 302	$\sim$6,920, 2950	
3,17-diacetate	264	10,200	A
6-Dehydroestrone	220, 262,	30,900, 8910,	A
	$\sim$ 272(i), 304	$\sim$ 6300, 2750	
19-Nor-1,3,5,6-cholestatetraen-3-ol	224, 266, 304	30,900, 9120, 1620	A
3-acetate	226, 264	31,600, 12,300	A
3-benzoate	230, 262	30,900, 10,700	A
3-(*p*-nitrobenzoate)	264	23,400	C
1-Methyl-6-dehydroestradiol	226, 266	37,200, 8900	A
3,17-diacetate	222, 264	28,800, 9100	A
1-Methyl-6-dehydroestrone	228, 268, 306	30,900, 7940, 1910	A
3-acetate	222, 264	27,500, 8510	A
1-Methyl-19-nor-1,3,5,6-cholestatetraen-			
3-ol	228, 266,	$\sim$ 25,000, $\sim$ 7900,	
	$\sim$ 275(i), 304	$\sim$ 6300, $\sim$ 1600	A
3-acetate	224, 266	26,300, 8710	A
$\Delta^{8(9)}$			
2-Methyl-7-methoxy-1,2,3,4,9,			
10-hexahydrophenanthrene-			
1,2-dicarboxylic acid dimethyl			
ester	275	18,500	A

TABLE A.14 — (contd.)

Compound	λ_{max} (mμ)	ε_{max}	Solvent†
Conjugated benzenoid ring A — *(contd.)*			
$\Delta^{8(9)}$ — (contd.)			
α-Monodehydrodoisynolic acid			
7-methyl ether	~ 275	~ 15,800	A
3-Hydroxy-1,3,5,8-estratetraen-16-one	273, 336, 363	14,500, 230, 170	A
3-methoxy	273	17,800	A
8-Dehydro-14-isoestrone (isoequilin-A)	275	16,000	A
3-methoxy	275	16,000	A
3-methoxy (racemic mixture)	270, 335	15,800, 32	A
$\Delta^{9(11)}$			
2-Methyl-7-methoxy-1,2,3,9,10,11-			
hexahydrophenanthrene-1,2-di-			
carboxylic acid dimethyl ester	264, 299	20,900, ~ 3200	A
β-9-Dehydro-14-isoestradiol	264, 300	18,000, 3000	A
9-Dehydro-14-isoestrone	264, 299	~ 18,000, 3000	A
3-methoxy	264, 299	~ 18,000, ~ 3000	A
8-Hydroxy-9-dehydro-14-isoequilin	270	16,500	A
6-keto:			
β-Estradiol-6-one	256, 326	8000, 3000	
3,17-diacetate	~ 250, ~ 300	~ 9000, ~ 1900	
Miscellaneous:			
$\Delta^{1,1'}$-2′-Keto-2-methyl-7-methoxy-			
3,4,9,10-tetrahydro-1,2-cyclo-			
pentanophenanthrene	258, 280(i)**,	10,700, 5000,	A
	360	27,500	
Benzenoid ring B			
3-Hydroxy-5,7,9-estratrien-17-one	270, 278	345, 240	A
22-Dihydroneoergostatriene	~ 224, ~ 269,	~ 10,000, ~ 400,	A
	~ 277	~ 250	
Epineoergosterol	270	500	E
Neoergosterol	268	500	A
Norsterol	270		
Conjugated benzenoid ring B			
Δ^3			
3-Methoxy-3,5,7,9,22-ergostapen-			
taene	270, ~ 280	16,200, ~ 15,000	E
3-Methoxy-3,5,7,9-ergostatetraene	270	20,500	E
3,5,7,9-Ergostatetraen-17-one	268	4600	

TABLE A.14 — (contd.)

Compound	λ_{max} (mμ)	ε_{max}	Solvent†
Conjugated benzenoid ring B — *(contd.)*			
Δ^3 — *(contd.)*			
Neoergostapentaene	$\sim$ 224, $\sim$ 231, $\sim$ 268, $\sim$ 308, $\sim$ 314, $\sim$ 323	$\sim$ 25,100, $\sim$ 27,000, $\sim$ 6300, $\sim$ 200, $\sim$ 80, $\sim$ 100,	A
22-Dihydroneoergostatetraene	$\sim$ 224, $\sim$ 230, $\sim$ 268, 308, $\sim$ 314, $\sim$ 323	$\sim$ 20,000, $\sim$ 18,000, $\sim$ 8000, $\sim$ 400, $\sim$ 200, $\sim$ 250	A
Δ^{11}			
3-Acetoxy-11-dehydroneoergosterol	270	11,500	
Benzenoid rings AB			
β-*dl*-Equilenane	231, 282, 322	93,300, 5760, 910	A
3-Desoxyequilenin	$\sim$ 282, $\sim$ 321	$\sim$ 5000, $\sim$ 600	A
cis-3-Methoxy-16-equilenone	229, 265, 275 283(i)†, 319, 334	64,600, 5890, 5750 3890, 1860, 2340	A
trans-3-Methoxy-16-equilenone	232, 269, 278, 287(i), 323, 336	64,600, 5130, 5620, 3890, 2040, 2450	A
Equilenin	230, 270, 282, 292, 328, 340	—, 7080, 7420, 5500, 3800, 4790	A
17-(2,4-dinitrophenylhydrazone)	370	102,000 §	C
Isoequilenin	267, 278, 289, 325, 338		A
α-6-Methoxy-17-equilenone	225, 240, 303	28,800, 42,700,6460	A
Tetradehydroneoergosterol	250, 280, > 340		E
3-acetate	240, 280		
22-Dihydrotetradehydroneoergosterol acetate	280	4900	E
7-Methylbisdehydrodoisynolic acid methyl ester	268, 276, 286, 315, 333	$\sim$ 5600, 6580, $\sim$ 4500 $\sim$ 2000, 2720	A
1-Methyl-17β-dihydroequilenin	$\sim$ 236, $\sim$ 272, $\sim$ 284, $\sim$ 295, $\sim$ 329, $\sim$ 344	$\sim$ 79,000, $\sim$ 7000, $\sim$ 6900, $\sim$ 5600, $\sim$ 2000, $\sim$ 2500	A
3,17-diacetate	$\sim$ 234, $\sim$ 278, $\sim$ 316, $\sim$ 330	$\sim$ 100,000, $\sim$ 8900, $\sim$ 2200, $\sim$ 2500	A
1-Methylequilenin	$\sim$ 235, $\sim$ 273, $\sim$ 285, $\sim$ 297, $\sim$ 330, $\sim$ 344	$\sim$ 63,000, $\sim$ 5600, $\sim$ 6300, $\sim$ 4500, $\sim$ 2000, $\sim$ 2500	A

TABLE A.14 — (contd.)

Compound	λ_{max} (mμ)	ε_{max}	Solvent†
Benzenoid rings AB — *(contd.)*			
1 Methylequilenin — (contd.)			
3-acetate	~ 236, ~ 278, ~ 316, ~ 330	~ 80,000, ~ 7100, ~ 1800, ~ 2500	A
1-Methyl-19-nor-1,3,5,6,8-cholestapentaen-3-ol(?)*	~ 240, ~ 258, ~ 264, ~ 282, ~ 299, ~ 315, ~ 340	~ 32,000, ~ 16,000, ~ 16,000, ~ 5000, ~ 7900, ~ 4000, ~ 2000	A
6-Methoxy-17-equilenone-15-carboxylic acid	243, 300	38,900, 6160	A
Conjugated benzenoid rings AB			
Δ^{14}			
14-Dehydroequilenane	255, 285, 295, 305	45,700, 12,600, 15,500, 12,900	A
3-Methoxy-14-dehydroequilenane	245(i), 254, 263, 281, 292, 303	33,900, 45,700, 44,700, 13,800, 18,600, 17,800	A
16-Hydroxy-14-dehydroequilenane	245(i), 254, 262, 283, 292, 305	34,700, 46,800, 41,700, 13,500, 16,600, 13,500	A
14-Dehydro-17-equilenone	251, 281, 292, 303	49,000, 12,300, 14,400, 11,500	A
3-Methoxy-14-dehydroequilenin	253, 262, 294, 305, 333, 350	46,800, 45,700, 15,800, 14,800, 2190, 1740	A
6-Methoxy-14-dehydro-17-equilenone	260, 302, 330, 347	44,700, 8710, 4170, 2950	
$\Delta^{14(20)}$			
3′-Keto-3,4-dihydro-1,2-cyclopentanophenanthrene	219, 241, 250(i), 260(i), 270, 280, 324, 335, 360(i)	38,000, 6610, 7240, 17,000, 38,000, 46,800, 14,200, 15,500, 8910	A
$\Delta^{1,1'}$-2′-Keto-3,4-dihydro-1,2-cyclopentanophenanthrene	219, 238, 245, 255(i), 266, 276, 316, 360(i)	20,900, 13,200, 13,300, 18,600, 36,300, 42,700, 29,500, 4900	A
$\Delta^{1,1'}$-2′-Keto-2-methyl-3,4-dihydro-1,2-cyclopentanophenanthrene	220, 231, 246, 257(i), 266, 275, 315, 360(i)	21,900, 16,200, 11,600, 16,600, 32,400, 38,000, 25,700, 4070	A

TABLE A.14 — (contd.)

Compound	λ_{max} (mμ)	ε_{max}	Solvent†
Conjugated benzenoid rings AB — *(contd.)*			
Δ^{14} — (contd.)			
$\Delta^{1,1'}$-2'-Keto-2-methyl-7-hydroxy-3,4-dihydro-1,2-cyclopentano-phenanthrene	226, 263(i), 268(i), 283, 342	19,500, 20,000, 27,500, 28,800, 24,500,	A
7-acetate	222, 235(i), 258(i), 268, 277, 318, 353(i)	20,900, 12,900, 19,100, 33,900, 39,800, 26,900, 6030	
7-methoxy	226, 262(i), 274(i), 281, 333	21,900, 22,400, 28,200, 31,600, 27,500	A
$\Delta^{1,1'}$-2'-Keto-3'-hydroxy-2-methyl-3,4-dihydro-1,2-cyclopentanophen-anthrene	219, 239, 247, 260(i), 268, 277, 318, 360(i)	20,900, 12,000, 12,200, 17,800, 30,900, 36,300, 27,500 4790	A
$\Delta^{1,1'}$-2',3'-Diketo-2-methyl-3,4-di-hydro-1,2-cyclopentanophen anthrene	220(i), 236, 271, 280, 291, 333(i), 345	18,200, 23,400, 15,800, 18,200, 14,100, 16,600, 17,000	A
Δ^{14}-15-carboxylic acid:			
Methyl 14-dehydro-17-equilenone-15-carboxylate	219, 243, 247, 264, 310	29,500, 20,000, 20,000, 26,900, 17,800	A
Methyl 3-methoxy-14-dehydroequi-lenin-15-carboxylate	223, 265, 323	30,200, 25,100, 18,200	A
Methyl-6-methoxy-14-dehydro-17-equilenone-15-carboxylate	213, 224, 269, 311, 354	24,500, 25,100, 24,000, 12,900, 5890	A
Methyl-11,12,13,17-tetrahydro-16H-cyclopentanophenanthrene-16-keto-15-acetate	220, 236, 267, 277, 316	24,600, 10,000, 38,000, 45,700, 25,700	A
Δ^{15}-17-one:			
15-Dehydro-17-equilenone	230, 270, 321	77,600, 6760, 660	A
Δ^{15}-carboxylic acid-17-one:			
15-Dehydro-17-equilenone-15-carboxylic acid	228, 273	89,100, 7760	A
3-Hydroxy-15-dehydroequilenin-15-carboxylic acid			

TABLE A.14 — (contd.)

Compound	λ_{max} (mμ)	ε_{max}	Solvent†
Conjugated benzenoid rings AB — *(contd.)*			
Δ^{15}-carboxylic acid *17-one:* — *(contd.)*			
3-methoxy	235, 318, 334	77,600, 2880, 2690	A
3-methoxy methyl ester	235, 275, 318, 333	57,500, 5370, 2090, 2090	A
6-Hydroxy-15-dehydroequilenone-15-carboxylic acid			
6-methoxy	215, 243, 296, 327	39,800, 43,700, 5890, 3240	A
6-methoxy methyl ester	242, 296, 325	41,700, 5890, 2570	A
$\Delta^{11(12),14(18)}$:			
3′,5-Dimethyl-1,2-cyclopenta-nophenanthrene	260, 280, 298	$\sim$ 58,000, $\sim$ 13,000, $\sim$ 9500	

† A = ethanol; AA = alkaline ethanol, usually 0·1 N; C = chloroform; E = ethyl ether; M = methanol.

* Many of the compounds in this group have an inflection near 220 mμ.

** (i) signifies an inflection.

*** For summary see Fieser and Fieser, *Steriods*, p. 327, Reinhold (1959)

§ The extinction coefficient is too high.

TABLE A.15. ULTRAVIOLET ABSORPTION OF STEROIDS CONTAINING PHENYL CHROMOPHORES

Compound	λ_{max} (mμ)	ε_{max}	Solvent†
Diphenylcarbinol:			
3α-Acetoxy-24,24-diphenylcholane-12α,24-diol	255	780	A
(3α,12β-Dihydroxypregnyl-20)-diphenylcarbinol	~ 262	~ 600	A
3α-Acetoxy-12α,22-oxido-22,22-di-phenylbisnorcholane	~ 260	~ 600	A
Phenyl ketone:			
24-Keto-24-phenylnorcholane	243, 280	12,800, 1030	A
3α,11α-Diacetoxy-24-keto-24-phenyl-norcholane	243, 280	12,500, 980	A
Diphenylethylene:			
1'-Methyl-1'-(3α,11α-diacetoxyetio-cholanyl-17)-2',2'-diphenylethylene	245	11,800	A
1'-Methyl-1'-(3α,12β-dihydroxyetio-cholanyl-17)-2',2'-diphenylethylene			
3-acetate	~ 252	~ 12,200	A
3,12-diacetate	~ 252	~ 12,200	A
1'-Methoxy-1'-(3α,12-dihydroxyetio-cholanyl-17)-2',2'-diphenyl ethylene	~ 250(p)*	~ 20,000	A
3-acetate	~ 250(p)	~ 20,000	H
3,12-diacetate	~ 250(p)	~ 20,000	H
3α,11α-Diacetoxyternorcholanyl-diphenylethylene	250	17,200	A
3α,11α-Diacetoxybisnorcholanyl-diphenylethylene	250	17,200	A
3α,12β-Diacetoxy-24,24-diphenyl-23-cholene	~ 250(p)	~ 20,000	C
Diphenylbutadiene:			
3α,12α-Diacetoxy-24,24-diphenyl 20(22),23-choladiene	~ 310(p)	~ 17,800	C
3α-Acetoxy-12,21-dibromo-11-keto-24,24-diphenyl-20(22),23-chola-diene	325		
Diphenylhexatriene:			
3α-Acetoxy-20-keto-21-(1,1-di-phenylacrylal)pregnane 20-enol acetate	245, 335	16,200, 47,600	A
3α,12α-Diacetoxy-20-keto-21-(1,1-diphenylacrylal)pregnane 20-enol acetate	245, 335	18,500, 51,000	A
Conjugated phenylenone:			
Dehydroepiandrosterone-16-benzylidene	223, 295	8300, 24,600	A

TABLE A.15. — (contd.)

Compound	λ_{max} (mμ)	ε_{max}	Solvent†
Conjugated phenylenone: — (contd.)			
3β,14-Dihydroxy-17-keto-5-andro-stene-16-benzylidene	221, 290	8300, 24,700	A
3β,11α-Diacetoxy-20-ketopregnane-21-benzal			
-17α	294	23,400	A
-17α	294	22,900	A
-17β	294	22,500	A
-17β	294	24,000	A
3α,12α,20-Triacetoxy-17-pregnene-21-benzal	~ 294, ~ 304, ~ 320	~ 33,000, ~ 33,500, ~ 22,750	
Conjugated phenyldienone:			
3β-Acetoxy-17-keto-14-epiandro-stene-16-benzylidene	234, 256, 335	12,600, 8500, 22,400	A
3β-Acetoxy-17-keto-5,14-androsta-diene-16-benzylidene	234, 256, 335	12,600, 8710, 23,500	A
3α-Hydroxy-20-keto-21-(1,1-di-phenylacrylal)pregnane	242, 338	13,900, 31,800	A
3α,12α-Dihydroxy-20-keto-21-(1,1-diphenylacrylal)pregnane	242, 338	12,300, 29,000	A

† A = ethanol; C = chloroform; H = hexane.
* (p) signifies a plateau.

REFERENCES

1. P. BLADON, H. B. HENBEST and G. W. WOOD, *J. Chem. Soc.*, 2737 (1952).
2. H. P. SIGG and T. REICHSTEIN, *Helv. Chim. Acta*, **39**, 1507 (1956).
3. A. LARDON and T. REICHSTEIN, *ibid.*, **41**, 904 (1958).
4. K. STICH, G. ROTZLER and T. REICHSTEIN, *ibid.*, **42**, 1480 (1959); R. E. HAN-SEN and M. BUELL, *Analyt. Chem.*, **31**, 878 (1959).
5. M. GLOVER, J. GLOVER and R. A. MORTON, *Biochem. J.*, **51**, 1 (1952).
6. S. R. M. REYNOLDS and N. GINSBURG, *Endocrinology*, **31**, 147 (1942); D. G. EDGAR, *Biochem. J.*, **54**, 50 (1953); M. W. NOALL, H. A. SALHANICK, G. M. NEHER and M. X. ZARROW, *J. Biol. Chem.*, **201**, 321 (1953).
7. L. DORFMAN, *Chem. Revs.*, **53**, 47 (1953).
8. D. KRITCHEVSKY, *Cholesterol*, ch. 7, Chapman & Hall, London (1958).
9. R. P. COOK (Ed.), *Cholesterol*, ch. 2 and 3, Academic Press, New York (1958).
10. A. STOLL and E. JUCKER, *Modern Methods of Plant Analysis* (edited by K. PAECH and M. V. TRACEY), vol. 3, p. 153, Springer, Berlin (1955).
11. W. M. SPERRY and M. WEBB, *J. Biol. Chem.*, **187**, 97 (1950).
12. L. S. GALLOWAY, P. W. NIELSON, E. B. WILCOX and E. M. LANTZ, *Clin. Chem.*, **3**, 226 (1957).
13. F. E. LUDDY, A. TURNER and J. T. SCANLAN, *Analyt. Chem.*, **25**, 1497 (1953); **26**, 491 (1954).
14. V. R. WHEATLEY, *Biochem. J.*, **55**, 637 (1953).
15. H. K. HANEL and H. DAM, *Acta. Chem. Scand.*, **9**, 677 (1955).
16. H. SCHÖN and K. F. GEY, *Z. physiol. Chem.*, **303**, 81 (1956).
17. A. ZLATKIS, B. ZAK and A. J. BOYLE, *J. Lab. Clin. Med.*, **41**, 486 (1953).
18. B. ZAK, *Amer. J. Clin. Pathol.*, **27**, 583 (1957); B. ZAK and E. EPSTEIN, *Clin. Chim. Acta*, **6**, 72 (1961).
19. H. L. ROSENTHAL and L. JUD, *J. Lab. Clin. Med.*, **51**, 143 (1958).
20. R. L. SEARCY and L. M. BERGQUIST, *Clin. Chim. Acta*, **5**, 192 (1960).
21. R. L. SEARCY, L. M. BERGQUIST and R. C. JUNG, *J. Lipid Res.*, **1**, 349 (1960).
22. R. L. SEARCY, L. M. BERGQUIST, R. C. JUNG, R. CRAIG and J. KOROTZER, *Clin. Chem.*, **6**, 585 (1960).
23. L. L. ENGEL and B. BAGGETT, *Recent Prog. Hormone Res.*, **9**, 261 (1954).
24. P. TALALAY, *Methods of Biochemical Analysis*, **8**, 119 (1960).
25. H. B. FRIEDGOOD, J. B. GARST and A. J. HAAGEN-SMIT, *J. Biol. Chem.*, **174**, 523 (1948).
26. J. B. BROWN, *Biochem. J.*, **60**, 185 (1955).
27. W. S. BAULD, *ibid.*, **63**, 488 (1956).
28. S. KOBER, *Biochem. Z.*, **239**, 209 (1931).
29. J. B. BROWN, *Advances in Clinical Chemistry*, **3**, 157 (1960).
30. W. S. BAULD and R. M. GREENWAY, *Methods of Biochemical Analysis*, **5**, 337 (1957).
31. E. DICZFALUSY, *Acta Endocrinol.*, Suppl. 12 (1953).
32. J. B. BROWN, *J. Endocrinol.*, **8**, 196 (1952); *Ciba Foundation Colloquia on Endocrinology*, vol. 2, p. 132 (1952).
33. H. W. MARLOW, *J. Biol. Chem.*, **183**, 167 (1950); G. F. MARRIAN and W. S. BAULD, *Biochem. J.*, **59**, 136 (1955).
34. W. M. ALLEN, *J. Clin. Endocrinol.*, **10**, 71 (1950).
35. G. ITTRICH, *Z. physiol. Chem.*, **312**, 1 (1958); **320**, 103 (1960).
36. W. KLYNE, *The Chemistry of the Steroids*, Methuen, London (1960).
37. W. ZIMMERMANN, *Z. physiol. Chem.*, **233**, 257 (1935); **245**, 47, (1936); *Vitamins and Hormones*, **5**, 1 (1944).
38. W. ZIMMERMANN, *Chemische Bestimmungsmethoden von Steroidhormonen*, Springer, Berlin (1955).

39. L. L. ENGEL, *Methods of Biochemical Analysis*, **1**, 479 (1954).
40. P. L. MUNSON and A. D. KENNY, *Recent Progress in Hormone Research*, **9**, 135 (1954).
41. H. WILSON, *Arch. Biochem.*, **52**, 217 (1954).
42. I. E. BROADBENT and W. KLYNE, *Biochem. J.*, **56**, XXX (1954).
43. D. H. R. BARTON and P. DE MAYO, *J. Chem. Soc.*, 887 (1954).
44. C. J. W. BROOKS and J. K. NORYMBERSKI, *Biochem. J.*, **55**, 371 (1953).
45. A. E. KELLIE and E. R. SMITH, *Nature, Lond.*, **178**, 323 (1956).
46. C. J. MIGEON and J. E. PLAGER, *Recent Progr. Hormone Res.*, **9**, 235 (1954).
47. N. H. CALLOW, R. K. CALLOW and C. W. EMMENS, *Biochem. J.*, **32**, 1312 (1938); (cf. M. R. C. Committee on Clinical Endocrinology, 1951); A. S. ZYGMUNTOWICZ, M. WOOD, E. CHRISTO and N. B. TALBOT, *J. Clin. Endocrinol.*, **11**, 578 (1951).
48. A. F. HOLTORFF and F. C. KOCH, *J. Biol. Chem.*, **135**, 377 (1940).
49. W. ZIMMERMANN, H. U. ANTON and D. PONTIUS, *Z. physiol. Chem.*, **289**, 91 (1952); W. ZIMMERMANN, *ibid.*, **300**, 141 (1955).
50. G. PINCUS, *Endocrinology*, **32**, 176 (1943).
51. M. L. GIVNER, W. S. BAULD and K. VAGI, *Biochem. J.*, **77**, 406 (1960).
52. R. BORTH, *Vitamins and Hormones*, **15**, 259 (1957); H. BRAUNSBERG and V. H. T. JAMES, *J. Clin. Endocrinol.*, **21**, 1146 (1961).
53. C. C. PORTER and R. H. SILBER, *J. Biol. Chem.*, **185**, 201 (1950).
54. P. K. BONDY, D. ABELSON, J. SCHEUER, T. K. L. TSEU and V. UPTON, *J. Biol. Chem.*, **224**, 47 (1957).
55. S. A. SIMPSON and J. F. TAIT, *Recent Progr. Hormone Res.*, **11**, 183 (1955).
56. V. C. BARRY, J. E. McCORMICK and P. W. D. MITCHELL, *J. Chem. Soc.*, 222 (1955).
57. L. L. ENGEL, *J. Amer. Chem. Soc.*, **57**, 2419 (1935); J. C. P. SCHWARZ and M. FINNEGAN, *J. Chem. Soc.*, 3979 (1956).
58. R. H. SILBER and C. C. PORTER, *Methods of Biochemical Analysis*, **4**, 139 (1957).
59. D. H. R. BARTON, T. C. McMORRIS and R. SEGOVIA, *J. Chem. Soc.*, 2027 (1961).
60. L. J. MARKS and J. H. LEFTIN, *J. Clin. Endocrinol.*, **14**, 1263 (1954).
61. D. H. NELSON and L. T. SAMUELS, *ibid.*, **12**, 519 (1952); K. EIK-NES, D. H. NELSON and L. T. SAMUELS, *ibid.*, **13**, 1280 (1953).
62. C. J. MIGEON, A. A. SANDBERG, E. L. BLISS and A. R. KELLER, *ibid.*, **16**, 253 (1956).
63. A. M. RIONDEL, M. C. SANZ and A. F. MULLER, *Acta Endocrinol.*, **26**, 57 (1957).
64. E. M. GOLD, B. SERENA and S. COOK, *J. Clin. Endocrinol.*, **20**, 315 (1960).
65. R. E. PETERSON, A. KARRER and S. L. GUERRA, *Analyt. Chem.*, **29**, 144 (1957).
66. P. K. BONDY and G. V. UPTON, *Proc. Soc. Exp. Biol.*, N.Y., **94**, 585 (1957).
67. W. J. REDDY, D. JENKINS and G. W. THORN, *Metabolism*, **1**, 511 (1952).
68. R. H. SILBER and C. C. PORTER, *J. Biol. Chem.*, **210**, 923 (1954).
69. W. J. REDDY, N. A. HAYDAR, J. C. LAIDLAW, A. E. RENOLD and G. W. THORN, *J. Clin. Endocrinol.*, **16**, 380 (1956).
70. D. EXLEY, S. C. INGALL, J. K. NORYMBERSKI and G. F. WOODS, *Biochem. J.*, **81**, 428 (1961).
71. J. K. NORYMBERSKI, *Nature, Lond.*, **170**, 1074 (1952).
72. J. K. NORYMBERSKI, R. D. STUBBS and H. F. WEST, *Lancet*, II, 1276 (1953).
73. J. I. APPLEBY, G. GIBSON, J. K. NORYMBERSKI and R. D. STUBBS, *Biochem. J.*, **60**, 453 (1955).
74. J. I. APPLEBY and J. K. NORYMBERSKI, *ibid.*, **60**, 460 (1955).
75. J. K. NORYMBERSKI and R. D. STUBBS, *ibid.*, **64**, 168 (1956).
76. J. Y. F. PATERSON and G. F. MARRIAN, *Mem. Soc. Endocrinol.*, **2**, 1 (1953); G. F. MARRIAN, *Recent Progr. Hormone Res.*, **9**, 303 (1954).
77. B. E. LOWENSTEIN, A. C. CORCORAN and I. H. PAGE, *Endocrinology*, **39**, 82 (1946).
78. R. W. H. EDWARDS and A. E. KELLIE, *Biochem. J.*, **56**, 207 (1954).
79. G. C. BUTLER and G. F. MARRIAN, *J. Biol. Chem.*, **119**, 565 (1937); **124**, 237 (1938).
80. R. I. COX, *Biochem. J.*, **52**, 339 (1952).
81. A. M. BONGIOVANNI and W. R. EBERLEIN, *Analyt. Chem.*, **30**, 388 (1958).
82. S. B. BARKER and W. H. SUMMERSON, *J. Biol. Chem.*, **138**, 535 (1941).

83. N. B. TALBOT and I. V. EITINGON, *J. Biol. Chem.*, **154**, 605 (1944); L. F. FIESER, M. FIELDS and S. LIEBERMAN, *ibid.*, **156**, 191.

84. C. SOBEL, O. J. GOLUB, R. J. HENRY, S. L. JACOBS and G. K. BASU, *J. Clin. Endocrinol.*, **18**, 208 (1958).

85. R. W. H. EDWARDS, A. E. KELLIE and A. P. WADE, *Mem. Soc. Endocrinol.*, **2**, 53 (1953).

86. H. BREUER and J. GERTZ, *Clin. Chim. Acta*, **5**, 544 (1960).

87. A. ZAFFARONI, *J. Amer. Chem. Soc.*, **72**, 3828 (1950); G. DIAZ, A. ZAFFARONI, G. ROSEN-CRANZ and C. DJERASSI, *J. Org. Chem.*, **17**, 747 (1952); A. ZAFFARONI and R. B. BURTON, *J. Biol. Chem.*, **193**, 749 (1957).

88. S. BERNSTEIN and R. H. LENHARD, *J. Org. Chem.*, **18**, 1146 (1953); **19**, 269 (1954).

89. W. J. NOWACZYNSKI and P. F. STEYERMARK, *Arch. Biochem.*, **58**, 453 (1955); *Canad. J. Biochem. Physiol.*, **34**, 592 (1956).

90. A. M. BONGIOVANNI and G. W. CLAYTON, *Bull. Johns Hopkins Hosp.*, **94**, 180 (1954).

91. M. BELL and H. VARLEY, *Clin. Chim. Acta*, **5**, 396 (1960).

92. A. KLOPPER, E. A. MICHIE and J. B. BROWN, *J. Endocrinol.*, **12**, 209 (1955).

93. M. I. STERN, *ibid.*, **16**, 180 (1957).

94. J. ZANDER, *Nature, Lond.*, **174**, 406 (1954); J. ZANDER and H. SIMMER, *Klin. Wochschr.*, **32**, 529 (1954).

95. H. REICH, K. F. CRANE and S. J. SANFILIPPO, *J. Biol. Chem.*, **198**, 713 (1952); *J. Org. Chem.*, **18**, 822 (1953).

96. I. CLARK, *Nature, Lond.*, **175**, 122 (1955).

97. K. HINSBERG, H. PELZER and A. SEUKEN, *Biochem. Z.*, **328**, 117 (1956).

98. W. H. PEARLMAN, *Recent Progr. Hormone Res.*, **9**, 27 (1954).

99. A. A. FORIST, *Analyt. Chem.*, **31**, 913 (1959).

100. B. CAMBER, *Clin. Chim. Acta*, **2**, 188 (1957); *Oxosteroids: The Use of Phenolic Hydrazines for Detection, Characterisation and Estimation*, H. K. Lewis, London (1960).

101. P. S. CHEN, *Analyt. Chem.*, **31**, 292 (1959).

102. I. F. SOMMERVILLE, *J. Clin. Endocrinol.*, **17**, 317 (1957).

103. R. I. COX, *J. Biol. Chem.*, **234**, 1693 (1959).

104. P. CRISTOL and M. F. JAYLE, *Bull. Soc. chim. Biol.*, **42**, 655 (1960).

105. M. L. LEWBART and V. R. MATTOX, *Analyt. Chem.*, **33**, 559 (1961).

106. W. J. NOWACZYNSKI, E. KOIW, J. GENEST, R. TELLIER, I. MORIN, A. LA FLAMME and P. ROBINSON, *Canad. J. Biochem. Physiol.*, **35**, 425 (1957).

107. S. C. SLACK and W. J. MADER, *Analyt. Chem.*, **33**, 625 (1961).

108. J. J. KABARA, J. T. MCLAUGHLIN and C. A. RIEGEL, *ibid.*, **33**, 305 (1961).

109. G. V. VAHOUNY, R. M. MAYER, J. H. ROE and C. R. TREADWELL, *Arch. Biochem. Biophys.*, **86**, 210 (1960).

110. W. NOCKE, *Biochem. J.*, **78**, 593 (1961).

111. O. NEUNHÖFFER, K. THEWALT and W. ZIMMERMANN, *Z. physiol. Chem.* **323**, 116 (1961).

112. R. NEHER, *Advanc. Clin. Chem.* **1**, 127 (1958).

113. G. V. MANN, *Clin. Chem.*, **7**, 275 (1961).

114. R. I. DORFMAN (Ed.), *Methods in Hormone Research*, vol. 1, Academic Press, London (1962); C. H. GRAY and A. L. BACHARACH (Eds.), *Hormones in Blood*, Academic Press, London (1961).

BIBLIOGRAPHY

In the following list of suggested further reading, the emphasis of each monograph or review is indicated by the marginal notes:

> (a) theoretical including structure-spectra correlations;
> (b) instrumentation and techniques;
> (c) collections of absorption data.

a.   G. N. Lewis and M. Calvin, *Chem. Rev.*, **25**, 273 (1939).

a.   W. West (Ed.), *Chemical Applications of Spectroscopy in Technique of Organic Chemistry*, vol. 9, Interscience, New York (1956).

a.   E. A. Braude, in *Determination of Organic Structures by Physical Methods* (edited by E. A. Braude and F. Nachod).

a.   L. N. Ferguson, Relationship between absorption spectra and chemical constitution of organic molecules, *Chem. Rev.*, **48**, 385 (1948).

a.   E. A. Braude, Ultraviolet absorption and structure of organic compounds, *Ann. Rep. Chem. Soc.*, **42**, 105 (1945).

ab.   A. E. Gillam and E. S. Stern, *Introduction to Electronic Absorption Spectroscopy in Organic Chemistry*, 2nd ed., Arnold, London (1957).

b.   L. Heilmeyer, *Spectrophotometry in Medicine*, Hilger, London (1943).

ab.   G. F. Lothian, *Absorption Spectrophotometry*, Hilger, London (1958).

b.   F. Ellinger, Absorption spectral data on natural products. *Tabulae Biologicae*, **12**, 291 (1937).

a.   J. R. Partington, *Advanced Treatise of Physical Chemistry*, Longmans, London (1954).

ab.   W. C. Price, Advances in ultraviolet spectroscopy. *Rep. Progr. Physics*, **14**, 1 (1951).

b.   H. H. Cary, *Rev. Sci. Instr.*, **17**, 558 (1946).

abc.   *Analytical Chemistry*, Annual bibliographical collections on ultraviolet spectrophotometry, e. g., **23**, 12 (1951), **24**, 14 (1952), **28**, 579 (1956).

bc.   R. A. Morton, *The Application of Absorption Spectra to the Study of Vitamins, Hormones and Co-enzymes*, Hilger, London (1942).

bc.   R. M. C. Dawson, D. C. Elliot, W. H. Elliot and K. M. Jones, *Data for Biochemical Research*, Oxford (1959).

bc.   K. Paech and M. V. Tracey (Eds.), *Modern Methods of Plant Analysis*, 4 vols., Springer, Berlin (1955–1956).

b.   D. Glick (Ed.), *Methods of Biochemical Analysis*, (1952 Vol. 1, *et seq.*).

abc.   M. Resterner and D. Brück, *Methods of Organic Chemistry* (Houben-Weyl), vol. 3, part 2, p. 593, Thieme, Stuttgart (1955).

c.   Landolt-Börnstein's, *Zahlenwerte und Funktionen aus Physik, Chemie, Astronomie, Geophysik und Technik*, vol. 1, part 3, Springer, Berlin (1951).

a.   A. Maccoll, Colour and constitution, *Quart. Rev.*, **1**, 16 (1947).

b.   R. A. Morton, *Practical Aspects of Absorption Spectrophotometry*, Royal Institute of Chemistry, London (1938).

c.   H. M. Hershenson, *Ultraviolet and Visible Absorption Spectra*, Index for 1930–1954, Academic Press, New York (1956).

c.   R. A. Friedel and M. Orchin, *Ultraviolet Spectra of Aromatic Compounds*, Wiley, New York (1951).

c.   A.P.I.Research Project 44, *Ultraviolet Spectral Data* (Index Card System), Carnegie Institute and U.S. Bureau of Standards.

a.   G. HERZBERG, *Molecular Spectra and Molecular Structure*, Van Nostrand, New York (1950).

b.   M.G.MELLON, *Analytical Absorption Spectroscopy*, Wiley, New York (1950).

c.   *International Critical Tables*, vol. 5, p. 359, McGraw-Hill, New York (1929).

c.   H.E.UNGNADE and M.J.KAMLET (Eds.), *Organic Electronic Spectral Data*, Interscience, New York (1960); Vol.I (1946–1952); Vol.II (1953–1955).

a.   C.N.R.RAO, *Ultraviolet and Visible Spectroscopy. Chemical Applications*, Butterworth, Washington (1961).

a.   H.H.Jaffé and M.Orchin, *Theory and Applications of Ultraviolet Spectroscopy*, Wiley, New York (1962).

a.   S.F.MASON, *Quart. Rev. Chem. Soc.*, **15**, 284 (1961).

INDEX

434

OTHER TITLES IN THE SERIES ON
ORGANIC CHEMISTRY